RESIDENTIAL CONSTRUCTION AND DESIGN:

Techniques for the Modern Builder

Frederick Uhlen Hop

Prentice Hall, Englewood Cliffs, New Jersey 07632

15282305

Library of Congress Cataloging-in-Publication Data

HOP, FREDERICK UHLEN.
   Residential carpentry.

   Includes index.
   1. House construction. I. Title.
TH4811.H63 1988   690   87-2488
ISBN 0-13-774761-6   025

Editorial/production supervision
and interior design: COLLEEN BROSNAN & PATRICK WALSH
Cover design: WANDA LUBELSKA DESIGN
Manufacturing buyer: S. G. OSBOURNE
Page layout: CHARLES PELLETREAU

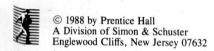

© 1988 by Prentice Hall
A Division of Simon & Schuster
Englewood Cliffs, New Jersey 07632

Printed in the United States of America

10 9 8 7 6 5 4 3 2 1

ISBN 0-13-774761-6   025

Prentice-Hall International (UK) Limited, *London*
Prentice-Hall of Australia Pty. Limited, *Sydney*
Prentice-Hall Canada Inc., *Toronto*
Prentice-Hall Hispanoamericana, S.A., *Mexico*
Prentice-Hall of India Private Limited, *New Delhi*
Prentice-Hall of Japan, Inc., *Tokyo*
Prentice-Hall of Southeast Asia Pte. Ltd., *Singapore*
Editora Prentice-Hall do Brasil, Ltda., *Rio de Janeiro*

CONTENTS_____

PART II
CONSTRUCTION TECHNIQUES
54

PREFACE

Writing this book was a labor of love, a labor born of a desire to see homes built efficiently and with pride, a love of wanting to help those who need the information to carry out an objective.

Old systems that have come and gone are occasionally referred to historically only to give a depth of understanding of the evolution in house building and to assist the remodeler. There is no massive collection of obsolete diagrams from which the reader must guess the current technique.

All systems and techniques of construction described and illustrated have been used successfully on full-scale projects. Their feasibility is proven. These techniques are based on the good standards of the industry and accepted building codes.

This text concentrates strongly on the mating of design to readily available materials. This system is referred to as *modular development*. Such a philosophy of building eliminates the huge waste piles so characteristic of construction sites. It is in line with present conservation objectives.

There are many techniques described herein which are found in no other published source. The author describes step by step how to accomplish these tasks. Other techniques are fresh and new and field tested. There are designs and tables herein never before seen in print. Val-

uable information and design concepts are presented for highly efficient fuel-conserving structures. These concepts are well within the present-day scope of the average home builder and the professional contractor.

As a method of attack it is advised that the learner read all of Part I first. As Part II is read, it will be helpful to refer back to the design paragraphs in Part I that correlate with the subject at hand.

Good luck in your undertaking. Remember that pride is one of the important wages of a job well done.

OBJECTIVES

Why would a person read a book of this type? Probably not for recreation. More likely a search for knowledge has begun, knowledge to satisfy an intellectual curiosity or a realistic survival need. This book deals with both objectives. Its content comes from the roots of the workplace.

The objectives in Part I are twofold. A major emphasis is placed on the proper design of the structural components of a residence. It is important to know how the parts should be assembled for maximum strength and endurance. Part I deals with the technology of design and layout. It explains the structural role of each component by itself and in an assembly. For those readers with limited background in construction, a good practice will be to refer to Part II while reading Part I and match the design philosophy with the construction methods. Bear in mind that this text is not just an instruction manual. It is a philosophy of creating a structure in which a worker can take great pride.

In the planning stage of Part I, the reader is presented with enough technical information to make sketches and drawings with structural components properly placed for strength and economy. Floor planning and the cosmetics of a house design are touched on for three reasons: (1) to save the builder from making a significant blunder in design or construction, (2) to provide some guidelines to meet those problems which crop up for which there are no readily available answers in other books, and (3) to meet the specified minimums of universal building codes.

The objectives of Part II are also twofold. One objective is to lay a foundation of logic for sustaining some construction techniques while discarding those that are obsolete. The craftsman will feel comfortable when the *reasons* are known for a system of construction. By contrast, the craftsman can only be mystified and unfulfilled when reduced to simple instruction-following.

The second objective of Part II is to give extensive detail of the many systems that are currently used in the construction of a residential structure. Also, Part II includes a host of practical innovative ways to do a job. Comparisons with older, frequently abandoned techniques will equip the reader to make value judgments in picking his course of action.

It is easier and more enjoyable to make something when the principles are understood. The lowest level of appreciation comes from simply following instructions. A greater level of enjoyment is reached when it is known why things are done a certain way. The ultimate appreciation comes when one has possession of enough knowledge to make quality choices. Then you are a decision maker. Decision makers are not necessarily happier persons than instruction followers, but they are unquestionably higher paid. With knowledge and decision-making capacity comes responsibility. The worker at a lower level can usually cop-out successfully when something is done according to the supervisor's instructions and it does not turn out well. There is no excuse when a person is left to his or her own judgment and skill. Building codes are made to prevent poor judgment from becoming reality in the form of structures that are unsafe. For the sake of human safety, codes are mostly directed at structural soundness.

In this text a concern for safety, both during construction and after tenancy, will be demonstrated. There is also an interest in pride. The construction industry has gone through cycles of pride. In some times and places pride was (and still is) placed in the skill, quality, and perfection of a structure. At other times and places the emphasis has been placed on the dollar. We have quality builders and we have money-oriented builders. It is the author's belief that these two philosophical objectives need not be widely separated.

In the past fifty years we have seen examples of the two building philosophies. The economics of the building industry fluctuate with the general economy. In good times more money is available and the demand for housing units increases. This encourages many new builders who are not fully equipped with knowledge or responsibleness to jump into the trade. It encourages short cutting on time, quality, and good materials. For some ''builders'' it is a good climate in which to make a lot of fast bucks and get out when the going gets tough. Unfortunately, the outcome is often lawsuits and bankruptcy. Occasionally, a fortune is made and pride is taken in that accomplishment, as though that were the only objective.

The good-quality builder seems to survive better the ups and downs of the national economy. He is not forced to shut down as much or as frequently. His employees are often older and their employment records are more stable. In hard times those consumers who are able to hire a contractor tend to prefer the old-established firm. They prefer and will pay for good-quality construction.

The ''quality'' debate will probably go on forever. As with other elements of life, it is a question of quality versus quantity. It is an objective of this text to show that one need not be wholly sacrificed for the other. Knowledge, the ''know-how,'' can frequently provide the avenue to quality construction at a reduced cost. From the information in Chapter 1 it was made clear that knowledge about modularity could effect a savings in material and labor and cause better construction. The author believes it is important that workers at all levels have some understanding of the whys and wherefores of a technique or process. Only with this type of knowledge can value judgments be made on the job. Therefore, the methods and procedures to follow in Part II will attempt more than simple directions. It is hoped that the conscientious reader will come away with a feeling for basic principles. Specifically, it is hoped that he or she attains a usable skill for coordinating principles into a system of building. The end result should be a sound, safe, attractive structure in which a large measure of pride will be a substantial by-product.

The author's objective in presenting the information in this text is to enable learning to take place. Hopefully, the reader's objective will be to learn, not just to copy. It is the author's conviction that true self-appreciation in the construction business does not come from the single act of following oral or written instructions. It comes from an understanding of the logic that is in the instruction. Such an acquisition of knowledge will make it possible for the learner to emerge from the mastering of this text with the skill to choose better courses of action. The results of his or her handiwork will then be a great source of pride and satisfaction.

ACKNOWLEDGMENTS

A number of individuals and organizations have been supportive of my desire to write and illustrate this book. In their behalf I dedicate this labor of love.

- To the administration and staff of Westark Community College at Fort Smith, Arkansas, for the moral and mechanical support and a mutual sense of joy as the project developed.
- To Katy Brake, through whose capable hands flowed every word into print; for her patience and constant resolve.
- To Don Goodwin for his unswerving loyalty and encouragement from the beginning to the fulfillment of the project.
- To Jack Gorham for his photographic contributions.
- To my son, John Frederick Uhlen Hop, for his specialized assistance with the tables and illustrations.

- To my wife, Leila, for her many hours of sustaining help and to my family who have been so caring and supportive while permitting me to put this project ahead of many other priorities.
- To firms and organizations who have permitted the inclusion of special references and materials.
- Arkola Sand and Gravel Co.; Fort Smith, Arkansas
- United Steel Products Co.; Montgomery, Minnesota
- Southern Forest Products Association; New Orleans, Louisiana
- Petit Jean Lumber Co.; Fort Smith, Arkansas

The cover of this book is from a photograph of one of the author's double-walled houses which contains many of the innovations and the high quality features recommended in the pages to follow.

Frederick Uhlen Hop

Chapter 1

EFFECTIVE PLANNING

REASONS FOR PLANNING

Many structures have been erected without written or drawn plans. The simplicity of the pioneer's one-room log cabin is an example. The design and method was so simple and well known that about the only planning involved related to the location of a door, a fireplace, a window or two, and what direction to face the front. All of these plans could easily be made on the site during the actual construction.

Today's home is a far cry from the American log cabin. There are probably some small houses being constructed with nothing but the simplest line sketches of a floor plan. An experienced builder can produce a building from such a hastily devised sketch. It may turn out to be a suitable structure. The novice builder or the amateur who attempts to build without good plans is courting disaster in both time and money.

When no plan or an inadequate plan is used, a characteristic of trial and error soon dominates the activity. This usually creates serious problems. When an error is discovered, there are two alternative decisions from which to choose. The most obvious possibility is to redo that which has been done incorrectly. The thought of such an alternative when constructing a house may be so painful that it is rejected routinely. An example of a significant error is found in the technique of spacing structural members. Incorrectly spaced floor joists can lead to a number of costly and time-consuming retrofits of materials that go on the floor at a later stage. It can also destroy the straight-line bearing characteristic of rafters, studs, and joists, which is a basic structural objective.

Unfortunately, errors are prone to be discovered after a lot of work has been completed. The floor joist example is a case in point. An entire floor frame may be completed up to the last set of joists before a spacing error is recognized. Such a situation will usually encourage an acceptance of the alternative decision to leave the completed work as is and adapt to it. Unfortunately, some typical errors in construction become compounded throughout the remainder of the structure. This causes continual adaptation and waste in the form of additional material and throwaway excess.

The reason for obtaining or making good and complete plans is to avoid problems and achieve a satisfactory goal. The objective of the plan itself is to provide an illustrated guide to the erection of a specific structural design. It is more practical to work out the problems and revisions on paper than with wood or masonary.

IMPORTANCE OF DOCUMENTING

The human mind is a marvelous storehouse of facts and knowledge. However, it is not necessary to memorize and store extensive plans and specifications. Nor should the mind be expected to provide on-the-spot infallible plans. Good plans, like any invention, are usually the result of some exploratory thrusts. The beginning experimentation takes place on paper in the form of sketching. An idea becomes a mental picture and is put down on paper. With lines and figures and words, a design begins to appear.

Soon the design takes on many forms. There is the exterior appearance form (elevations). There is the interior arrangement and size of rooms to be visualized (floor plan). As the conception progresses, many more details will go down on paper for future reference. Gradually, the process of brainstorming and graphic recording will produce enough documentation that the final development process can begin. Alternative ideas are evaluated and choices are made. Specification lists are made to note desired features. After the sketches and specifications have been evaluated and revised, the formal drawing takes place. The collection of all the drawings that are made is reproduced and stapled into a packet which is referred to as the *plan* or the *blueprint*. This is the documented road map to building a specific structure.

SPECIFICATIONS

There is another form of instruction in addition to the plan. It is known as the specifications. The specifications are word notations and descriptions of building methods and materials. This written information is found in charts and tables and in descriptive form.

Simple Specifications

Simple plans of uncomplicated nature or size may have all the specifications placed on the blueprints. They will be found as notes near the item they describe or prescribe. Other specifications may be found in column and blocked form. These are called *schedules* or *conventions*. For example, windows and doors may be given a code number on the floor plan. A window and door schedule is presented in bordered form somewhere in the plan set. In the schedule will be found the full description of each different size, shape, and type of window and door unit, with a corresponding code number or letter that is to be used in the house. Electrical plans are coded in a similar manner.

Printed Specification Manual

The larger or more complex a construction project, the more important it becomes to spell out the specifications.

This is particularly true when there are innovations and original design features. It is of particular value when code compliance is necessary. Written specifications also provide a reference for estimating costs and drawing up a contract.

The second form of planning documentation is the printed specification manual. This booklet is usually of typing paper size. Several copies will be run off on office reproduction machines, such as photocopiers and word processors. The small booklet type is bound with staples. Larger ones require spirals. Several copies are required. Separate copies are needed for bidders, the general contractor, subcontractors, loan agencies, municipal permit offices, and the owner. Each copy will accompany a set of blueprints. Homes of modest size and budget seldom require a separate specification manual. When the investment exceeds $50,000, it is well to consider the written specification manual as a necessity together with the complete graphic plans. The long-term advantages will outweigh the initial cost. The specification manual is made up by the architect or designer. It is extremely important that this person be well versed on current materials, availability, and cost in addition to modular methods of design (the key to conceptual economy).

WISDOM OF PLANNING

The wisdom of thorough planning cannot be overemphasized. This is especially true of builders with less than full experience and those who have built just enough to be overconfident. Many builders, aspiring to be professionals, have gone out of business in the first few years. Seldom was the reason for this a lack of skill. Usually, it was because of inadequate or faulty planning. In this text the author presents the type of information that will equip the would-be builder either to make adequate plans or to choose suitable plans. In the building of a home, it is better to correct the problems or errors on the drawing board rather than on the structure. It is frequently a tragic mistake to work with real materials when no specific plan exists on paper to guide the project to a successful conclusion.

REVIEW TOPICS

1. What is meant by the statement that early construction errors tend to be compounded as building progresses?
2. What objectives are made possible through the use of a good plan?
3. What do good plan drawings tell you?
4. Arrange the following elements of planning in the order in which they will normally occur by placing a number 1, 2, or 3 in the parentheses.

(   ) Formal drawing
(   ) Researching and brainstorming ideas
(   ) Freehand sketching

5. Explain what a floor plan is.

6. Describe a call out.

7. What is the difference between a set of plans and a specification manual?

Chapter 2
CHARACTERISTICS OF MODULARITY

MODULAR DESIGN

The words "modulus," "module," "modular," and "modularity" are used to mean several different things in the construction industry. The word *module* means a standardized component. *Modular design* refers to a coordinated system that makes use of standardized material units without waste. *Modulus* refers to the size of the unit. The term *modularity* is used herein to denote a concept of design that features maximum construction efficiency and minimum material waste through the use of modular components.

There are other, related uses of these terms. In the plumbing industry, the one-piece fiberglass combination tub and shower is called a "module." The plywood companies some years ago designed a straight-line floor frame assembly that accepts full sheets of plywood. It was labeled a "modular system of joist spacing." When factories began to fabricate parts of homes, the assembly lines made modular units that would fit together on the site. These were called "panelized" or "modular" homes.

DESIGNER'S OBJECTIVE

Throughout these various meanings there is one common objective for the designer. The objective is to draw a structural plan that makes use of modular materials. Unfortunately for the builder, not many architect-drawn plans are available that emphasize modularity. The typical architec-tural emphasis is likely to be focused on the aesthetic features, the beauty of a design. It then falls to the builder to try to adapt the existing material modules to an uncoordinated plan.

TEXT OBJECTIVE

An objective of this text is to show how a plan can be modular as well as attractive. It is usually possible to coordinate a pleasing appearance with economically structured design. The reader will learn the significant and telltale dimensions which denote a plan that considers modularity. With some study and a little practice, the student will be able to assess the superior plan, the plan that requires the least amount of revision. By applying this knowledge, thousands of dollars can be saved on a single modest house project.

BASIC MODULUS MATERIALS

Production of two material units has enabled the concept of modular construction to become a reality. One of these was the development of the precast concrete block; the other was the lamination technique that gave us the plywood sheet (Fig. 2-1).

When builders realized the coordination potential between these two modules and others like them, the industry began a significant change in construction technique. Both

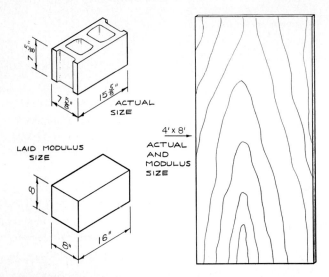

FIGURE 2-1   The concrete block and the plywood sheet are standardized units that form the basis of modularity in the United States.

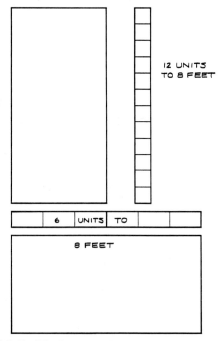

FIGURE 2-2   Blocks and plywood moduli coordinate to form a spacing system.

of the materials were standardized on the 4″ modular cube. Roughly speaking, all coordinating modular materials to follow are based on the division of 4. For example, the width of plywood (4′) coordinates with the length of three laid blocks (16″ modules × 3 = 4′); plywood in lengthwise position (8′) coordinates with six blocks (Fig. 2-2). The most common standardized block is the stretcher. It measures 16″ long, which includes the mortar joint when laid in a course. The height and most common depth of the basic block are both 8″ laid in a wall.

CALCULATIONS

Material Coordinating Formula

With this simple bit of coordinating knowledge, the designer has a mathematical tool at his disposal. It will be referred to as the *3-for-4 theorem*. The applications are many. There are three concrete block units for every 4 running feet (linear horizontal distance). Knowing this, we can accurately assess the length of a block foundation simply by counting the blocks. More significantly, the designer will recognize the specific linear dimensions that accept full blocks without remainders. For every three blocks there are 4′ of length. To find the feet when a quantity of block units is known, *divide* the quantity by 3 and *multiply* the result by 4.

> Formula: Units ÷ 3 × 4′ = length
>
> Sample problem: 36 units ÷ 3 = 12 × 4′ = 48′

Assessing Dimensions for Modularity

To determine whether a dimension fits the unit modulus, simply multiply the dimension by 3/4. When the result is a full number, it means that the dimension is evenly divisible by 16″ (the block length modulus). It will accommodate full block units. There will be no fractional joist and stud spacing at one end of the house left over since these wood parts are usually spaced on the 16″ modulus. The following are problems using sample dimensions that are modular.

> 3/4 × 60′ = 45 units   3/4 × 48′ = 36 units
>
> 3/4 × 41′–4″ = 31 units   3/4 × 42′–8″ = 32 units

Computation by Calculator

When a dimension ends with inches, the feet and inches should be converted to inches before dividing. By so doing the result will be in full numbers when the dimension proves to be modular. An inexpensive calculator operates with decimals. The moduli for blocks and frame spacing are 4″ (1/3 of a foot) and 8″ (2/3 of a foot). These inches are the excess beyond the foot length of one block (1′-4″) and two blocks (2′-8″). Neither 1/3 nor 2/3 can be multiplied on a calculator with complete accuracy. Take the following example using the dimension forty-one feet four inches of foundation length (41′-4″). Three for four is three-quarters or 75 one-hundredths.

0.75 × 41.333333 = 30.999999

We know that 3/4 of 41'-4" is actually 31 full units of 16" spaces. It can be arrived at mentally with ease by going to the root number (the closest 4' module) and adding the additional single unit. Forty feet is the closest root number divisible by 4. Forty feet times three-quarters nets 30 units plus the one additional unit gives 31 units. If the dimension is 42'-8", we could go to the 44 root module and subtract one unit, or we could use the 40' module and add two units. To use the calculator with complete accuracy, let us transpose the sample dimension of 41'-4" into inches first. Next divide by the 16" unit modulus. Set up for calculator or long hand, the problem looks like this:

$$41' \times 12" = 492" + 4" = 496" \div 16" = 31 \text{ units}$$

Note that this comes out exactly even, as it should when the dimension is modular.

Let us take an example that is *not modular* in any sense. $3/4 \times 45'\text{-}10" = ?$ Setting up the problem, we have

$$45' \times 12" = 540" + 10" = 550" \div 16"$$
$$= 34.375 \text{ units.}$$

Nonmodular Figures

Feet that are trailed by the following inches are never modular for the application of plywood or concrete blocks: 1, 2, 3, 5, 6, 7, 9, 10, and 11. These figures will always produce an odd-sized space in the framing structures (floors, walls, ceilings, and rafters). In the foundation they will require cutting or breaking of blocks. The only inch figures following feet that are modular are 4 and 8. It will also be found, a little further on in this study, that the 4" figure is modular only when preceded by an odd-numbered foot and the 8" figure when preceded by an even-numbered foot. 41'-4" is modular. 42'-8" is modular. 41'-8" and 42'-4" are *nonmodular*.

MODULAR PLANNING

Many synthetic materials have been coordinated to make the modularity principle possible. A common brick lays up six to a block face (some newer magnum sizes do not modularize with blocks). There are many sheet materials that modularize with blocks. These are: fiberboard (Celotex), hard board (Masonite), Styrofoam, gypsum wallboard, particle board, and all the types of plywood and paneling. Their common modulus is 4' by 8'. Common ceiling tile sizes are 12" × 12", 16" × 16", and 24" × 48". The odd nonmodular 9" × 9" floor tile has been phased out in favor of the current modular 12" × 12" units. One of the few

remaining nonmodular areas in construction is the bathroom with its 5' tub and 4 1/4" tiles.

Modular Plan Dimensions

There are key plan dimensions that the designer should memorize. The memorization should be of the graphic visual type. The person should see in his mind's eye a visual image of the material and be immediately able to associate the size to the image. This is not a monumental assignment. It is like the games we had as children: the Lincoln logs, the erector sets, and more recently the snap-together plastic toys.

Visualizing Unit Coordinates

Visualize the stretcher block. It is 8" high and 16" long. Now visualize a sheet of plywood standing vertically on top of three blocks lying end to end (Fig. 2-3). Three 16" blocks measure 48" end to end, which is the same as the width of the plywood. Now lay the plywood down on edge horizontally. Picture six blocks under it. Six units of 16" equal the 96" length of the ply sheet. When visualizing these two materials, one should also think in proportionate sizes. Both the block and the plywood are twice as long as they are wide. Focus mentally on two squares comprising the rectangle. This visualizing helps greatly to maintain correct proportions when sketching details of construction.

Characteristics of Structural Members

The next step in this exercise is to consider the manner in which the modular materials fit onto or are attached to the

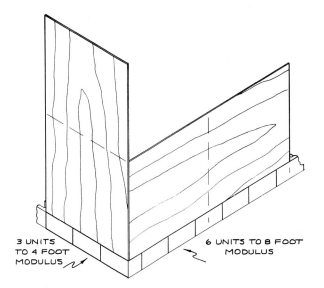

3 UNITS TO 4 FOOT MODULUS

6 UNITS TO 8 FOOT MODULUS

FIGURE 2-3 Visualize the concrete and wood moduli as double squares when sketching in addition to the 3-for-4 concept.

structural members. Structural members, such as floor joists, wall studs, and roof rafters have standard girth dimensions. *Girth* means the cross-section thickness and width. These sizes will vary only slightly due to the effects of moisture or dryness, which cause them to swell or shrink. Girth has little relation to modular planning. Length and spacing of structural members has a direct influence on modular coordination. All the larger members (2 × 6 through 2 × 12) come in even lengths starting with 8′ and ending with 24′. This structural lumber is referred to as *dimension lumber*. There is one modular exception in the dimension lumber category. This is the precut stud. "Precuts," as they are nicknamed, come precisely cut to identical lengths of 92 5/8″. The length has been established as a universally coordinated module to fit interior wall covering modules of drywall and paneling. It coordinates with a single sole plate and a double top plate to form the required height.

Four-Foot Modulus

The most significant dimensions that are first encountered in designing or assessing a plan will be the exterior overall dimensions. When a block is the unit modulus of the foundation and will be coordinated with modular sheathing above, the most economical dimensional sizes will be those which are divisible by 4′. Foundation rectangles of the following overall dimensions are examples of perfect modules: 24 × 40′, 28 × 52′, and 28 × 60′. Wings or ells off a rectangle will coordinate perfectly when they follow the same rule. These major modules (divisible by 4) will create the potential for little or no waste throughout the floor, the exterior walls, and the ceiling joists. Any departure from this size formula will automatically raise the cost of the house by causing waste through leftover materials. The same modular principle applies to poured concrete foundations that will have wood-framed structures upon them.

Split Modulus

The next significant module may be called the split modulus or "mod" for short. It incorporates dimensions which are divisible by 2′. There are unique characteristics of the split mod to visualize and understand. A foundation of 26 × 40′ will accommodate an even number of block units even though the 26′ is divisible by neither 16″ nor 4′. On one of the 40′ sides there will be 30 blocks; on each of the split mod 26′ ends, there will be 19 blocks; on the back side there will be 29 blocks (Fig. 2-4). No blocks will need cutting. This factor occurs because of the 8″ depth of the block, which carries around the corner to fill the half unit module (26′ ÷ 16″ = 19 1/2 units). Since blocks are laid in a staggered-course pattern in foundations, the next course will have 30 blocks on the back side of the foundation and

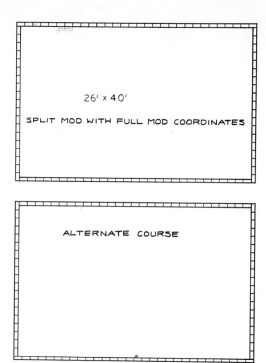

FIGURE 2-4 Split-module dimensions can fit full block layouts when well planned.

29 1/2 on the front. The split mod can be correlated with blocks as illustrated. The split-mod dimension *does not* correlate with stud spacing of 16″. There will always be a half-space (8″) module left over with dimensions that are divisible by 2 but not divisible by 4. This is a minor factor, as it only involves the addition of one stud per wall. The split mod remains modular with sheathing and siding modules that are installed vertically. A sheet is cut in half. The cutoff half fills out the opposite side or end of the house. For example, 26′ ends of a house frame will each take 6 1/2 sheets, 13 full sheets in all.

Sixteen-Inch Modulus

The third choice of desirable exterior dimensions is any multiple of feet that can be divided equally by 16″ (1 1/4′). Examples of these house dimensions are: 25′-4″ × 38′-8″ or 26′-8″ × 45′-4″. These figures, although common in divisibility by 16″, pose completely different considerations for coordination in a wood structure, which are explained in sections to follow.

Common Spacing Modulus. Floor joists and wall studs are most commonly spaced 16″ apart. Three spaces form the major modulus similar to the concrete block coordinates. On four wall studs, which make up three spaces, visually place a vertical sheet of plywood (Fig. 2-5). Now associate horizontal major mod dimensions with

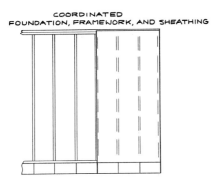

FIGURE 2-5 Visualize the coordination of blocks with standard sheets and both with stud spacing. Stud quantity (16″ OC) will be 3-for-4 plus one to close the end of the wall.

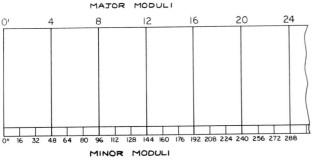

FIGURE 2-6 Think major and minor modules when designing. This will contribute to a plan that will save significant material and labor cost.

the plywood and begin to lengthen the wall. A pattern begins to emerge of full units fitting neatly together. See two sheets, then three, then four sheets in place. Mentally note, "four sheets equal 16′—four modules of triple blocks equal 12 blocks—behind the plywood, 12 stud spaces net 13 studs." Add another sheathing module and recompute. This visualizing technique turns the mind into an effective computer of materials and dimensions. Continue the exercise by adding units of plywood. The significant major module dimensions are now clear (Fig. 2-6). Our early training in arithmetic probably left us with the common skill of counting by twos, either odd or even. Now we are developing the design skill of counting by fours.

Effect of 16″ Spacing on Wall Length. Consider the effect of adding a single or double 16″ unit of linear space to the full 4′ modules. A house dimension of 40′ will accept 10 full, uncut sheets of sheathing placed vertically on the wall (discounting window and door openings at this point). Add one 16″ minor module of length and space. Now there is an odd space left over at one end of the wall. A vertical third of a sheathing sheet is required to cover this space. Another third will be used on the opposite wall. There is a third of a sheet left over.

Effect of 16″ Modulus on Floor Length. In the example of a plan length of 41′-4″ (10 major mods plus one minor mod), the floor sheathing will also be affected. Floor sheathing is placed with the long direction running across the joists. The plywood length being 8′, a 40′ floor will accept five full sheets per course (Fig. 2-7a). A 41′-4″ floor will require an additional one-sixth of the length of a sheet (Fig. 2-7b). Additional labor time is required for the cutting that is necessary on every course. The 40′ floor (or any dimension divisible by 8) will require sheet cutting (in half) only every other course because the end joints are staggered. The first, third, fifth, and so on, courses will accommodate full sheets. The second and fourth and sixth courses will take the two halves that were cut with one pass of the saw and used to start and end the course. The same characteristic exists with linear frontal dimensions that have two additional 16″ moduli added to the basic fours (Fig. 2-7c). Use the 40′ basic four as an example again and add two units of 16″. This makes 42′-8″. This dimension is now two units beyond the major module of 40 and one unit short of the next module of 44.

Modularity Patterns in Dimensions

By visualizing actual figures in modular dimensions, a consistent pattern emerges. The skill of recognizing this pattern makes it possible to evaluate the effects of specific

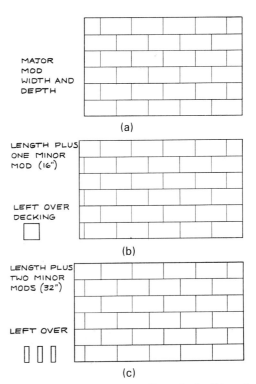

FIGURE 2-7 (a) Major module floor deck; (b) major plus one minor module floor deck; (c) major plus two minor modules.

dimensions on labor time and material usage. Assume that after sufficient practice the major 4′ moduli from 4 to 100′ can be readily recognized. For each 16″ minor module added to a major module, there will be 1′-4″ added. The foot number is always odd. The inch number is always 4. When two minor moduli units of 16″ (32″) are added, it is discovered that the inch figure is always 8 and the preceding foot number is always even. Therefore, the single minor unit extension with an odd number plus 4″ and double unit addition with an even number plus 8″ emerges as a recognizable pattern. Examples: a major module is 40′. That module plus one minor module is 41′-4″. The same module (40′) plus a double minor module is 42′-8″. The principles to be followed are:

- Odd-numbered feet following a major module plus 4″ comprise major modules of 4′ plus one minor module of 16″.
- Even-numbered feet following a major module plus 8″ comprise major modules of 4′ plus two minor modules of 16″ (or the next higher major module minus 16″).
- Overall dimensions ending in inches other than 4 or 8 are *nonmodular*.

Visualizing and memorizing these principles will enable a consumer or builder to recognize whether a plan has been developed with modularity as an objective. Unfortunately, most plans on the market today, available across the counter or through the mail, are not based on modularity. As a designer you are now in possession of the principles that are needed to revise the exterior overall dimensions of such plans. By so doing, material cost can be saved or additional floor space can be gained at little or no cost. As a final exercise let us view a series of linear dimensions. To make the characteristics stand out, the major 4′ modular figures are circled. For practice, continue the figures on up to 100′.

⟨20⟩-0	21-4	22-8	⟨24⟩-0	25-4	26-8
⟨28⟩-0	29-4	30-8	⟨32⟩-0	33-4	34-8
⟨36⟩-0	37-4	38-8	⟨40⟩-0	41-4	42-8
⟨44⟩-0	45-4	46-8	⟨48⟩-0	49-4	50-8

Modularity Considerations with Floor Joists

The most efficient depths (spans) for a wood floor are 12′, 16′, 20′, 24′, 28′, and 32′. Thirty-two feet is a maximum depth with the use of a pair of single joists end to end across the span. Sixteen feet is the maximum possible span found on most stress tables for a 2 × 12 joist. Fabricated truss joists will be required above 16′. There is no dimension

lumber readily available above 12 nominal inches. For practical considerations the house depth of 28′ should not be exceeded unless a thorough understanding of the structural loads from above exists. The problem associated with spans of joists between 14 and 16′ long is springiness in the floor. Although the longer and larger joist may carry the weight adequately, the floor may not feel rigid when walking on it.

The next most efficient depth modules are those divisible by 2′ as far as the floor is concerned. The primary consideration is the available lengths of joists and the construction methods to coordinate the joists with plywood sheathing widths. Therefore, the 2′ dimension lumber modulus is our focal design interest when considering the total span.

Optional Placement of Girders

Girders are beams of steel or built-up wood designed and placed to support the interior ends of joists and bearing partitions. Girders do not have to be centered between foundations as long as the lumber girth of the joists is large enough to meet the span code of the longest joist used. Below are some feasible combinations of floor depths.

20′ depth

> Two 10′ joists butted
> One 12′ and one 8′ joist butted over a girder

22′ depth

> One 10′ and one 12′ joist butted over a girder
> Two 12′ joists lapped over a centered girder

24′ depth

> Two 12′ joists butted over a centered girder
> One 12′ and one 14′ lapped over an off-centered girder

26′ depth

> One 12′ and one 14′ butted over a girder
> Two 14′ joists lapped over a centered girder

28′ depth

> Two 14′ joists butted over a centered girder
> One 14′ and one 16′ lapped over an off-centered girder

Effect on Plywood Sheathing

The plywood sheathing modulus to be considered when designing floor depth is 4'. This is because the plywood will be placed with its long direction across the joists (at right angles). Therefore, each course of sheathing is 4' wide.

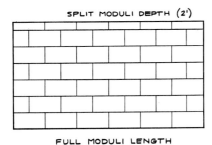

SPLIT MODULI DEPTH (2')

FULL MODULI LENGTH

FIGURE 2-8 Split-module depth with full-module length requires ripping of sheets lengthwise.

Floor depth dimensions divisible by 4 and floor lengths divisible by 8 will net 100% use of plywood sheets. For example, a floor 24 × 40' will take exactly 30 sheets of plywood. Six courses deep times five sheets long equals 30 units. Full use of plywood can be achieved with the 2' split-mod depths when the length dimensions of the floor are held to figures evenly divisible by 8. An example of this would be a floor size of 26 × 48'. The only additional cost in such a dimension will be the labor required to saw the last course of sheathing lengthwise into 2' widths (three sheets cut into six pieces; Fig. 2-8).

Visualizing Material Quantities

There is a fringe benefit in mastering the technique of visualizing the coordination of materials to dimensions. Figuring out a bill of materials becomes an easy mental exercise. Much of it can be accomplished with little mathematics. It is a simple system of counting units instead of computing areas by square feet. For example, the conscientious student will find it quite possible to answer quickly and accurately such questions as: How many sheets of sheathing are needed for the exterior walls of a rectangular house that is 24 × 48'? The visual process kicks into gear and grinds out 6 units on one end, 12 units on a side; 6 + 12 = 18 × 2 = 36 sheets.

Counting Dimension Lumber Needs

There is one exception to the counting method. When inventorying for dimension units (joists, studs, and rafters), the problem is one of space and perimeter as contrasted to area coverage. The sheathing unit that covers three 16" wall spaces will have four studs. Look at the back of your hand with your thumb folded back out of sight. There are

three spaces, but four fingers. The 3-for-4 theorem is used by simply adding one lumber unit to close the last space. Visualize two sheets of plywood. There are now six studs plus one for 8' of coverage (seven studs in all). The 3-for-4 spatial concept can be memorized as a fractional multiplier once the visualizing skill has been learned. Regardless of the total length of a house, there will be three stud space units for each 4' with the 16" spacing system. Add one stud to the space count to obtain the quantity of common studs. An additional stud is added for each corner. This 3-for-4 plus one on the end formula will be accurate for partitions with no openings and no intersections. For an intersection add one stud. For a single door add one stud. The one displaced by the usual 32" rough opening will provide a trimmer for one side, so only one additional stud is required to make the other trimmer. For larger doors, double doors, or wider arches, no extra count need be added, as the displaced studs from the opening will take care of both trimmers.

Exterior walls are a different story. The doorways are fairly standardized, with 3' entry doors the most common and frequently used for front and rear entry. Often there will be a dinette or patio door which displaces enough studs to provide its own trimmers and have one or two left over. The window openings, by virtue of their variable height, are less predictable. Sometimes, displaced partial studs will compensate for the rough sill material that is required below a window.

Two simple methods of estimating a stud count for exterior walls are available. A fairly close estimation will be to compute the perimeter in feet. Count one stud for each linear foot. The second tried and true method is to use the floor plan. Put a little X where each stud is on the plan. Then count the Xs.

Modular Partition Intersections

The example above assumes the placement of the partition at a point that will utilize one of the studs already in the intersected wall. This will seldom, if ever, happen unless the plan has been specifically designed for it to happen. In order for it to occur intentionally, the dimensions on the floor plan must place one side or the other of the frame in line with the edge or center of the "on-centered" stud in the frame it intersects (Fig. 2-9). When dimensioned to the edge of this stud (the preferred method), a dimension will read in multiples of 16" plus 3/4" (half the thickness of the stud). Examples are 12'-0 3/4", 13'-4 3/4", 14'-8 3/4", and 16'-0 3/4". Each of these examples places the partition on the far side of the on-center stud. A dimension that places the partition on the near side will read in multiples of 16" minus 3/4". These dimensions will read 11'-11 1/4", 13'-3 1/4", 14'-7 1/4", and 15'-11 1/4". On the plan the dimension line arrows must

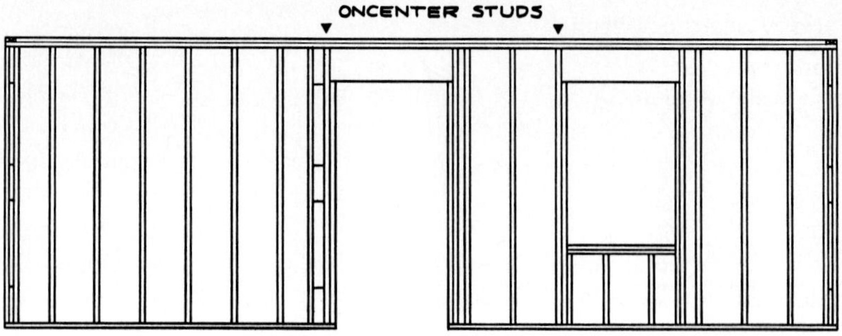

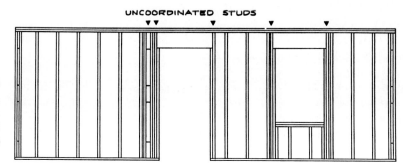

ONCENTER STUDS

FIGURE 2-9 A modularly planned typical wall saves labor and materials. The stud count averages one stud per linear foot.

UNCOORDINATED STUDS

FIGURE 2-10 A nonmodular plan disregards material and spacing, causing waste and inefficiency. There will be many more ill-spaced studs to buy and narrow spaces to insulate.

clearly show which side of the frame wall is being aligned to the stud in the frame it intersects. Plans with dimensions to the center of the frame wall indicate a disregard for modular coordination. Such a plan forces the layout carpenter to straddle the location with the wall, thus requiring two extra studs at each intersection (Fig. 2-10). The other alternative is to move the partition toward the closest stud. This involves a plan revision which may involve major changes. The well-planned modular system makes layout and construction simpler and less costly.

It is possible, and not difficult, to design a house plan with most of the intersections coordinated modularly. The saving in studs and labor is substantial. Floor plan layout is simpler and more accurate. Parallel placement of walls is made easy because a stud on the opposite wall may be used as a reference point. Wiring and insulating require less time and fitting. The floor frame will also benefit. Since the floor joist is below the stud, the modularly coordinated partition will run alongside the edge of the joist. Where a trimmer joist is specified for partition support, it will be placed on the side of the joist that puts it directly under the partition. This removes the necessity of using cross blocks to support the sheathing. All benefits taken into consideration, the modularly placed partition is superior.

CONCLUSIONS ABOUT MODULARITY

The challenge to the designer who accepts modularity as an objective is to devise a construction plan that will net three results: (1) an economical use of materials, (2) an efficient use of labor, and (3) a structurally sound and pleasing home. From the foregoing descriptions of the sig-

nificance of key modular dimensions some specific and some general conclusions can be formulated.

Specific Conclusions

There are trigger points of recognition that let us know at a glance what figures are completely modular, those which are partially modular, and those which do not take modularity into account at all. As a final review, study the list of examples below of exterior dimensions in the three categories.

1. **Completely modular:** all of the 4′ multiples. *Examples:* 4, 8, 12, 16, 20, 24, 28, 32, 36, 40, 44, 48, 52, 56, 60, and so on.
2. **Semimodular:** feet and inches figures other than the foregoing which are multiples of 16″. *Examples:* 21-4, 22-8, 25-4, 26-8, 29-4, 30-8, 33-4, 34-8, 37-4, 38-8, 41-4, 42-8, 45-4, 46-8, 49-4, 50-8, 53-4, 54-8, 57-4, 58-8, and so on.
3. **Nonmodular:** any dimension whose feet are followed by inches other than 4 or 8 and which do not conform to the pattern in the semimodular list above. *Examples:* 25-7, 36-9, 41-5, 46-4.

Note the pattern that exists in the semimodular column. Each of these dimensions has a characteristic that creates uniformity. The odd-numbered feet are all followed by 4″. The even-numbered feet are all followed by 8. When the major mod fours are put into this pattern, a rhythm of triads is felt. This can be a valuabale memorization tool (in the same manner as children are taught the alphabet to music). Let's try it with a beat.

"Forty-one four" (1-beat pause)

Forty-two eight" (1-beat pause)

Forty four (4-beat pause)

Forty-five four (1-beat pause)

Forty-six eight (1-beat pause)

Forty-eight (4-beat pause)

Chant the numbers like a march. Start at 1 foot 4 and go to 100. Soon the significant numbers are locked in memory.

The nonmodular column is characterized by figures that have no relationship to material size. A key tip-off here is the odd inch. However, the even inches of 4 and 8 are also nonmodular unless properly preceded by odd and even feet as explained previously. There is one exception to these principles, which is the house plan that specifies brick or stone veneer siding. The overall dimension may include the depth of the brick or stone. It may be an odd figure that includes the sum of each depth of veneer at opposite sides or ends of the house. In such cases one must look for other significant dimensions from the interior parts of the floor plan to arrive at the actual frame size of the plan.

General Conclusions

1. Modular development produces less waste and therefore provides greater economy.
2. Modularly designed structures require less labor cost.
3. The amount of extra time spent on the drawing board to make a plan modular is small compared to the savings that will be realized.
4. It does not require an architect's degree to produce a satisfactory modular plan.
5. There are relatively few plans on the market that are basically modular.
6. Any deviation from the modular concept will require additional capital outlay (an extremely important factor to quantity builders).
7. Modularizing an existing plan may frequently provide added living space at little or no additional cost.

APPLICATION OF THE SYSTEM

Before leaving the discussion of modular development, a word of encouragement may be in order. To the student who has had no exposure to building, no hands-on or visual association, the techniques described in this chapter may seem confusing or overwhelming. Words are seldom as clear or impressive as action. When you begin the actual construction, much of the instruction will begin to fall in place, to make sense. In the meantime, an excursion to as many house building sites as you can find will be extremely helpful. A mental photograph in the memory bank can be drawn out and examined over and over. Take along a tape measure, preferably one that is 16' long or more. Check out spacings and material sizes. See if the framework adheres to the modular concept. Begin the eyes-on experience. It will be very helpful when you begin to sketch your own design and again when you assist at laying out and assembling the real materials.

For those readers who have had some experience, the material presented so far will ring some bells. The principles just described are a fresh approach, unique in print at the time of this writing. The remainder of the text will follow the same style. Practical, field-proven construction methods and systems of design are presented for your consumption. It is recommended again that the remainder of the text (Part II) be read entirely before starting a house project. The combined study of theory (Part I) and construction technique (Part II) will reinforce a more complete understanding of principles and practice. It will lead to a more successful outcome as seen in the finished product.

REVIEW TOPICS

1. Describe the meaning of modularity.
2. What is a module?
3. What does "modulus" means?
4. Explain why it is important for a builder to understand these terms.
5. What wood product is the standard modulus of the construction industry?
6. What masonry product is the standard modulus of the construction industry?
7. Explain what the 3-for-4 theorem means.
8. Explain how a designer and/or builder can use the 3-for-4 theorem.
9. What results from a house plan whose dimensions ignore the principles of modularity?
10. Explain how modular dimensions on a plan can be distinguished from those that are nonmodular.
11. Explain why a 24'-deep floor is a full-mod size, whereas a 26' floor is called a split-mod size.
12. Explain why the purchase of construction lumber is mostly a unit cost problem instead of a board-foot problem.
13. List three or more reasons why it is advantageous to design partitions to intersect the exterior wall adjacent to a common stud.

Chapter 3
CONVENTIONAL DESIGNS

SOURCES OF TYPICAL DESIGNS

There are many plans available from sources such as lumberyards, supermarkets, drugstores, bookstores, and mail-order ads in home magazines. To get a look at a lot of plans under one cover, a common source is the categorical booklet of plans (Fig. 3-1). This catalog cuts down the search by presenting many plans with certain common features. Catalogs are available in such categories as split-level homes, ranch-style homes, period Americana homes, duplexes, log homes, and vacation cottages. In the early 1980s more solar and earth-sheltered plans became available.

CHARACTERISTICS OF THE CATALOG PLAN

The catalog plan is usually presented on a page or a half-page. It shows a floor plan and an artist's perspective view in color or black and white. A short descriptive paragraph points out some features and gives the total square footage.

Much like the artist's presentation of a new automobile in a magazine, this view of a home may be a little unrealistic. A contract builder is accustomed to hearing a statement like: "It looks different than it did in the picture." It is usually a matter of proportion that makes the difference. The actual house on a lot appears to be higher, the roof steeper, and the house generally less attractive during construction. Those towering trees and broad expanses of winding concrete drive shown by the artist are frequently missing.

FIGURE 3-1 Typical book of plans.

Living-Area Square Feet

The rooms inside the real house can be a real shocker. What appears to be a spacious area on a floor plan turns out to be small or cramped for its intended use. It is easy to fall into demoralizing traps in the planning and building of a house. Some folks begin their project by setting a square-foot maximum that they can afford. *Square footage* refers to the quantity of square feet in a floor plan. A house 26' × 52' is said to contain 1352 square feet of living area. In reality it contains significantly less. The wall thicknesses take up floor space. The more walls, cabinets, built-ins, and closets, the less living area remains.

Cost by Square Foot

A common method of estimating the cost of a home is to arrive at a dollar-per-square-foot analysis. This is a broad and extremely variable ballpark method. It is realistic only when all conditions and specifications can be duplicated from a currently documented project. Many variables will affect the square-foot analysis. Some of them are the cost of a lot, sewer, and water; utility availability and type; accessibility of materials; inflationary rate; mortgage interest rates; cost of materials; local building codes; geographic area; and so on. A factor seldom considered is the ability of the builder to avoid waste. Some of this can be dealt with successfully by developing a nearly perfect modular plan.

BLUEPRINT CHARACTERISTICS

The typical blueprint on the market has changed very little as to drawing technique since being introduced. Had it kept up with the modular concept of construction, the dimensioning technique would be considerably different. In this unit the past and present drawing techniques will be explained so that the reader can achieve the skill of reading a conventional plan. In Chapter 4 the student will be introduced to a new system based upon modularly placed dimensions that are accurate and real.

Typical Blueprint Sets

The typical ''blueprint'' that can be purchased from a catalog may contain as little as one large page of drawings or it may contain many large sheets of drawings, details, and written information. A *universal plan* is one that is intended to be applicable for any part of the country. The consumer should be aware that certain characteristics of a structure are more fitting for particular environmental conditions. For example, flat roofs and low-pitched roofs are poor choices for heavy rain and snow zones. Similarly, a long, sprawling structure with many ells, wings, and corners will present excessive exterior wall surface for heat loss in cold-climate country. A split-level or tailored house with a garage in the lower level is designed for a hillside lot. Such a plan usually fits a specific incline direction. It would be misplaced on a level lot. One of the first things to consider when choosing a plan from an illustrated advertisement is whether the design fits the locality and building site.

MODULAR VERSUS NONMODULAR DESIGN

With the skill developed from Chapter 2, the reader should be able to recognize overall dimensions (OD) that are modular, as well as the degree to which they are modular (major, split, or minor). Some plans for sale do have modular exterior dimensions. These are desirable from the standpoint of material economy. Savings can be had in the foundation, the floor frame and covering, the exterior wall frame, the ceiling, and the roof.

Interior dimensioning is not usually found on the illustrated advertising plan. There is more apt to be a width-and-length figure displayed somewhere near the center of a room to indicate an approximate size. These figures are sometimes rounded off in full feet (usually to the higher number). Some other catalogs will have plans that give these room figures in both feet and inches. Rarely do either of these advertising systems express an exact room size. To find out how close to reality the figures are, one can add all the figures running down one side of the house plan. When the sum equals the overall outside dimension, it is evident that the wall thicknesses were included in the room-size figure. This is misleading. When a room in question is at the corner of the house, it is particularly deceptive. The exterior wall may use up 4 1/2″ of space and the parallel half of the partition one-half that amount (the other half would be subtracted from the adjoining room). When a room is labeled 12' long, its actual length may be 11'-5 3/4″ (12 minus 4 1/2″ and minus 2 1/4″). Should this same room be labeled 14' in the other direction (12 × 14) the room could actually be 11'-5 3/4″ × 13″-5 3/4″. If the draftsman chose to round it off to the nearest inch, it may be stated as 11'-6″ × 13'-6″ (Fig. 3-2). When adjacent room figures along the length or depth of the plan are added and the total falls short of the overall dimension, it indicates that the wall thicknesses are not included in the room sizes (a more realistic representation). For example, should the sum of the rooms be about 1' less than the overall (OA) dimension and there is just one interior partition, the assumption can be made that the draftsman has allowed approximately 4″ of depth per wall thickness (two exterior and one interior). Another example includes a closet. Visualize two bedrooms separated by a closet on the end of a

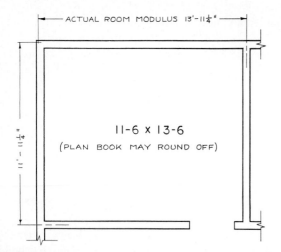

FIGURE 3-2   Plan book room dimensions are not exact.

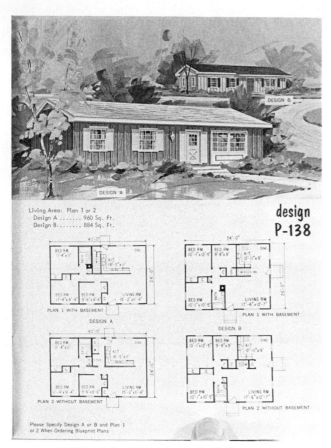

FIGURE 3-3   Typical plan book floor plan.

24'-deep plan. Each room is labeled 11' in the depth direction. The standard minimum depth for a closet (framing dimension) is 24" (2') in most building codes. Therefore, the total thickness of the wall materials must all be taken off the room figure. The amount to subtract will vary a little depending on the material thicknesses that are used throughout and the optional wall alignment that is used on

the exterior. On the catalog plan room sizes must be estimated from what little information is deduced (Fig. 3-3). On a blueprint with material specifications it should be possible to be quite accurate in finding the real size of a finished room.

A common modulus that helps determine a bathroom size is the 5' bathtub. There are other tub sizes, but by far the most common tub is 5' long. When a bathroom is shown with a tub crossing one end, that room is most likely to be 60" wide between the faces of the studs.

READING DIMENSIONS

Overall dimensions on a conventional plan have been standardized for many years to mean the total distance between the corners of the foundation. Chapter 2 explains the modular significance of concrete foundation blocks (the 16" modulus).

Unlike blocks, poured concrete has no modulus because it comes in a fluid state. Whatever can be formed can be poured. The modular significance is not in the finished material. It is in the concrete forms. It is also in the wooden framework that goes on top of the concrete. Long-lasting reusable forms made of magnesium or aluminum come in standard-sized units that interlock. There are several sizes of fillers to accommodate horizontal lengths other than combinations of full-form units. The designer who intends to specify a poured concrete foundation should find out the size of the standard and filler form units that are available from local contractors or rental establishments. This knowledge is needed before getting locked into specific dimensions on a plan.

A brick-veneered house may have an overall set of dimensions that includes the depths of brick ledges. A brick ledge is a shoulder in the masonry foundation or block upon which brick or stone veneer rests. The horizontal width of the ledge is usually a 1/2 to 1" greater than the horizontal depth of the veneer to be used. The brick is usually laid flush with the exterior face of the foundation. The additional space (1/2 to 1") behind the brick and the brick comprises a module of depth that coincides with the foundation brick ledge. The presence or absence of the ledge depth in the plan dimensions must be taken into consideration when interpreting a plan. Modularity for framing with wooden products must exclude the masonry brick ledge. For example, a 26 × 48' framework veneered with brick on a 4" ledge will show up on many plans with overall dimensions of 26'-8" × 48'-8". It is a perfect module plan for the wood framing when the brick is discounted.

The overall dimension is taken from the farthest extension of the foundation (Fig. 3-4). The width of the brick ledge may vary in accordance with the method of forming as well as the size of the brick or stone. In a wooden form

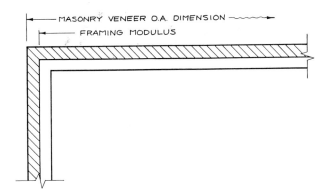

FIGURE 3-4 The foundation line is the starting point of dimensions.

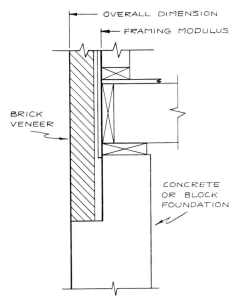

FIGURE 3-5 Brick-veneer siding adds 8″ to the framing modulus.

kit the brick shelf is usually formed by an insert box around the upper perimeter inside the main form. The sum of the depths of the shelves on the opposite sides of a foundation are seldom modular. To have a minimum of 4″ of bearing for floor joist ends and a 4″ brick ledge it is necessary to have a minimum 10″-thick foundation (Fig. 3-5). The joist header and sheathing account for the other 1 1/2 to 2″ of space. This makes a situation where the overall dimension appears to be nonmodular. In reality the part of the foundation on which the house frame rests may be modular, although the overall dimension does not appear to be. If it is a question of which modularization is preferred, the overall brick dimension or the wooden frame lines, this author will choose the wood frame. The rationale is that no latitude exists with the wood units down the linear dimensions of a plan, whereas bricks and stone are assembled in conjunction with fluid mortar. The vertical joints can be tightened up or lengthened out to make a significant

adjustment in overall length. A poured foundation is easily adapted with forms. A wood unit can be shortened only with resultant waste.

With this understanding some new dimensions may be considered modular when brick veneer is indicated on the plan. For example, a wood-sided house 28′-8″ × 48′-8″ is not modular. This same dimension with brick veneer *is* modular since one can assume that 4″ on all sides is provided for the brick. This leaves a perfect modular size of 28 × 48′ for the framework of the house. The floor plan of such a design will show a double-depth exterior wall. The outer half of the wall is striped with section lines to indicate that it is masonry. This is the drawing symbology that tips off the reader to interpret the overall dimensions.

Openings in a foundation, such as those for windows in a basement wall or crawl space vents, are dimensioned from side to side of the actual concrete opening. Some architects dimension to the center of a masonry opening (Fig. 3-6). This forces the contractor to use the window or door specifications to find out the precise "rough opening" for masonry that is required. Concrete is so perma-

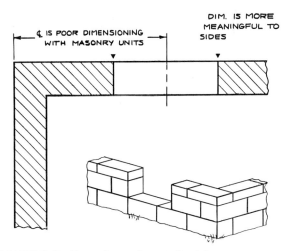

FIGURE 3-6 Poor dimension method for masonry openings.

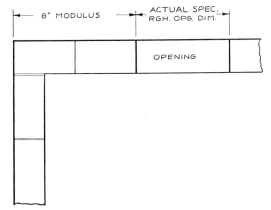

FIGURE 3-7 Openings in block foundations should fit the units when practical.

nent after setting up that alteration becomes a serious problem if an error is made. For this reason the full amount of width and height that is required will (should) be shown on the foundation plan. These figures are to be taken literally and reproduced exactly on the job. It is of the utmost importance that these dimensions be thought out very carefully before being placed on a plan. For example, with block walls, an opening should be designed to fall at an existing mortar joint (end of a unit) and the exact rough-opening size of the window unit from the manufacturer's specifications must be known in advance (Fig. 3-7).

INTERPRETING THE FLOOR PLAN

Interpretation of a floor plan is the art of making small changes in the plan for structural or economic improvement without altering the basic design. Unlike the concrete openings, dimensions on the floor plan are open to interpretation (change). What this really means on a conventional plan is that the draftsman has usually created a design, a grouping of rooms, without consideration for the structural framework under or around the rooms. It is left to the builder to deal with the complications that arise. Some professional builders will make no changes. It is their belief that the architect is responsible. Whatever the architect orders via the plan will be delivered regardless of added cost. Extra material is used where needed as well as extra labor time. The amateur, on the other hand, may not recognize nonmodularity or the need for additional strengthening members. A poorly placed partition calls for additional floor joists. The amateur may simply omit this requirement. Such a structural weakness may be completely covered from sight when the house is completed. Only after the structure begins to settle and the materials shrink and stabilize do the cracks and sags appear.

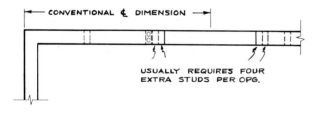

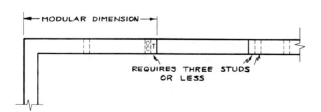

FIGURE 3-8 Moving a rough opening saves a stud.

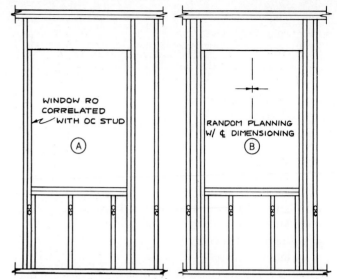

FIGURE 3-9 (a) A window opening coordinated with the wall framing is better dimensioned to the OC stud edge. (b) An opening dimensioned to the centerline seldom correlates with the OC studs, causing extra labor, extra materials, and inefficient construction.

One of the simplest alterations of a floor plan is the shifting of a window to the right or left. On each side of a window opening there is a shortened stud called a *trimmer* which holds up the header above the window (Fig. 3-8). The *header* crosses the window opening and supports the roof so that no weight is placed on the window casing. The trimmers are nailed to a stud on each side. The most common spacing for all the studs is 16". Window openings in a wood-frame wall are traditionally dimensioned to a centerline (Fig. 3-9). This location will most often put both of the trimmer and stud combinations somewhere in the space between common stud locations. A saving of one stud can always be accomplished by moving the rough opening to the right or left a few inches (toward the closest common stud). The trimmer is then nailed to a common on-center stud which is already there.

In the early years of our country, many homes were built with symmetrical fronts. Examples are the colonial, the federal, and the saltbox. These designs did not permit altering of window locations on the front. On the front, for example, the windows were spaced equally from the corners of the house or evenly spaced apart from each other. Frequently, they were precisely aligned with dormers above. Contemporary designs have departed from the symmetrical plan. Most contemporary designs have the potential for shifting an opening a few inches right or left without complication. Labor time and materials are saved. Less custom cutting and fitting of insulation are required since one narrow space has been eliminated.

The kitchen window over the sink is an exception to the rule. This window is most frequently surrounded on both sides with upper cabinets. The manufacturer's standardized cabinet widths will often dictate the precise location of this window. It must not be altered.

Moving a door opening does not present quite as much flexibility as most windows. The location of a door relates to a desired traffic route. Altering the location to save a stud may be unwise if it causes an unnecessary jog or twist in the walking pattern for years to come. A door at the end of a hallway may look better precisely centered with equal wall space on either side of the trim. This is especially true when these spaces are narrow.

Moving a partition from its designated location requires in-depth understanding of several principles. It presents the most perilous of changes but also the most rewarding economically.

The greatest potential is with the partitions that are parallel to the floor joists. Three questions are important: Can the partition be moved without damaging room size? Will a shift of location save a full joist? Can a shift of location be accomplished without undue complication to adjacent construction? When the answer is "yes" to all three questions, there is a potential for saving two studs and one joist and considerable labor. The location of a partition is indicated on a conventional plan by a dimension to the centerline of the frame. It is the blueprint interpreter's job to figure out how close the partition will be to an on-center joist. When it is over the joist or directly alongside it, the location permits the addition of a single joist trimmer nailed directly to the on-center joist for the required support. In an optimum design, the exterior wall studs will bear directly over the joists. The partition will line up off the edge of an on-center stud (Fig. 3-10). This will save a stud in the adjoining wall at each end of the partition, as the on-center stud is then a part of the intersection post. The added floor joist trimmer will be placed fully under the partition against the on-center joist. When

it appears unwise to shift an unmodularly placed partition to this location, there are two possible methods of strengthening the floor frame under the partition. One is to add an extra set of double joists directly under the partition (costly). The other method is to add one extra joist under the partition and block it to the closest on-center joist. These methods are described and illustrated in Chapter 6. A third alternative is to use several solid blocks between the on-center joists. This method prevents the partition, which is flexible until covered, from sagging the subflooring. This method, which does not add strength but only stiffness, is satisfactory when a trussed roof is used because the ceiling weight is not placed on the partition. Blocking the on-centered joists under the partition does not add appreciably to the load-carrying capacity. This method is not satisfactory when a nontrussed conventional ceiling is used. Part of the weight of a conventional ceiling and the partition are placed on the floor. This calls for strengthening of the floor frame by adding one or two joists as described.

PHILOSOPHY OF PLAN REVISION

Whether or not the builder should engage in minor alteration of a plan, or make major changes, or make any changes at all is dependent on several things. Some of these are:

1. The extent of the builder's experience or knowledge
2. The feasibility of the plan
3. The cost objectives (the budget)
4. The construction time schedule

Builder's Knowledge

A builder's experience and knowledge play a major role in any alteration that is considered. To venture into unknown areas of change without adequate supplementary planning is to court disaster. For the first-timer this means that getting educated is of utmost importance. It requires research, study, and field trips. It requires the banking of knowledge through the acquisition of reference material, the noting of information gained from experts (not the clerk at the supply yard—he does not have time), and graphic recording (sketching details on site). An important element for the amateur is in-depth curiosity. For the experienced person, an open mind and a desire to upgrade methods is helpful. One should not seek out simple instruction. It is important to know *why* a system is being used. If a resource person cannot adequately explain why an operation is done a certain way, it is subject to question. Many builders do things a particular way because the method has been handed down from one generation to another. This type of learning is sometimes difficult to change when conditions warrant a change. Experience does not automatically equate to

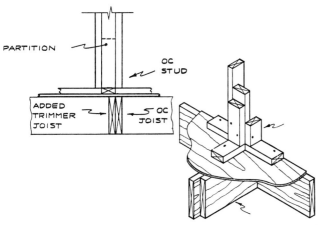

FIGURE 3-10 Coordination of partition with OC stud and joist.

knowledge. A case in point is the coming of the roof truss. Many builders failed to alter their interior header designs (trusses eliminate the need for interior bearing walls and smaller headers are adequate in certain locations). "If it was right for grandpa, it is good enough for me" is a statement that does away with progress. Overbuilding or underbuilding is the result of a lack of up-to-date knowledge. It is costly and sometimes unsound.

Plan Feasibility

The feasibility or practicality of the plan can dictate much change. Several characteristics are important. The older the plan, the less likely that it was developed around current materials. The universal plan sold through catalogs is apt to be 5 to 50 years old. Rather than upgrade the basic floor plan, the companies that reproduce these plans will include an option detail page. On this page will be drawings of construction details. Each part will feature four or five different ways of assembling a particular part of the house. Usually, all but one of these methods is obsolete. Sometimes all of them are. In any case, it requires some fieldwork to determine the best alternative. It takes visits to many building sites. One trip to one site is not adequate. It may be the obsolete or unsatisfactory example that is observed. Several samplings are needed so that a value judgment can be made. A cross-country excursion is most valuable, as the entire local scene may represent a uniformly antiquated building system.

A custom-made plan by a local firm is likely to hold better potential for successful building execution than the mail-order plan. When questions arise, the architect is available to answer them. There is also a better chance that the plan will be oriented to the specific building site as well as to the geographic area. The architect is familiar with the availability of certain materials in the area and will avoid prescribing unobtainable items.

Budget

Cost objectives can play an important role in plan alteration. Many things can be done to an existing plan to either increase or reduce the cost. One objective may be to enhance a modest plan by using more costly materials on the aesthetic features. More expensive thermal barriers may be specified with long-range economy and current comfort as objectives. When maximum space on a limited budget is the objective, the above-mentioned things may be reversed. Even in the structural part, savings can be achieved by a careful study of the codes. Applying maximum spans and spacing can save a lot of material. *One of the significant areas of savings potential is in modular revision. A plan revised to modular dimensions can gain several hundred feet of space at little or no extra cost. Therefore, the budget under which one is privileged or forced to operate can be an important controlling factor in the type and amount of plan changing.*

Construction Timetable

The construction schedule is an important factor to the professional tract builder. Profit or loss is affected by the number of house units completed annually or by the total square footage. When construction is limited to several standard tried and proven plans, the work is likely to move along at a predictable pace. Making changes in a plan is time consuming. The professional builder must constantly make comparisons between the cost of labor and the cost of materials. Unfortunately, the current pattern is to throw away a lot of usable material because of the added labor cost required to salvage it. We see mounds of "scrap" being bulldozed into holes or loaded on dump trucks. The individual homebuilder is not usually faced with this dilemma. Time is not as important. About the only loss he may incur by extending the building schedule a month or two is the rent he may be paying or the inflation of material costs. This is not all lost by comparison because there will ultimately be taxes on the new property. In times of high inflation he may suffer the cost of higher-priced material as time passes. On the other hand, a great many home builders have regular jobs. In times of inflation their salaries keep pace, so any loss is relative. He also has the potential of buying material at low seasonal times because he can wait with no direct effect on his income.

CONCLUSIONS

The conventional plan is more of a guide toward a visual conception of a house than it is a specific road map. It can be altered and revised to accommodate a better mating of structural materials than it usually contains. To revise a plan successfully, a person must prepare by learning principles and investigating successful current practices. There is no substitute for knowledge and skill. Without knowledge a prospective builder can aspire to nothing greater than imitation. Imitation is a gamble with obsolescence and inferiority. It may cause unintentional code violations. It can result in the reproduction of poor practices. The acquisition of knowledge and skill, by comparison, is a noble objective that will produce confidence and pride in a job well conceived and well done.

REVIEW TOPICS

1. Explain what is meant by the term "square footage" in a house plan.

2. Explain why a room may turn out to be smaller than the size given on a catalog illustration.

3. Explain the effect that brick veneer has on your assessment of the modularity of the overall dimensions seen on a plan.

4. Explain why an overall dimension of 28'-8" × 48'-8" on a brick-veneered house plan is modular but is nonmodular on a wood-sided-frame house plan.

5. Should a layout carpenter make changes at the building site from the plan furnished to an owner by a local architect? Why?

6. What is a universal plan?

7. What is a specific or custom plan?

8. Can a knowledgeable person revise a nonmodular plan and gain square footage at about the same cost or sustain the same footage at a reduced cost?

9. What three things on a conventional plan can usually be moved, thereby affecting savings of both material and labor?

Chapter 4
DRAWING
THE MODULAR PLAN———————

IMPORTANCE OF PLANNING

There are many fine textbooks available that teach the art of drafting. Such is not the primary purpose of this chapter. The main objective in this chapter is to pull together the information given thus far into a usable planning skill. Toward this objective the reader has been exposed to the importance of adequate planning and to the significance of modularity in home building. Not many over-the-counter blueprints are basically planned on modular principles. Few if any are dimensioned modularly throughout. Let us review some familiar planning techniques and delve into the advantages of some new and proven skills.

Conventional floor plans are seldom related to the specific location of structural components of the floor and walls. In this chapter it will be shown how plans can be laid out and dimensioned in a new way that coordinates the plan with the structure. This technique will make interpretation of a plan unnecessary. The builder can follow the plan to the letter. There is now no other known source of the technique you are about to learn. Why bring it into existence? Because it is much simpler. The advantages of a modularly drawn plan are that it:

- Needs no on-site alteration
- Eliminates hidden structural problems
- Is a direct form of communication from the drawing board to the builder
- Requires far fewer dimensions on a crowded plan

As a final persuader, the system has been field tested for over a decade and found to be eminently successful. The author is not naive about the acceptance of a new or radical departure from the conventional. He does, however, have hopes that the students of architecture and building trades who read this text will see the advantages that are involved. Perhaps these students will be the first to break out of the old mold. It takes some courage.

FLOOR PLANNING

In actual construction a structure rises from the ground and continues on up until the highest part is put in place. There are five basic sequential units of construction:

1. The foundation and/or basement
2. The floor
3. The walls and partitions
4. The ceiling and roof
5. The trim and finish work

Construction progresses in that order. The initial planning of a home, when you are ready to put something down on paper, starts with the indoor living areas. This is called *floor planning*. There are many features and factors that will be coordinated into a total property concept. All the desirable things one wants in a home should be written down like a shopping list. When all these things are brought together, the first drawing to consider will be the floor plan.

Definition of a Floor Plan

A floor plan appears to be a top view where one looks down into an open house. It is actually a sectioned view. Imagine that a huge saw cuts through a house horizontally at a point halfway up the walls. The top is taken away. Like the Jolly Green Giant we gaze down into the open rooms. We see the arrangement of all the areas, the partitions, the doors and windows, the cabinets, the permanent fixtures, and semipermanent appliances. The floor plan provides this view and includes dimensions to locate each feature.

Principles of Room Arrangement

A study of this subject should be made from one or more of the architectural planning resources found on library shelves. Only a few basics and pitfalls will be covered here, as the main objective of this text is to coordinate modular concepts into planning.

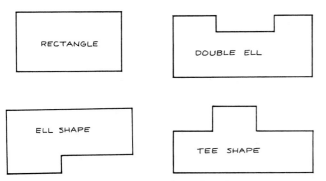

FIGURE 4-1 Basic floor plan shapes.

Three basic perimeter shapes of houses make up the largest percentage of construction. These are the rectangle, the ell, and the tee (Fig. 4-1). Any other shapes that have 90° corners are variations of the basic three. A tee and an ell sometimes evolve off the rectangle when a particular area in the plan seems too small. A room may simply be pushed out beyond the rectangle, thus creating an L shape.

Criteria and Rules for Planning

Making a choice of perimeter shape is dependent on such influences as the budget, aesthetics, climate, lot size, terrain, surrounding houses, family composition, family living style, and others. The budget will influence the size and complexity of the proposed house. Only so many square feet and so many corners can be turned for a specified amount of construction money. In a highly fluctuating economy, it is wise to plan a structure that will use only 80% of the money available. The 20% cushion will usually be used up by unpredictables. Without such a cushion, the

financial situation is usually overextended. Generally speaking, the rectangular floor plan, not in excess of 28′ deep, will net the most economical shape to build and maintain. Each additional ell attached to the basic rectangle adds exterior wall surfaces. This drives up the cost of heat and air conditioning.

When attractiveness is the overriding objective and money is no deterrent, any conceivable shape is within reach with only one design limitation. That limitation is found in the roof. Some shapes cannot be roofed properly for adequate drainage. When a plan is really being extended here and there, the planner should attempt to place a roof diagram on it before too much time is expended on interior arrangements. There must be a downhill draining direction for each roof segment.

Considering the climate of the area is important. A study should be made of temperature variations, sunny days per year, and the angle of the sun on the shortest and longest day of the year in the specific latitude. The sun's angle, for example, will have a direct bearing on the length of a roof overhang that should be planned in coordination with the window heights on the east, south, and west sides of a house.

Lot size and shape can force a limited choice of floor plan shapes. A narrow, deep lot can limit the house plan choices to narrow-fronted styles with rear-approach garages. A hillside plot may dictate a multilevel plan. A high water table in the ground can rule out a basement or crawl space and dictate a slab. The laundry, furnace, water heater, and recreation areas normally found in a basement will have to be accommodated in the slab-floor plan. Considerable extra space footage will be required.

Existing houses in a neighborhood will influence the style and shape of your plan. Some conformity of style is desirable to sustain the continuity of a neighborhood. When one house is totally out of synchronization with the other homes in an area, it looks out of place and is sometimes considered to be the monstrosity of the neighborhood. Such a house will rarely bring its full value at sale time even though the structure is a good buy in every other respect.

Family size and life-style are considerations in developing a plan. Children's rooms need to be segregated from adult rooms. A major fault in the traditional American floor plan is the clustering of all bedrooms, with their nearly nonexistent sound privacy. Grandparents need secluded areas. Families that enjoy outdoor eating and lounging will opt for the plan with easy access from kitchen to patio and pool.

Basic planning rules govern where rooms should and should not go. There are criteria from experience regarding sizes, sight lines, and traffic routing. Not all codes cover these items. The emphasis of a code is usually based on safety. Those items that are usually covered in codes are noted in the following list. Other items relate to simple liveability. Criteria and good practice rules for floor planning are:

1. An entrance area (foyer) is desirable. A front door directly into a living room provides no privacy. A primary entrance should include at least a minimum sight barrier.
2. The traffic routes should not pass through conversation or activity areas. Alternative routes are needed.
3. A minimum corridor width of 40″ is desirable (36″ is a minimum cited in many codes).
4. Minimum primary entrance door width is 36″ (code). Secondary entrance is 32″ minimum.
5. Minimum interior passage door width is 30″. Minimum bathroom door is 24″ (code).
6. Limit corridor length to the shortest possible amount. Use the wheel-hub concept.
7. Minimum closet depth is 2′ (code). Small rooms need larger closets. The smaller the room, the greater the need for storage space.
8. Sight access into the main bathroom should not be possible from anywhere except the adjoining corridor (code).
9. A washer and dryer should not face onto a traffic lane (a principle frequently violated).
10. Doors should swing away from living areas and against an adjacent wall so that they are out of the way when in the open position.
11. Minimum window size: 4% ventilation, 10% light (percentage of room square-foot area) (code). Cross ventilation in corner rooms is advantageous.
12. Show kitchen cabinets 24″ deep on the floor plan.
13. The horizontal minimum length of a stairwell is 10′ (more is desirable). Any less length will not provide adequate height.

PRELIMINARY SKETCHING

Sketching is a primary step in the development of a plan. Most people feel that they cannot draw or sketch. However, if they follow some simple techniques, their lack of confidence can usually be overcome.

Proportion and Parallelism

There are two areas of plan sketching skill where assistance is most needed. One is making parallel lines. The other is keeping proportionate sizes. There are methods and tools to eliminate both of these problems.

Graph paper with 1/4″ grid lines is an ideal material with which to get started. The most common scale for floor plans on a formal blueprint is 1/4″ equals 1′. The squares on the graph paper provide a measuring modulus simply by counting them. To control parallelism of walls and partitions, one simply sketches on top of or parallel to the light green or pink grid lines. Any 8 1/2″ × 11″ graph paper will contain enough squares for a plan up to about 40′ long. A pencil is the only tool needed. One third of a square is about the thickness of a wall. As an example, take the wall-lineup system, where the exterior surface of the studs is flush with the foundation. The wall will be exactly 4″ from the building line (foundation line) to the interior face when 1/2″ wallboard (drywall) is used for wall covering on top of 2 × 4 studs. The actual size of the stud is 3 1/2″. A partition with 1/2″ wallboard on each side will be 4 1/2″ deep. The difference is unimportant when sketching on grid paper. The important thing to keep in mind is that the major modules are four squares (4′). This places the 16″ spacing modules 1 1/3 squares apart. The grid makes it easy to visualize the hidden structural members of the plan. This aids in the coordinated placement of partitions, joists, and studs.

Basic Room Clusters

After studying a number of rectangular floor plans, it will be noted that some standard room arrangements exist. Most of the smaller plans (two- and three-bedroom) have only a few variations. The living room is in one corner of the house. The eating area and kitchen are in an adjacent corner. The bedrooms and bathroom occupy the other end of the rectangle (Fig. 4-2). Closets are sandwiched in between the rooms as much as possible so that additional corners do not jut out into living areas and traffic routes. Corridors should be traffic hubs, not long thoroughfares. Stairways and corridors are most efficient at the core or central part of the rectangle, where they pass between other rooms.

Where there is one bathroom, it should be readily

FIGURE 4-2   Basic two-bedroom layout.

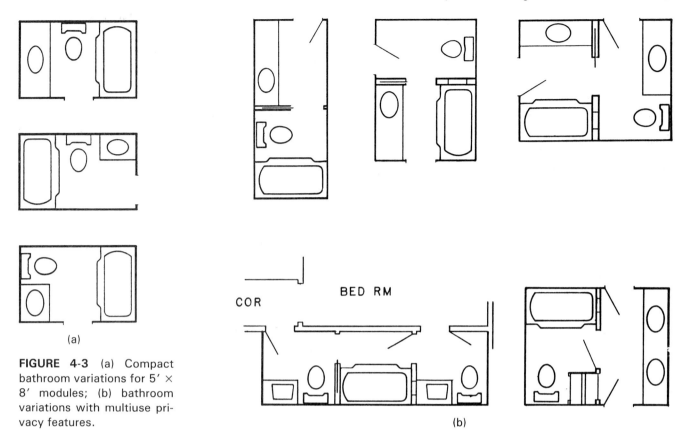

FIGURE 4-3 (a) Compact bathroom variations for 5' × 8' modules; (b) bathroom variations with multiuse privacy features.

accessible from all bedrooms and not too far from the kitchen. Two types of bedroom–bath clusters are most common. One places the bathroom (Fig. 4-3) and one bedroom side by side on one side of the house. The other bedroom (or pair) is placed across the corridor on the other side of the house. This cluster of four rooms takes up one end of the rectangle. To save money the bathroom can be grouped behind the kitchen partition in such a way that

long plumbing pipes are minimized (Fig. 4-4). The other variation places the bathroom between two bedrooms at the end of the rectangle. This arrangement is limiting, as it creates narrow bedrooms with all but the deepest-spanned plan.

Sound privacy is an important objective to keep in mind. This can be achieved by placing closets between rooms (Fig. 4-5). Often they can be designed back to end

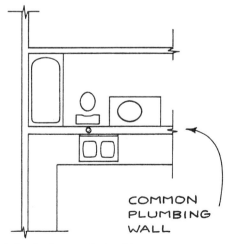

FIGURE 4-4 A clustered plumbing arrangement provides installation economy.

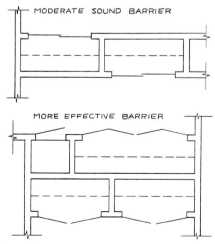

FIGURE 4-5 Closets may be arranged to provide a sound barrier function between adjoining rooms.

or end to end in such a way that there is no single wall between any two bedrooms for sound to penetrate.

Where to Start

There are two ways to go about the task of sketching a floor plan. One is to use the knowledge just gained and attempt to invent a plan from scratch. Recognizing some pitfalls in advance may be helpful. One of these the author calls the "golden-line syndrome." An idea goes from the imagination to the paper. Some lines appear. Soon there develops a structural or conceptual conflict, a roadblock to progress. The mind goes into negative subconscious nonproductive gear. "I cannot accept what I see. I have too much time invested to discard it." The tendency is to stick with it in the vain hope that a problem can be resolved or be rationalized away. The lines become very valuable, painfully so. They are your offspring, and you will not throw them out. The solution is in the second quote, ". . . too much time invested. . . ."

Brainstorm the plan when working from scratch. Plan from the beginning to make four or five fast plans. Stop progress immediately on any plan that is bogged down by the same problem. Start the next trial run. After several attempts there will be enough plans from which to choose. Keep at it until a potentially successful plan is reached.

The resource-and-revision system is another method of attack. Research is made of all the available plans. Choices are boiled down to a few. Desirable features are lifted from these plans and placed on your sketch. Size and space adjustments are made to conform to the modular ob-

jectives. List all the desirable features you want and try to work them in. Soon you have a feasible sketch that is ready for drawing to a precise scale.

DRAFTING THE FLOOR PLAN

Drafting a plan that is suitable for blueprinting will require some equipment and tools. Essentials are an architectural scale, a triangle, two or more grades of pencils (hard and soft), and a board with a slide bar or a T-square (T-squares have been obsolete since the 1940s but are usable). It takes much more manipulative skill to draw with a T-square than with a slide bar, but with some practice an adequate job is possible. The cost of these items, including a board with a slide bar, will be much less than hiring a professional to produce a drawing for you.

Drafting Is a Language

Drafting is sometimes referred to as the language of lines (Fig. 4-6a). For simple designing, two primary line widths are used. The object being drawn should stand out boldly so that the shapes of things are very clear (Fig. 4-6b). To produce this effect, a soft-lead pencil is used. All lines that are part of the structure will be drawn as object lines. Some consistency of line thickness (width) can be maintained if the lead point is maintained at about the same sharpness throughout the drawing. The lead point can be kept sharp longer simply by revolving the pencil in your thumb and first finger as the pencil is pulled across the paper (Fig.

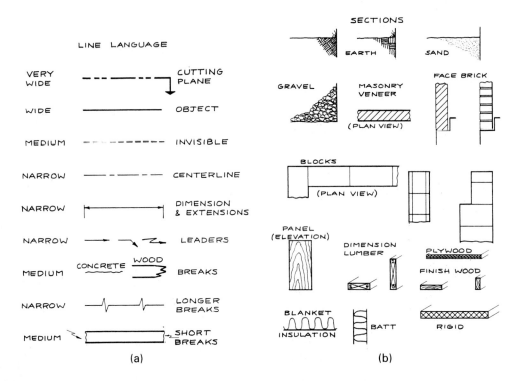

FIGURE 4-6 (a) Drafter's alphabet of lines; (b) architectural symbols.

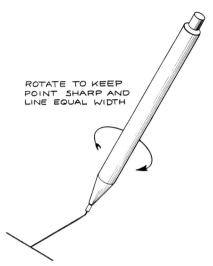

ROTATE TO KEEP
POINT SHARP AND
LINE EQUAL WIDTH

FIGURE 4-7 Rotating a drawing pencil improves the quality and consistency of a line and keeps the point uniformly tapered.

4-7). Whenever possible, the pencil should be pulled away from your body. This will produce more consistent line thickness. Pushing the pencil instead of pulling quickly puts a flat surface on the end of the lead. Because the point is tapered, it widens as it is worn away. The farther it is pushed, the wider and fuzzier the line becomes. Start the drawing by making all object lines very lightly. This can be accomplished with either hard or soft lead as long as very little pressure is applied. Hard lead is preferred for the first light outlining. Keep the lines just dark enough to be seen. Then it is easy to erase runover corners or to make changes. Heavy-pressured lines frequently engrave the paper and become impossible to eradicate. Also, the light-line technique of starting helps a person to avoid the golden-line syndrome because it is so easy to change lines. The object lines used for walls, partitions, foundations, and so on, will be darkened to their finished width only after all dimensional corrections and changes have been concluded.

Thin lines are used to denote all other features of the plan, such as dimension lines (with their extension lines), centerlines, electrical switch lines ("legs"), and notation arrows. It is a mistake to think that line quality is light or dark. Actually, the lightness or darkness comes from the width of the line. For successful blueprinting, all lines must be dark enough to be impenetrable by the light rays of the machine. A hard-lead pencil is used to make narrow lines because it can be sharpened to a finer point, resists breaking, and stays sharp longer.

There are several other qualities of lines as seen in Fig. 4-6. It will be sufficient for the beginner to master the two-line-width technique. More line qualities may be put to use as experience and the scope of drafting advances.

Choosing the Reproduction Method

It is usually necessary to have several copies of the floor plan. This means that an original drawing that can be reproduced is needed. Years ago, copies of drawings had to be made by copy drafters (tracers). Now, this job is done by several mechanical and electronic means. One is the blueprint maker. Another is the copier-type reproducer, such as the Xerox machines. The most sophisticated is the CAD (computer-assisted drawing). The blueprinter does not produce a true blueprint. The name "blueprint" came from the early technique, which produced a blue background and left white lines. The modern white printers produce a white background with blue or black lines, depending on the paper used. Builders and architects still refer to the copies as "blueprints." They are actually "whiteprints."

Inexpensive reproductions can be made using a copier. No special transparent drawing paper is required. Any good-quality white paper can be used for the original. The only serious limitation is the size of the reproduction that can be obtained. Machines that are available to the public in post offices and shopping malls do not reproduce anything larger than legal-sized paper (8 1/2" × 14"). Nevertheless, a floor plan up to about 28' × 56' can possibly be reproduced by this method. Obviously, there will be no room left on the paper for conventions or details. Two advantages of this simple method are a minimum reproduction cost and a very compact plan. It can be stapled to a scrap piece of plywood or carried around the job on a clipboard. The disadvantage is that many more sheets will be needed to cover all the other details and specifications.

For those who plan to make whiteprints from the original drawing, it will be necessary to purchase a good-quality vellum tracing paper. This paper is available in several sizes. Some standard sizes are designated by letter. A size is 9" × 12", B size is 12" × 18", C size is 18" × 24", and D size is 24" × 36". Note that in each step up, the smaller dimension is doubled. This makes it possible to cut the paper down from the D size into the smaller standard sizes. Other proportioned sizes in between these can be purchased. The size of a drawing board to buy, the general size of the houses that will be drawn, and the paper size that will be purchased should all be coordinated before buying either a board or paper.

Transferring the Sketch to the Drawing

Having used the square counting method on the grid paper, most of the locations that require dimensioning will be well defined. The accuracy of pencil lines on a sketch is not important. The object on a working plan is to pinpoint with complete accuracy the locations of all corners and openings. To do this, it is necessary to know the actual size of

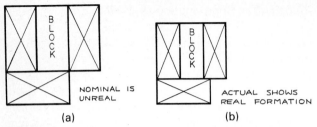

FIGURE 4-8 (a) Unreal nominal representations are often misleading. (b) Actual scaled drawings are true representations.

each designated piece of material. Some books on the market today have drawings, mostly details, done in nominally sized materials that are unrealistic and misleading, (Fig. 4-8a). A "two by four" is not 2″ × 4″ in delivered size. It is 1 1/2″ × 3 1/2″. Correct dimensioning is not possible when nominal designations are used. The drafter may label parts by nominal designations but must never use nominal sizes in the dimensions that are placed on a drawing. It must be constantly remembered that the carpenter works with actual sizes, not nominal designations (Fig. 4-8b). **Dressed lumber sizes** were changed in the late 1960s. Prior to that time nominally designated 2″-thick wood was dressed to 1 5/8″ for many years. Today, all mills plane the dimension lumber to 1 1/2″. This makes the job much easier for the layout person on the building crew because the larger 1/2″ modulus can be used instead of eighths of an inch. The tongue of a framing square has always been 1 1/2″ wide. No longer is it necessary to draw an edge mark and place an X next to it to show on which side of the mark the stud should be lined up. Now a mark can be traced on each side of the tongue, and the stud accurately placed between the marks (Fig. 4-9). There is no confusion whatever when the stud goes between the lines.

Strangely, there was no communication from the tradesman at the building site to the drafter at the board when this lumber size change occurred. Architectural schools did not pick up on the potential that was present in this seemingly insignificant change. Let us proceed to find out how this and our modular knowledge can be put to work on the drawing board.

IMPROVED DIMENSIONING SYSTEM

Stacked dimensions of significance (Fig. 4-10) are more important to the builder than a string of irrelevant dimensions whose total equals an overall figure. A main feature of the system about to be described is that all measurements are taken from the same starting point. This beginning point will be referred to as the *zero point* or *POB* (point of beginning). The zero point is most often going to be the corner of the building or another modular reference point from which to take a measurement. The layout person measures from this point. Why go back to this point when measuring for partitions or window openings?

The psychology is simple and proven by experience. Placement errors on the job are seldom made because of an inability to read the tape measure. Errors come in two other ways. One is mathematical error. The other error potential comes from visual and manipulative limitations of the tools and the operator.

Mathematical errors are common when dimensions are accumulated from one spot to another, to another, and still another. Few layout persons can add a series of feet, inches, and mixed denominator fractions in the mind reliably. Such a problem forces them to do addition with pencil and paper to work out the totals from a starting point. Why do we need singular dimensions from a starting point? When measurements are made by resetting the tape from place to place, an element of inaccuracy creeps in no matter how hard the workers try to be accurate. Experiment with a simple example. Use a ruler to measure a long room.

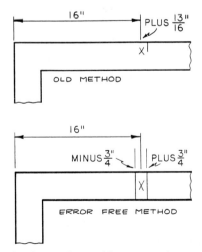

FIGURE 4-9 Old-style marking was edge to edge. Current marking of both sides is more trouble-free.

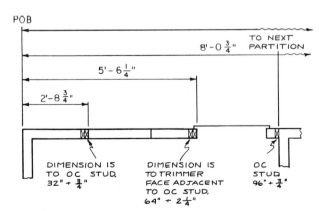

FIGURE 4-10 "Stacked" dimensions that originate from POB are more meaningful for the carpenter.

Then use a tape measure that is longer than the room. It is humanly impossible to gain the same accuracy with the shorter measuring instrument. Each time it is moved, an element of inaccuracy is introduced. Every measurement in the construction of a house should be made with a tape measure of sufficient length to go from the POB to the object being located. Tape measures of 16, 25, 50, and 100' are desirable on any full-size house project. Accuracy is the result of operator attitude, an understanding of where error potential lies, and adequate equipment.

See Fig. 4-10 for examples of stacked dimensions. These dimensions need not go all the way across the house when modular overall dimensions exist (another good reason for modularity). Take a sample house length of 48'. Suppose that there are five intersecting partitions and four windows along the wall. Nine location dimensions are needed. An overall dimension can go on whichever side of the house has the least other dimensions. Four of the dimensions may zero point from the left side. The remaining five dimensions may zero in from the right building line (zero point). Remember that using either end of the building line for the POB works only when the overall dimension is divisible by the stud spacing modulus (usually 16" but sometimes 24" as with 2 × 6 studs). With this system of dimensioning there remains a space (a room or area) near the middle of the exterior wall that is undimensioned. It does not require dimensioning for layout purposes. It may be dimensioned for checking purposes, although it is not really necessary. Because the plan is drawn to a scale of 1/4" to 1' it is a simple matter for the layout carpenter to "scale" the distance off the plan with a tape measure. Scaling means laying the tape measure on the plan and finding the distance to the nearest spacing module. One inch on the tape equals 4' on the plan. An undimensioned central locality, as an example, might measure 4" and about 5/16". At a scale of 1/4" = 1' a point on the tape a little beyond the 5/16" mark but short of 3/8" equals 4" (one-third of a foot). In the example this indicates a modular room length of 17'-4". The layout person can check this out quickly by counting the stud spaces between marks already placed on the plates. In this example if the spaces do not check out to be 13 spaces (3 for 4'), there is an error in one of the other dimensioned areas.

A dimension should tell a precise distance from the zero point to the vertical surface of a partition frame. There it forms a corner with an on-center stud of the wall it intersects. Placing a dimension to the center of a partition creates needless mathematics. There is no logical reason for a plan to focus on the centerline of a partition when it is one edge of the partition stud that will be the lineup surface. The choice of which partition face to dimension to will depend on whether you want the partition in the space to the right or the left of the on-center (OC) stud. This will have been determined at the time of sketching on the grid paper. It is now time to figure out the exact dimension to the location.

Calculating Exact Dimensions

Take an example where the first opening in an exterior wall adjacent to the corner of the house is a window (Fig. 4-11). You choose to coordinate the side of the window that is closest to the corner (the zero point) with the first 4' modulus point (three 16" stud spaces from the corner). A mea-

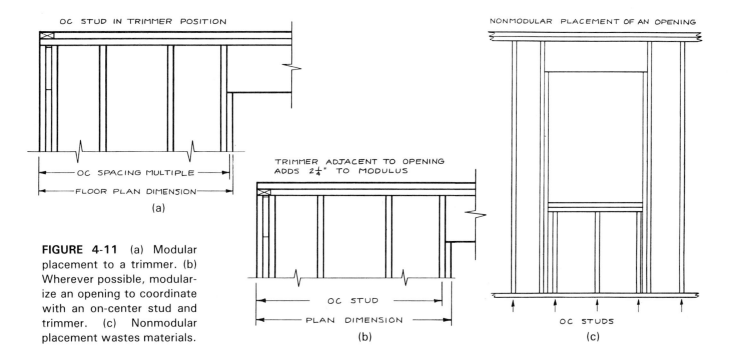

FIGURE 4-11 (a) Modular placement to a trimmer. (b) Wherever possible, modularize an opening to coordinate with an on-center stud and trimmer. (c) Nonmodular placement wastes materials.

surement of 4′ from the corner will reach the OC stud in the center of its thickness. The edge of that stud beyond its center will be 3/4″ farther from the zero point (half the thickness). A 2 × 4 trimmer is required, nailed to the stud, to support the header over the window. This adds another 1 1/2″. The combined distance is 4′ + 3/4″ + 1 1/2″, for a total of 4′-2 1/4″. This is the significant dimension to enter on the plan.

To find the other side of the window opening, a rough-opening (RO) figure may be entered opposite the window. The rough opening is the exact horizontal and vertical space to be framed around into which the window unit will be placed. This information will come from the window manufacturer's specification sheet. Take the figures very literally. Do not alter them. There may be two different ROs listed, one for masonry and one for wood-frame construction. The masonry one is larger, as it provides for the window molding to be pocketed inside the masonry. Ignore the masonry RO, as it applies only to full masonry walls. The brick-veneer house frame will use the frame RO figure. When a spec sheet shows an "overall size" (OA) for a window casement which is larger than the RO column, it can be assumed that the OA designation is for an opening in masonry. When the RO is entered on the floor plan drawing, the figures must be followed with the letter W to indicate width and H to indicate the height of the opening. These entries eliminate the need to reference to a window schedule.

Framing around a bathtub is another example of special dimensioning on the plan to save material. It is not mandatory to place the partition intersection adjacent to a stud in the intersecting wall, but it presents advantages. Let us take an example where the first partition has been purposely located on the side of the stud closest to the POB that occupies the 14′-8″ distance from the starting point (Fig. 4-12). On the other side of this partition is the bathroom. The tub is to be located against the exterior wall and parallel to it. The tub is a standard 5′ model. The tub is framed directly against the stud surfaces, so the opening will be exactly 5′ (60″). Five feet is nonmodular; however, it can be modularly adapted to save a stud. When one end

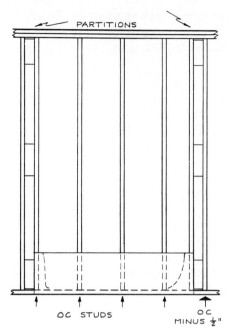

FIGURE 4-13 Move the on-center partition post stud to fit the standard tub opening dimension.

of a 5′ tub room is coordinated to an OC stud, both ends will save a stud by simply offsetting the second partition 1/2″ on the partition post so that it is exactly 5′ from the first partition (Fig. 4-13). This will not materially affect the corner bearing surfaces on which the wall board is placed. Normally, the nailing surface on each side of the corner that is formed is a stud thickness (1 1/2″). By offsetting the partition 1/2″, the surface that remains on the tub side of the partition post is reduced to 1″. Drywall (gypsum board) should be applied to the exterior wall first (on the 1″ corner surface) so that a full inch of corner surface will remain on the interior side of the corner for nail backing. The carpenter must remember to put the partition at the 5′ mark on the T post and not routinely over the partition spacer blocks as is customary on other partition Ts.

Closet framing presents an example that puts the partition farther away from the OC stud, requiring an additional stud. This occurs when a single closet intersects the exterior wall at its end or when two minimum-depth closets are placed back to back and their ends intersect the exterior wall. This is a case in point where it is not imperative that a dimension go all the way back to the zero point. The distance is short and standardized. One reference from the zero point to the OC-connected partition is adequate. From that point on, a closet depth dimension or call out is all that is needed. A *callout* is a specification denoting commonalities or unique features. A common specification callout such as "ALL CLOSETS ARE 2′ DEEP" placed in one of the longest closets will be information enough for the whole plan. Where there are one or two closets of non-standard depth, the call out may read "ALL CLOSETS 2′

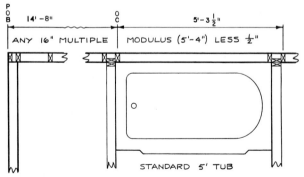

FIGURE 4-12 Modular placement of a 5′ bathtub.

DEEP UNLESS OTHERWISE NOTED." The layout person finds it a simple operation to lay out the 2' depth location using the blade of the framing square (24" long) or tape measure.

The closet that is framed in the rough to a 24" depth will be slightly less when finished. For example, the installation of 1/2"-thick gypsum wallboard will reduce the actual depth to 23". A rough-opening depth of 23 to 24" can be achieved by using two of the 16" stud spacings in the exterior wall. The space from edge to edge of the studs spanning the two spaces is 30 1/2" (32" center to center). Conventionally placed intersecting partition studs will subtract 3 1/2" of space from each side. The remaining RO space for closet depth is 23 1/2". The 1/2" undersize amount can be regained by moving each partition out 1/4" on its partition T post or 3/4" out to produce a 25" RO with a resultant finished depth of 2'. The gap that results between the post spacer blocks is of no significance.

A deeper closet may be framed modularly by using the two 16" spaces but placing the partition intersecting studs both on the same relative sides of the OC outer wall studs. They will both be either on the right side or the left side as you face the exterior wall. The 32" centering is then reduced by only one set of 3 1/2" spacing blocks (Fig. 4-14). The remaining rough-opening depth is 28 1/2". With 1/2"-deep wall covering, the finished closet will be 27 1/2" deep.

Both of these spacing systems make use of the OC studs in the exterior wall frame. The dimensioning from the point of beginning must reflect the actual spaces spanned and the real material thickness of the components. One might think that the regard for such precise planning was not worthy of the effort. The misplacement of a partition intersection would be of minor significance. The mandatory placement of an occasional and uncoordinated T post between OC studs is not significant in a house plan if it occurs in only a few places. A complete disregard for modular placement, however, increases cost dramatically when the quantity of window and door openings and the total intersections of inner and outer walls is considered. Added to this will be the waste materials that will accrue from the modular wall-covering materials. Everything considered, the modular planning task is well worth the time and effort expended.

Regardless of which OC stud is chosen for the attachment of the intersecting partition, the dimension from POB (point of beginning) will reflect a 3/4" plus or minus factor from the modular OC dimension to the stud. The 3/4" figure is half the thickness of the stud. When it is desirable to place the partition intersection on the far side of the stud, the half thickness becomes a plus from POB instead of a minus. Using the same example of an OC stud at 14'-8" from POB, a partition placed on the far side is dimensioned 14'-8 3/4" to the face. Placed on the close side it will be dimensioned 14'-7 1/4". By following this system of plus or minus 3/4" from the modular stud OC position, it is immediately obvious that the partition is modularly placed. Such a plan is extremely easy to read. It eliminates a lot of mental exercise (mathematical checking) and makes layout a simple exercise in association of parts.

Window and Door Dimensioning

In the stacked dimensioning system, door openings are dimensioned to the same POB as window openings (the face of the trimmer next to the opening). Only one of the two trimmers can be placed against an OC stud, as none of the standard door widths coincide with stud spacing. The dimension should be referenced to that trimmer so that the modular association can be recognized. Door sizes are standardized. Rough openings for exterior doors need to be 2 1/2" larger than the finished door. For interior doors, the opening will be 2" wider than the door. Therefore, it is unnecessary to dimension the width of the opening or to dimension both sides from a reference point (zero point). Whenever it is possible to place one side of the opening next to an OC stud, it may be dimensioned in the same way as described for window openings, the sum of the spaces plus 2 1/4" (half a stud plus the trimmer thickness). Should a design call for a doorway to be precisely centered in an entrance or foyer, no dimension line is required. In fact, it is undesirable. A simple centerline is drawn through the opening into the area in which it is to be centered (Fig. 4-15). The door width is indicated in feet and inches parallel to the door symbol line. The layout person will have no difficulty laying out the opening. One simply lays out the two partitions, finds the center point between them, and marks off half the rough opening to the right and left of the center point.

There is a lot of unnecessary dimensioning and duplication on conventional blueprints. Door dimensions are an example. Most of the interior passage doors are of the

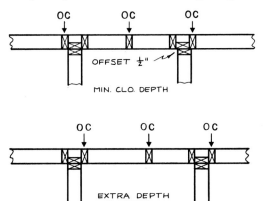

FIGURE 4-14 Standard and oversized closet modular placement.

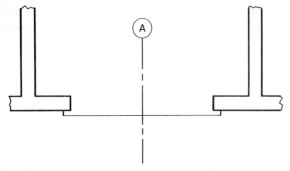

FIGURE 4-15 A centerline in the doorway indicates a door centered in a corridor.

same width (30″). It is only necessary to label the exceptional doors (those that are different). A callout can designate all others. It is a waste of time and space to enter the height of standard doors. All regular home doors are currently standardized at 6′-8″. It takes a special order to get any other height. A notation in the door schedule is all that is needed. Any exceptions can be taken care of on the plan in the old way. The conventional way to call out a door-opening size is to give the finished door width and height in feet and inches without the feet and inch marks. This method was adopted by most architects and drafters after the door manufacturers began the system. A typical door may be stamped on the edge like this: 2-6 × 6-8, meaning a door size of 2′-6″ × 6′-8″. A 3′ door reads 3-0 × 6-8. One should not confuse 3-0 to mean 30″ or 2-0 to mean 20″. 2-0 means 2′ and 0″. Suppose that we have an unusual home with a special entrance that has an oversized door 40″ × 7′. It would be shown as 3-4 × 7-0.

More recently, this system has been further simplified. The dashes are being left out and sometimes the height. All that one sees is a foot figure and a figure smaller in size above and to the right signifying the added inches (Fig. 4-16). A 30″ door is labeled 2^6. The reader must be

FIGURE 4-16 Coded door sizes on new doors.

alert so that this figure is not interpreted as a 26″ door. Similarly, a 3^0 is 36″, not 30″. This system is a step forward in cutting down on the quantity of figures that are needless on a crowded drawing.

Windows have also undergone size designation changes. The quantity of specified dimensions as well as the meaning varies with manufacturers. Some cased windows will have rows of specs across the top and up the side of the window symbol on their specification sheets. There will be specs for the overall dimensions (sometimes listed as ''masonry opening''), for rough openings in wood frames, for ventilation opening size (sash opening), and for individual glass pane sizes or total light area. To top off all this description there is usually a model number that may or may not be coded to the sizes given in the specifications. There are other manufacturers of brands who have simplified the specifying and ordering task by coding the sizes similarly to the door system. There are aluminum window units on the market, for example, which bear only a name and number. The description ''Colonial 3030'' with one manufacturer means a window with a single hung lower sash, six or eight lights per upper and lower half, and a size dimension that frames into a 3′ square opening. A 3844 window is for a 44″-wide by 52″-high opening (3′-8″ × 4′-4″). The numbers read in sequence to mean feet and inches of width by feet and inches of height for a rough opening in a wood frame. It is simple and effective communication when one knows the code.

Being aware of the differences in descriptive technique makes it necessary for the planner to investigate sources and brands at an early stage of the plan development. Such information must be firmed prior to actual framing of the structure. After framing has begun, any changes will be costly in time and money, patience, and morale.

Interior partition framing should follow some continuity that will be reflected in the dimensions. The studs in a centrally located partition that runs parallel to the girder under the floor should be placed on the same centers as the exterior walls (Fig. 4-17). This will cause the ceiling joist to bear directly over the stud, which in turn bears directly over the floor joist. Like the exterior walls, the spacing zero point will be the building line, the outside side of the exterior wall. The designer must keep this in mind when he intends to use one of the OC studs as a unit of a rough door post. The dimension line arrowhead will touch the outer wall at the exterior surface that aligns with the foundation. Doors that are intended to be directly adjacent to an intersecting partition need no dimension whatever (Fig. 4-18). It takes one stud and one trimmer off the partition face to form the corner and start the opening. The one stud is also an integral component of the partition post to which the door opening is adjacent. This first stud with a trimmer attached comprises 3″ of distance from the partition. From

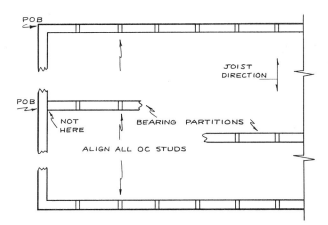

FIGURE 4-17 Align bearing interior studs with exterior studs.

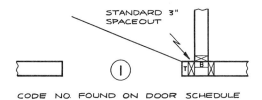

FIGURE 4-18 A door adjacent to a partition requires no locater dimension.

there to the other side of the opening, it is door width plus 2″. When the door is not labeled, it indicates a 30″ door, so the rough opening is 32″.

Partitions parallel to the ends of a house (usually parallel to floor joists) are said to be *nonbearing*. They are parallel to ceiling joists and therefore do not support the ceiling. The studs in these partitions are spaced from the interior surface of the exterior wall frame. Measuring from that surface, the first stud will be against the partition post spacer blocks in the exterior wall. The next stud will straddle the 16″ mark, the next one the 32″ location, and so on. This system should be followed without exception. It provides an index to the location of the studs after the walls are covered. Baseboard, ceiling mold, shelf brackets, and pictures can be installed without searching blindly for the stud. One has only to subtract the wall covering thickness from the first 16″ spacing modulus. From there on, all the studs will be behind the 16″ modulus. Wallboard is placed on the exterior walls first so that an inch of surface remains on the first interior stud to back up the interior sheets of wall covering.

ADAPTING CONVENTIONAL DIMENSIONING TO MODULARITY

For some experienced designers, the transition from the conventional method of dimensioning to the system just

described may be too great a change to make all at once. It is possible to make modular arrangements of structural components and continue dimensioning to the center of a partition. To place a partition adjacent to an OC stud, the dimensional distance to that stud from a reference point will be increased or decreased by 2 1/2″ (Fig. 4-19). The 2 1/2″ is the sum of half the thickness of the OC stud plus half the width of the intersecting partition stud (3/4″ + 1 3/4″ = 2 1/2″). A 2 × 4 stud is 1 1/2″ by 3 1/2″ in cross section. Suppose that a designer desires a living room on the corner of a plan to be about 20′ long. The adjoining partition can be placed on the far side of the fifteenth stud space (three spaces for every 4′). The actual length of the room from frame face to face will be 19′-9 1/4″. Three-quarters of an inch is added to the interior end of the room (half the stud thickness). Then 3 1/2″ is subtracted from the other end (the exterior wall depth). A dimension from the zero point to the center of the partition in this case will be 20′-2 1/2″. From that point on to the next partition center, the dimension will be the total sum of the spaces (modular figure divisible by 16″) when the partition intersects on the same side of the OC stud as did the first wall (the far side in the example above). When it intersects on the near side of the stud, 2 1/2″ will be subtracted. Therefore, all partitions will have one of three characteristics (see Fig. 4-20).

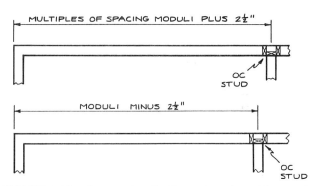

FIGURE 4-19 Conventionally dimensioned partition modularly placed from point of beginning.

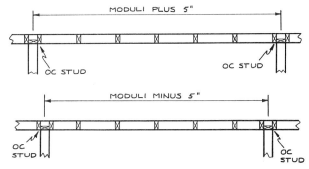

FIGURE 4-20 Conventional dimensioning between modularly placed partitions.

- If both interior partitions intersect on the same respective side of an OC stud, the distance from center to center will be the same as the sum of the spacings.
- Where the partitions are placed on the outsides of the OC wall studs, the center-to-center distance will be the sum of the spacings plus 5″.
- Where the partitions are on the insides of the OC wall studs, the distance center to center will be the sum of the spacings minus 5″.

With this knowledge it is possible to recognize a modularly oriented plan that is dimensioned center to center on the partitions. Most plans on the market are not, thus causing waste or revision by the layout carpenter.

DIMENSIONING SYMBOLS

The symbols used to dimension can be a source of pride or embarrassment. It does not require a lot of skill to make them pridefully. A little practice and determination will get the proper result. The telltale part of a drawing that will brand one as a slovenly amateur quicker than any other is the manner in which the dimension arrowheads are formed. Another giveaway is lettering, especially the indiscriminate mixing of capitals and small letters and longhand figures with lettered figures. An objective of this text is to instill a sense of competence and pride in workmanship.

There are three recognized symbols in use at the ends of dimension lines. They are an *arrowhead*, a large *dot*, and a *slash* (Fig. 4-21). The slash is least preferred. It is too indistinguishable among all the other lines on a drawing. Instead of clarifying terminal points, the slash frequently confuses. Dots are placed dead center over the intersection of the extension line and the end of the dimension line. This does not vary whether the dimension line ends at the extension line or carries on through to another point. The art of dot making is to make them all the same size and round. The size should not get out of hand. Maximum diameter should be about twice that of a type period.

Arrows take some practice (Fig. 4-22). Bear in mind two objectives. The width of the arrow fins should not ex-

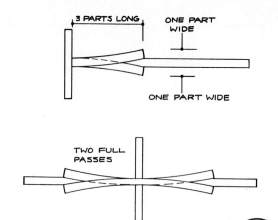

FIGURE 4-22 Magnified view of arrow drawing techniques.

ceed one-third the length. The length should be about 1/8″ to 3/16″. Start at the intersection of the extension and dimension lines and stay on the line for a little ways before starting to flare out. Go back and repeat the flare to the other side of the line. The extension and dimension lines are narrow. The arrowheads may be made with a softer pencil. Even though you stay on the dimension line, the arrowhead will appear darker because it is slightly wider. When you have developed enough expertise to be prideful making single arrows, try some doubles. Change the routine a little. Make the double arrowhead in two passes only. Start on the left side of the extension line. Place the lead point just above the dimension line. Sweep down onto the line and carry through across the extension line. Wind up this single stroke the same way you made the upper half of a single arrowhead. Return to the left side and reproduce the motion on the underside. Keep one thing in mind. The arrowhead should be slim and sharp pointed. The flared end is no wider than one-third the length of the arrowhead (1/16″).

Dimension figures are made in the printed style (Fig. 4-23). Longhand figures are never used on any kind of drafting. The figures may be placed in a space, a break in the dimension line, or may be placed 1/16″ above the line. Above the line is the traditional architectural system; however, it takes a lot more space and may not be practical

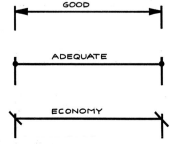

FIGURE 4-21 Dimension line terminus indicators.

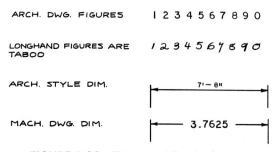

FIGURE 4-23 Figure and line techniques.

with the stacked dimension system. Whichever technique is practiced, use the same system throughout. Figures are given in feet and inches with an 1/8″ dash between. A dimension less than 1′ may be given in inches only. Practice is the key to good-looking figures, arrows, and letters.

DRAWING THE FOUNDATION PLAN

Now that the shape and size of your floor plan has been firmed, the foundation can be drawn with ease. This is the correct order of planning. One should never make a plan for a foundation first. That would cause a forced confinement to a predetermined area and make floor planning very difficult. Obviously, the foundation and floor plan require exact coordination. When a floor plan has been developed on the modular principle, the foundation will also be modular. This provides the option of either poured concrete or precast concrete blocks for the building material. A nonmodular floor plan does not exclude blocks for the foundation, but it causes waste and extra labor.

Wall Thickness

The foundation view is taken horizontally through the wall similarly to the floor plan. It is a section view. The heavy outlines will show the outer and inner edges of the foundation wall. The thickness of the wall may vary depending on the load it will carry. A minimum thickness for a habitable one-story structure is 8″ (most codes). When a brick ledge is specified in a block wall, the blocks from the ledge surface down to the footing will be 8 × 12 × 16″ (Fig. 4-24a). Eight-inch stretchers and caps will form the ledge backup and floor joist bearing. With poured concrete a 10″-thick wall with a formed 4″ ledge may pass the code in a particular area. Two-story frame houses (no brick ledge) usually require 12″ blocks or 10″ solid masonry foundation walls. These figures denote minimum practice as found in most building codes (Fig. 4-24b). Local codes should be researched on this point before starting the drawing.

Other Features

There are several other features of a foundation plan that require showing. They are the footing outline under the wall, openings in the wall, and any other footings such as those under the girder columns and fireplaces. These parts of the foundation are below the sectioning line that represents the main view. They are drawn with an intermediate line width when the drafter chooses to use three qualities of line emphasis. The shape of the line indicates a semi-invisible interpretation. It will be about 3/4″-long dashes with about an 1/8″ space between.

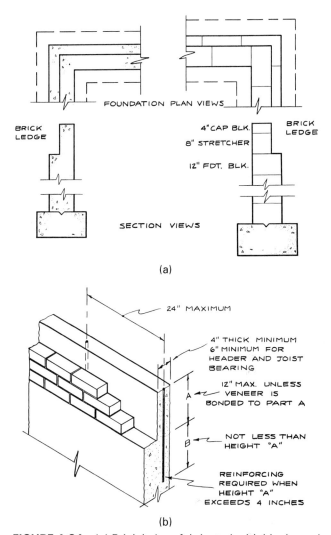

FOUNDATION PLAN VIEWS

BRICK LEDGE

4″ CAP BLK.
8″ STRETCHER
12″ FDT. BLK.

BRICK LEDGE

SECTION VIEWS

(a)

24″ MAXIMUM

4″ THICK MINIMUM
6″ MINIMUM FOR HEADER AND JOIST BEARING

12″ MAX. UNLESS VENEER IS BONDED TO PART A

NOT LESS THAN HEIGHT "A"

REINFORCING REQUIRED WHEN HEIGHT "A" EXCEEDS 4 INCHES

(b)

FIGURE 4-24 (a) Brick ledges fabricated with blocks and formed in concrete; (b) codes for brick ledge size and reinforcement based on FHA–MPS.

Both sides of the wall footing are shown. The wall is centered over the footing so that an equal projection extends inside and outside of the wall. There is an accepted formula for the *minimum-sized* footing proportion to the wall thickness for a one-story structure. The depth of the footing should not be less than the thickness of the wall. The width should not be less than twice the wall thickness. This formula is best remembered by visualizing the diagram in Fig. 4-25a. It will be noted that the two conditions above cause a projection ledge on the footing which is one-half the wall thickness. This means that to abide by the code, the wall must be centered on the footing. Remember that this formula is a minimum standard. It is nearly impossible to produce this exact shape and hold all components in perfect alignment while pouring concrete into forms. It is difficult to construct forms perfectly. Stakes do not go in where you what them to. For these reasons builders tend to make footings a little larger than the minimum.

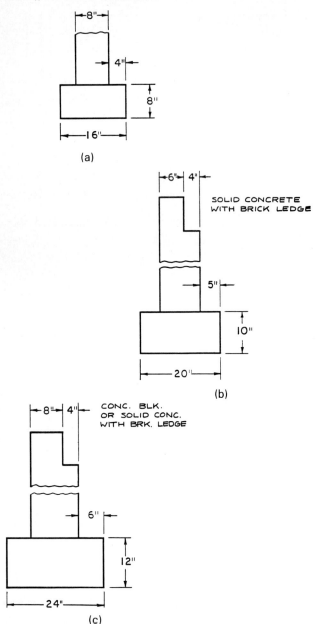

FIGURE 4-25   (a) Minimum footing for a one-story residence; (b) brick ledge foundation minimum; (c) concrete block brick ledge combination minimum sizes.

This gives some space to manuever the wall into the correct location without the danger of violating the ledge projection rule. Standard backhoe buckets that dig the trench will control the trench width to some extent. A footing can sometimes be poured without forms in earth that does not collapse. It is common practice to dig such a footing with a scoop of a size larger than the minimum footing width that is required. Keep in mind when drawing as well as when laying out a footing that the footing straddles the wall location, *not the building line.* The wall thickness is all

inside the building line. Only the exterior projection is outside the building line.

Pier or column footings (Fig. 4-26) are simple rectangular slabs of concrete. The size required depends on several conditions. A conventional roof (nontrussed) will cause more weight to be transferred to the girder pier pads. This extra weight comes from the ceiling of the first floor (in a one-story house). When roof trusses are used, this weight is transferred to the outer walls. It is an engineering feat to determine the exact minimum size of a pier/column footing. Some rules of thumb may help guide the designer who does not have access to engineered sources. A pad 24″ × 24″ square by 12″ deep is usually considered adequate for a one-story house with columns no farther apart than 8′. The formula calls for the depth to be not less than half the surface width (least dimension). Should the designer choose a little larger surface such as 28″, the depth should be increased to 14″. Adding surface size without adding depth defeats the load-bearing capacity, as the column focuses its pressure at the center of a pad. It can break through a wider pad easier than a smaller one under some ground-bearing conditions unless the added depth is provided.

Locating the column foundation pads with dimensions is done with the use of centerlines instead of extension lines (Fig. 4-27). Only one pad requires dimensions or a uniform callout when they are all the same size. The dimensions for locating the pads will reference to the exact center of where the column or pier will rest. The desired location is a place that coordinates several factors. This is

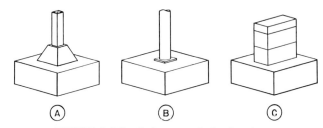

FIGURE 4-26   Column and pier footings.

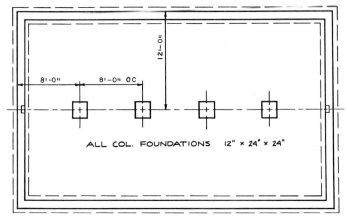

FIGURE 4-27   Dimensioning method for column and pier pads.

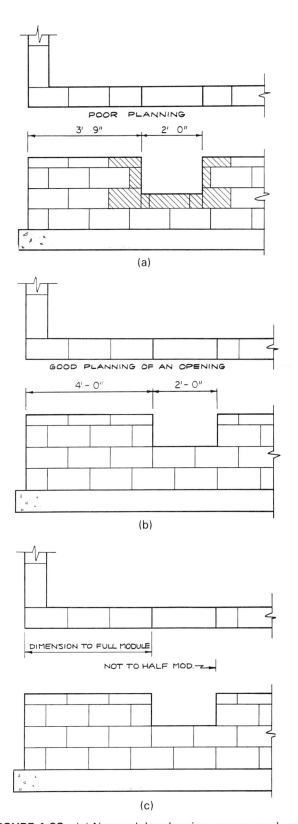

POOR PLANNING

3' 9"   2' 0"

(a)

GOOD PLANNING OF AN OPENING

4' - 0"   2' - 0"

(b)

DIMENSION TO FULL MODULE

NOT TO HALF MOD.

(c)

FIGURE 4-28 (a) Nonmodular planning causes much on-site custom cutting of blocks (shaded area). (b) Recognition of unit moduli and good planning eliminates waste of labor and material. (c) Make dimensions as meaningful to the mason as possible in modular terms.

explained fully in Chapter 6 in Part II, under the subject heading of girder construction.

Fireplace and chimney footings may be designed and made as integral additions to the perimeter foundation footing. This occurs when the fireplace is part of the exterior wall of the house. The weight of the fireplace and chimney that is placed on the footing and the composition of the bearing soil (known as the foundation bed) will determine the size of the footing that is needed. This requirement is so variable that it is suggested the designer seek out professional help before attempting to specify.

Wall openings in the foundation will include such things as a crawl space access, ventilators, basement windows, and walk-out doors. Where several openings are standardized, the drafter may dimension only to the centers of the openings. Where there are different sizes of the same type of opening, it will aid the mason to have a dimension to one edge of the opening followed by an opening height and width stated in the opening. This removes the necessity of looking for a schedule and cross-referencing symbols to find the needed information.

Openings in basement or crawl space walls made of blocks can actually be laid up with a minimum of measuring when dimensions reference to a corner POB. Openings will be modular when the distance from the foundation corner is a multiple of 8″ (a half-block) or 16″ (a full block) (Fig. 4-28). The mason can actually leave an opening in the correct location without the use of a tape measure by simply counting units in a lower course. The key to successful dimensioning is to keep in mind how you can tell the assembler of parts (units) where they go or where they are omitted with the least amount of writing and drawing. Avoid the tendency to fill in every blank expanse that does not have a dimension set in it. Only put up those road signs that will get the craftsman to his destination quickly and unerringly.

DETAILING THE FLOOR FRAME

Only after the floor plan has been firmed can the floor frame be planned. This is not an essential plan. Many experienced builders will construct the floor frame using only the floor plan. Nevertheless, it is a good problem-solving exercise to draw the frame plan. It can reveal the conflicts between stairwells, girders, and foundation openings that sometimes occur.

Two Types of Joist Symbols

There are two graphic forms for showing the floor frame. One is the single-line representation, the other is the full-thickness presentation.

The single-line technique is used when drawing space is at a premium and small scale is desirable. It is symbolic. The spacing shown is actual size (to scale) but the thickness of the dimension lumber (1 1/2") is represented with a single line. Whenever two lines are side by side, it is interpreted as two boards. This can be a little confusing, as the average print reader of details is conditioned to larger details, where both edges of a board are shown. Once the concept is understood, the drawing pace will move along rapidly. Drawing the single-line representation (Fig. 4-29) will cause less strain on the eyes and the patience than the full-thickness drawing. For every actual board there is a line shown. A gap is left at points where the end of one board meets the end of another. Without the gap it would appear to be one piece. Lapped boards are separated with a little space, as the line is actually a centerline of the board it symbolizes. Each unit or feature will be called out with a label in at least one place. Duplications need not be labeled. Callouts will be squiggle-arrowed or straight-arrowed to the item being signified. These are called "leaders." Labeling will include such callouts as "OC joist," "double joists," "band header," "band joists," "bridging" (with girth size or type), "blocks," and "butt straps." A three-dimensional notation of the size is part of the callout (2" × 10" × 14' joists, etc.).

The full-thickness representation (Fig. 4-30) shows a realistic bird's-eye view of the floor frame. The thickness of each board is shown as one would see it. It is more easily understood because it looks real. All thicknesses of the material are drawn to their actual size. *Materials should never*

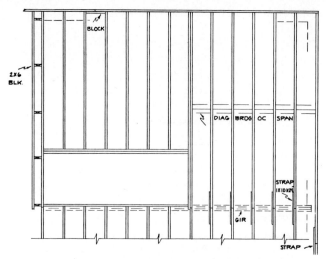

FIGURE 4-30 Partial full-thickness joist plan.

be drawn to nominal size. They do not fit together the same (the nominal illustration is a false representation unfortunately found in many texts). A 2" joist is drawn 1 1/2" thick. A 1 × 8 × 24" wood strap is drawn 3/4" thick, 7 1/4" high, and 24" long. Corner joists are shown lapped and butted exactly as you intended them to be. The wood sill under the floor frame is shown with a semi-invisible long-dash line. Only one dash need be shown between each joist (there would scarcely be room for more).

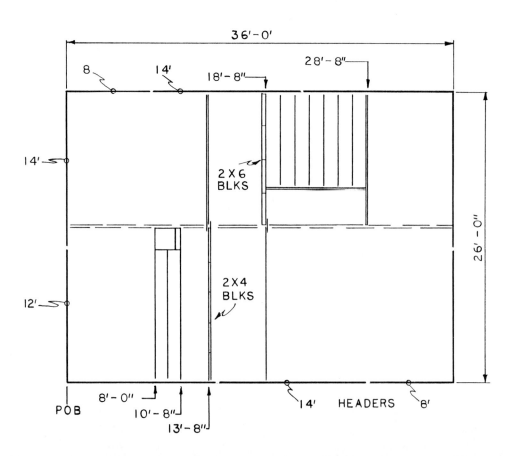

FIGURE 4-29 Single-line joist plan representation.

Dimensioning the Floor Frame Plan

Dimensioning a floor frame should follow one simple objective. Dimension only the significant layout locations. Do not duplicate obviously related positions. Overall dimensions may vary from the foundation. Some plans call for the header box (the perimeter of the frame) to be set in on the foundation an amount equal to the thickness of the sheathing. When this arrangement is specified, a medium-wide foundation line is drawn outside each corner of the frame. Dimensions will originate from this "building line." The setback at the ends is subtracted from the first and last space between the joists. This must be kept in mind when drawing the joists, the same as it is when actually laying them out on the sill and headers. The zero point is the foundation vertical surface and the surface of the sheathing that will later be placed over the set-in headers. When the specifications call for a header band that lines up vertically with the foundation, all dimensions reference directly to the ends, sides, and corners of the frame.

Modified Modular Frame Plan

An objective that has been advised consistently throughout this text can be achieved in the design of the floor frame. A modular floor plan makes it an easy matter to simplify the floor frame drawing. No carpenter needs to see a drawing of every joist in a floor in order to install one in each regular place. What he needs is a plan showing the exceptions. Such a plan is easily drawn in a fraction of the time it would take to duplicate all the OC joists (a 60'-long house has 92 joists, including the end bands). Drawing commences by laying out the perimeter box (headers and bands). Next are drawn only those OC joists that are next to any extra trimmers. The extras are those under partitions and alongside openings. To indicate the joist centering system, the end joining system (butted or tied), and the bridging (at the center of the joist span), a few sets of regular OC joists may be drawn at one end of the floor. Do not dimension these. Use callouts to indicate the features. Dimensions will be placed to the center of the significant OC joists that are adjacent to the extras. The plan reader can see at a glance which side of the OC joist the "doubler" goes.

A quick way to check out the joist plan (another name for the floor frame plan) is to overlay or underlay it with the completed floor plan. The doublers must fall under the partitions as planned when correctly located. If they do not, something is inaccurate. When it is difficult to see through the vellum, hold the two drawings against a window pane.

If the drafter has access to a light table, the overlay technique can be used from the outset. A clean sheet of vellum is taped over the floor plan (use a blueprint, as the lead will come off an original) and both are taped to the glass top of the tracing table. A fluorescent light underneath makes the floor plan lines clearly visible. Keep in

mind that the wall studs of the bearing walls and partitions have been purposely lined up directly over the joists. By visualizing the intersection post, one member of which is an OC stud, the OC joist can be drawn alongside the partition. One of the sides of the joist will coincide with the side line of the partition. The other side line of the joist trimmer to be added will be under the partition. This overlay tracing method makes it possible to locate and draw a major part of the joist plan without measuring. It is a significant time saver and eliminates much potential error.

One caution is important. The dimensioning that follows must reflect mathematical and modular precision. The draftsman must *never "scale" a drawing* and assign dimensions. Scaling, in this sense, means tracing something and measuring it on the architect's scale and then dimensioning it as whatever it appears to measure. The actual full-sized measurements, arrived at mathematically and modularly, are the only figures to use for real dimensions.

DETAILING WALL SECTION VIEWS

In a set of house plans, each view must correlate precisely with all others. Some views cannot be drawn by measurement alone. They must be projected from information gained from a detail drawing. A section drawing cuts through some location of the structure and exposes the parts to view. Making section details helps visualize the relationship of the materials and their proportionate sizes.

Frame Wall Section

Probably the most useful and basic section in a plan set is the wall section (Fig. 4-31). A complete section would start with the foundation footing and end with the capping shingles on the roof ridge. A view including this much detail could have as many as 50 parts or more to be labeled. It is not usually necessary to go to this extent to determine significant heights.

Significant Heights of the Wall Section

The height of the wall structure itself is controlled by the standardized sizes of the material units in it. When using standard precut studs, the wall height has two possible variable units: the floor joist height and the sheathing thickness. Floor joist height will be greater when the span of a floor is longer (a deeper house from front to rear). Example: a 24'-wide house may require 8" joists, a 26' or 28' span may require 10" joists, and a 30'- or 32'-deep structure would require 12" joists. These three nominal sizes are actually 7 1/4, 9 1/4, and 11 1/4" high. Therefore, the house grows in wall height by 2" increments as the floor depth increases. The three joist sizes mentioned cover all conventional home varieties. When the precut stud is used, the interior frame walls above the floor sheathing are standardized at a height of 97 1/8". The bulk of home

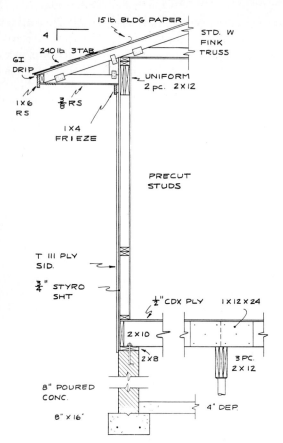

FIGURE 4-31   Typical wall section drawing.

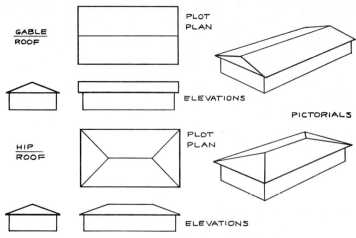

FIGURE 4-32   Two basic roof styles.

designs will have one of three standard exterior heights from the top of the foundation to the top of the wall plate. The wood parts and sizes starting at the bottom are as follows: 1 1/2″ sill plate, 7 1/4″ header and joist, 1/2″ subfloor (occasionally 5/8″), 1 1/2″ sole plate, 92 5/8″ precut stud, and a 3″ double upper plate (two flat 2 × 4s). The total height of this assembly is 106 3/8″. Substituting a 2 × 10 joist will make it 108 3/8″. A 2 × 12 joist makes it 110 3/8″. By far the largest quantity of house plans today will call for the 2 × 10 joist, so the most common height is 108 3/8″. Where 5/8″ plywood is used for subflooring, 1/8″ more height is added. Because of this commonality it is not necessary to dimension stock parts in a wall section. Each part is called out nominally.

   Drawing window and door sections is also a waste of time. Manufacturers supply all this information. The only construction information needed is the rough-opening width and height. Where the uniform header system is used (two side-by-side 2 × 12s) over all exterior windows and doors, the rough-opening height is standardized at 82 7/8″. This is arrived at by subtracting the height of the header and top plate (11 1/4″ + 3″ = 14 1/4″) from the total wall height of 97 1/8″ (sole 1 1/2″, precut stud 92 5/8″, and double top plate 3″). Door sills of prehung doors are seldom cut into (let into) the subfloor as they used to be when oak was the common material. Today's superior

weathertight aluminum threshold is installed on top of the subfloor or on top of both the subfloor and the underlayment floor. In either case the door profile on an elevation view may be shown realistically at 81″, compared to the measured height (80″) of years past, when rough openings were cut to be 82″ high.

DESIGNING THE ROOF

There are several roof styles from which to choose. The designer should consider the following things before beginning a drawing: the neighborhood styles, the geographic influences (sun, rain, wind, snow, and temperature variation), and building complexity. The average family moves about five times in a lifetime. Some builders feel that resalability merits consideration. Odd designs and mismatched roof slopes are more difficult to sell.

Basic Designs

Two basic designs make up the largest percentage of roofs built in the United States. These arc the gable roof and the hip roof (Fig. 4-32). The gable-roof house has vertical walls at the ends of the house closing in the triangular area formed by the slant of the roof. This area is called a *gable* (Fig.

FIGURE 4-33   Typical gable roof.

(a)

(b)

FIGURE 4-34 (a) Typical hip roof; (b) gambrel roof.

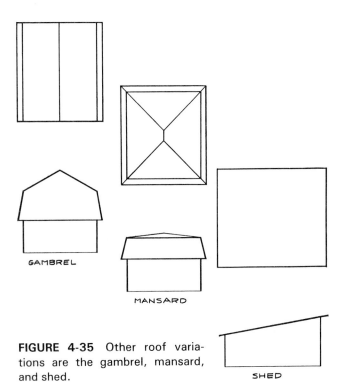

GAMBREL

MANSARD

FIGURE 4-35 Other roof variations are the gambrel, mansard, and shed.

SHED

4-33). The hip roof slants toward all the exterior walls (Fig. 4-34a). Other roof designs are modifications of these two types. The exception is the flat roof. It has no pitch (slant), which is the basic qualification of a roof. Other styles, such as the gambrel (Fig. 4-34b), mansard, and shed (Fig. 4-35), simply combine the slants into different profiles.

Drawing Roof Pitches

The pitch of a roof means the angle of the surface as it rises away from horizontal. In the construction business, this is not given in degrees. It is stated as so many inches of rise above the upper plate surface per 12″ of run (Fig. 4-36). The measuring line is a line on the face of a conventional rafter which is parallel to the edges and runs from the top outer corner of the upper plate to the vertical centerline of the ridge board. The *measuring line* is the *hypotenuse* of the roof triangle. The *rise of a roof* is the vertical distance from the top surface line of the upper plate to a point on the ridge where the pitch line intersects the centerline of the roof profile. The *run* (Fig. 4-37) is the horizontal distance from the outer edge of the upper plate to the centerline. The *span* is twice the run or the total distance from the front building line to the rear or opposite building line.

   The majority of roofs are laid out and built to a specific pitch given in whole numbers (Fig. 4-38). The pitch designation may be stated as a fraction or as a set of whole numbers. A roof that is 12′ high at the center and has a run of 12′ may be referred to as *half-pitch*. The rise in this case is one-half the width of the full roof triangle (an equilateral). The baseline of this triangle is twice the length of the run. The baseline distance, which is the depth of the house, is the *span*. To refer to a pitch fractionally, the rise number is placed over the span figure and reduced to its lowest

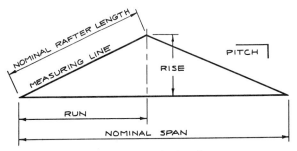

FIGURE 4-36 Roof triangle terms.

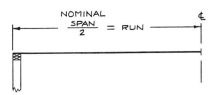

FIGURE 4-37 Roof run.

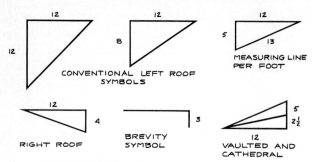

FIGURE 4-38   Sample pitch symbols.

common denominator: 12 over 24 pitch becomes "one-half pitch." All the even-numbered pitches may be stated in this manner. One-sixth pitch, quarter-pitch, one-third pitch, and half-pitch are common terms. The carpenter and architect are more apt to use the proportionate whole-number designations. Orally, the half-pitched roof would be expressed as "12 in 12". This means that in every 12″ of run there will be 12″ of rise. This manner of verbalizing is better fitted to the odd pitches. "5 in 12" is more descriptive than "five twenty-fourths."

The 12″ of run is a *unit of run*. When the quantity of run units is multiplied by the rise in inches per run unit, it gives the actual rise at the centerline in inches. A house that is 26′ in depth has a run of 13 units. If the specifications called for a 5-in-12 pitch, the rise would be 65″:

$$\text{pitchnumber} \times \text{run units} = \text{rise in inches}$$

$$5 \times 13 = 65''$$

House depths that are not in even feet involve fractional computation. The problem for a house depth of 26′-8″ (13′-4″ run with a 5-in-12 pitch) is laid out like this:

$$5 \text{ pitch} \times 13 \: 1/3 \text{ run units} = \text{rise in inches}$$

$$5 \times 13 \: 1/3 = 66 \: 2/3''$$

Laying Out the Rafters

To lay out a roof-line detail for conventional rafters, follow the procedure shown in Fig. 4-39.

1. Draw an end view to scale of a set of upper plates. The outer edges will be the span distance apart.
2. Draw the roof triangle baseline between the plates. This is the underside of the ceiling joist.
3. Draw a centerline vertically and measure the actual rise up the centerline from the baseline.
4. Connect this rise point with the outer corners of the upper plates using a narrow, long, dashed line. This is the measuring line.

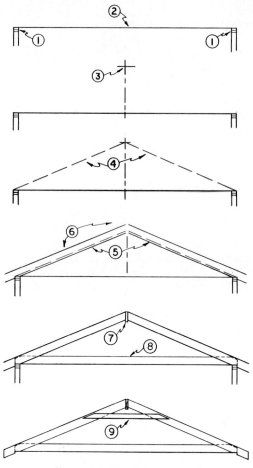

FIGURE 4-39   Roof drafting.

5. Draw a line parallel to the measuring line starting from the interior corners of the plates.
6. Measure perpendicular to this line at the top and bottom of a distance equaling the rafter width (actual size). Draw the upper line of the rafter through these points.
7. Draw in an end view of the ridge board. Straddle the centerline. Choose a board width large enough so that all the plumb cut rafter end bears on the board. This usually means that the ridge board will be one size larger than the rafter.
8. Measure up from the baseline the height of the ceiling joist and draw it in.
9. Draw a horizontal collar beam (1 × 6 or 2 × 4) at a point two-thirds of the distance above the baseline. A collar beam is usually required for each 4′ of house length.

This is the basic layout for a conventional set of rafters and ceiling joists. Overhangs have no effect on this layout procedure. The overhang is a simple extension of the rafter lines. Overhang and soffit design is discussed later in this chapter.

Drawing W and M Trusses

The Fink and the Howe trusses, nicknamed the W and the M, are laid out in a similar way. Steps 1, 2, and 3 are the same. The measuring line, step 4, may be drawn in solid, as it is the lower edge of the upper truss chord. The rafters on a truss are called *upper chords*. The lower edge of the upper chord coincides with the measuring line. The upper chord sits on the pitch-cut scarf of the lower chord. There is no birdsmouth bearing seat on a truss as found on the bottom of the conventional rafter. The height of the rafter (its vertical girth) is all above the measuring line. There is no ridge board where trusses are used. The upper end of the chords meet and bear against each other on their plumb cuts.

Placing the webs on a truss drawing is a precise matter. Webs are the tension and compression braces connecting upper and lower chords. The locations have been worked out through engineering principles and stress tests to assure the greatest possible strength. Changing the intersection locations by more than the width of a web board will weaken the load-bearing capacity of a truss.

On the lower chord of the W truss, the webs should be placed on third points (Fig. 4-40). This means one-third of the *clear* span (the distance across the span from the interior face of the upper plates). This is the actual unsupported span, not the nominal span (building depth). Dividing the nominal span is a commonly practiced error in design. The webs adjacent to the center will meet at the peak. The outer webs will contact the upper chord at quarter points. Quarter points are locations one-fourth and three-fourths of the way across the clear span as projected vertically to the upper chords. To turn Fig. 4-40 into a scaled

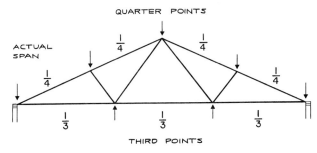

FIGURE 4-40 W truss diagram.

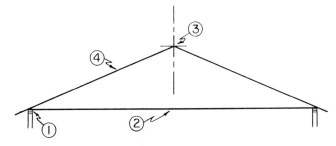

FIGURE 4-41 W truss detailing: steps 1 through 4.

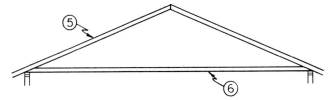

FIGURE 4-42 W truss detailing continued: steps 5 and 6.

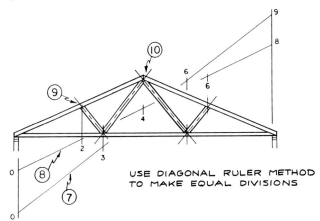

USE DIAGONAL RULER METHOD TO MAKE EQUAL DIVISIONS

FIGURE 4-43 W truss detailing continued: steps 7 through 10.

detail, the upper chords are placed above the measuring line, and the lower chords are placed above the baseline. The centerline for the webs will meet the lower chord on its top surface, intersecting the vertical centerline of the third point. This places the bearing axis directly over the third point.

The steps for laying out the W truss are as follows (Figs. 4-41 to 4-43):

1. Lay out a set of upper plates.
2. Draw the roof triangle baseline by connecting the top of the plates.
3. Draw a vertical centerline and mark the top rise point on the line.
4. Connect this point with the outside top corner of each top plate.
5. Measure the depth of the upper chord perpendicularly to the hypotenuse line at the peak and at the top plate. Connect these points to form the upper edge of the top chord.
6. Measure the depth of the lower chord vertically above the baseline. Draw this line parallel to the baseline for the lower chord.
7. Divide the clear span by 3 (inside to inside of the plates). Place a short centerline through the lower chord on these two third points.
8. Divide the clear span by 4 along the baseline. Project these quarter points to the top edge of the upper chord.

9. Draw a diagonal centerline from the third point on top of the lower chord (not the baseline) to the quarter point on the top chord in each half of the truss. Draw the outer webs by straddling the diagonal centerlines.

10. Connect two more diagonal centerlines from the third points to the rise point (underside of the peak). Straddle these centerlines with the inner webs.

There are several variations of joint junctions that can be made where the webs intersect the chords (Fig. 4-44). Different pitches will benefit from one or another design. Objectives are to create as few miter cuts as possible at the third points and the peak (the quarter-point intersection will always be a single miter) and to keep the webs superimposed over the centerline. Whether it is centered exactly is of less importance than the intersection techniques. Consideration should also be given to the potential nailing surface that will be presented under a gusset that holds the joint in place. Too sharp a pointed end on the web will make for a poor nail anchoring and gluing surface. Where nail plates or gang nails are used, inadequate holding may also result.

The M truss has three vertical posts. The one in the center is called the *king post*. Two smaller ones at the quarter-point locations are called *queen posts*. A web on each side runs diagonally from the top of the queen post to the bottom of the king post. The quarter points are placed the same way as described for the W truss. All posts straddle their centerlines. Web ends may be varied from the diagonal line as described for the W truss. The lower ends should bear against the lower chord completely or partially and not solely against the king post.

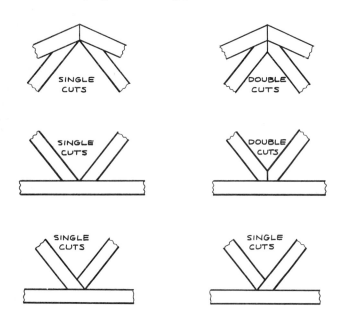

FIGURE 4-44   Web joint variations.

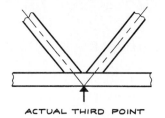 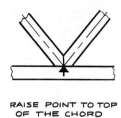

FIGURE 4-45   Compacting a lower web joint.

Large wood gussets will cover the members at the intersection points when centerlines intersect at the baseline. A smaller metal gusset will not. For this reason one of the standard joint layout variations is to raise the lower-chord centerline point to the top edge of the lower chord instead of the baseline (Fig. 4-45). This will make the joint intersection more compact. Where webs meet on the lower chord they should be directed equally at the vertical bearing line. The amount of fastening surface on the end of each web should be as nearly equal as possible. This will provide an equitable nailing surface for each web. The web centerlines may contact the third- and quarter-point centerlines at any point along the vertical girth of the chords. This minor variability will not alter the stress properties of the design. This alignment variability permits a design with a junction of webs and chords that is efficient to build.

Thermal Truss Designs

The energy crunch of the early 1980s caused both consumers and builders to consider better insulation factors in a home. One of the key heat-loss areas that could not be improved simply by adding more insulation was the limited area above the upper plate (Fig. 4-46a). The distance from the plate top to the underside of the roof sheathing could be as little as 2″ (conventional rafters with birdsmouth seats). With 2 × 4 trusses the depth is a shade over 3 1/2″ (the diagonal girth height through the sloping upper chord; Fig. 4-46b). In all but the southernmost states current recommendations are for attic insulation with R values (resistance to heat loss) between 30 and 40. To gain this level of efficiency, it takes between 8 and 12″ of insulation depth over the ceiling. Different types of insulation material have different values per inch of thickness. To accomplish this depth over the exterior plate, a truss design with a short cripple stud to raise the upper chord is available (Fig. 4-47). The builder can request any height of cripple desired. The method is effective but expensive. It requires an additional joint with two more gussets and sometimes an extra web per side. It opens a greater area on the face of the building above the plate which must be sheathed to contain the insulation. When early American homes had open rafters tails, this closure piece was called a *bird stop*. It can now be more appropriately referred to as an *insulation stop*.

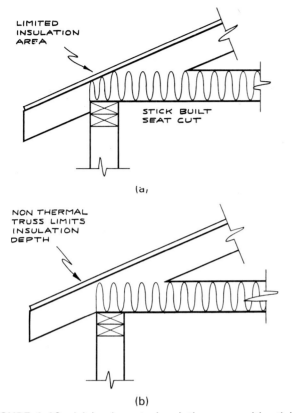

(a)

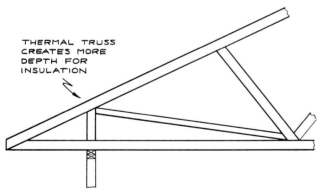

(b)

FIGURE 4-46 (a) Inadequate insulation area with stick-built roof. (b) A truss provides a bit more insulation space over the plate.

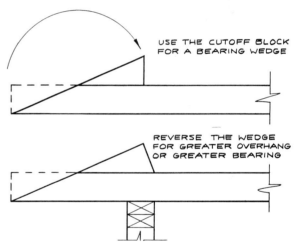

FIGURE 4-47 Cripple stud thermal truss design.

Extended Lower Chord

Another simple way to raise a truss is to extend the lower chord length by 2′ more than the span (Fig. 4-48). This can be done on pitches of 2, 3, and 4 in 12 without substantially altering the bearing condition over the plate. One objective should be kept in mind. At some point across the width of the surface of the upper plate one should be able to draw a vertical line that does not leave the surface of the lower and upper chords. There should be a bearing line

through the contact point of the chords. When the lower chord extends so far that a gap exists between the chords above the plate it can be remedied by filling the gap with a wedge (Fig. 4-49). This wedge is ready made from the scarf cutoffs at the end of the lower chords (the rake cut line). The wedge is inserted between the chords. A single gusset on each side covers both joints, and the wedge. When the economy of this system is explained to the truss maker, it frequently becomes the choice over the cripple

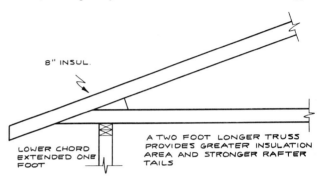

FIGURE 4-48 Extended chord thermal truss.

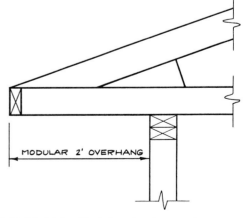

FIGURE 4-49 Filler wedge.

FIGURE 4-50 Modular plancier overhang truss.

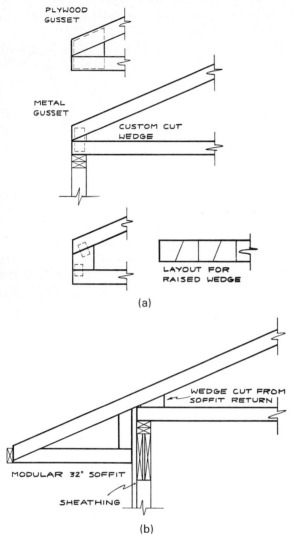

(a)

(b)

FIGURE 4-51 (a) Wedge-raised thermal truss; (b) thermal truss with conventional height soffit.

design. A truss with 2 × 4 chords will contain about 8″ of cavity above the plate with this design. Another variation of this design is to use a lower chord 4′ longer than the span. With a 2′ overhang (Fig. 4-50) this design provides a ready-made soffit nailing framework. Cut the wedge block from the top chord (Fig. 4-51a). Coordinate the design with a facia backer for a completely modular overhang (Fig. 4-51b). Still another variation uses span-length chords with a simple custom-cut wedge.

VENTING THE SOFFIT AND ROOF

Building codes usually prescribe the minimum ventilation area in terms of proportion to the square footage of the ceiling or attic. The Federal Housing Administration (FHA) requires 1 square foot of free venting area to every 150 square feet of ceiling. A 1500-square foot house will require 10 square feet of free vent area. At least 50% of the vent area must be in the upper part of the roof (at the peak or in the gable ends, etc.). The remaining 50% may be in the eave or cornice. Free vent area literally means no obstruction to airflow. All vents have screening or fins or both. An 8″ × 12″ soffit vent does not qualify for 96 square inches of venting area. Probably 75% of that is a more realistic estimate. It is a good practice to overplan venting area. If the specifications require 12 square feet, 16 square feet will more closely meet the requirement.

Eave vents are important on both gable- and hip-roof houses. It was once thought that they were a characteristic of hip roofs only. Big gable vents are effective when there is a direct air current into one or the other. The suction created on the off-wind end, aided by the pressure from the wind against the other end, will circulate much of the hot air out of the central and upper portions of the attic. It will not pull it up from the eave area to any extent when there are no eave vents. To do this there must be a fresh-air inlet source. The most efficient source is a fully vented eave. This can be achieved with an on-site constructed continuous screen or with manufactured venting soffits of aluminum or steel in sheets or rolls. The next-most-efficient eave vent is the combination of several small vents. These may be placed at intervals down the eave between rafter tails on a rake soffit or between soffit lookout returns on a horizontal soffit. The vents adjacent to the ends of the house should vent into the first rafter space that enters the attic. It is difficult to remove the pocketed air above the ceiling corners unless the vent is directly below the corner.

A planned air corridor (duct) between the rafters up and over the ceiling insulation is necessary (Fig. 4-52). Eave venting is not effective without some form of retainer over the insulation to prevent it from closing the aperture. There are several brands of manufactured vent stops on the market designed to fit 16″ and 24″ centered rafters. Stops can be made on site (Fig. 4-53) with a variety of materials. An effective material is rigid 1″ Styrofoam ripped to 14 1/2″ width for 16″-OC rafters or 22 1/2″ for 24″

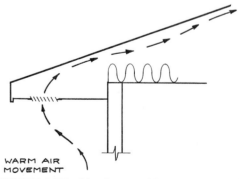

FIGURE 4-52 Venting corridor over the plate.

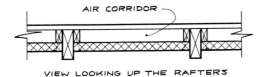

VIEW LOOKING UP THE RAFTERS

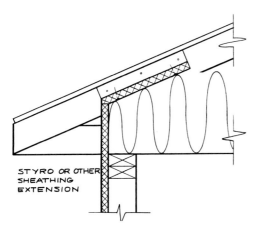

STYRO OR OTHER SHEATHING EXTENSION

FIGURE 4-53 Site-built venting corridor.

rafters. The length required will vary with different roof pitches and insulation depths. A 1″ × 2″ strip is nailed to the rafter face flush with the roof sheathing. Below this comes the rectangular Styrofoam. It can be nailed to these reversed ledger strips with four 1 1/2″-long roofing nails. The size of this backer strip should be coincided, designed in width to create an opening above the stop that will equal the square-inch capacity of the soffit vent that it accommodates. When the duct needs to be kept high to allow more insulation below, it may be logical to make two ducts for each vent below. There are two advantages of Styrofoam for the duct material. The R rating is about twice that of fiberglass; therefore, the insulating space lost to the open duct is regained by the higher efficiency of the Styrofoam. The second advantage is the relatively low cost compared to hard materials such as 1/4″ plywood or Masonite, with their low R ratings.

Gable vents are advisable regardless of what other types are used in conjunction. When wind is coming parallel to the ridge, a gable vent is fairly effective. When there is no wind, the effectiveness drops off dramatically. Only the rising hot air close to the ends of the attic finds its way out. Attics with only gable vents can run a temperature in the middle of the attic as much as 30 to 40°F above the outdoor temperature. Photographs and plastic items stored in attics with dark-shingled roofs have been known to melt where only gable vents exist. The gable vent also becomes less effective the longer the house is. The air in the attic moves very little lengthwise unless sucked or pushed. The rafters act as baffles that break up the movement. A combination of vents in the eaves and gables is

needed to create a circulation by draft as well as convection.

Eave and gable vents are not likely to be enough when a house is more than twice as long as it is wide. Four options are left. A continuous ridge vent is the most effective of all vent types when combined with continuous eave venting. An attractive and effective site-built vent is described in Chapter 10.

Static roof vents are available. These are single vents installed over an appropriate 10″-diameter hole in the roof. They are screened and have metal covering to shed rain and snow. The drawback is that it takes too many of them to be used as a single system. They do not add to the beauty of a home and are therefore usually placed on the backyard side of the roof ridge. The static roof vent is effective for a long roof that needs some additional central venting. The static vent should be installed as close to the ridge as shingle lapping will permit.

The nonpowered turbine appears to be working when it turns. In reality, when there is no wind, the movement of the turbine is being caused by the movement of the hot air rising through the fins. Since this air has to push the fins to make them turn, it is likely that the venting air would move out more efficiently if there was no turbine there. The turbine works best when there is some wind to turn it. The turbine is a comforting visual aid with or without wind; if it is moving, you can be assured that hot air is being exhausted.

The power venting roof fan works under all circumstances other than power failure. Its thermostat is set so that it comes on when the attic reaches a specified temperature. The small, fractional-horsepower motor in this fan takes very little electricity. In hot climates this cost is easily offset by savings in air conditioning. A single roof fan should be centrally located where used with eave and gable vents. In the southern and southwestern heat belts of the United States, two or more power fans are desirable. Ell-shaped or tee-shaped roofs could take advantage of a roof fan in each wing of the roof.

Two other options for ventilating or cooling bear mentioning. The gable power fan is an effective exhaust type. The problem with this fan is wind direction. Wind blowing against a gable fan can literally work it to death. A ceiling fan or roof fan, on the other hand, will function regardless of outside wind direction. A ceiling fan can cool a house measurably when basement windows are opened and first-floor windows and doors are closed completely or nearly so. The cool air from the basement is drawn through the first floor before being exhausted under pressure out the attic. The blower on a forced-air furnace which is located in the basement can also be used to force the cool air up into the living quarters. It is necessary to block first-floor cold-air returns, open a cold-air return in the basement, and leave the door to the basement open.

DESIGNING AN EAVE OVERHANG

Most present-day house designs have some overhang of the roof rafters. The advantages of shedding rain and blocking summer sunlight have caused designers to give more consideration to overhangs. There are structural limitations to how far a rafter may overhang the wall. An economic factor is the 2' modulus of the rafter length. Adding a few inches of overhang may be unnecessarily costly when it forces the purchase of rafters that are 2' longer. The same principle applies with the material in the soffit return. For example, if the surface material of the return is to be plywood, a 16-, 24-, or 32"-deep return will leave no waste. Size modules an inch or two under these figures will create negligible waste. By comparison a 36" return will cause 8 square feet of waste from a sheet of plywood or Masonite regardless of whether it is cut lengthwise or crosswise. This is an intolerable 25% waste factor. The overhang economy will be determined by a compromise of the rafter-length modulus, the return depth (pitched or horizontal), and the soffit material modulus. Metal soffit material, such as aluminum and steel, comes in a variety of shapes, lengths, and widths. The ribbed interlocking type which runs from eave to wall frequently comes in 10' lengths. This length adapts to cutting 15 and 30" soffit depths (divisions of 120"). Roll types also have specific widths to bear in mind.

How can the designer cause an economical combination of rafter tail and soffit depth? It involves a compromise of several specifications. Roof pitch will have a predominant control upon overhang. The constant factor affecting the overhang profile is the level of the top of the windows and doors in the wall. Most contractors are currently using the uniform header, which is made of two 2 × 12s side by side. The double plate laid on top nets 3" of height. By adding this to the 11 1/4" of header, it is found that the rough opening of the window is 14 1/4" below the top of the wall. When conventional rafters are specified, this distance is further reduced by the seat cut in the rafter, which lowers the underside of the rafter tail. The window is likely to have a brickmold or other type of trim board across the top, which also takes up a couple of inches of height. There remains approximately 12" of height (rise) above the rough opening when trusses are used and the lower surface of the upper chord intersects the outer corner of the top plate. This has been the usual method of assembly; however, there are several methods of placing the truss at a higher level to gain additional space for insulation. A conventional rafter will sit about 2" lower than a truss due to the seat cut. The distance (rise) from the top of the window trim to the underside of the conventional rafter will be about 10". A line extended horizontally from the top of the window trim intersects the underside of the rafter tail. This intersection point denotes the maximum horizontal overhang that can be obtained. Soffit thickness must also be subtracted when a roof pitch (slant) is steep and the over-

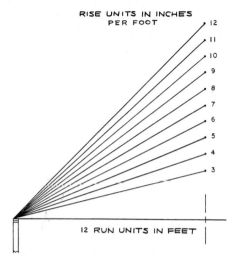

FIGURE 4-54   Common roof pitch angles.

hang is smaller. As a general rule, longer overhangs may be had with lower-pitched roofs.

Estimating the maximum overhang that is feasible is possible by using a technique of proportion. Practicing this technique may net some satisfaction, as it is impressive. The technique is based on the use of the roof truss conventionally set directly on top of the plate. As explained earlier, the roof pitch triangle from this setup is simple (Fig. 4-54). The horizontal base of the triangle is the ceiling line, which originates from the top surface of the upper plate. The pitch line (the hypotenuse of the triangle) is the lower surface (under edge) of the upper chord of the truss. These two lines intersect at the building line at the top of the upper plate (this may be the outer corner of the upper plate or the sheathing depending on whether the wall frame has been ''set in''). The horizontal depth of the maximum potential overhang can be established within an inch by drawing the detail to larger scale. The larger the scale used, the most accurate will be the analysis. To accomplish this way of finding the overhang, the drafter simply lays out a diagram in the following steps (Fig. 4-55).

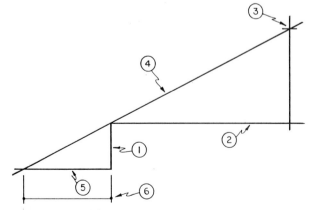

FIGURE 4-55   Layout steps for diagramming an overhang.

1. Draw a vertical wall line 12″ high to a scale of 1″ = 1′.
2. Draw a ceiling line off the top end of the wall line.
3. Establish a rise point above any run unit point along the ceiling line.
4. Draw the pitch line through the rise point and through the intersection of the wall and ceiling lines. A truss chord intersects the outer plate corner. A conventional rafter intersects the interior corner of the plate with a line parallel to the measuring line. Allow this pitch line to extend down and beyond the wall line at least as far as the bottom level of the wall line.
5. Draw a horizontal line from the bottom of the 12″ wall line across the paper until it intersects the pitch line. This is the maximum-depth soffit line.
6. Scale (measure) this soffit line. This is the maximum possible overhang using standard wall components (2″ brickmold trim, 12″ nominal window headers, and nonthermal trusses).

This is the basic manner of laying out the section detail. One has only to add in the material thicknesses and heights of the components to produce a finished drawing. Details should be drawn to large scale.

The technique above is methodical and routine. Another method is mathematical. It is done by mental visualization quickly and accurately—the part that impresses. The key to the process is found in the height figure from the top of the window trim to the underside of the rafter. Place this number over the rafter pitch number as a numerator. Multiply this major fraction times one unit of run (12″). The result is the maximum horizontal overhang. Several of the even pitches can be done mentally (or simply memorized). Others will require a little pencil and paper or calculator manipulation. Following are some examples of both. Visualize a 12-in-12 pitched roof triangle with an eave overhang (Fig. 4-56). On the house side of the building line, a single unit of run and rise (12 in 12) forms a right triangle whose legs are equal. Extending the pitch line (the hypotenuse of this triangle) an equal amount below the baseline and returning it to the vertical building line, we find an identical triangle. The rise of the roof pitch in this example is 12″. The rise from window trim point to top plate is also 12″. The unit of run is 12″. Since both rises are the same, the eave run will be equal to a unit of ceiling run (12″). A formula evolves:

$$\frac{\text{eave rise}}{\text{roof rise}} \times \text{unit of roof run (12)}$$

$$= \text{maximum horizontal overhang}$$

Let us put the 12-in-12-pitch figures into the formula:

$$\frac{12''}{12} \times 12'' = 12''$$

To show that a pattern develops, try putting quarter pitch (6 in 12) and then one-eighth pitch (3 in 12) into the formula:

$$\frac{12}{6} \times 12 = 24'' \quad \text{and} \quad \frac{12}{3} \times 12 = 48''$$

These three pitches produce perfect modularity of soffit-covering materials that come in 4′ × 8′ sheets (plywood, hardboard, etc.). The overhang depths can easily be memorized by visualization as the triangles are proportionate in inverse order to the numbers:

12 to 12 = 12   6 to 12 = 24   3 to 12 = 48

(Fig. 4-57). Since the numerator of the truss example is always 12 and the multiplier is a unit of run (always 12),

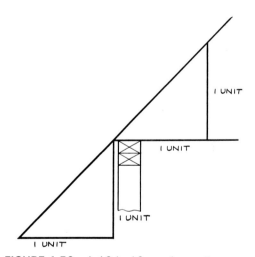

FIGURE 4-56 A 12-in-12 overhang diagram.

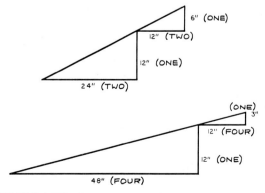

FIGURE 4-57 Reverse ratio diagrams of overhang.

one step in the formula can be bypassed. Use 144 (the 12 × 12) as the numerator over the denominator in question (the pitch number). By this simple division, the horizontal overhang maximum figure is reached in one division problem. Some of the pitches do not net even inches. An example is 7-in-12 pitch: 144 ÷ 7 = 20.57″. Converting 20.57″ to the tape measure would interpret as 1′-8 9/16″. Following is a list of pitches showing the maximum horizontal overhang that results under the specifications noted earlier.

Pitch	Eave Rise (In.)	Maximum Overhang (In.)
12	12	12
11	12	13.09
10	12	14.4
9	12	16
8	12	18
7	12	20.57
6	12	24
5	12	28.8
4	12	36
3	12	48

Bear in mind that any variable in design or material sizes will usually alter the eave rise number. For example, a high facia on the ends of the rafter tails (one greater than a 1 × 6) will cause a horizontal soffit to return at a lower level. This must be compensated for by shortening the rafter tail and consequently the overhang. Accommodating variations necessitates using the initial formula in its entirety. Two examples follow.

Example 1: Conventional Rafter. The plumb-cut height is 1 1/2″ in the birdsmouth (the vertical cut of the seat cut). The trim around the window is rough-sawn cedar of 3 1/2″ width (excessive height compared to the short formula). Subtracting these quantities from the 14 1/4″ vertical space above the rough opening leaves an eave rise of 9 1/2″. The specified pitch is 5 in 12. Placing the numbers into the first basic formula gives the following problem:

$$\frac{9.5}{5} \times 12 = 22.8'' \quad (1'\text{-}10\ 13/16'')$$

Example 2: Raised Thermal Truss. The upper chord of the truss design has been placed on top of a square-cut 2 × 4 lower chord, which effectively raised it 3 1/2″. The nominal eave rise is now 17 3/4″. Over the windows 2″ brickmold is used. A 6″ frieze board is desired above the brickmold. The actual frieze height is 5 1/2″. The sof-

fit will be aluminum in a J channel which takes up 3/4″ of height. Our computation is

$$14\ 1/4 + 3\ 1/2 = 17\ 3/4 - 2$$
$$= 15\ 3/4 - 5\ 1/2 = 10\ 1/4 - 3/4$$
$$= 9\ 1/2'' \text{ of eave rise}$$

The specified pitch is 4 in 12. Putting the numbers in the formula nets

$$\frac{9.5}{4} \times 12 = 28.5'' \quad (2'\text{-}4\ 1/2'')$$

maximum potential horizontal overhang

Keep in mind that economy of material use is a give-and-take consideration. It would be foolish to extend a soffit depth to be more modular and in the process cause rafter lengths to overrun their length module to the next longer size. A combined consideration is the objective. All material elements that are affected must be considered.

Sun-Ray Control

Control of sunlight entering the home is an important consideration. It has a direct bearing on the economy of heating and air conditioning a home. Frequently, too little attention is given to the orientation of a home. Eaves are designed too short to keep out sun's hot summer rays (Fig.

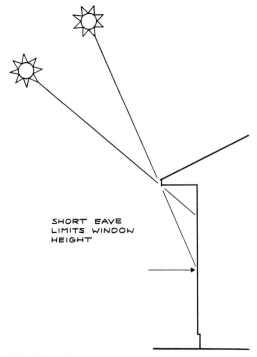

SHORT EAVE
LIMITS WINDOW
HEIGHT

FIGURE 4-58 Short eave permits entry of summer sun.

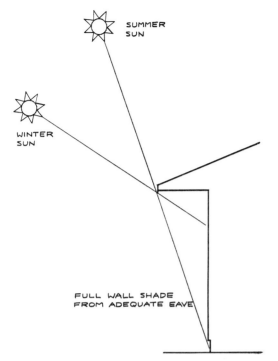

SUMMER
SUN

WINTER
SUN

FULL WALL SHADE
FROM ADEQUATE EAVE

FIGURE 4-59 Adequate eave adapts to all seasons.

4-58). No analysis is made to coordinate the eave depth
with the window height in accordance with the angles of
the sun on the longest and shortest days of the year. Sun
shining into the house in the winter to assist the heating
needs is a desirable and free solar source of energy. Shade
from properly designed eaves is equally desirable in the hot
months of the year in many of the warmer climes. To
achieve these two objectives, it is necessary to know the
lowest and highest angles of the sun in a particular geographic area (Fig. 4-59). It varies with each latitude. When
these angles are known, it will be possible to plot two sun
ray lines on a wall and roof section view. These lines will
tell how much overhang is needed to shade out the summer
sun on the east, south, and west sides of the house. It will
show the lowest point on the wall that a window sill should
be so that direct rays of the sun do not enter the house in
the summertime.

Consideration of the affects of solar heat have historically had an effect on house design. Short eaves and steep
roofs typify northern and New England styles. Long eaves
on low roofs, the ranch style, originated in the southwest,
where the sun shines hottest and the most.

Some combined principles evolve from this exercise.
To gain a combination of the greatest eave shade and the
greatest window height, a low-pitched roof is necessary.
Horizontal soffits limit the overhang more than rake soffits.
A *rake soffit* is one where a soffit material is nailed directly
to the underside of the rafter tails. The rake soffit or exposed tail overhang can extend a little farther than a horizontal return soffit even though the eave drops below the

top of the window height. It should not extend to a point
that obstructs the view from inside the room, nor should it
nullify the light-admitting purpose of the window glass.
Obviously, the rafter tails must not extend so low as to
obstruct the opening of storm doors.

Designing the Rake Overhang

The rake overhang is by far the least complicated type to
draw and build. Its simplest form is the open-rafter tail design. The tails extend beyond the plate a uniform amount.
The opening over the upper plate between the rafters is
blocked with single boards or with a notched frieze board.
This closure keeps out birds, bats, and rodents. To draw
this detail the drafter extends the rafter lines to a cutoff
point that is correlated with the rafter length modulus and
the top of the windows in the wall beneath. The junction
of the lower edge line of the rafter with the horizontal line
projected from the window top will generally be the limit
of the overhang. The exact point will vary a little depending on the existence of a facia board and its height. The
facia is a trim board nailed across the ends of the rafter
tails.

The rake soffit detail drawing will start out the same
as the exposed tail. It is then closed in with some form of
boxing. In regions where wood is still the dominant material, the soffit "skin" may by plywood or hardboard
(Masonite). Stained rough-sawn fir or cedar plywood are
popular materials when combined with rough cedar or red-
wood board and batt siding. In areas where consumers put
an emphasis on maintenance-free surfaces, the soffit covering is likely to be aluminum, vinyl, or steel. To draw the
rake soffit, one has only to close in the underside of the
rafter tails with the material of choice. Some of these materials will require furring strip backup nailers perpendicular to the rafter tails.

Two standard tail-cut choices are available to the
designer (Fig. 4-60). One is called the *square cut*. The other
is the *plumb cut*. The tail of the square cut, as the name
implies, is cut square to the edge of the rafter. This cut is
the easiest to make. It coordinates smoothly with the rake
soffit. All converging materials at the end of the tail meet
flush and at right angles, so there are no voids behind the
joints. Square-cut tails are attractive when boxed. The system is practical when no rain gutters are to be installed.
The overhanging shingles cause the rain to drip out away
from the facia, thus prolonging the life of stain or paint.

The plumb-cut tail is cut on a vertical line. It is
customary to coordinate the plumb-cut tail with the horizontal soffit. Occasionally, one sees a square-cut tail combined with a horizontal soffit in arid zones of the United
States. The plumb-cut tail is fitted with square-edged
sheathing and facia. These materials do not require beveling. Many obsolete drawings perpetuate the facia with an

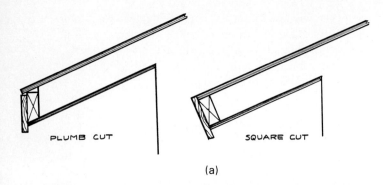

(a)

(b)

(c)

FIGURE 4-60 (a) Two basic eave tail cuts; (b) boxed rake soffit; (c) open tail soffit.

upper edge beveled to match the roof pitch. Since the coming of metal drip edge in the late 1940s the practice of beveling has been discontinued. Beveling is not necessary because the drip edge covers all the voids completely.

Designing the Horizontal Eave Soffit

The horizontal boxed soffit requires considerably more time and material to construct. It requires backup materials called nailers on which the soffit skin is fastened. On a conventionally built rafter system the boards crossing from the end of the tails back to the wall face are called plancier or cornice frames. These terms are also used to describe short rafters horizontally placed which form part of a gable overhang. When the eave overhang is part of a truss, this short horizontal board is called a *soffit return* (Fig. 4-61). Another backup nailer board is nailed to the surface of the wall from one end of the house to the other. The soffit returns are end nailed at right angles to this nail backer. The assembly is put together at ground level in manageable sections. It is hoisted and fastened in assembled sections. The loose ends are surface nailed to the rafter tails. A cross-section drawing of this assembly will show only the sectioned end of the nail backer that is nailed to the house.

The third member of the boxing framework is the facia backer. It is usually a 2 × 4. It serves a dual function.

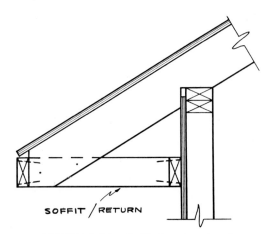

FIGURE 4-61 Soffit framing detail.

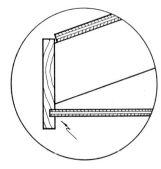

FIGURE 4-62 Grooved facia and soffit detail.

As the name suggests, it forms a rigid backing on which to nail the facia boards. It is a very difficult task to create a straight facia when it is nailed directly to the rafter tails. The nominal 1″-material is too flexible. It requires much shimming and cutting. The use of a backer board behind the facia also provides a good nailing surface on the lower edge for the soffit panels (Fig. 4-62). The grooved facia system is seldom seen anymore. The routing of the groove is too costly. The high cost of craftsmanship has done away with many good joinery systems in favor of fast fabrication with stock materials.

The boxed corner soffit (Fig. 4-63) can take many forms. A primary objective when designing the backup framework is to support it structurally compared to hanging the parts from toenails (the latter method inevitably results in sagged roof corners). A good means of support for the boxed corner is the soffit nailer on the wall face. It can be extended beyond the end wall of the house to a point where the flying return meets it. The fly return, as it is nicknamed, is scarf joined to the underside of the eave end of the fly rafter. The vertical back side of the boxed corner is then flush with the front face of the house.

Another support system may be used when it is desirable to make this corner boxed triangle appear a little deeper. The upper member of the upper double plate on the front and rear walls may be extended out beyond the wall as far as the fly rafter (Fig. 4-64a). This permits the triangular box to continue back along the end wall another 3 1/2″. Some designers feel that this adds to the appearance by giving the impression of a longer overhang (wider soffit). The vertical riser frame piece used to form a nailing backer is face nailed to the end of the extended plate. This, added to the extended soffit backer, provides two strong members from which to hang the boxed corner frame. The joint at the lower corner between the return and the riser is

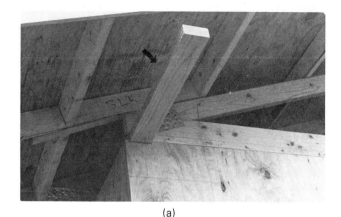

(a)

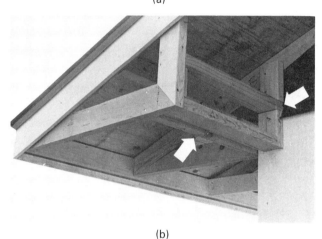

(b)

FIGURE 4-64 Top plate extended to support a triangular boxed corner soffit; (b) completed boxed corner soffit framing. The eave soffit nailer is also extended to help support the bird box.

a 45° miter so that nails will be long enough to penetrate each piece. A horizontal return to the gable end wall is nailed behind this joint to complete the three-surfaced corner (Fig. 4-64b). All the nail positions in this corner should be predrilled to prevent splitting. A split joint is an inferior joint.

Many homes will be observed where the triangular facia piece on the corner box is lined up directly below the rake facia (flush fitted). This is a difficult piece of joinery. The slanting upper edge of this piece is a scarf that is cut diagonally across the grains of the wood. Its entire length exposes end grain. The fit must be perfect and the joint should be glued. This type of craftsmanship is fading away. An alternative design may be used; (Fig. 4-65). The triangular facia piece can be neatly recessed. The exterior surface of the triangular facia is made flush with the back side of the rake facia. It is tucked up under the edge of the rake facia that hangs down below the fly rafter. This system looks neat. It produces a little distinctive shadow line under the rake facia. There is no surface joint to make (no

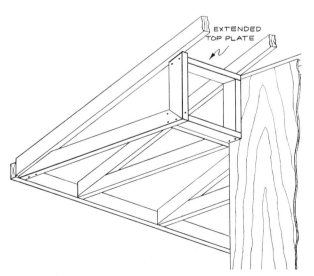

FIGURE 4-63 Boxed corner soffit framework.

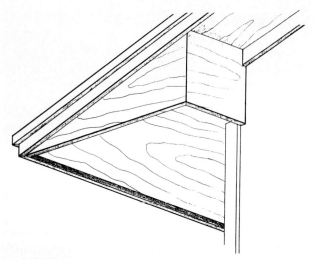

FIGURE 4-65 Facia dropback on a corner soffit.

edge joinery to open up when the wood shrinks). Rain and sun will not penetrate the grain and peel the paint or warp the board.

DRAWING THE ELEVATIONS

An elevation is a view of a particular side of a house. It is a designer's conception which shows the outline of foundation, walls, and roof. It shows the location of windows, doors, steps, chimneys, and other parts. It must be drawn precisely to scale so that an accurate impression is displayed. It is common to make the four or more elevation views to the same scale as the floor plan (1/4″ = 1′). However, if one does not wish to place this much emphasis on the elevations, they can be made to a smaller scale and grouped on the same page. For a very conventional-appearing house, a front view only may be adequate. Elevations provide views to specify some items that do not appear elsewhere in a plan—things such as rain gutters with downspouts and spill pans, chimneys with flashing and projecting flue liners, concrete step profiles and railing, window and door shutters, window and door stylings, siding characteristics, gable and overhang appearance, foundation and roof ventilators, and other aesthetic features.

The technique of elevation drawing is based on measurement and projection. When a height or width is to be repeated at several places on a drawing, it is simpler and more accurate to use the slide bar and/or triangle and project the point to the needed location. To accomplish the projection method the drafter can tape the floor plan above the elevation sheet. A reproduction is preferred so as not to damage the original. It can be folded to position just the one wall to be drawn. All the vertical lines on the elevation can be projected down with very light guidelines. Next, a section schematic of the wall may be drawn to right or left of the elevation position (on the paper or on a separate

sheet; Fig. 4-66). Previously drawn section views cannot be used, as they are usually made to a much larger scale. The section drawing may and should be used as a reference to be sure that no details are omitted. Any omission such as subflooring or a sill will produce an inaccurate and misleading appearance. Floor and ceiling heights are indicated with a few thin dashed lines extending perpendicularly from the elevation. Making the section schematic for projection purposes should not be a lengthy or laborious task. Only the barest bones are shown to indicate heights that project into horizontal lines on the elevation. Heights that are needed for transfer are (starting at the bottom on a front elevation) the footing profile, foundation, grade level, bottom siding line, floor level (to reference door bottoms), underside of window header (to reference window tops), bottom and top of facia, and roof peak.

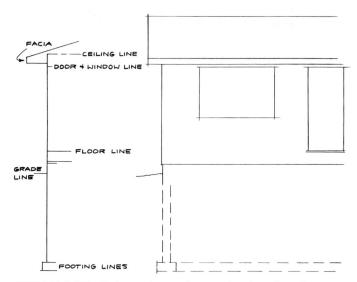

FIGURE 4-66 Schematic section to aid elevation drawing.

End elevations are most efficiently drawn by projecting them off the end of the front and/or rear elevation if the paper size and drawing scale permit. All heights are transferable. The drawing will progress at an efficient pace. Items projecting from the roof must be cross-correlated to show the accurate location on both views. Vertical lines on end views can be projected by taping the folded floor plan above the drawing paper in the same manner as described for the front view.

To gain a mental picture of these projection methods, one may visualize a master layout as follows. A floor plan is centered on a large square table. A sheet of drawing paper is positioned perpendicular to each of the four edges of the floor plan sheet. On each sheet a profile view is created by projecting all the characteristics of the adjacent side of the house perpendicular to the floor plan. It is like unfolding a cardboard cube so that each side is on the same plane as the top or bottom.

REVIEW TOPICS

1. Explain why all dimensions on a plan should be based on actual-size materials instead of nominal callout designations.

2. Explain why interior bearing studs should be aligned with exterior bearing studs in a house.

3. What is meant by modular placement of a window or door opening?

4. Can an on-center stud be utilized in the role of a trimmer stud?

5. *True or False.* Modular placement of a window opening usually nets a saving of at least one stud.

6. *True or False.* The location of doorways that are centered between partitions and windows that are specifically aligned between kitchen cabinets should not be altered by the layout person.

7. How much should one on-center stud at a surrounding partition junction be moved to accommodate a 5′ bathtub that crosses the bathroom?

8. Explain why openings in block foundation walls should be spaced in from the corners and apart from each other a distance divisible by 8″.

9. What is the difference between a single-line and a full-thickness representation of a floor joist plan?

10. Why must the drafter be mathematically correct when dimensioning instead of scaling a drawing?

11. Diagram (draw) and indicate the minimum footing formula with the letter W representing the foundation wall thickness.

12. Describe how to place and dimension an opening for a window on a foundation plan where concrete blocks are specified. State the modulus in your description.

13. Starting at the bottom, list all the wood parts of a frame house, from the sill plate to the top of the top plate. Place the actual size of each piece that contributes to the height to the right of its name. Place a line under the last piece and give the total height (sum of the pieces).

14. Name the two basic roof styles and illustrate each with a top view.

15. Explain the difference between nominal run and clear span.

16. From what point on the wall top plates are third points and quarter points established?

17. Describe and illustrate two ways to design the bearing ends of a truss to that it will qualify as a thermal truss.

18. From a conservation standpoint, what service objectives should an overhanging eave be designed to do?

Chapter 5
FOUNDATIONS

FOUNDATION BED

In the United States there are three general types of soil composition: sand, clay, and rock forms. The portion of the earth upon which a home will bear (rest) is called the *foundation bed*. The supportive characteristics of the foundation bed are directly related to the soil composition. Generally, sand is the least supportive, followed by clay. Rock is the most supportive. These characteristics, and all variable gradations in between, will affect the design of the foundation that is required under a house.

Conventional Assumption

The conventional assumption is that a load of weight placed on a foundation will exert compression forces straight downward parallel with the lines of the earth's gravity (Fig. 5-1). When a foundation bears directly on a bed of solid rock, the assumption is basically true. This is why many large buildings require pilings that go clear down to "bedrock" to assure that there will be no sinking.

Characteristics of Sand and Clay

Sand is the poorest material for a foundation bed because it is easily displaced both vertically and laterally. The pressure focus of a footing is shaped like half an egg (Fig. 5-2). When aimed from a load on ground level it sinks easily, as though being pushed into the ground like a pointed stick. The same foundation placed below ground level is more

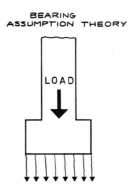

FIGURE 5-1 The basic assumption of the earth's bearing surface is like rock.

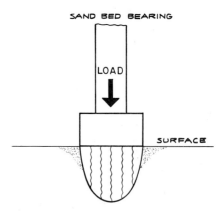

FIGURE 5-2 Sand permits foundation to penetrate and pivot as shown in this profile.

stable in its vertical axis. It gains vertical stability from the compacted support of the earth on each side of the foundation. The deeper it goes into the earth, the more vertically reinforced it becomes. At a certain point of depth it will be detrimental to go deeper. With added depth the foundation material mass increases in weight. The additional weight becomes excess load on the footing. It may cause an unnecessary spearing effect. This counteracts the support factor that is sought with the footing.

Footings in sand or loose soil should be designed with a minimum of two principles. The design of the footing girth and depth sometimes needs to be altered at the site at the time of excavation. Many homes are built from plans that did not include preliminary soil testing (the universal plan). In such circumstances it is necessary to make a value judgment on the spot. Your trench may need to be wider or deeper or both.

Principle 1. In all localities where frost line codes exist, the minimum depth should be adhered to strictly. The earth below the frost line remains stable year round. The objective is to have a stable foundation bed, so the footing must be below the frost line. A few inches of leeway is always advisable. A particularly severe winter may drop the frost line lower than ever recorded. Some protection against such a possibility is a wise procedure.

Principle 2. Under loose soil conditions (sand, gravel, etc.) it is wise to add supportive characteristics to the environment and the footing design. Going a little deeper in sand will add beneficial sidewall support (Fig. 5-3). This will counteract the tendency for walls and footings to tilt and shift. Note in Figs. 5-2 and 5-3 how much the support base of the pressure dome broadens when lowered into the earth. Even in southerly climates where the ground surface seldom or never freezes, it will be wise to lower the footing into the ground to gain the side support of the compacted soil.

More stabilization can be gained by broadening the base contact area of the footing. The most common shape

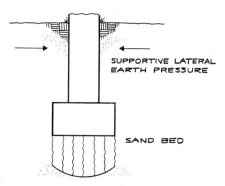

FIGURE 5-3 The penetrating profile improves some with the support of lateral mass.

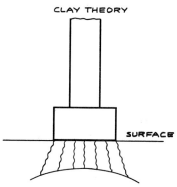

FIGURE 5-4 Clay and mixed forms of organic soil are more supportive than sand.

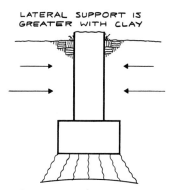

FIGURE 5-5 Side support by earth composition adds to stability.

of foundation is the inverted tee. The design limitations of this arrangement are discussed later in this chapter.

The characteristics of clay are intermediate in the foundation bed analysis (Figs. 5-4 and 5-5). Clay is less predictable than sand. Excavation at times when the ground is frozen or in hot, dry times of year may give the impression of a hard, stable foundation bed material. The same surface during the groundwater-running months of the year will reveal an easily compressible and shifty medium. A footing that is dug too deep in places should never be filled back in with clay. When the undisturbed level is exceeded in depth, it is wise to simply let it be filled with concrete. The small additional cost is minor compared to the problems caused by a collapsed footing.

FOUNDATIONS

Trench Foundation

The trench foundation (Fig. 5-6) is a combination footing and wall poured simultaneously. No forms are used below the ground level. This requires that the soil be stable and tight. It must not collapse into the trench during the pouring of the wet concrete. Trench foundations are seldom

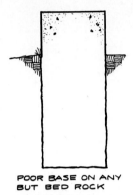

FIGURE 5-6   A trench foundation has a limited base width in proportion to the total mass.

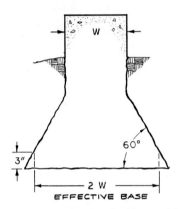

FIGURE 5-7   The flared footing looks good in a diagram but is extremely difficult to produce in actual construction.

used anymore. There is too much handwork involved. Reinforcing with steel is difficult if not impossible. Any portion above ground must be formed on a surface that is usually uneven. The bearing surface that meets the foundation bed is too small in comparison to the quantity of weight mass in the wall. The trench foundation is rarely specified for modern construction.

Flared Footing

The flared footing is similar to the trench foundation in all characteristics (good and poor) except one. The bottom is flared out (Fig. 5-7) by careful hand digging. This provides a better contact surface with the foundation bed. The flared wall at the footing level should not be less than 60° from horizontal. It is readily seen that such a shape is difficult to carve out of the earth unless the trench width is wide enough for a person to stand in. Few residental homes would require a foundation wall thickness of that great a width.

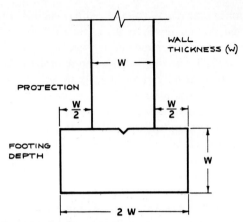

FIGURE 5-8   The formula for a minimum proportion of the universal inverted T footing.

Inverted-Tee Footing

The inverted-tee footing and foundation gets its name from the profile (Fig. 5-8); it appears like an upside-down T. This is the most universally used foundation shape in existence for homes today. The primary excavation is done with large machines, leaving only minor adjustments to be done with hand tools. Forms are required in sandy and loose soil to contain the poured concrete in the desired location and level. In stable soil it is frequently possible to pour the footing in an open trench with only depth-gauge stakes spaced a few feet apart. The stakes should be removed as quickly as an area has been poured and the wet concrete is no longer moving. A half shovelful of wet concrete is placed where the stake is removed. This sustains the level and prevents a low spot. The foundation wall is poured at a later date after the footing has hardened and gained strength.

Pyramid Footing

Poor soil conditions may make it desirable to increase the contact base of the footing without increasing the thickness

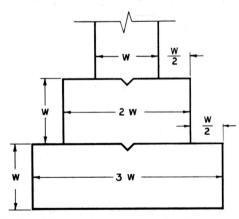

FIGURE 5-9   The minimum proportion formula for a pyramid (stacked) footing.

of the foundation wall. This can be accomplished by one proportionately smaller footing atop another. The design is sometimes called a **stacked** or **pyramid footing**. The same basic formula is used as for the single inverted tee. The bottom footing of the design is one unit of wall thickness greater in width than the one above. This means that the projections will be uniform throughout (Fig. 5-9). Each level of a stacked footing is poured at different times. Forms for the higher-level footing are a little more difficult to hold in place because they cannot be staked directly into the ground. Antispreader bars are run out over the lower footing and nailed to stakes that are driven alongside the first poured footing.

Inclined Step Footing

The inclined-step footing is designed specifically to advance from one footing depth to another (Fig. 5-10). It is used on slopes and hillsides. By stepping up or down from one plateau level to another, both excavation area and concrete are saved. A specific formula exists which governs the maximum rise that should not be exceeded. Violation of this principle will set up a condition that makes it possible for the foundation and the structure on it to slough off (slide) downward toward the low side of the gravity pull. All step footings should be carefully reinforced with lateral, continuously joined reinforcing bars of steel. The rise

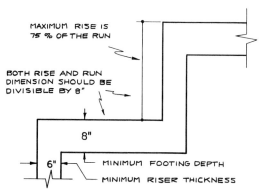

FIGURE 5-11 Stepped footing minimum proportion formula.

of the step footing should not exceed three-quarters of the run (Fig. 5-11). For example, a horizontal section of the footing is 4' long. The vertical step-up part of the footing should not be over 3' high from one surface to the other. The minimum thickness of the vertical part is 6". The minimum thickness of the horizontal section is 8", as it is with continuous-level footings.

    Forming the step footing is somewhat complex. The higher the steps, the more difficult it becomes. Generally, the steeper the incline, the more difficult it will be to pour. Under the highest-rise conditions it may be necessary to pour in stages, taking one level at a time. Several hours may be required between pourings to allow lower levels to solidify enough so that spill-out does not occur (soft concrete that overruns the forms). Obviously, pouring commences at the lowest levels and proceeds toward the highest levels. Theoretically, it is best to pour any footing or wall *monolithically* (all at once). When a delay such as that described above is forced on the builder, it becomes critical that the continuous steel reinforcing be well placed where the riser meets the step. The bars should be bent to run through these turns without being exposed above or below the form. A joint in the rebar should not be made at any place in the riser unless it can be field welded.

LAYING OUT THE BUILDING LINES

The footing location is obviously dependent on the desired location of the aboveground structure that will rest on the foundation. A bore test of the foundation bed is a wise step to take where the subsoil condition is not known. A localized condition may exist that could cause a decision to move the proposed location of the foundation.

Regulated Locations

In rural areas there is usually little or no regulation of building sites. The landowner is customarily at liberty to pick his or her own spot. Once a location is established,

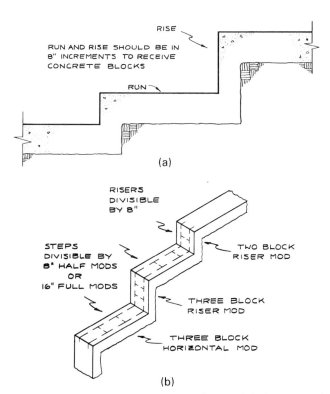

FIGURE 5-10 (a) Section view of a modularly stepped footing, a profile segment. (b) Steps and riser heights should be made to fit concrete stretcher block modules.

there will usually be health-oriented regulations from the county or state. These rules (laws) restrict the proximity of the well and the septic system to each other and to the house.

In a city a code usually exists that defines limits and boundaries which must be observed. There will be a *minimum dropback* rule. This means that a house cannot be placed any closer than a specified number of feet to the front property line. A *side clearance* rule prevents houses from being built too close to each other by restricting the distance that a structure may be to the side lot lines.

Layout Procedure

The steps to laying out the location of a house are as follows (Fig. 5-12 through 5-14)

1. Locate the corner boundary stakes of the lot.
2. Establish the lot reference line (usually the property line nearest the street).
3. Determine the desired or required dropback and side clearance.
4. Establish the longest building line of the house.
5. Triangulate one adjacent end or side of the house line.
6. Lay out the remaining lines by parallelism.
7. Check accuracy by diagonal measurement of the rectangles.
8. Make final adjustments. Do not alter the baseline.

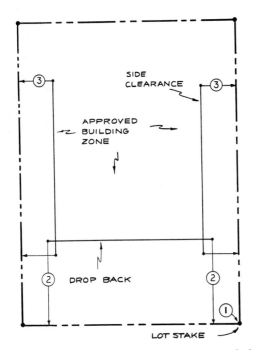

FIGURE 5-12 Laying out a foundation: steps 1 through 3.

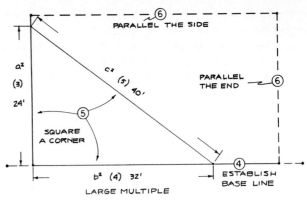

FIGURE 5-13 Establish a baseline and lay out a rectangle: steps 4 through 6.

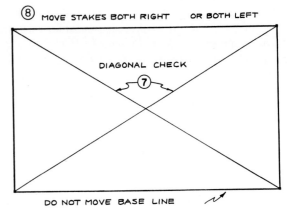

FIGURE 5-14 Check for squareness by comparing diagonal measurements: steps 7 and 8.

In the city it is frequently possible to locate the boundaries of a lot without employing a surveyor. Usually, there are stakes on the property or on adjacent plots of land which can be used as reference points. When a paved street exists with a curbing, the task is further simplified. A city plot map will show the width of the right-of-way easement. The contractor can measure the distance from curb to curb and find the center of the road. If the right-of-way easement is 60', the private property line is a parallel line 30' from the center of the road. A word of caution: Many lawsuits have been created by failure to establish lot boundaries accurately. Roads, especially graveled ones, are not always centered between easement boundaries. When any doubt exists about the exact boundaries of a lot, the least expensive solution may be to employ a surveyor. Check with your municipality first, however, as the service may be provided at no cost.

After the location of the front lot corners is known, the front *reference line* of the house can be staked out. A string line can be stretched taut between lot stakes. It must be clear of all obstructions, such as trees, bushes, and even weeds. A builder's level or transit is a more sophisticated instrument for this task. It can be set up with its plumb bob pointing to the center of one of the lot corner stakes. The target pole is placed on the stake at the other side of the lot. The vertical cross hair in the scope is aligned on the target pole. The pole is held in vertical alignment with the cross hair. This makes the target pole plumb. Any point on the ground along this sight line will be on the lot line and will provide a reference point from which to measure.

The dropback distance is simply measured from the lot line in two places if the house is to be parallel to the lot line. The measurements should be at right angles to the lot line. Greater accuracy will be attained when the two measurement points are considerably farther apart than the length of the baseline of the house. At this point in the layout a string may be placed around a single stake at each end of the line. Position the string on the inside of the stake (the side toward the house).

Side clearance is established in the same way. There is usually more flexibility with side clearance than with dropback. Some codes specify a precise dropback. The builder must comply so that all houses in the block are dropped back the same amount. With side clearance there is usually only one objective. That is to guarantee a minimum distance between houses. If your house plan is 40′ wide, the lot is 100′ wide, and the side clearance regulation is 10′, there will be 40′ of leeway. The house may be placed anywhere in the 80′ from right to left. Many lots are not rectangular. The side clearance rule will apply to the corner of the house that is closest to the lot line. The rule usually applies to the foundation line. It is wise to check the ordinance as it may apply to any part of the structure such as roof overhangs, driveways, patios, or porches. Seldom will a wise builder court trouble by building right up to the minimum side clearance line. It would be a rare case if the house plan took up all the available footage between side clearance lines.

Now that the point of side clearance has been fixed on the front building line a reference exists from which to measure off the other front corner. These two front corner points should be accurately fixed. Use solid stakes driven firmly in the ground. A nail may be driven in the top of each stake at the exact corner point. This is the baseline of the house. When properly established it must not be altered for any reason from this time forward. All squaring adjustments will be made by moving the other stakes and lines.

A house is not always laid out with the front line as the baseline. A U-shaped house, for example, with wings on the front and a straight building line at the back would use the back line as a baseline (Fig. 5-15).

The Pythagorean theorem provides a simple means of squaring the first corner of the house layout. The theorem states that the sum of the square of the length of two sides of a right triangle equals the square of the hypotenuse. Among builders this is known as the 3-4-5 rule. In mathematics class it is taught as the formula $a^2 + b^2 = c^2$. Substitute 3, 4, and 5 for a, b, and c and the formula works

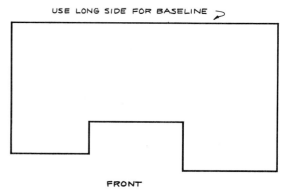

FIGURE 5-15 The longest side makes the best baseline for laying out a rectangle.

out as follows: $3^2 + 4^2 = 5^2$, which is $9 + 16 = 25$. To put this to use squaring the first corner of a house layout, the builder simply measures 4′ down the baseline from the corner point. Hold one tape measure on this point and stretch it out to the 3′ point along the side line of the house, which is intended to be at right angles. Another person will hold the end of a second tape on the 4′ mark on the baseline. This tape will be stretched along the hypotenuse of the triangle. The 3′ mark on the first tape is brought together with the 5′ mark on the hypotenuse tape. The 3′ and 4′ lines now form a 90° corner. When working alone, stiff wire stakes are useful to hold the ends of your 50′ and 100′ tape measures.

In actual practice the numbers used should be the largest possible multiples of 3, 4, and 5 (Fig. 5-16). *The greater the size of the triangle, the more accurate it will be* (Fig. 5-17). For example, a 24′ × 40′ house will fit a multiplier of 8 perfectly: $8 × 3 = 24$, $8 × 4 = 32$, $8 × 5 = 40$. Measure 32′ along the baseline. The hypotenuse (40′) and the side line (24′) will meet at the exact back corner of the house. For any other house depth, a multiplier can be used that will keep the baseline point within the

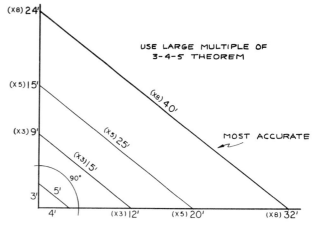

FIGURE 5-16 The theoretical 3-4-5 triangle lacks accuracy for laying out.

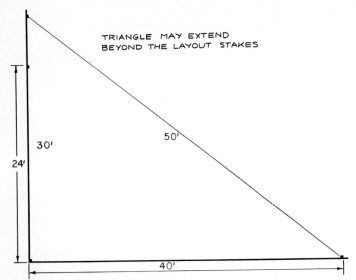

TRIANGLE MAY EXTEND
BEYOND THE LAYOUT STAKES

30'

50'

24'

40'

FIGURE 5-17 Use the largest possible proportionate triangle for greatest layout accuracy.

length of the house. Using the same house dimensions as an example (24 × 40'), the product of 10 also nets a perfect number. It places the "4" figure of the formula precisely on the other corner of the house along the baseline (10 × 4 = 40) (this is another example of the benefits of the perfect modularity characteristics of the 24 × 40' house dimension). The formula "3" figure multiplied by 10 nets 30', which is measured along the 24' side. The fact that 30' is farther out than the 24' house depth poses no problem. The junction of the 30' side is matched with the 50' hypotenuse and the junction is staked (nail on a stake). Then the 24' depth is measured along the 30' line from the baseline and marked on the string. A corner stake is driven and an accuracy nail is placed. Accuracy is important throughout this procedure and should be practiced habitually. Any corner can be squared using the Pythagorean theorem regardless of the house dimension.

When coordinating the junction of the triangle leg with the hypotenuse, be sure to have the figure lines meet on the adjacent sides of the tapes, preferably the inside edges. The tape measures should not be twisted. The more a tape is twisted, the shorter it becomes. Check the loops on the end of your tapes. Some tapes start the zero point on the inside of the loop, others on the outside. Those with a hinged hook start on the inside face of the hook. A bent-out hook will give a long measurement. When working with a partner or team, decide in advance what relative points of reference will be used. Loops and hooks will be butted against stake nails or looped over them. Consistency is the name of the game. The thickness of nails, string, and stakes may seem relatively unimportant at this stage in the rough layout. The understanding of principles and the development of accuracy habits is important. It will be found as construction progresses that most problems develop from

the compounding of small, seemingly insignificant errors in measurement, judgment, or attitude.

Now that two sides of the house line have been established, it is a simple matter to find the final stake of a rectangular plan (Fig. 5-18). Two tapes are used. Each is started from the open corner stakes that were placed last. In the 24 × 40' example the point being sought will be found on the parallel tapes at the intersection of the 24 and 40' marks.

If all measurements and practices were completely accurate, the result of the layout process so far would net a perfect rectangle. Such perfection seldom occurs. Many little obstacles can throw off the results of our efforts. Stakes get kicked and the accuracy nail is no longer on point of focus. String lines on long sides sway out of straightness on a windy day. Rough ground makes a tape "run long." Or if the tape is held high enough to clear piles of dirt or obstacles, it is too high over the stakes to establish an accurate point directly below. A new employee or "volunteer helper" references differently. Any of these variables can cause an inaccurate rectangle or combination of rectangles (the L and U shapes).

The final proof check is done by taking two diagonal measurements across the rectangle(s). The distance is usually an odd figure. It is of no importance to know what the distance should be, although it is a simple problem to compute (the side squared plus the end squared nets the diagonal squared). It involves a working knowledge of square roots or a calculator. The square root of the 24 × 40' sample is 46.647615' or approximately 46'-7 3/4". This knowledge is overly technical. The figure can easily be found by halving the difference between the two measured diagonals. Let us say that one of the diagonals measures 46'-8 1/2", the other measures 46'-7". Halfway between these figures is 46'-7 3/4". When the diagonals are unequal, a parallelogram exists. The line parallel to the

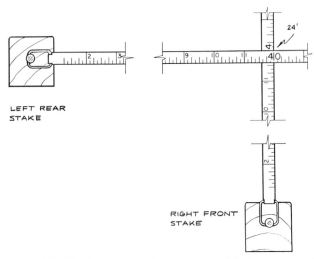

LEFT REAR STAKE

24'

RIGHT FRONT STAKE

FIGURE 5-18 Locate the last corner with two crossed tapes.

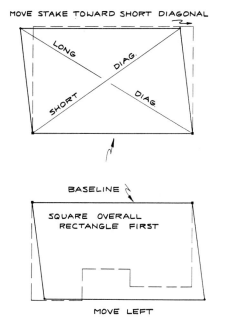

FIGURE 5-19 Correct unsquareness by moving two stakes.

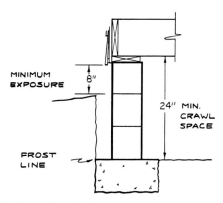

FIGURE 5-20 Minimum crawl space excavation.

baseline must be shifted in a right or left direction until the diagonals become equal (Fig. 5-19). *Never move the baseline* upon which the dropback and side clearance have been established. Both stakes must be moved exactly the same amount in order to sustain an accurate length. The amount of movement is proportionate to the fraction composed of the baseline length over the diagonal length. In the example, half the difference of the diagonals is 3/4″. 40/46.65 of 3/4″ reduces it about an 1/8″, so a 5/8″ shift of the two points will equalize the diagonals.

TYPES OF EXCAVATIONS

Excavations for a house foundation can be uncomplicated or complex. A house to be built on a concrete slab in a southern climate may require no more than a shallow trench. Many footing trenches of this type have been dug by hand. The bulk of the earth was taken out with a long-handled round-point shovel. The side and bottom would be straightened and smoothed with a square-point shovel. Few trenches are dug by hand anymore. The backhoe tractor is currently used for most foundation excavating. The scoop on the backhoe is interchangeable. Different widths can be attached. The builder should clarify three things with the machine operator before digging commences: (1) the exact location of the excavation, (2) the depth of the excavation, and (3) if it is a trench, the maximum acceptable width.

Crawl space and full basement excavating has much in common. The main difference is the depth. The crawl space height from earth level to the underside of the

floor joist should not be less than 2′ so that a person can get around under the floor to work on the plumbing cleanouts, furnace ducts, and wiring. This minimum height provides for adequate air circulation and ventilation. A height between 2 and 3′ is reasonable.

The actual excavation depth to provide the crawl space height desired will depend on several variables. One of the most important factors relates to the amount of foundation that will be exposed on the exterior. The FHA–MPS code states that a minimum of 8″ must be exposed (Fig. 5-20). To achieve this minimum foundation exposure (the objective being to keep the house profile low), the main part of the excavation would have to be at least 16″ deep and the footing part (trenched perimeter) 24″ deep. This would be the case on a building site where all the excavated dirt was to be hauled away. On a flat lot where a little slope in the yard is desired (away from the house), some of the excavated dirt can be used by spreading it around the foundation. It is always advisable to have the yard slope downward away from the house toward the street or a drain source. This will run off the rainwater and prevent unnecessary dampness or flooding of the crawl space. In such a contour design, the buildup of the grade line at the foundation will be subtracted from the excavation depth. For example, if a foot of dirt is to be filled back above the existing ground level, the excavation can be a foot shallower.

Climate affects the required depth of an excavation. The surface level of the excavation does not necessarily have to be more than 2′ below the floor joists; however, the footing level may have to be much lower. In some of the northernmost parts of our country, along the southern Canadian border, the frost line hovers between 4 and 5′ below grade. In such a circumstance the footing is placed several feet below the crawl space floor level. This requires a general excavation to a specified intermediate depth followed by a perimeter trench of considerably greater depth (Fig. 5-21). This is one of the reasons why most northern homeowners are sold on having a full basement. For a relatively small additional investment the intermediate excavation can be lowered. After the house is built, a concrete

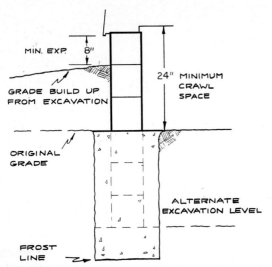

FIGURE 5-21 Deeper footing excavation is required for lower frost lines.

floor is poured in the basement. The usable square footage of the house is doubled at relatively small cost by having a full basement.

MARKING THE EXCAVATION LOCATION

A popular way to mark the building lines for the backhoe operator is to use lime. The simplest method is to spread a thin line by hand. The lime can be fed out through the fingers onto the ground directly under the string lines. The hands should be washed clean as soon as the marking is complete. A lime spreader such as the ones used by athletic departments to mark football fields is an ideal tool for laying out excavation lines (building trades classes take note).

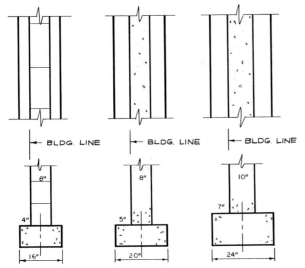

FIGURE 5-22 Relation of the footing to the building line.

It must be made clear to the backhoe operator that this chalk line, which is about 2″ wide, represents the building line, not the footing line. If any confusion exists on this point it will be well worth the contractor's time to place a set of double chalk lines, one representing the outside perimeter, the other the inside perimeter of the footing. Remember: *The footing is not centered under the building line* (Fig. 5-22). It is centered under the wall. The building line is on the exterior surface of the wall. The outer edge of a 16″ footing will be 4″ outside the building line when an 8″ foundation wall is to rest on it. The inside edge of the footing will be 12″ inside the building line. A 20″ footing will be trenched 6″ outside the building line and 14″ inside the line to fit the 8″ wall. A complete understanding between the machine operator and the layout contractor is crucial at this point. Should the ground be broken incorrectly, it will necessitate calling back the machine to widen the trench in one direction or the other. It may then require forms for the incorrect side of the trench. For a full-depth basement, forms are usually required for the footing anyway. It is too difficult for an operator to see over the edge and efficiently judge the depth, width, and straightness of the trench within an excavation. His machine is on ground level unless the excavation has been made with a bulldozer. The bulldozer leaves a ramp at one or both ends of an excavation, providing an access for a backhoe.

BUILDING LINE LAYOUT FOR BASEMENTS AND CRAWL SPACES

Laying out building lines in an excavation embodies the same methods of measurement and squaring as those used in the initial positioning of the anticipated house at ground level. It is more complex, however, because the dropback and side clearance must be determined at points below ground level.

The task is accomplished through the use of batter boards (Fig. 5-23). A batter board set is made up of three 2 × 4 stakes tied together in an ell formation by a pair of 1 × 4s or 1 × 6s. One formation of batter boards is positioned on ground level outside each of the house location corners. They should be driven into firm ground as close to the corners of the excavation as possible. Piles of excavated earth should not be deposited or stockpiled at the corners of the excavation. Such an error will make the placement of batter boards more difficult. The length of the horizontal batter boards is mandated by the width of the excavation that exceeds the actual foundation. Each batter board must exceed the width of the working trench that will remain outside the completed foundation wall. For example, an excavation is accurately dug to provide 2′ of working space around all sides of the anticipated foundation

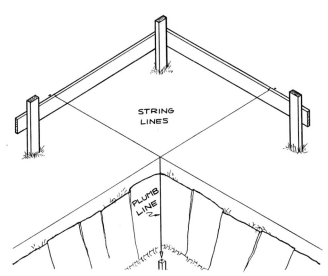

FIGURE 5-23 Batterboards are used above grade level to square corners in an excavation.

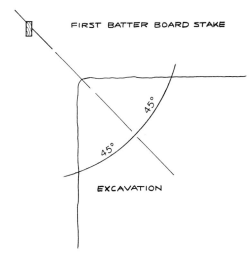

FIGURE 5-24 Place first batterboard stake by visually bisecting the excavation corner.

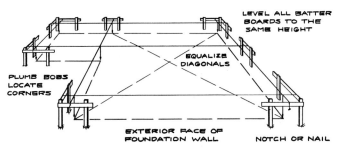

FIGURE 5-25 A full set of batterboards is used for L, T, and U shapes.

wall. String lines are tied between the batter boards to represent the sides of the house (the building lines). The ends of these strings are adjusted back or forth on the batter boards until the intersections where they cross each other are at the specified corner locations from the original layout. To have enough batter board length for this string maneuvering, the board length should be about three times the width of work space outside the anticipated wall. In the example this space is 2′, so the boards would be made 6′ long. If the excavating was not done too accurately or if a wider working space is provided, the batter board length would need to be longer. This batter board length formula assumes that the stakes can be driven within 2′ of the edge of the excavation. In loose soil the banks of the hole cannot be sheared vertically. Some slant is necessary to prevent the sides from collapsing inward. In such cases longer batter boards are necessary, as the stakes will be farther away from the building line.

The first of the three stakes at each corner is placed at a diagonal position from the anticipated building line corner (Fig 5-24). Try to visualize an imaginary line bisecting the building line corner. Extend it out onto the ground level. Place the first stake on this imaginary line. The second and third stakes are placed next to form a right angle. The batter boards are nailed to the stakes in a level position. Each of the four sets should be as nearly at the same elevation as possible. After the strings are attached some stakes may be driven lower to bring the string intersections within 1/8″ of each other. The batter board set will have to be moved should it be found that either batter board position is not within the range of the projected building line.

House plans having L, T, or H-shaped building lines will have one or more corners where a single batter board

is used (Fig. 5-25). A single batter board is nailed to two stakes on the far side of an excavation opposite the interior corner of the wing.

After establishing the precise corner locations with intersecting strings, the next procedure is to transfer these location points down into the pit so that the footing can be laid out. The intersection crossing point should be marked on each string with pencil lead. These marks are held together while a plumb-bob string is tied to the intersecting strings. The plumb bob should hang about 1″ above the top of a corner depth stake. This stake is driven until its top is at the exact level desired for the top of the footing. When the plumb bob has stopped swinging, a nail is driven into the top of the stake directly below the point of the plumb bob. The first two points to be established in this manner are the corners of the baseline of the house.

The quantity of batter boards that is necessary for an accurate layout depends on the number and direction of the corners in the house plan. A rectangular plan will usually require only two single batter boards (Fig. 5-26). One is placed outside each end of the baseline of the house.

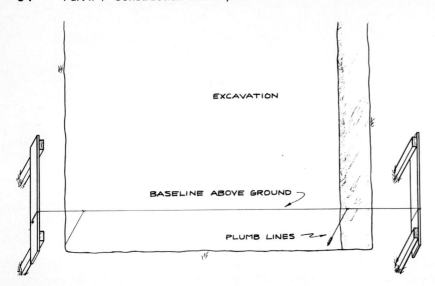

EXCAVATION

BASELINE ABOVE GROUND

PLUMB LINES

FIGURE 5-26 A single line and two single batterboards may be used on the baseline only. The foundation is laid out in the pit.

Each board straddles the baseline. The transit is set up again on its original bench mark. The lot line is reaffirmed. The dropback distance is used to place the baseline string at the correct place on the batter board. A small V notch may be cut in the edge of the batter board to stabilize the string in its final resting place. The side clearance is reestablished and marked on the baseline string with pencil lead. The length of the house is measured along the string. A second mark is placed on the string and the two house corners of the building line are established. This whole procedure can be done with two stakes if they can be placed accurately and securely and the ground clearance is unobstructed.

One of the advantages of excavating with a bulldozer is that the dirt pile is usually stockpiled at one end of the house. This leaves an unobstructed area along the baseline, which simplifies the layout. On the other hand, the backhoe advantage is that the dirt which is to be taken from the premises can be loaded directly into trucks while digging. This saves the separate loading operation that is required when a bulldozer is used.

When the two corners of the baseline have been established in the pit, the remainder of the layout will proceed exactly as it did on ground level.

CRAWL SPACE EXCAVATION

Where a crawl space is designed to have the dirt floor surface on or near the top surface of the footing, the layout procedure is the same as described for the basement. Batter boards and plumb-bob referencing will be required on all corners when the footing is more than a few inches below the crawl floor surface. This is because the intersection points must be projected down below the surface. Therefore, the diagonal checking must be done between the string line intersections that are derived from the batter board setup.

LAYING OUT PIER AND COLUMN FOUNDATIONS

The lateral location of pier and post foundations is accomplished by doing in full scale what was described in Chapter 1. One reminder—when the foundation pads are spaced apart equally, the first and last spaces will be measured from the exterior surface of the wall (the building line; Fig. 5-27). In practice one can easily check out the final correctness by measuring the first and last spaces from the end building lines. If they are designed to be equal and they are not, an error exists somewhere.

A centerline stake is placed at each end of the foundation. If the girder is to be centered between the front and rear building lines, the two stakes will be placed at the exact center of each end of the foundation. It is irrelevant whether the measurement is taken from the outside or the inside of the perimeter forms or from the building lines. The center will be at the midpoint of the total distance. It

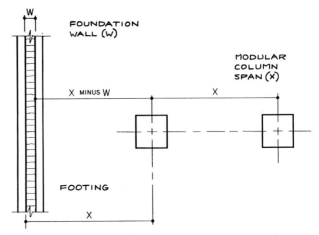

FOUNDATION WALL (W)

MODULAR COLUMN SPAN (X)

X MINUS W   X

FOOTING

X

FIGURE 5-27 Correct modular column pad location stems from the foundation building line (exterior of wall).

is necessary to take the measurement from the same relative place on each side (outside to outside, etc.).

Where a girder is off-centered and parallel, the measurement should be taken from the corners of the building line that is nearest the girder location. A string is then placed between the two stakes. The spacing of the pier pads is plotted down the string. A centering and depth stake is driven below the string at the specified column or pier location.

Elevation of Pier Pads

The depth of the pads is important. It varies from the wall footing elevation in most crawl space designs when piers are made of block units. When blocks are used to assemble a foundation wall, they make a convenient material unit for assembling the piers. An immediate cautionary note: A solid pier is best. Hollow piers are permissible, but at least the top block should be a solid unit or filled with concrete. The solid unit deters termites. It furnishes a better surface for the girder. There are a number of ways of filling the top unit only. One is to lay screen wire in the last joint. Another is to stuff wadded mortar sack paper into the block cores so that the concrete or mortar groat will not pass through.

Pier footing elevation will vary from about 3/4 to 4 3/4″ from the foundation wall footing elevation. This is caused by the variance between block height, and wood girder height, and the sill. The blocks lay up in courses of 8″ height. The actual height of a wood girder is 7 1/4″ for a built-up girder assembled from 2 × 8s. A 10″ girder is 9 1/4″ high; a 12″ girder is 11 1/4″ high. A sill plate is seldom used on top of a wood girder. This has a 1 1/2″ effect on the elevation of the pad. The top of the girder is flush with the top of the perimeter sill. The top wall course of 8″ blocks plus the sill board equals 9 1/2″ of height. With a 10″ nominal girder (9 1/4″) the pads can be laid with their top surfaces on the same elevation level as the perimeter footing (Fig. 5-28). The 1/4″ lower desparity can easily be made up by slightly deepening the mortar joints or by shims under the girder. A 1/4″ leeway is considered by many contractors to be an advisable way to design. Shimming is preferable to notching out the underside of a beam should the pad be too high. Having the pad low is preferred to having it high.

Using the same philosophy, the pad elevation used with an 8″ girder (7 1/4″) should be 2″ higher than the footing (Fig. 5-29). The 12″ girder (11 1/4″) is laid 2″ below the perimeter footing surface elevation (Fig. 5-30). Any variable in block size in the wall or pier will require a specific analysis of the pad elevation. To avoid this type of computation, the contractor can use the 10″ girder and simply duplicate units in the wall and piers. For example, when the wall contains all 8″ hollow units and the top

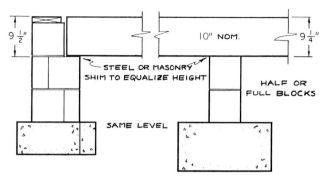

FIGURE 5-28 Pier foundation pads may be at same level as the wall footing where 10″ wood girder is used.

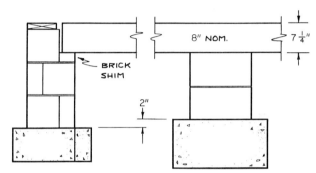

FIGURE 5-29 The pad will be 2 to 2 1/4″ higher for an 8″ girder.

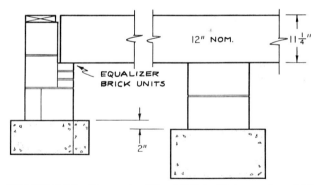

FIGURE 5-30 The pad will be 1 3/4 to 2″ lower for a 12″ girder.

course is filled, the piers will be the same (less one course, which is taken up by the girder). When a designed wall has a 4″ cap block, the pier should have a 4″ cap block.

Elevation of Column Pads

Column footings usually apply only to basements. In the basement situation the top of the pad is on the same level as the perimeter footing. There are three principal types of columns; the wood post, the telepost, and the adjustable screwjack. All of these have a length adjustment that makes the pad footing elevation noncritical.

The obsolete wood post was set on a plinth (a taper-sided concrete pedestal of 8″ height), which in turn rested on the pad (Figs. 5-31 and 5-32). The concrete floor was poured on top of the pad and around the plinth (English spelling: plynth). The common 4″ depth of floor allowed for 4″ of plinth to extend above the floor surface. This prevented the wood post from decaying as quickly from dampness. The height adjustment from the plinth top to the underside of the girder was achieved simply by cutting a post to the correct length. The advent of pressure-treated lumber, which is more decay resistant, has given new life to the feasibility of wooden columns.

The telepost (Fig. 5-33) is adjustable for height. It does not require a precise pad surface elevation. The telepost derives its name from the design. A pipe of a smaller diameter telescopes inside a larger pipe. There are holes through each pipe spaced a few inches apart. The larger pipe is placed on a steel base plate directly on the foun-

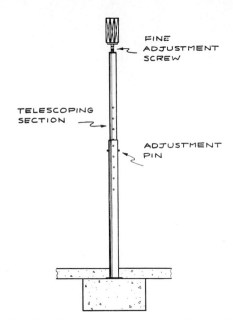

FIGURE 5-33   The telepost has two adjusting features.

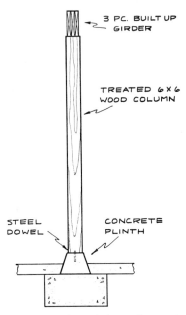

FIGURE 5-31   A wooden girder column should be elevated on a plinth (a concrete pedestal).

FIGURE 5-32   Plinth form and the extracted plinth.

dation pad. The smaller pipe is inserted in the top of the lower section. The upper pipe has an inset collar on top with a threaded shaft. On this screw shaft a top plate is placed. This plate may first be nailed or lag bolted to the underside of the girder. There are alignment pinholes near the center of the pipes. Two steel pins are furnished to immobilize the telescoped sections. On good-quality teleposts each cross pin will have shallow flat grooves to lock them in place when the load is placed upon them. The top screw is then adjusted with a rod handle until the girder surface is on a level with the sill plates on the outer walls. The combination of the hole adjustments and the range of the threaded jack shaft provides a range of height that is adaptable to any pad footing elevation within its height range. A cautionary note: There are many inexpensive lightweight teleposts on the market which are designed only for auxiliary purposes such as shoring up a sagging member. *These are not adequate for new construction in many cases.* The load limit is usually stated on the box.

The screwjack post (Fig. 5-34) is a one-piece steel pipe with a screwjack insert in the top. It is adjustable within the range of the threaded screw. It is more suitable than the telepost for a permanent column. Because of its one-piece characteristic it is less apt to buckle under a heavy load. It may be installed with the screw on top or on the bottom. Some contractors believe that the screw should be on the bottom. After the concrete floor is poured around the screw, curious children or pranksters cannot change it. Lowering the column could allow the girder and walls above to settle, with resulting damage to plaster. Other contractors opt for the upper screwjack location. Their

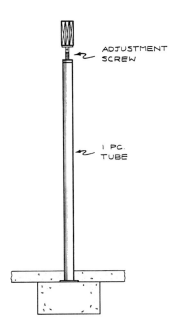

FIGURE 5-34 The screwjack column is an adjustable full-duty type.

rationale is that the girder and other framing materials shrink in size during and after construction. By periodically checking the straightness of the girder with a string line during construction, the builder can eliminate settling to some extent. Any amount of sag indicates that the screws should be raised until the girder is level and straight across the columns.

Setting the Pad Form

Even though the top of the form elevation may not be critical, it is wise to see to it that it is level. A 28 or 48″ level is placed on top of the depth gauge stake (Fig. 5-35). The 28″ level will be used across the form box from side to side. A 48″ level is long enough to span diagonally from corner to corner. When a corner is low it can be raised a little by compacting some dirt or placing a suitably sized

rock under the form. If a form will not stay firmly in place with compacted dirt on the outside, it will have to be staked and nailed. One stake at each corner (a total of four stakes) will secure it adequately both vertically and laterally. Supporting the height of the form with stakes will require nailing through the stakes into the form. A sledge hammer or other heavy object needs to be held against the form on the inside. Without such a backup, the stake will be pounded loose from its mooring and the form will be driven away from its intended location. A concrete block is a handy backstop. In firm soil it may not be necessary to make forms. The shape of the pad perimeter is of little importance. A circular scooped-out basin of adequate diameter (30″) and 12″ depth is actually more efficient than a square pad. Some attempt should be made to make the perimeter shoulder as vertical as possible. A dishpan-shaped depression loses its efficiency as the sides slope upward and outward. An excellent precast pad can be formed in half of a round washtub. Moving such a pad onto location is difficult unless equipment is available and a steel lift loop is cast in the top of the pad. When concrete is being mixed at the site, it is a simple matter to cast-in-place with a bottomless washtub. The tub form is put in place upside-down. A very dry mix is shoveled into the form to the desired depth. It is compacted with a rod tamper (a 2 × 4 on end does nicely). In a few minutes the tub can be jiggled free and carefully raised. The tub must not have horizontal corrugations, as this will prevent release. The same system is possible with wood. All the pads can be made with the same form. The form is made with sides that are tapered somewhere between 15 and 30° (Fig. 5-36). It is put in position with the large face down like an upside-down flower box. The individual homebuilder can save a considerable amount of wood cost by using the same form for all the pads when he mixes his own concrete.

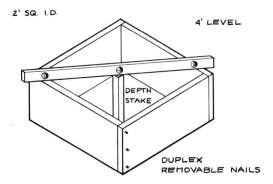

FIGURE 5-35 Leveling a column foundation form.

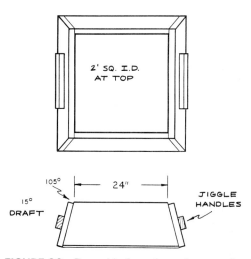

FIGURE 36 Reusable form for column pads.

CONSTRUCTING THE FOOTING FORM

Form construction can be an expensive item in the budget unless the lumber can be used again. Some conscientious planning can reduce the cost from several hundred dollars to practically nothing. The key to cost saving is fourfold:

- Plan to use form lumber of a size that can be reused elsewhere in the house.
- Design the forms so that the boards do not require cutting.
- Assemble the forms with duplex nails and disassemble by pulling all the nails (no hammering on the boards).
- Clean all the lumber immediately by hosing, scraping, and wire brushing until it is usable for construction.

The methods to achieve each of these objectives are as follows.

Objective 1. Reuse of the form lumber can usually be achieved by coordinating floor joist size and the footing girth. For example, a 24'-depth house plan usually requires 2 × 8 joists and a minimum footing depth of 8". A 26'- to 28'-deep house requires 2 × 10 joists. Although the latter may not require more than an 8" depth footing, additional depth may be advisable in some circumstances. The 9 1/4" joist (the actual size of the 2 × 10) would not be considered oversize.

In reality, none of the dimension lumber sizes fit the footing depth requirement exactly. To produce an 8"-deep footing it is necessary to scoop the trench at least 3/4" deeper than the 7 1/4" form board. If an 8" footing is to be poured into 2 × 10 forms (9 1/4" high), it can be ac-

complished in one of two ways. The form boards can be recessed 1 1/4" deeper into the earth than the foundation bed level. The second way is to place the forms on the foundation level and not fill the form to the top. A double-notched screed board (Fig. 5-37) is used to float the surface of the concrete level at a point 1 1/4" below the top edge of the footing. This leaves an 8" depth of concrete in the 2 × 10 form.

Objective 2. In most designs the majority of joists in the floor will be full-length stock units. In the butted and spliced system, approximately 1 1/2" will be cut off (the amount of span taken up by the box header). The joists that will be used first as forms should be left full length for this initial forming phase.

On a rectangular house plan, it is possible to construct a foundation form without cutting any boards. It is accomplished by lapping and overrunning. First, the notion must be dispelled that the sides of the footing must be perfectly straight. They do not have to be. Codes and proportion formulas deal in minimums. Where the side of a footing juts out 1 1/2" due to a lapped form board, there will be no effect on the soundness of the footing. The little bit of extra concrete needed to fill the jut-out is insignificant.

Start the interior form boards at the corners and work toward the middle. A string line is stretched between the corner points. The boards are kept outside the string line. When the boards come together, one of them is simply swung out away from the string and lapped against the other board. The top edges are made flush and a pair of form nails is driven in. A stake is placed against the lap. This method can be repeated on all the sides of the interior form (Fig. 5-38).

The exterior form boards may follow the same design. Another option is practical for assembling the outside form boards. If the size of the excavation is large enough, the board at the corner may run on past the board to which it will be nailed (Fig. 5-39). When room does not exist to accommodate the amount of surplus length that exists, it is backed up and lapped like the interior ones.

Foundation shapes that include small protruding wings or ells may require cutting of one or more pieces. Such an extension is needed for step foundations and fire-

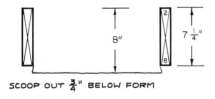

SCOOP OUT 3/4" BELOW FORM

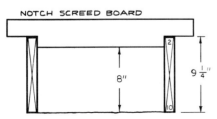

NOTCH SCREED BOARD

FIGURE 5-37 A notched screed board is used where forms are too high.

LAP INTERIOR FORMS

STRING LINE

BUTT OR LAP EXTERIOR FORMS

FIGURE 5-38 Form boards to be used later as structural members are left full length.

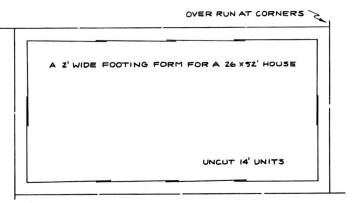

FIGURE 5-39 This single-line representation shows a complete footing form made up of uncut 14' lengths which will later be used for floor joists.

places. Here again, a careful examination of the floor plan may reveal an opening in the floor plan that requires headers and tail joists. A tail joist is any joist that extends from an opening in the floor frame to the foundation wall or to the girder. By determining the lengths of these shorter members in advance, it may be possible to cut pieces for the footing form which will be long enough or exceed the length needed later. By overrunning two of the protruding corners it becomes necessary to custom cut only one piece of lumber.

Pier and column footings can be made in several ways. The form is a simple open-bottomed box. Boards that are cut the same length to make the box must be one thickness longer than the opening size that is specified. A 24″ × 24″ pad will require 25 1/2″ lengths of form boards. When nailed together each succeeding corner lap must progress in the same direction. Failure to do this will net a rectangle, not a square. Should the form builder choose to assemble the box like a stool, laying one side across the upright ends of the two ends, the top board being nailed must be two thicknesses longer than the opening. The two boards being end nailed will be the exact length of the opening.

As an example, consider that the specifications call for a footing 12″ deep by 24″ square. The material will be 2 × 12 stock (see Fig. 5-40). In the first instance each

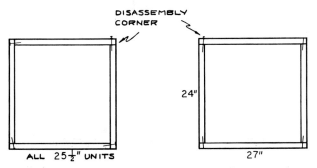

FIGURE 5-40 Column form joints with different advantages.

board is cut 25 1/2″ long. The nails are placed on the surface on one end only. In the second instance two of the boards will be 27″ long and two will be 24″ long. The two longer boards will have surface nails on both ends. The uniform-length system has a slight advantage. Matching of sets (two long and two short boards) is not required when cutting or assembling. When the forms are used over and over again, some boards are broken by disassembly. Replacing a piece or two from other broken sets is more easily accomplished. It is possible to use a form many times if it is assembled with double-headed scaffold nails. Some manufacturers call this double-headed design a duplex nail.

To remove the form, pull only the nails from one corner. Scoop enough dirt away from the form so that the corner can be spread open a few inches. The form is now free to be lifted off. Replace the nails immediately into their original holes. Handle the forms carefully. Stack them neatly and they will be in good shape for the next job. Banging forms of any kind apart with a hammer is a destructive practice.

Objective 3. The next objective is to *preserve the wood from damage* and unsightliness. Most lumber species split readily when a nail is driven close to the end of a board. Think of a board as a lot of long, hard, stringy bands held together by soft tissue. A nail is a steel wedge. It drives through the soft tissue and presses the hard fibers apart. The closer the nail is to the end of the board, the more apt the board is to split. A good rule of thumb is: *Nail no closer to the end grain than the thickness of the board.* If there is sufficient lumber length on the outside perimeter forms, allow the corner board to run on past the corner. By so doing the nails will not be close to the end of the board. The inside form corners will have to be nailed with regular nails since duplex heads would embed in the concrete. The natural tendency of novice carpenters is to start the nail in a position aimed dead center into the end of the other board. With 2″ lumber (1 1/2″ thick) this places the nail 3/4″ from the end grain of the first board. In a majority of cases this position will cause the 16d common nail to split the board. Another practical nailing rule states: If the wood splits, use a smaller-diameter nail or tap a pilot hole (drill a hole for the nail so that the wedging effect is eliminated). A nail can only be placed 3/4″ from the end of a 1 1/2″-thick board safely when a hole has been drilled for it. A better choice is to use 16d box nails. They are smaller in diameter and still have the needed length for penetration. Even with the smaller nail it is wise to follow the thickness rule. Back away from the end 1 1/2″. Slant the nail to penetrate just inside the edge of the other board. It will penetrate and follow down the porous soft grain.

The technique of disassembly is equally important to the preservation of the wood. Boards that are driven apart from one another by pounding seldom survive the abuse.

The result of pounding is usually split boards with many unsightly dents and bruises. Forms put together with scaffold duplex nails, by contrast, can be disassembled with very little damage. It does not take an excessive amount of time. On the contrary, the knockdown time will be shortened when the technique is perfected. What it does require is an attitude of conservation. One should visualize every plank as a $10 bill or every successfully extracted nail as $1 gained. The reclamation project will seem like a $100-an-hour achievement. It is!

Make the task easy as well as profitable. A hammer is the least effective tool for pulling nails in the 12d to 20d class. The leverage is inadequate. The nails are of such a length that they are bent beyond reuse when pulled with the hammer. This inadequacy can be eliminated to a certain extent by pulling the nail in two stages. Place the claws of the hammer under the exposed head of the duplex and pull until the second head is exposed above the surface (Fig.

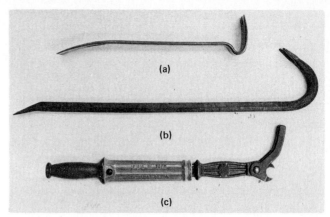

FIGURE 5-42   (a) Wonder bar; (b) wrecking bar; (c) nail puller.

5-41a). Reset the claws under the intermediate head. Hold a small scrap block of wood under the head of the hammer and complete the extraction (Fig. 5-41b). The nail will release before it is bent to any detrimental degree. It can be used many times when pulled in this manner. Rip hammers are poor nail pullers. When the flat of the straight claw is reached, it will take much more energy to continue the pull beyond that point. The hammer head has to pivot on the flat top rather than on the gradual curve as it does on the claw hammer. This puts a distinct dent in the surface of the wood. The rip hammer is useful when separating two boards by driving the claws in between the ends of the boards.

There are several tools designed specifically for pulling nails. Three of them should be in every carpenter's kit. The *wonder bar* (Fig. 5-42a) is a small but effective tool. There are three openings on the wonder bar for pulling nails. Both ends of the bar are chisel shaped with a V slot. Either of these ends can be forcibly driven under the head of a nail by pounding on it with a hammer. A keyhole on the shank of the wonder bar will pull the nail whose head is above the surface.

The tool that provides the greatest leverage is the crowbar or *wrecking bar* (the name should be "reclaiming bar"; Fig. 5-42b). This bar is shaped like a shepherd's crook or an elongated question mark. Its cross section is hexagonal. The nail-puller claw is on the crooked end. The other end is slightly bent and chisel shaped for prying and lifting. The bar is available in several lengths. The 35″ length makes it possible for a person to pull many of the form nails from a standing position. The pry end is handy for prying stakes apart from the form boards. It can also be used as a lever to raise the boards out of the ground with the stakes still attached.

A third valuable tool for reclamation and redo work is the *nail puller* (Fig. 5-42c). It will remove a nail whose head has been driven below the surface to a point that none

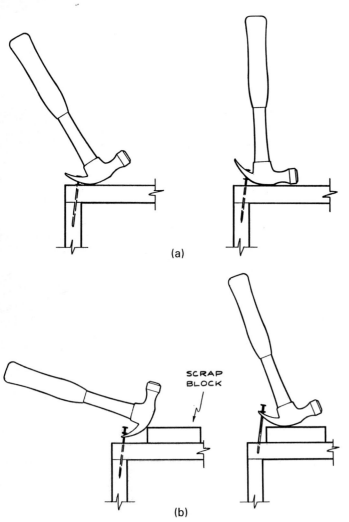

SCRAP BLOCK

FIGURE 5-41   Pull a form nail in four steps to avoid bending the form nails.

of the other tools can successfully get a hold of it. The nail puller has two pincher jaws, one mounted on a pivot pin. A ram handle is on the other end. The jaws are placed outside the nailhead. While one hand holds the jaws on target, the other hand slams the ram handle down. This drives the pinchers into the wood. When the handle is tilted, the pinchers close under the nailhead. The handle is pulled toward you. The lever action pulls out the nail. The pinchers pivot on a shoe, which is the fulcrum. The jaws should be placed parallel with the grain of the wood so that they will drive in easier. The nail puller will extract just about any nail whose head can be seen. It leaves two deep indentures alongside the nail hole. It is the tool of last resort—an invaluable tool when others fail.

Objective 4. The fourth objective is to *strip and clean the wood*. The nails should be pulled completely out of each board as soon as the board is detached. This is a wise safety practice. A board lying on the ground or swinging through the air with a nail sticking out is an unnecessary menace to personnel on the job. A few moments of delay in removing a single nail can mean a disabling accident for you or a fellow worker. Reserve a nail pocket in your apron for the reclaimed form nails.

Any nail-pulling tool has a tendency to flip the nails through space. Two precautions should be observed.

- **Wear protective eye gear.** The wise carpenter will wear goggles, shatterproof safety glasses, or a face shield when pulling nails. The wise contractor will require it.
- **Develop the skill** of easing off the pressure on the pulling lever (the handle part) of the puller as the nail comes farther out of the wood. Never jerk a nail loose. If you have gloves, a gloved hand can be held over the nail just before it exits the wood. An attitude of carefulness will prevent needless accidents.

Remove and clean one form board at a time. When forms are removed the next day after the footing is poured, the cement that remains on them can easily be scraped off. It is still "green" and soft. An excellent tool for scraping is the 4″ masonry chisel. Sometimes the cement is still soft enough that it can be hosed and brushed off with a fiber brush. Hosing should be done with the board in a perpendicular or tilted position so that the wood does not have time to absorb a lot of water. Stand each board on end after hosing until all the water has run off. In a few minutes reverse the ends so that the end that was on the ground can begin to dry. *Do not leave wet or damp boards in direct sunlight.* It takes only a few minutes for some boards to warp so badly that they are unusable. When forms are not removed for several days, the cement will be much harder.

Where it is very thin on the boards, it will be powdery. This powder can be wire brushed away. Brush in the direction of the grain. One or all of these methods may be used to restore the usefulness of the board. In a crawl space, a little cement on a joist is not objectionable. The cleaning can be limited to those surfaces that will come in contact with other materials, such as the bearing ends and the upper edge. The immediate area around a required saw cut must be freed of any cement in order to maintain sharp blades.

Stack all the cleaned boards up off the ground. Place thin spacer strips between each layer. Cover the stack from the weather in a place out of the sunlight whenever possible. When you are ready to use the reclaimed lumber, inspect any area on a board that requires sawing. Check for hidden nails. Remove the remaining cement or cement powder. Cement powder looks harmless, but it is abrasive and will quickly dull a saw blade. Carbide-tipped blades will last longer than regular blades when working with reclaimed lumber. Nonetheless, the abrasive powder will gradually wear away the keen edge of carbide teeth as well as steel teeth.

REINFORCING THE FOOTINGS

Under all but the most perfect foundation bed conditions it is well worth the cost to reinforce the footings of a foundation with steel. Concrete has great compression strength even though it does not have much ability by itself to resist bending or stretching. Footings under foundation walls of a house are comparatively long, narrow perimeter ribbons of concrete. The footing is particularly susceptible to cracks across the width and depth. Weaknesses can exist in the foundation bed. A vein of sand or gravel may run across a segment of an otherwise stable bed. Weaknesses can develop during construction. Rains can wash away parts of the trench. Water standing in low spots can turn a stable area into unstable mud. A weakness will be built in if the trench is dug too low in spots and then filled back in with loose dirt. Such an area will not support the footing with the same firmness as the undisturbed earth in the remainder of the trench. Tamping is helpful but is not a substitute for the original firm earth.

Objective of Reinforcement

An unreinforced footing may fail by giving way to movement in one or more of three directions. It may stretch—moving in an outward lateral direction. It may collapse downward due to failure of the foundation bed. These two directions are common to basement footings and those which are under slab floors. The third direction is inward. The crawl space foundation is susceptible to exterior pressures from backfill. There is no basement floor to prevent

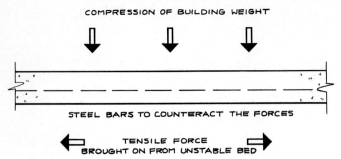

FIGURE 5-43 Compression and tensile stress on a foundation footing (a perimeter segment).

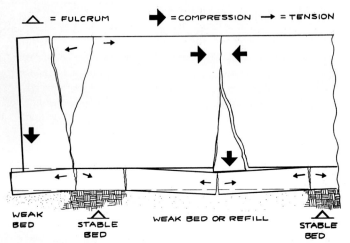

FIGURE 5-44 Typical foundation failure which probably could have been avoided by a proper-sized footing and adequate reinforcing in the footing and wall.

the foundation wall and footing from being pushed in. There is no counteracting dirt on the inside of the foundation wall as there is with the ground-level slab floor.

The objective of steel in a footing is to immobilize it against sideward and downward pressures (Figs. 5-43 and 5-44). Side pressures are referred to as lateral. Downward pressures are called *compression stress*. When a perimeter footing attempts to pull apart lengthwise, it is said to be under *tensile strain*. All of these strains can be counteracted by embedding steel reinforcing bars of adequate size and quantity in the footing. The shortened name of this steel is *rebar*. The objective is to place rebar in a continuous band around the perimeter footing. Two or more of these unbroken bands of steel will help the perimeter footing to hold together in all directions. The concrete may crack, but it is not apt to separate or change levels.

Rules for Installing Rebar

There are four basic rules for placing and securing rebar:

- Bend the bars around corners. Do not end bars at a corner unless they can be welded in place.

- Stagger the ends of the lap joints of the bars that are side by side. The joint of one bar should not be closer than 4' from the joint of an adjacent bar.
- Lap ends of bars to be joined between 12 and 16".
- Wire the lapped ends of the bars in at least two places or weld.

Placing the Steel by the Rules

Rebar comes in 20' lengths. That used in house foundations is usually size 3, 4, or 5. The diameter is the numerator designation over the denominator eight. (No. 3 is 3/8, No. 4 is 1/2", and No. 5 is 5/8"). There are both hard and soft bars. Soft can be cut with a hacksaw or long-handled bolt cutters. Hard bar requires an abrasive cutting saw blade in a power saw or a cutting torch. When the rules are followed (continuous bands and bent around the corners) there will be only one cut to make per band. If the last lap is not too great to be excessively costly, there could be no cutting.

Start positioning the first set of bars around a corner (Fig. 5-45). Lay out a bar on the ground. Step off or measure 4' from the end of the bar. Place your boot on the bar. Reach down, grasp the bar, and bend it sharply up at right angles to the ground. Step off 8' on the next bar and repeat the process. If there are to be three parallel bands, step off a third bar to the 12' point and bend it. Place the three bars in the trench around the corner spaced one-fourth of the trench width apart (with two bands, place them one-third of the width apart). The ends of all the bars are now staggered apart from each other approximately 4'. From this point on add full 20' lengths, bending them around the corners as you come to them. Work in one direction or both until the perimeter is surrounded.

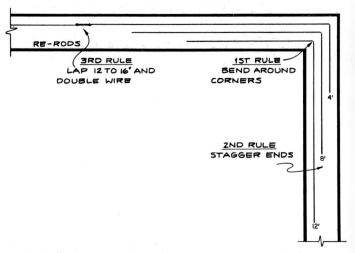

FIGURE 5-45 Bend and start the first rods at a corner to set off a staggered end syndrome. Stagger a minimum of 4', lap, and double wire each joint.

Lap wiring is done at a point 2 to 3″ from the ends of the bars. Each lap joint should have two wires. Tie wires are available for the purpose. They have looped ends so that the fingers are not damaged from hand twisting. Most bars have some form of ribbing. It is important that the bars be tightly placed and wired together so that the ribs interlock. This prevents the bars from sliding past each other. It also prevents the bars from slipping in the concrete.

The bars must be supported in some manner above the bottom of the trench. The bars should be between one-third and one-half the way up into the footing from the bottom. When concrete forms are used, wire can be suspended across the forms to support and separate the bars. Some builders believe that the bars can be pulled up into the wet concrete from the trench bottom while the concrete is being poured. This is a poor technique. Frequently, it cannot be accomplished quickly enough. Many times it is simply forgotten. The depth positioning of the bars is impossible to determine uniformly. The rods must be probed for with a hooked rod. They are difficult to find in time. Spacing them apart from each other is seldom done accurately. There is no assurance that the rods will not sink in a mix that is too thin. Ready-mix drivers are famous for asking if you would like the mix watered a little "so that it will move around better." Do not permit it. *Wet cement makes weak concrete.* Adding water after the plant-specified mixture has been put in the mixer voids the company's guarantee of strength. The bars must be held in place firmly enough that the cascading ready mix will not push them out of position. When forms are not used and the concrete is poured in an open dirt trench, it is a little more difficult to stabilize the rods. Some builders drive stakes to a desired level and nail the rod to the stake top. The nail is driven alongside the rod. It is then bent over the rod like a one-legged staple. The stake is left in the concrete. This is a questionable practice. The stake may rot out in time, leaving a strength void in the concrete. The rod is exposed to ground moisture and will corrode at a more rapid pace than does fully embedded steel.

Another method of supporting the rods is to bend a small section of 6 × 6 reinforcing mesh into an arch (Fig. 5-46). These arches are placed at intervals close enough to prevent the rods from sagging more than 1″. The rods are tie wired to the arches.

Reinforcing an Oversize Footing

The angle of effectiveness of the forces projecting downward through a footing is 60° from level. Any widening of the footing without deepening causes ineffective mass, which may be more detrimental than good (Fig. 5-47). In some foundation bed environments it is advisable to have a broader bearing base on the footing to provide more "table" support. In the same instance it is not advisable or

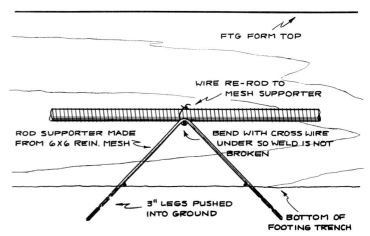

FIGURE 5-46 Rebar supports made from 6 × 6 grid mesh reinforcing.

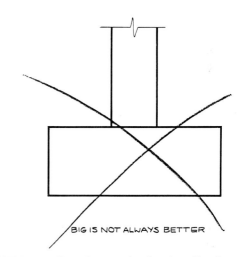

FIGURE 5-47 Grossly oversize footing. Not formula proportioned.

desirable to widen the wall or the footing depth to sustain the correct proportion because it would add excessive mass and weight. Widening the footing beyond the formula maximum may create a fracture potential. A downward compression force is concentrated by the wall on the center of the widened footing. The extended footing projections counteract the force at the outer edges. When more than enough compression weight is present, the footing may rupture lengthwise (Fig. 5-48).

This problem can be overcome by reinforcing crosswise. In addition to the longitudinal rebars, cross bars are embedded in the footing. They are placed across the trench and securely wired to the other bar bands (Fig. 5-49). In this stress circumstance all the bars should be closer to the bottom of the trench since any fracture of this kind will tend to start from the bottom surface of the footing and work its way up toward the inner and/or outer surface point of the wall.

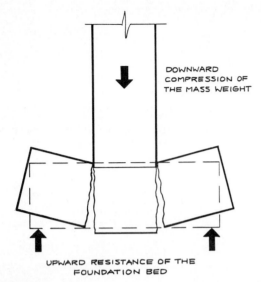

FIGURE 5-48 Too much width (projection) may cause lengthwise rupture.

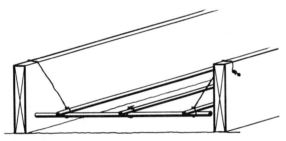

FIGURE 5-49 Cross bars will help spread the compression stress throughout a wide footing.

The quantity of cross bars will call for same value judgment. The width of the footing will not gain effectiveness by being wider than three times the wall thickness. Some precepts to go on are the following:

- The wider the footing, the more cross bars are needed.
- The weaker the foundation bed, the more cross bars are needed.
- Space the bars equally apart when the foundation bed is of the same consistency throughout its perimeter.
- Place more cross bars (closer together) over areas where the foundation bed is notably less stable than the rest of the footing area.

A cross bar every 2′ will usually do under the most undesirable bed conditions. A bar every 4′ may be adequate when some insurance is desired but conditions are not severe.

Holding the Forms in Place

The shape and location accuracy of the completed footing will be no better than the quality of the form construction. Poor footings may result even though good materials are used. Conversely, a satisfactory footing can be produced with wood that is far from good in appearance. It is not the quality of the form material that determines the finished product so much as it is the form builder's ability to have the fluid concrete end up where it is supposed to be. To accomplish this result, the forms must be held firmly in their desired position throughout the pouring phase. There are several methods and devices to secure the forms.

Stakes are a common means of preventing footing forms from moving away from their location. The builder of many homes can profit from the use of steel stakes over a period of time. They are easier to drive. There are holes provided for nailing. The lifetime of a steel stake is long, provided that they are not lost at disassembly time. It pays to paint all steel stakes a bright color that contrasts with earth and grass. Wood stakes, by contrast, are usually expendable. They will constitute a repeated outlay of money for each job. Most lumber companies supply 2 × 2 and 1 × 2 stakes in 16 and 24″ lengths. 2 × 4 stakes are available from some custom-cutting yards.

The spacing of stakes along a form is governed by the flexibility of the form boards. Forms made of 1″ stock will require a stake every 3 to 4′. Forms of 2″ stock may require a stake every 6 or 7′. If a form board is bowed (curved lengthwise on the flat vertical surface), it will be difficult to stake it in a straight line.

Spreader boards and blocks will help position bowed form boards. There are two ways to use a spreader. A spreader block can be made of any scrap board that can be cut to a length the same as the specified footing width. 2 × 4s do nicely. The spreader block is placed between the forms when either or both form boards are bowed in. In this circumstance, a stake is first placed as far out toward the end of each form board as possible. This will make it

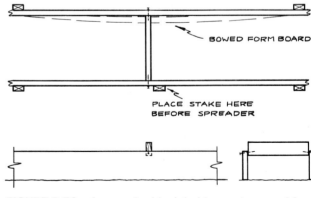

FIGURE 5-50 A spreader block holds apart warped form boards that are inclined to bow inward.

easier for the form board to be bent into a straight line. The rest of the stakes are placed between the ends of a bowed form board only after the spreader block has been wedged into place and temporarily nailed (Fig. 5-50).

A container board is used to hold in form boards that are bowed out. It must be longer by several inches than the footing width. The container board is nailed to the top of one form board. It must be firm. Two nails on each side may be advisable when there is great stress in the bow. After the first side is secured, the forms are drawn together until they are the correct distance apart. Then the second end is firmly nailed with duplex nails. Prefabricated spreaders can be made and used over and over again by the professional builder. A combination spreader that will accommodate both inward and outward bows is shown in Fig. 5-51.

Spreaders of both types can usually be removed within an hour after the concrete has been placed. The concrete will be set enough to prevent the form from moving. Keep in mind that fluid concrete is very heavy. In its first rush down the chute it can "blow out" an insecure form.

Each type of concrete work has the characteristic of being permanent. When a mistake in judgment or attitude is made, the end result is extremely difficult to change or remedy. One should approach any concrete job with the attitude that once the die is cast, there is no turning back. The essence of form construction is found in two elements: accuracy and sturdiness.

Accuracy of footing form construction is found in two spheres. *The surface of the footing must be level*. The sides must be straight in the sense that the projections beyond the outer and inner wall lines must not be less than the minimum specified. A lapped form board, as described earlier, will always be lapped outside the form line.

The levelness of the footing is usually attained by setting depth stakes in key locations within the form. They are pounded into the ground until the top surface is at a uniform level. The transit or construction scope level is probably the most universal instrument for setting stakes. Old-timers made use of a garden hose filled with water. With the hose lying in a trench, the end would be turned

up to the height desired on one end. The other end was then lowered until the water appeared at the end.

Straightness of the form sides is achieved by laying them to a string line. The corner form boards are placed in position first. Strings can be run between the corners inside the forms. Some builders run these strings on the building line. They will then measure from the string to the form board to assure that it equals or exceeds the specified projection. Other form builders will run a string along the location of the outer edge of the intended footing. With this method it is important not to allow any board to touch the string. When a board touches a string, there is no way of knowing whether it is pushing it out of alignment. String lines should be placed inside the form because the area outside the form will have stakes and braces which will obstruct the string. A string line is reliable for assuring straightness. It is not reliable on great lengths for checking levelness because it can sag.

POURING THE FOOTING

There are several prerequisites to the actual pouring of concrete for a foundation footing. Whether the concrete is to be mixed at the site or delivered ready-mixed, all preparations should be completed before mixing is started. When water is added to the other ingredients for concrete, a process called *hydration* begins. Once begun, it cannot be delayed. Only a limited amount of time is available to place the fluid concrete before it sets up into an immobile mass. On hot, windy days the workable time limit is very short. It can be as little as 20 to 30 minutes from the time the concrete flows from the chute. On cool, cloudy, or damp days the time could extend to an hour or more. Regardless of the climatic conditions, time will not stand still while details are completed in preparation for the pouring.

Access to the Site

Consideration must be given to how the footing area will be reached with the concrete. The site-mixed job will require space close to the trench for the mixer, the piles of aggregate, a water barrel, and runways to wheelbarrow the mixed concrete around the footing form. It will require a water supply and electricity if the mixer is powered by an electric motor.

The ready-mix job will require drivable access to several points around the footing trench. An approach to the corners is preferred in some instances, as the wet concrete can be pulled down two directions simultaneously. The side approach will be required in addition to corners when the sides are long. The chute should be located to put the concrete in at angles to the form (as nearly parallel as possible). It is swung to right and left. A backer board in-

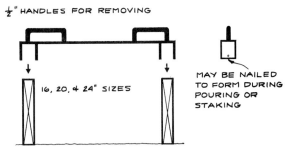

FIGURE 5-51 This steel form gauge is used as a temporary spreader/container while stakes are set.

side the form is helpful to prevent excess overfill and spill-out. In the ideal dumping setup, the truck can drive along parallel to the trench, filling it progressively. This arrangement provides for a minimum of hand pulling of the wet concrete with hoes and shovels. The quantity of handwork required to place the concrete will be directly related to the ease with which the footing site can be approached.

When a combination of difficult terrain and excavation deposits makes it impossible to approach the site, other ways of depositing the concrete will have to be planned. It may be necessary to have planks on hand. These will be used to make runways for wheelbarrowing the concrete to the desired location. Pushing a wheelbarrow full of wet concrete requires a lot of strength and control. It is extremely difficult over rough or soft ground. Some ready-mix companies will furnish a wheelbarrow and extra chutes upon request.

Delivery and Setup Time

Setup time must always be considered before ordering ready-mix. All the conditions discussed in the foregoing paragraphs will affect the amount of time it takes to place the wet concrete. Other elements are involved. One is the distance from the ready-mix plant to the site.

The hydration process begins from the moment that water is introduced into the mixture. The chemical action creates heat, evaporation, drying, and hardening. Additional water should not be added to a carefully measured mixture for the purpose of slowing down the hardening rate. This is called *retempering*. Concrete engineering specialists advise against retempering, as it weakens the final strength of the concrete. Many ready-mix companies have a statement on the bottom of their delivery slip that contains a blank to be filled in by the driver showing the number of gallons of water added "at the customer's request." The sentence goes on to state that such an addition of water voids the company's guarantee of the specified strength. It is a great temptation to "water down" the mix when pouring concrete into any horizontal form. It makes it easier to move it around. It flows and self-levels. Unfortunately, the mixture breaks down. The heavier stone aggregate sinks to the bottom. The sand and the lighter cement parts are left on top. The hydration process is swamped with water. The excess water rises to the top. It puddles in low spots or runs off, carrying with it the rich cement binder.

Slump Test

To assure a suitable stiffness of the wet concrete mixture, a slump test is performed by an inspector. Any reputable ready-mix company will perform the test regularly at the mixing plant. On a large government-controlled job such as a highway overpass, an inspector will perform a field

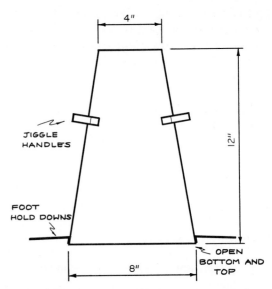

FIGURE 5-52   Typical slump tester (mold).

test on the concrete as it comes from the ready-mix truck. The slump test is performed with an open-ended cone-shaped cylinder (Fig. 5-52). The container is 12″ high. It is placed on a flat surface with the small end up. It is filled with the concrete taken from the mixer chute. It may be tamped gently with a small rod to remove any air bubbles and voids. The inspector will then grasp the handles and with a jiggling motion raise the cone straight up off the concrete. A correctly-watered mix will not slump more than one-third of the height of the cone (Fig. 5-53). Any more slump (collapse) than this is an indication of too much water in the mix.

The homebuilder is not likely to perform such a formal test at the building site. He should, however, be conscious of the slump characteristics of the concrete that he accepts. Water can easily be added to the mix from the tank on the truck after it has left the plant. Some unforeseen delay along the route may motivate a driver to add water. A simple site test can be made. Take a shovel full of concrete from the chute after a few cubic feet have been passed. Dump the full shovel vertically in a clear space in the forms. It should stand up at least half as high as the shovel blade. It is the consumer's prerogative to question the qual-

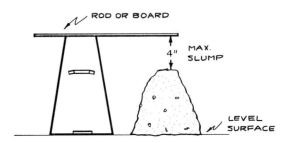

FIGURE 5-53   Measure the slump from a horizontal straightedge on top of the empty mold.

ity of a product. When it is obvious that a mix will not meet a slump test, the consumer may place an immediate call to the company requesting that a representative come to the site and test the concrete. Time is of utmost importance in this situation. A few minutes of delay can lead to a situation where the concrete begins to stiffen due to the advanced hydration stage. Such a condition produces a false slump test. There is a great deal of tension around a concrete job that is not going right. There is also an atmosphere of delusion that none of these principles of quality really matter because all the concrete will be covered from sight. Suffice it to say that no house can be any better than the foundation on which it stands. Probably no more serious problems can be cited in the building industry than those caused by a careless attitude that results in a faulty foundation. *The key to success is knowledge, adequate preparation*, and a bit of good luck with the weather.

Manpower Needs

Perhaps this paragraph should have been titled "person-power needs" since the building industry is experiencing an inflow of women into the labor force. Such an impact may never be felt in the concrete sector, however, due to the strenuous nature of the work. Concrete work is always a race against time. The only way to successfully win the race day after day is with enough adequately experienced hands at work. The author has gone to great detail to impress the reader with the one factor about concrete work. *Once begun, there is no turning back.* How many workers are needed to do a job? The question has many conditional answers. On every job there is the need for an experienced leader. Someone must know how to place the concrete, where to put it progressively, and how to finish it. This is not a job for an amateur or a slightly experienced novice. There is also a role for laborers. One or more persons must pull the wet concrete into position with hoes, shovels, rakes, or come-a-longs.

The shape and purpose of the finished concrete affects the size of the labor force needed. A narrow perimeter footing poured from a chute that can be moved alongside could easily be handled by an experienced worker and one helper. As the shape of the pouring gains in surface area, more help is needed. The principle involved is the quantity of concrete surface that will be exposed to the air. Any slab of considerable size will take more workers than a footing, even though it may involve the same cubic volume of concrete. The greater the exposed area, the more rapidly the surface will set up. When a surface requires finishing, such as steel troweling or texturing, it must be accomplished at a specific stage and in a relatively short period (only minutes). The finishing time may be about as long as it took to dump the concrete. Remember that setup takes place at a particular interval after water is introduced. When one

truckload of concrete arrives a half hour after the first load on any given day, the concrete from the second truck will be trowellable about 30 minutes later than the first batch. This may work out well if there is 30 minutes of troweling time involved in the first load. However, if it is setting so fast that the troweling must be accomplished in 15 minutes (a hot, sunny, windy day), a delay will be experienced at the junction between the first and second loads.

Another variable affecting the size of the labor force needed is the complexity of the project. Hillside sites that require two or three step footings will take longer to fill. With concrete there is no more time. It must be made up with more help. Remember that an experienced concrete mason can accomplish as much or more than three or four well-intentioned neighbors. He knows when, where, and how to make the significant moves. He possesses a built-in timer gained from hard-earned experience.

Functions of Footing Pouring

The first basic job in the pouring of a footing is to place the concrete in the trench or the form. A primary objective is to get the whole trench filled without interruption. Large commercial footings sometimes have to be poured in segments. When this is required, specific requirements are placed on the manner in which the segments are joined together. The residential builder should not consider breaking off the job at one point and continuing the next day. Few, if any, residences will be of such a magnitude that it would be necessary. Nor should the builder allow a stoppage to occur due to unwise planning. When the ready-mix dispatcher says, "We can't get to you until after 4 p.m.," put off your order until the first delivery the next morning. Waiting on ready-mix is like waiting in the doctor's office. How long the driver gets held up on the job before yours is anybody's guess. On the other hand, if you have a mid-day delivery, be ready ahead of time. Your driver may have had a couple of easy dumps or a cancellation. Here he comes 40 minutes early and your help is still having coffee 3 miles away. What do you do? You pour. If you are lucky, the sympathetic driver may lend a hand. He knows better than most that his load waits for no man.

Once begun, *the filling and spreading should not stop until the form is filled.* While the filling is going on, another operation, called *rodding*, should be taking place simultaneously. Rodding means to poke a steel rod down into the concrete along the edges of the form. This allows voids to be penetrated by surface air so that they will fill up with concrete. The stiffer the mix, the more voids are apt to form. These voids are most often found along the edges of the forms. A pointed mason's trowel is an effective rodding tool. Slide it in between the form and the concrete. Plunge it up and down from the surface to the bottom of the form. Heavy aggregate (stone) is eased away from the form. Water and binder are drawn to the steel trowel. It fills in behind the tapered blade of the trowel on the withdrawal stroke, thus allowing the voids to fill. This operation can be done with a pointed shovel with much less back bending than with a hand trowel. Some codes make reference to this operation with a typical statement such as: "All concrete in forms shall be well rodded or spaded, especially at corners and intersections." Rodding also works the concrete in around the steel reinforcing.

Screeding is the process of leveling the surface of the concrete so that it is level or parallel with the form. Any straight board longer than the footing width can be used to scrape the surface of the concrete. A 1 × 6 is effective. The excess concrete is pushed ahead of the board. Low spots are filled with the excess in front of the screed board. A sawing motion works effectively. The jiggling effect brings a little moisture up, which in turn helps produce a relatively smooth surface. *Footings do not require troweling*: in fact, troweling is inadvisable. A slightly rough surface will bind better to block walls or poured walls.

Spreader blocks can usually be removed a few minutes after pouring. Any depression left by the block is then filled during the screeding operation. **Container boards**, nailed on the surface to hold the forms in, *should not be removed* before the next day. The concrete can be compacted under these spreaders so that it rises to an equal level in the form.

The final operation on the footing may be *grooving a centerline* under the wall (Fig. 5-54). A groove in the footing under the wall accomplishes two objectives. It locks the wall into the footing so that side pressures from backfill or hydraulic pressure from water-laden earth do not push in the wall. A basement wall will have the concrete floor to counteract this pressure at a later date. The crawl space foundation will not usually have this benefit of a slab. Although seldom seen, the footing groove is equally effective in locking concrete blocks in position provided that a little grout is dumped in the block holes.

Another feature of the groove is its moisture-barrier potential. A light stream of asphalt tar can be poured in the groove. When a concrete wall is subsequently poured, the tar forms a water-repelling gasket between the footing and the wall.

There are simplified methods of producing the groove which are currently being practiced. Years ago 2 × 4s were embedded in the concrete. It was a poor and wasteful system. They were difficult to remove. If taken out too soon, the result was usually cracked and broken-out edges of the concrete. When removal was delayed a day or two, the concrete would be so hard around them that the wood would have to be mangled any way possible to get it out. The system was never used to any extent even though it is still shown in many texts as though it were a feasible forming method.

IMPRACTICAL AND COSTLY FOOTING KEYS

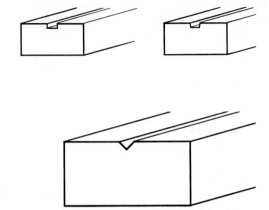

PRACTICAL AND EXPEDIENT TYPE GROOVE

FIGURE 5-54 The V channel is practical, expedient, and cost-free.

A groove-forming board that works satisfactorily is a board with a single side or both sides beveled. The single or double bevel provides the taper needed for easy release. A 2 × 6 ripped once down the center with the saw blade set between 15 and 30° will provide two lengths of groove board. If the boards are to be left in the concrete until hardening has set in, it will require as many linear feet of boards as there are in the centerline of the perimeter foundation wall. This is an unnecessary expense.

A 2 × 2 sled board can eliminate this expense (Fig. 5-55). A 2 × 2 from 2 to 4' long, pointed on both ends, is pressed into the concrete surface. A pair of nails or V blocks are placed on the 90° corner edges for hand holds. The opposite 90° V edge of the sled is pressed into the concrete. It is then worked forward and backward like a brick mason's joint-grooving tool. The sled is worked into the concrete surface until it is embedded halfway. It is moved progressively around the footing perimeter. There are two critical aspects. The groove must be parallel and centered under the wall location. This is done by eye, as

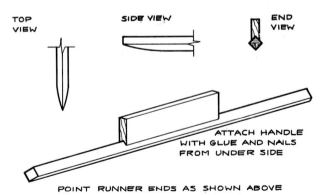

POINT RUNNER ENDS AS SHOWN ABOVE

FIGURE 5-55 A practical sled runner for grooving a footing is made from a 2 × 2 and a 2 × 4. Glue the handle on and nail it from the underside.

there is no time for measuring or gauging. The second element is judging the correct timing. The concrete must be set up enough so that the groove does not fill back in behind the groove runner. It must also be malleable enough that it can be impressed. Grooving in this manner requires pushing down the stone aggregate. This is possible only during a short interval of time. Start the operation early while the ''mud'' is soft. Two or three trips around the footing will be preferred to a frustrated half-trip that is too late.

The specifications of a foundation plan may call for **steel anchoring dowels**. These are short lengths of rerod. A portion of this anchoring pin will stand exposed above the footing surface. The dowel pin will be pushed into the wet concrete as soon as it is firm enough to support it vertically. The amount exposed above the concrete should be 4″ or more. Intervals will be in accordance with the specifications. The purpose of dowels is twofold. Like the groove, the dowel helps prevent lateral movement of the wall that will be cast around it. Another function is to provide a firm anchor to which vertical reinforcing rods in the wall can be attached. The vertical rerods are wired to the anchor dowels just above the footing. This prevents them from being moved out of position when the concrete is dumped into the wall forms.

TREATED WOOD FOUNDATION WALL

By now the reader has some familiarity with the two most common types of foundation walls, the concrete block wall and the poured concrete wall. There is a third type that is popular in some areas. It is the treated wood basement foundation (Fig. 5-56). This foundation is made of toxic-

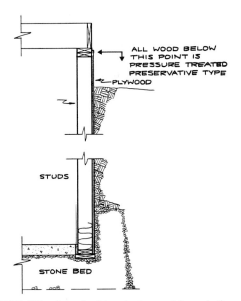

FIGURE 5-56 A typical treated wood foundation rests on a bed of gravel.

treated lumber which resists the deteriorating elements of the subsoil environment. It is said to be impervious to termites and dry rot. The system of construction is not beyond the capabilities of the average home builder. It is unique and should be attempted only after thorough study and close attention to detail. This information can be obtained from plywood companies or firms that pressure-treat lumber.

MONOLITHIC FOUNDATION FLOOR

In the concrete trade, monolithic means poured at one time to form an integral unit. A monolithic foundation and floor is a one-piece combined footing, wall, and slab floor. The advantage of the monolithic system is that one pouring of concrete provides a completed job.

Forming the Monolith

Most of the forming of the monolithic foundation and floor is placed around the exterior perimeter building lines of the structure. It is something like a super-sized sandbox. Where soil is firm it is sometimes possible to form only that portion of the foundation that is above the grade level (the ground surface). In shifting soil, forms will be needed from the slab surface down to the foundation bed.

In colder parts of the country the monolith is not popular because the frost levels are deep. A deep trench would require extensive formwork and materials. Another disadvantage of the monolith in cold country is the heat loss that occurs through the slab which is in direct contact with the exterior exposure area of the foundation. A number of techniques have been devised to counteract the heat loss using insulation barriers of Styrofoam. Most of the techniques involve suspending the rigid strips of Styrofoam in the fluid concrete during the pouring stage. The technique is difficult and seldom accomplished with optimum results.

Because there is only one form wall to be built around a monolith, it requires sturdier bracing. During the pouring and hardening phase the compression forces of the fluid concrete are exerted outward as well as downward. This places great lateral pressure against the forms. Long 2 × 4 stakes are placed against the form boards with diagonal braces running from the top of the stake to a point far enough from the excavation to be in firm soil (Fig. 5-57). A ground stake is driven at the end of the brace. Where a shoring stake cannot be firmly seated below the foundation bed, a horizontal brace at ground level will be needed. All stakes and braces should be nailed together with duplex nails. A stake in the ground should be backed up during the nailing by a sledge hammer or other heavy solid object so that it is not jarred loose in its hole.

Interior forming of the sloping sides of the monolith may not be necessary if the earth is firm enough to sculp-

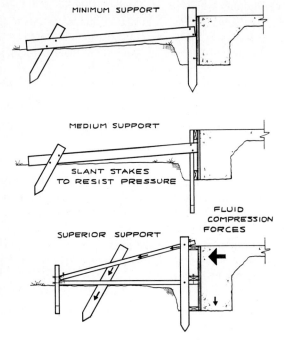

FIGURE 5-57 Forms can be made in many ways to support a monolithic slab foundation. (*Note*: Stakes are slanted to direct pressure into ground.)

ture to the desired shape. When it is not firm, some boards will need to be placed to hold back the sloping surfaces. All form boards used to retain higher levels of fill or compacted gravel should be removed as soon as the concrete reaches the level of the material they retain. A word of caution about monoliths is timely. There are a lot of published designs that appear interesting and attractive. Close examination reveals an artistic drawing of a system which may never have been built. In fact, the assembly of a form to create a mold for such a design could be an impossibility. When you consider a design, keep foremost in mind that the form must be shaped like a vessel to contain a liquid. It cannot have projections below the top level unless they are boarded over. Visualize the actual conditions at the site when the heavy forceful concrete cascades down the chute into the form. If the feasibility of a form design is questionable, the builder may choose to discard it or seek the advise of a reputable masonry contractor.

Reinforcing the Monolith

Reinforcement of a monolith is mandatory. Continuously embedded perimeter banding is a key factor in holding the extensive mass together. A pressure factor exists in the monolithic slab that is unique. The floor is resting on a dome of supportive earth. The foundation bed under the footing is at a lower level. The two levels frequently have different supportive characteristics and abilities. Any raising or lowering of either level independently of the other puts a strain on the unified monolith. Take the following

example. A severe winter drops the frost line to an unusual depth. The spring thaw creates greater subsurface moisture. The foundation bed under the perimeter, the footing, and wall part of the monolith becomes soft and spongy. The supportive characteristics for a few weeks are greatly lessened. Inside the dome under the 4″ floor part of the monolith the earth throughout the severe winter remained fairly constant due to the heat in the house and the constant earth temperature under the slab, which was not penetrated by the frost. The supportive character of the dome has not changed. The entire monolith was not initially being supported primarily by the dome. In a sense a portion of the weight of the footing and wall parts is now dangling unsupported from the interior dome. In reality the foundation is still supported but to a lesser degree than during stable seasons. With adequate reinforcing steel rods and grid the wall and footing portion will not settle and pull away from the floor. When inadequately reinforced the floor portion breaks loose and appears to rise. In reality the foundation parts are sinking. This condition is characterized by a crack in the concrete floor which runs around the perimeter inside the exterior wall. When steel grid reinforcing has *not* been run from the horizontal floor level down into the wall segment, the floor can separate and will appear to be at a higher level.

Another factor that tends to pressurize the foundation away from the slab floor is the compression force of the weight of the house. This is especially characteristic of the trussed roof house and the hip-roofed house. The trussed roof theoretically bears all the weight of the roof down the exterior walls onto the foundation. With a gable roof the weight is usually born by the two long exterior sides. The hip roof, whether trussed or conventional, distributes a large part of the roof weight onto all four exterior walls.

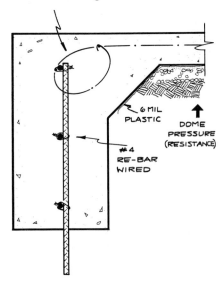

FIGURE 5-58 Adequate reinforcing is mandatory to prevent a monolith from breaking away from the floor portion.

In actuality the concrete slab between the exterior walls supports relatively little weight other than its own material (the partitions should have deepened floor thickness under them). Therefore, the compression exerted on the exterior perimeter by the bulk of the house weight is driving downward directly opposed to the upward pressure of the supportive dome (Fig. 5-58). The dome presents a central fulcrum. Since the fulcrum surface is broad based and the pressure is equal across its breadth, the crack will come at the turning point of the support, which is around the inside of the foundation. This weakness must be accommodated with steel reinforcing.

Slab Bedding

When cracks appear meandering diagonally across a floor, there are usually other causes. Much has been said about the benefits of undisturbed earth for any kind of concrete bedding. It is a rarity to see an uncracked slab that has been poured on fill. Most jobs are going to require some fill. Many will be 100% filled. To counteract the uneven settling that occurs with fill, a number of techniques have been practiced with varying success.

The quality of fill should have consistency. Mixtures of sand and loam clods and rocks will not comprise a consistent settling base. Where it is expedient to use fill from the site, some attempt should be made to layer it or mix it to some consistency. For example, one should not place stone in one area, clay in another area, and loose sand in yet another. Layering and power tamping will be beneficial. Place rubble and stone at the lowest level, followed by loam and dirt. Loose sand goes on top as a cushion. Some builders believe that dampening the fill by sprinkling aids the settling. It permits voids to be filled with the smaller grains of earth and sand that filter down. A suitable drying-out time is then required.

Most flatwork masons agree that a ground cushion under a slab will permit a slab to "float," which in turn avoids the pressures and stresses that cause cracks. A few inches of sand or light gravel is placed on the rough fill. Crusher dust is a favorite cushion material in areas where a stone quarry processes crushed rock. Once spread to a level and consistent depth, the cushion is thoroughly tamped. Any areas that give way are added to and releveled.

Plumbing and Ductwork

Due to the permanent characteristic of concrete, all plumbing and ductwork that needs to be under the floor must be carefully planned and laid out before pouring the slab. Having to break up a new slab to rectify an omission or an error in preparation is a project no housebuilder will ever want to repeat.

Local codes will dictate certain features of the underslab installation. Some characteristics are universal and wise. Copper water supply pipes, for example, must be one unjoined piece from one exit point to another. This mandates soft copper, which can be bent and curved. No hard copper with sweat-on fittings should be used under the slab. The logic of this is obvious. There are no joints to fail under the concrete.

The precise location of pipes and drains is important. A miscalculation of a few inches can sometimes be rectified later only by moving the intended partition location. Such an adaptation can affect a host of other things, such as closet depths, corridor widths, and even the lengths of ceiling joists. Be prepared with mathematically confirmed dimensions on the floor plan which refer to specific key locations on the perimeter forms. The forms are the only solid reference material in existence prior to the pouring of the floor. This requires that cross-referencing be done from building lines at right angles to each other. The plumbing layout person should never "scale" a blueprint to establish a location. Expressions such as "This looks about right," are the prologue to frustration and disappointment. Be precise.

Ductwork location is not quite as critical. Slab ducts are usually brought through the floor rather than in the partitions. As long as a hot-air register clears the baseboard, baseshoe, and an inch or more for the register frame the location is noncritical. Most heating design engineers specify that the registers be located under exterior windows. A few inches right or left of the centerline of the window will not affect the heat distribution. The furnace plenum location will require more precise placement. It will be necessary to know the exact dimensions of the furnace and the plenum exit on the furnace. Hot-air furnaces on a slab that push the heated air through underfloor ducts are called reverse-flow or counterflow types.

An upflow furnace is designed for location in a basement. Nonetheless, the upflow furnace is frequently found in slab houses. The heat ducts are in the attic. A single cold-air return is drawn through a louvered door or a register in a wall adjacent to the furnace room. This inefficient arrangement removes the necessity of ductwork under a slab floor. This may appear to be a more simple application for slab-floor homes, but it carries with it the penalty of lost heat from distribution ducts, even though insulated, that must pass through the attic. A further disadvantage of the upflow furnace on a slab floor is found in the location of the registers, which are usually placed in the ceiling or high on an interior wall. It is difficult to force hot air down toward the floor, as its natural inclination is to rise. The variance of temperature from floor to ceiling is usually greater when the hot air is introduced at or near ceiling level. In the face of this long-standing logic, proponents of the overhead duct system will debate their case at length and provide charts and written testimonials to substantiate their claims. As far as is known, no side-by-side test of identical homes has been made to compare the two different heating systems.

Hot-water baseboard convector heating systems are comparable to the plumbing water supply installation. The boilers are small and compact. All parts of the system are above the floor with the exception of the supply and return pipes. These pipes are 1/2 or 3/4″ soft copper and present no unusual installation technique. When individual lengths of convectors are used as compared to continuous baseboard, it will be necessary to know in advance whether the in and out supply line will connect at the same end or at opposite ends of the convector. When the supply enters one end and exists at the opposite end, the distance between the pipes must be exact. The pipe must connect into the convector quite close to the floor; therefore, there is not much adjustment potential.

All the copper pipes for plumbing and heating should have clearance sleeves placed around them where they exit the slab. The space protects the pipe from damage during construction. It also provides a little potential lateral movement to aid in the later hookup. A soft-copper pipe firmly cemented will seldom survive the construction work that takes place around it. It will be bent over right at floor level. To straighten it satisfactorily is nearly impossible. The plumber must then break out the concrete around the pipe and attempt to solder a fitting onto the flattened stub, which is below the floor surface. Sleeves for these pipes can be made from about anything that will stand up until the concrete sets (Fig. 5-59). Short lengths of plastic pipe, pop cans, beer cans, and soup cans with the ends cut out, all serve admirably. Ready-made sleeves are available from plumbing suppliers. Some of these resemble insulation sleeves. They are wrapped around the pipe and taped with duct tape.

None of the drain pipes, supply pipes, or ductwork should be in direct contact with the underside of the concrete slab. Each of these items will be trenched in with the top surface an inch or so below the slab bed. This permits a little of the cushioning sand to be spread over the conduits.

It is not prudent to leave the final inspection of the completeness and location accuracy of all the below-floor piping and duct work to the subcontractor. He does not have nearly as much at stake as the general contractor or the homeowner. No plumber would leave anything out intentionally. There is, however, much potential for overlooking items that require below-floor supply and drainage. Unlike the carpenter, who is provided many detail drawings, the residential blueprint rarely contains any plumbing details or schematics. The plumber works only from the floor plan. He can make out a general location for sinks, tubs, and water closets (toilets), but cabinetry symbols for

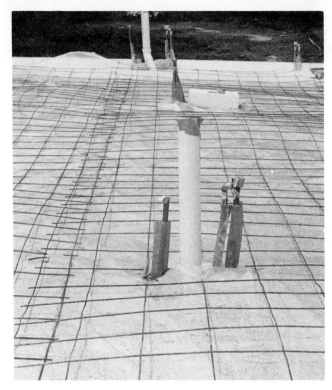

FIGURE 5-59 Pipe protectors help prevent pipes from damage during framing.

dishwashers, ice cube water supply lines, sprinkler petcocks, and anything unique may escape him completely. Without a detail plan he can scarcely be faulted. A final inspection by the homeowner prior to slab pouring is a wise precaution.

Moisture Barrier

All the earth materials under the slab are ready moisture carriers. Unless something is done to block this moisture, it will rise through the concrete slab. The dampness creates a problem for anything it contacts. Rugs and carpeting mold. Wood rots. Floor tiles come loose. Sometimes the health of the occupants is jeopardized. Many years ago tar paper was used under the slab. It was wet mopped with tar to seal the joints. Although its sealing properties were good and permanent, it was extremely difficult to complete a job without punctures from boot heals or hoe corners. When plastic film was invented the tar paper barrier became obsolete. Plastic sheets are available that will span most homes so that an entire floor can be covered with one piece. The 6-mil thickness will resist a certain amount of abuse, although it is easily punctured by the ends of reinforcing mesh wire or other sharp objects. The plastic is usually spread just before the reinforcing mesh is rolled out. The mesh helps hold it in place, especially on windy days. At points where plumbing pipes or other objects project above the floor, the plastic is carefully positioned. Then a small hole is cut in a plus shape (+) and carefully lowered over the pipe. Ductwork openings will be passed over by the plastic and left uncut until pouring has begun. The concrete is gently spread around the projecting duct, placing equal amounts on each side at a time. When the plastic becomes tight over the duct, diagonal cuts are made from corner to corner like an X. The plastic is eased over the edges and held up vertically while some more concrete is pushed alongside. The same system works well for any other floor-level openings, such as furnace plenums and floor drains.

Placing the Reinforcing Mesh

When space permits it is good practice to roll out the reinforcing mesh away from the floor. It can be cut to length and the sharp ends of the wires bent over immediately. These sharp points are dangerous to people and materials. If the end of a roll gets away from a worker, it can whip over in a large arch and plunge the dagger-pointed rusty wire into whatever is in the way. If it were a person's head without a hardhat, it could be a fatal accident. The bending over of these sharp wires will also prevent punctures in the plastic. When the mesh is first rolled out, it wants to recoil. It must be held down at the ends while someone walks down the wire and bends up a section with each step. It should have all bends and rolling contours corrected. When it is satisfactorily straight (horizontal), it is carried onto the floor area and laid in position. Adequate length is provided so that the ends can be curved down into the foundation-wall portion of a monolith. The ends of the wire mesh may be bent around one of the perimeter reinforcing rod bands in the trench. (Fig. 5-60). After all the mesh is installed, another rerod course is tie-wired at the top of the bend. This location is about 2 to 3″ below the slab surface level. This rod is important to the containment of the perimetrical strength at floor level. The mesh will not provide this circumferential protection adequately, especially on the slab side where the 60″ mesh widths are side by side. The mesh is made of welded wires on 6″ centers. A roll is 5′ wide by 150′ long. Laid side by side and tie-wired together every 1′, the mesh will prevent cracked concrete from changing levels. There is an inherent weakness laterally at every 5′ junction. The perimeter rerod of No. 4 or 5 size running continuously across these joints will prevent lateral separation of the mesh and the slab.

Reinforcing mesh is sometimes referred to on the job and called out on details as 6 × 6 No. 10 (or No. 9). The "6 × 6" refers to the size of the squares formed by the welds. The number is the wire gauge size used in light construction. Because two squares consistently equal a linear foot, it is not necessary to measure mesh if one prefers to step it off on the ground.

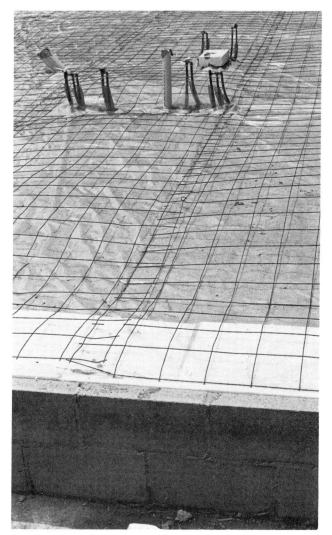

FIGURE 5-60 Reinforcing mesh is placed above (on top of) the plastic barrier very carefully to avoid punctures.

Insulating the Monolith

One of the drawbacks of the monolith is the difficulty of insulating it from heat loss and cold convection through the exterior exposed surface. Internal embedding of Styrofoam is not feasible, as it weakens the junction of the floor to the foundation wall. External methods are practiced with some success. Styrofoam sheathing may be extended over the external foundation face to a point well below the grade line (Fig. 5-61). Styrofoam is easily damaged, so it must be covered with some protective surface, such as aluminum, galvanized sheet metal, or copper (expensive). Treated plywood is also a viable protectorate. Such coverings provide an ideal transit area for termites and vermin. *Termite treatment of the earth is a must* when this system of insulation is used. Regular and consistent inspections should follow with regenerative treatment from time to time.

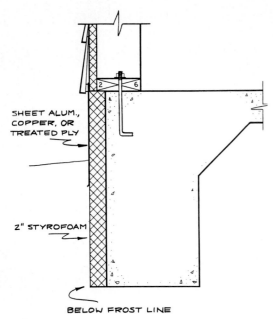

SHEET ALUM.,
COPPER, OR
TREATED PLY

2" STYROFOAM

BELOW FROST LINE

FIGURE 5-61 A feasible way to externally insulate the monolith to some degree.

Pouring the Monolith

Pouring a monolith is an exciting experience. In the space of a few hours a complete foundation and floor appears before your eyes. It is a good feeling to walk away from the monolith knowing that a major phase of the house building is complete. All the many details have been conquered and are now perpetuated in solid concrete.

It is important that the monolith pouring progress without delay or interruption. Arrangements are made for the trucks to roll in with the ready-mix at timed intervals. It will be efficient to have two trucks dumping simultaneously from opposite sides of the house (front and rear). The pouring should proceed down the long sides of the floor so that the leveling takes place across the narrow dimension, the span. The leading edge of the concrete will then be the shortest distance across the slab. This method requires less labor and provides more time for dumping.

Labor Force

All previous comments about the type of labor needed for pouring a footing apply to the monolith, with an additional role needed. The slab requires a smooth surface, as parts of it will probably be tiled, carpeted, or painted. Masonry finishing is a skilled trade. Small jobs are done by hand. The large slab is usually completed by the concrete finisher using a power trowel. The power trowel has three steel trowel blades operated in a circular motion. It is powered by a gasoline engine. The reliability of the small gas engine has improved in recent years. Nonetheless, an element of risk is always present. Should the engine fail to start, or if

it breaks down partway through the job, a backup machine must be readily available. Without another workable machine, all available personnel will be forced to jump in and attempt to hand finish the slab. Many contractors eliminate this risk by having two machines and operators ready from the start.

Placing the Anchor Bolts

Anchor bolts will be embedded as soon as the concrete is firm enough to support them from sinking. Start from the same end of the slab as the pouring began. Ease the crooked end in first with the bolt horizontally in your hand. As the bolt is pressed down, rotate it through an arced path. This will not displace as much cement as if it were pushed straight down. Pushing it straight down sometimes causes a void to form behind the bent end, which weakens its holding power. Tamp the surrounding concrete back to level with a small trowel or board. The bolt will be placed a specific distance back from the edge of the slab, which will position it in the center of the frame wall sole (sill plate). This distance varies according to the wall lineup system used, the thickness of the sheathing (when it butts on the slab), and the width of the sole (usually 2 × 4 or 2 × 6). The distance that the bolts are apart from each other will be in accordance with local codes and specifications (explained further later in the chapter). Remember not to place a bolt in any location that will be occupied by a stud. The amount of the bolt left exposed above the concrete should be about 2 1/2″. This allows 1″ of threads above the sole to accommodate the washer and nut when a spun-fiberglass sill sealer is used. A little more thread may be desirable if 1/2″ fiberboard is used for a sealer.

Other types of wall anchors are available. Galvanized sheet metal anchors may be embedded in the concrete. The exposed end is later bent around the sole and nailed. Another method is to nail the sole to the slab with concrete nails. When this is attempted with hand tools, it is usually only about 50% effective. Many nails do not penetrate adequately. They turn under or chip out the concrete. Holding power is inferior. Power-driven nails are more effective; .22-caliber impact guns fire nails that penetrate in one shot. It takes many nails to equal the holding power of a bolt. Power nails are especially useful for fastening interior partitions. Bolts are nearly impossible to place for interior partitions while the concrete is still soft. Bolts are preferred for the perimeter.

CONVENTIONAL SLAB FLOOR

A less complicated method of making a slab-floor foundation is to construct the three components one at a time (Fig. 5-62). The footing is formed and poured as the first

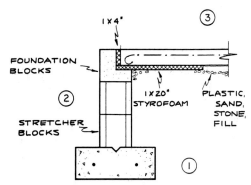

FIGURE 5-62 Three-stage slab floor construction.

step. The second step will be done by one of two methods. It may be a formed and poured wall, or a laid wall of blocks or bricks, or a combination of both. There are a variety of designs that provide a ledge for the slab. A ledge block is available which is specifically made to support a slab and provide an inch of space for rigid insulation. On a house to be brick veneered, the brick can be used as a means of forming and containing the slab.

In areas where it is desirable to insulate the slab from the foundation wall, the slab will not be in direct contact with the foundation. It will rest on a cushion of Styrofoam and will be isolated from the exterior by a vertical ribbon of Styrofoam. *No part of the concrete floor will have direct contact with the masonry that is exposed to the elements.* This makes it possible to pour the floor as an independent step, the third in the sequence. Because each step involves masonry that must harden before the next step is begun, it involves a minimum of 3 days no matter how many workers are put on the job. There is less risk of a breakdown or work interruption and consequently less tension. When working with brick or block walls, there is little or no forming to be done, with the possible exception of the footing. The footing can frequently be poured without forms. It might seem that a monolith could be created in less time due to the final dramatic pouring phase. In reality, the monolith requires so much more preparation and reinforcing that it may span as many calendar days as the three-stage job.

COMPUTING CONCRETE VOLUME

Ready-mix is sold by the cubic yard. It can only be purchased to the nearest quarter yard above a certain minimum. When ordering, the consumer will need to give the yardage quantity and the quality desired. Quality may be stated in one of two ways by the experienced or knowledgeable person. He may, for example, say "I want 3000-pound test." This means that the concrete will withstand a compression of a ton and a half after the twenty-eighth day of curing. He may express his desire in another way by saying "I want a 5-sack mix" or a 5 1/4-, or 5 1/2-sack mix. This means that for each fluid yard of concrete that is put together, so many sacks of cement will be in it. Most codes permit nothing less than 5-sack. For a few cents more, it is possible to upgrade the compression quality of your finished product by many pounds. A variance in the stone aggregate of the mix will also affect the compression strength. An inquiry should be made of your supplier so that you will know how much cement is needed per yard to cause a certain level of strength. Many companies use crushed and washed stone. Their mixes can be accurately proportioned and consistent from one batch to another. Some companies and individuals avail themselves of natural supplies of sand and gravel from pits and riverbeds. This is called pit run. It is neither screened nor washed. The sand and gravel mixture may vary from one vein to another. Such a mix can provide satisfactory concrete, but it frequently requires a larger proportion of cement per yard to equal the carefully controlled mix.

Computing Simple Volume

The computation required to find the volume of a slab involves only simple multiplication and division. Find the quantity of concrete to order for a sidewalk or a driveway by following these steps.

1. **Multiply** the thickness times the width times the length ($T \times W \times L$; woodworkers will recognize this as the beginning of the board-foot formula, which is simple volume).
2. **Divide** the result by 27 (the number of cubic feet in a cubic yard).

$$\frac{T' \times W' \times L'}{27} = \text{cubic yards}$$

Most slabs will have both width and length in excess of 1'. The thickness, however, is more likely to be in the range 4 to 6" (make it an exact 4, 5, or 6" depth intentionally). Therefore, the thickness part of the formula must be stated fractionally. An example would be a sidewalk 4" deep, 3' wide, and 25' long. The problem will be set up for longhand as $1/3' \times 3' \times 25' \div 27$. For calculator use, it will be $.3333333 \times 3 \times 25$, which calculates to 24.999997. This is actually 25 cubic feet since the $1/3$ cannot run out to infinity on a calculator. In the example sidewalk, there is a cubic foot for each running foot (linear) because it is $1/3'$ deep and 3' wide ($1/3 \times 3 = 1$). An order will be placed for 1 yard to accommodate the 25/27 yard that is needed.

Another example is a heavy-duty driveway for a dump-truck owner. Although he will prudently not park his truck on the driveway with a load in it, he will plan to use the driveway for regular overnight parking of the empty vehicle. This driveway will be designed for a greater load than the family car. The specs call for a 5″ depth, 12′ width, and 44′ length. The problem is set up as follows: $5/12 \times 12 \times 44 \div 27$. This type of problem provides an opportunity to practice cancellation:

$$\frac{5 \times \cancel{12} \times 44}{\cancel{12}} \div 27$$

The 12s can be canceled out, leaving a simple $5 \times 44 \div 27$, which equals 8.148 cubic yards. The ready-mix order will be placed for 8 1/4 yards.

Computing Perimetrical Volume

The teaching of perimetrical volume computation is a rarity in schools. Perimetric volume is the kind of problem found in a perimeter footing. The solution requires some special attention so that duplication of corner volume does not occur. There are three basic methods of calculating perimetrical volume.

Method 1. One method of finding the volume in a perimetrical footing is to *determine the centerline dimensions* (Fig. 5-63). Taking the linear perimeter sum of all the sides of a footing at the exterior edge or the building line and multiplying it by the cross-section dimensions will result in an incorrect answer. When the centerline sum of the footing perimeter is multiplied by the cross-section dimensions in fractional feet, it will net an accurate volume. This method involves the establishment of width and length dimensions from corner to corner of the footing centerlines. This poses a new analysis when working from plans, as there are no such dimensions on a plan. It is not difficult

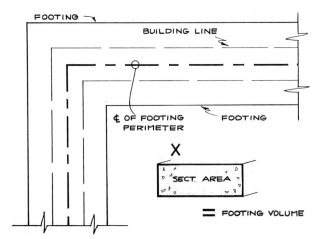

FIGURE 5-63 One method of computing the volume of a footing is to multiply the cross-section area (in feet) times the perimeter of the centerline and divide by 27 (a cubic yard in feet).

FIGURE 5-64 The centerline method is like finding the volume of a picture frame.

to arrive at these dimensions. The centerline locations will be half the thickness of the foundation wall inside the building line provided that the wall is centered on the footing. An exception exists when a brick ledge is involved. The problem is simplified when the dimensions are taken off the actual footing forms. One simply measures the distance between the outside form boards from one side of the house to the other or the distance between the inside forms (both measurements are taken on the interior surface of the forms). When the exterior figure is used, one footing width is subtracted (this is the same as subtracting two halves of the footing width, one from each side). When the interior measurement is used, one footing width is added to the net distance between centerlines.

On a simple rectangular foundation, the next step is to *find the sum of the centerline length* (two ends and two sides), which can be done by adding the lengths of one long side and one short side and multiplying by 2 (Fig. 5-64). With any other shape, all the sides are added. The total figure is then put into the volume formula as the length (L') and multiplied by the depth (thickness) and the width of the footing.

Consider a typical modular house plan whose building line is 24′ × 40′. The foundation wall will be 8″ thick and centered on the footing. Using method 1 to find the centerline, the centerline is 4″ in from the building line all around. The dimension of the width and length of the centerline is 23′-4″ × 39′-4″. The footing specified is 8″ × 20″. This size provides a 6″ projection. An exterior measurement across the span nets 25′. The interior measures 21′-8″ (assuming perfection). Add 20″ to the inside measurement (21′-8″) or subtract it from the outside measurement (25′) and the result is 23′-4″. The 40′ sides will calculate to 39′-4″ of centerline length (41′ minus 20″ = 39′-4″). Turning these dimensions into a long single cube by adding two sides and two ends (or one of each × 2) nets a solid 8″ × 20″ × 125′-4″. It will appear as follows when placed into the cubic yard formula. The depth is

2/3′, the width is 1 2/3′ and the length is 125 1/3′:

$$\frac{2/3 \times 1\ 2/3 \times 125\ 1/3}{27} = \text{cubic yards}$$

Remember that all inches must be stated as feet. To multiply this without the aid of a calculator, it will be written this way:

$$2/3 \times 5/3 \times 376/3 \div 27$$

Multiply all the numerators first, then multiply the denominators.

$$2/3 \times 5/3 \times 376/3 = 3760/27 = 139.26 \text{ cubic feet}$$

The cubic feet are divided by 27, to net 5.16 cubic yards (139.26 ÷ 27 = 5.16 cubic yards). The order must be placed to the next-higher quarter of a cubic yard, so the order will be for ''5 1/4 yards'' to make the 8″ × 20″ footing under a 24′ × 40′ foundation. Caution: Work with the actual distances measured from the forms, not the blueprint specifications. It is the real form that must be filled with concrete.

Method 2. Another method of finding footing volume is to *calculate the surface area* superimposed by the footing and then delete the area on the inside surrounded by the footing (Fig. 5-65). First, calculate the total volume of the area surrounded by the footing, including the footing volume. Then the area inside the footing which is not poured is subtracted, leaving the footing volume. To simplify the mathematics, it can be dealt with first as an area problem. Consider the same footing and foundation example as in method 1. The building lines are 24′ × 40′. The exterior dimensions of the footing are 25′ × 41′. The inside rectangle is 21′-8″ × 27′-8″. The problems are calculated as follows: The overall area, 25 × 41 = 1025 (area)

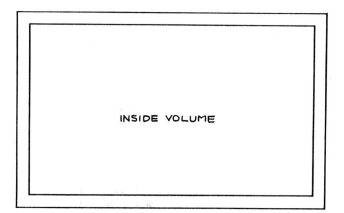

INSIDE VOLUME

TOTAL VOL. − INSIDE VOL. = FOOTING VOL.

FIGURE 5-65 Method 2 is to subtract the volume inside the footing from the total volume superimposed by the footing (including the footing) and divide by 27.

× 8″ (depth) × .666666 = 683.33 cubic feet. The inside superimposed area is 21.666666 × 37.666666 = 816.11 × .666666 = 544.07 cubic feet (done by calculator). By long hand the problem is 65/3 × 113/3 = 7345/9 = 816.11 × .6666 = 544 cubic feet. Subtract the cubic footage of the area inside the footing (544.07 cubic feet) from the total cubic footage superimposed by the footing (638.33 cubic feet): 683.33 − 544.07 = 139.26. The remainder is the cubic footage in the footing, 139.26 cubic feet. Divide by 27 to obtain the cubic yardage.

$$139.26 \div 27 = 5.16 \text{ cubic yards}$$

Note that the answer was exactly the same as that derived by method 1. To accomplish this kind of precision, it is necessary to use consistent practices in rounding off decimals when working by longhand. When using the calculator, it requires consistent use of the fractional-feet numbers. One should either round to hundredths throughout a problem or run the calculator out to its limit. For example, 4″ will be .33 and 8″ will be .67 if rounded. On a small seven-decimal calculator, these will be slightly more accurate when punched out to .3333333 and .6666666. In the examples above (methods 1 and 2), the latter method was used. Only the final answer was rounded to hundredths.

Method 3. This method may be called the *running-foot method* or the visual concept method of computing perimetric volume. This method calculates as closely as possible how many cubic feet there are in each linear foot of footing. The method has two areas of potential error to keep in mind. Any error or inaccuracy in the running-foot cubic calculation will compound as many times over as there are linear feet in the footing. It is best to use all the digits available on a calculator when developing this key multiplier, the cubic footage per running foot of footing.

A second potential error can occur when one fails to remember that the square in each corner must be counted only once. In method 1 where the centerline is used as a linear measure, a drawing of the footing may be visualized like a picture frame with mitered corners. With the running-foot method, visualize the footing like the door stiles of a screen door (Fig. 5-66). This means that each of the short-end linear dimensions will be reduced by two widths of the footing, one taken away from each side.

Apply the same sample footing calculated by methods 1 and 2. First, calculate the cubic area of a single running foot as accurately as possible. The girth of the footing is 8″ × 20″. .66666666 × 1.6666666 = 1.1111109 cubic feet. Take the two long sides in total. Two 41s will net 82 linear feet. The dimension across the ends is 25′. From this must be subtracted two 20″ widths or 40″ (3′-4″), as it has already been counted in the 82′. 25′ minus 3′-4″ =

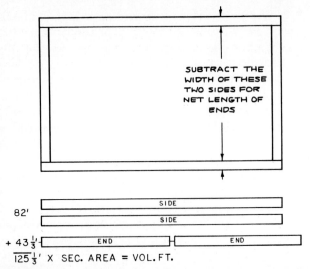

SUBTRACT THE
WIDTH OF THESE
TWO SIDES FOR
NET LENGTH OF
ENDS

82' | SIDE |
     | SIDE |

+ 43⅓' | END | END |

125⅓' X SEC. AREA = VOL. FT.

FIGURE 5-66 Method 3 lays the footing out in a straight line and turns it into a simple three-dimensional volume problem.

21'-8″. Two ends net 43'-4″. Therefore, 82 + 43.333333 = 125.33333 linear feet of footing. This is the identical figure derived in method 1 using the centerline. The next step is to multiply 125.33333 by the running-foot cubic quantity, 1.1111109, which nets 1.1111109 × 125.33333 = 139.25122 cubic feet. The last step: 139.26 ÷ 27 = 5.16 cubic yards.

Thus it is seen that any of these three methods will net accurate answers to the cubic perimetrical problems that are characteristic in footing volume calculation. Which method is preferred? The answer to that question is personal. When applied to simple rectangles, the three methods would appear to be comparable. Problems become more complex as the footing layouts vary from the rectangular. The problems are even more detailed when the structure is stepped up a hillside (multilevel). One principle is helpful in dealing with the more complex footing layouts. Segment the footing into several problems. Take individual sections that calculate easily. With step footings, separate the various levels. Calculate the riser sections separately from the horizontal parts. This is usually required anyway, as riser depth (the vertical footing) is usually less than the level-footing depth. When the cubic footage has been calculated for each section, a total is calculated. The total cubic footage is divided by 27 and the volume of the footing is then known.

From a practical point of view, the experienced contractor may order 1/4 yard or even a 1/2 yard more concrete than his calculations indicate. He knows and respects (even fears) the possibility that a short order can cause severe problems on a concrete job. Some ready-mix plants will not deliver less than 2 yards, which creates a dilemma when the initial order proves inadequate. Guesstimating cubic yardage is folly.

Calculating Poured Wall Volume

Calculating the concrete volume in a poured foundation wall employs the same principles used in the footing. The simple plan, not involving a brick ledge, is easily referenced from the blueprint. The perimeter of the wall dimensions will be found on the foundation plan. If there is no foundation plan, one may assume that the overall house dimensions are the same as the overall floor plan dimensions. Foundation wall thickness and height provide the remaining information to complete the perimetrical volume problem.

Calculating wall volume usually has one characteristic not common to footings. There are openings to be discounted. A simple crawl space foundation will have a number of ventilator openings. These are usually a uniform size. One need only find the volume of one opening and multiply that figure by the quantity of openings. There will probably be an access opening to discount also. Full or partial basements will have windows. Walkout basements will have door openings. Each opening of a different size will require a separate computation. The total cubic sum of the openings will then be subtracted from the total wall volume.

CALCULATING BLOCK UNITS

In Part I, in the study of modular design, it was learned that the quantity of blocks is more accurately assessed by the unit characteristic than as a surface area concept. Calculating blocks is more of a counting exercise than a volume problem. It is therefore best accomplished by visualizing. A course of blocks in a 40' wall will number 30 blocks since there are three blocks in every 4' of linear feet. On a 24 × 40' foundation wall, where 30 blocks are counted for the 40' length, 18 blocks are not counted for the 24' end but rather, 17. Although 18 blocks (three for 4') are visualized, the equivalent of one block must be subtracted because it has already been counted on the 40' side. Actually, half of it (8″) has been counted on each of the two 40' sides. In the next course, 18 blocks are visualized on the end and 29 on the 40' side because the blocks are staggered from course to course. It is found by this visualization and the method that a single course of blocks around a 24 × 40' foundation wall will contain 94 blocks, 30 on each long side and 17 on each end: 30 + 30 + 17 + 17 = 94, or 29 + 29 + 18 + 18 = 94 (Fig. 5-67).

As an example, consider a crawl space wall 32″ high. The specification calls for 12 ventilators, each of which takes up the space of a single block. There is an access opening of 24″ × 32″ (six block spaces). The calculation is more complicated because the blocks are not all of the same type. The large majority will be ''stretchers.'' At the corners, solid-ended blocks known as corner blocks will be

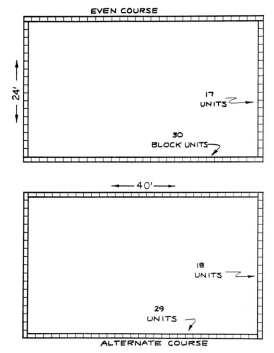

FIGURE 5-67 Alternate staggered covering does not affect the count.

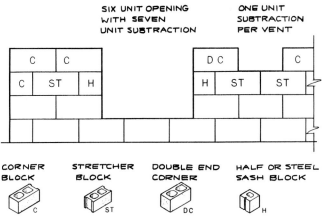

FIGURE 5-68 Openings in a block wall alter the bill of materials.

used. Every other course at the sides of an opening will require half-blocks. With these specifications, the counting process works out as follows. The wall is 32″ high, comprised of four courses (Fig. 5-68). If the foundation had no openings, 376 units would be involved. Subtract units from that figure where openings exist. The vents will remove 12 units. The blocks on either side of the vent may need to be corner blocks or steel sash blocks, in which case another 24 will be subtracted, so the vents will reduce the total unit quantity of stretchers by 36 to 340. The access opening (24 × 32″) eliminates 6 blocks. At least two half-blocks will be required, one on each side, to maintain uniform course staggering. Corner blocks will be used for the four remaining units next to the opening. This subtracts another 4

stretchers, so 11 more units are taken away from the 340, leaving 329. The wall has four exterior corners requiring corner blocks. Four courses times four corners nets 16 units to subtract. 16 from 329 leaves 313. The bill of materials is as follows:

313	Stretcher blocks	313
44	Corner blocks (or 20 corner blocks	20
	and 24 steel sash blocks)	24
2	Half-blocks (equals 1 block space)	1
359 total units		full unit spaces = 358

The size of all the openings equaled 18 blocks (12 vents and a 6-block access space). 358 plus the 18 block voids equals the 376 block spaces for the four-wall surface area.

Calculating a basement is done in the same manner as described above, with some additional variations (Fig. 5-69). The number of courses will be greater. A full-depth basement will contain 12 courses of 8″ blocks. This height may be varied downward to 11 1/2, 11, or 10 1/2 block units. A 11 1/2-block wall usually results from the use of 11 courses of stretchers capped by a solid 4″ block. The sight of a 4″ cap block on a wall, however, does not always indicate 11 1/2 units. A 12-unit wall may contain a solid 4″ termite barrier course below ground in addition to the 4″ cap block. In such a design, there will be 11 courses of stretchers (84″ of height) and two courses of 4″ solids (8″ total height), which totals to the same height as a 12-course wall of 8″ units.

Another variation, which is not obvious after the house is complete, is the full-size top cap block. It may be a regular stretcher that has been filled, or it may be an 8″-high hollow-domed cap block. The exterior appearance will be identical. The domed block is more costly than the stretcher. The final cost, however, may be less. It takes extra labor time and grout to fill all the cavities of the top

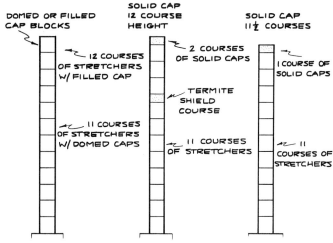

FIGURE 5-69 Typical block walls. Each has a different block count.

course of stretcher blocks. When done with mortar, it becomes an expensive technique. On the other hand, it may be feasible when some course aggregate is on hand to fill part of the holes and nonskilled labor is available in place of the higher-paid mason.

There is a bug in both the domed and the solid cap systems. Ignoring it will cause a great consternation. *Full blocks must start at the corners on the capping course that is parallel to the floor joists.* Also, it is mandatory that three hole blocks be used when anchor bolts are prescribed. Two hole blocks have a web in the center which falls directly under the vertical mortar joint (Fig. 5-72).

The only place that anchor bolts can be installed, where cap blocks are specified, is in the vertical mortar joint. Placing a full cap block at the corner perpendicular to the joists will cause every bolt in that wall and the opposite wall to be directly under the bearing end of a joist. The solid or domed corner blocks must be parallel to the joists. The solution to this potential dilemma lies in the first block laid on the footing. It must be faced correctly at the corner. The rule is:

- On an even-numbered block wall height, start the first course opposite to how the top course must be.
- On an odd-numbered block wall height, start the first course the same as the top course must be.

Planning ahead is truly the name of the game, followed by constant surveillance at critical moments.

An alternative solution to the anchor bolt and block coordination situation lies with the use of sheet metal anchors, which can be laid in the mortar joints with disregard for block webs. Frequently, the prevailing building code will prescribe closer spacing and therefore more sheet metal anchors. Look into this *before* the first block is laid.

ANCHOR BOLT SPACING

In Part I, there are several references to anchor bolt spacing. Some reminders concerning the proper locations and the potential problem areas are timely in the discussion of foundation wall construction. Remember first that all anchor bolts should be positioned between the joist locations, not under them or too close.

Measuring and marking the locations is accomplished accurately and reliably by first preparing a schematic layout record on paper. Start 12″ from the building line. Twelve inches from the end of the board is the maximum under the spacing rules. You will see from Fig. 5-70 how this location coordinates with the maximum bolt-to-bolt modulus. The sill boards on the end walls parallel to the joists may also have the first bolt placed about 12″ from

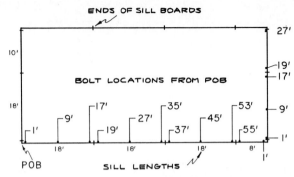

FIGURE 5-70   A schematic sketch indicating where the anchor bolts are to be placed using modular sill units and maximum spacing under the 8′ maximum rule. The 6′ maximum rule employs 14′ major module units.

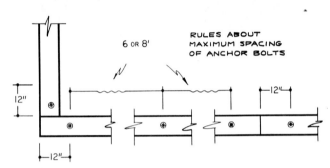

FIGURE 5-71   This graphic diagram shows the rules governing the placement of anchor bolts. *Example*: FHA, 8′ maximum apart; SBCCI, 6′. Both are 1′ maximum from ends of boards.

the building line. This distance will place it about 4 to 6″ from the end of its sill board (where sills are 8 or 6″ wide; Fig. 5-71).

The locations should be clearly and obviously marked on the forms with a red felt marker or carpenter's crayon before concrete pouring starts. In practice, some marks will be lost where screeding or spillover happens, so some locations will require remeasuring quickly and accurately while the concrete is setting up.

The second reminder or caution is to be conscious of the rule that each board must have a bolt *within* 12″ of each end. This means that you must not simply go down the wall placing a bolt every 6 or 8′ according to the maximum spacing rule (a very common error in the construction business). Such placement will violate the end proximity rule wherever a wall is long enough to require more than one board.

Many codes make no mention of sheet metal anchors. It is prudent to check on the spacing with your area building authority, as many inspectors recommend more of this type of anchor, especially in concrete blocks.

It is easier to avoid placing an anchor where a joist will rest on a block wall than on a concrete wall. You can tell at a glance whether the joists will sit above the bond

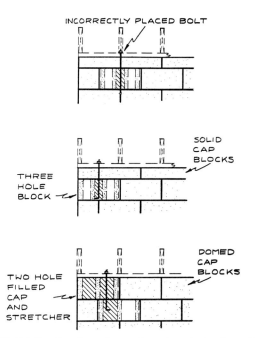

FIGURE 5-72 Section view of anchor bolts in a block wall.

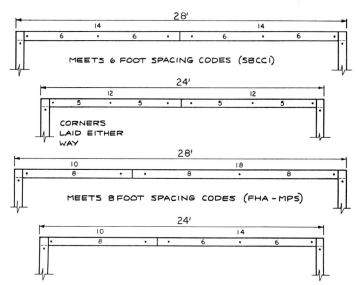

FIGURE 5-73 End wall anchor placement must accommodate the ends-of-board rule. Note that joist length sills always take one more bolt than the use of 14' and 18' boards combined with a shorter board.

joint or above the center of the block and thereby place the anchor in the bond or in the core that positions the anchor away from the joists (Fig. 5-72).

There is a potential with some of the sheet metal anchors for improved effectiveness. Some sheet metal anchors are shaped with two straps in such a way that instead of just folding both legs around the sill, one leg can be nailed to a joist face. In this case the anchor should be bonded into a core hole directly adjacent to the joist location so that it can run vertically right up the side of the joist without having to go diagonally across space. The nails should be angled to resist sheer stress as a nail would be angled for a coat-hanging hook.

Anchors of either bolt or sheet metal persuasion placed along the end walls or walls where the band header is parallel to the joists are not affected by joist spacing or placement (Fig. 5-73). The things to consider and remember are maximum spacing and board end locations.

WATERPROOFING THE FOUNDATION

Any discussion of foundation construction would be incomplete without some information about waterproofing, drainage, and disposal of unwanted moisture. Believe it or not, it is possible to have a relatively moisture-free basement in soil that carries a considerable amount of ground water. The author has, on several occasions, poured footings into forms that had filled with ground water the night before and subsequently constructed successful basements on them. Before casting judgment on the feasibility of such a venture, bear in mind that some of the greatest bridges

in the world have foundation piers and piles that were poured under water. Actually, concrete cures more uniformly under water. Nevertheless, it is advisable to pump out all the water possible in a house footing form so that the bearing bed is not allowed to be divested of its firmness. Earlier remarks about reinforcing are particularly important here. This is a case for plenty of rebar and a comparatively wide footing. Widths of 20 and 24" will take three rods of No. 4 size or larger (1/2" diameter). Once the footing is poured, the pump or pumps should be run continuously if water is present, until a permanent drain field is in place and operational. In severe conditions it may be advisable to construct the drain field and removal facility before pouring the footing.

Drain fields are made of perforated pvc pipe (polyvinyl chloride) or clay tile and washed gravel. The quantity of linear drain tile or pipe will be adjusted to the quantity of water that must be carried off. A minimum system is a single perimeter pipe surrounding the foundation wall, with an exit drain-off pipe. A floor drain may be piped into this perimeter system.

Obviously, a drain system must have an outlet; otherwise, it is nothing more than a collection and retention pipe. Water will simply sit in the low spots or glut the whole perimeter. No evaporation takes place because it is too far below the grade level to aspirate through the soil as a septic field does. A rural system requires ground terrain where the drain can be dumped at a ground level that is below the footing depth (Fig. 5-74). The slant of the drain pipe should not be less than 1/8" to a running foot. When 2' clay tile are used, the rule is 1/4" pitch per tile. One worker can lay such a drain effectively by taping a 1/4"

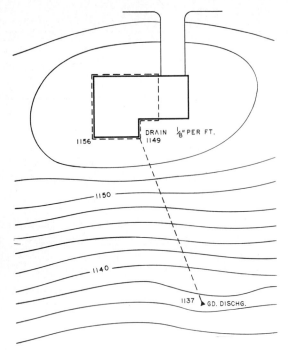

FIGURE 5-74 A topographic plan may be drawn to show how subground water is removed by a perimeter drain and aboveground discharge.

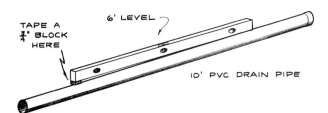

FIGURE 5-75 A 6' level with a 3/4" block taped under one end nets a 1/8" per foot fall in use on a 10' PVC drain pipe.

shim to one end of a 2' level and then, with the shim on the surface of the tile, lay it to a level bubble. A 10' pipe can be similarly installed with a 6' level and a 3/4" shim (Fig. 5-75). The use of depth stakes, a transit level, and string line will also provide a correct pitch.

Surface dumping requires a basement that is higher than some nonprohibitively faraway place that is acceptable for the discharge (Fig. 5-76). This could be a deep ditch along the road or a spot that is lower down a hillside on which a house is situated or a nearby stream. The exposed end of a ground spill drain should be protected from damage by moving machines and vehicles. A permanent stone or concrete protector is most durable. The possibility for erosion should also be considered and dealt with. Finally, a screen or grill of some design is needed to keep out rodents and snakes, which can clog the drain with nests and other blockage.

The urban drainage system has several possible alternatives. The footing drain pipe may be "plugged" into a storm drain in the street provided that the storm drain is lower than your footing drain and that the municipal authority approves. There is also the possibility that your drain can be directed into the city sewer line. Some communities will welcome the clean water, as it assists low-volume areas to move the contents of the sewer with better efficiency. Other officials may frown on such an arrangement, especially where sewers are already operating at capacity.

What if your footing drain is too low for all possible discharge hookups? The solution is to install a vertical sump-pump reservoir in the basement. The drain tiles are directed to the sump by mild gravity. Long runs will not permit a full eighth in drop per foot, but even level pipes will drain if open ended into a reservoir.

Sumps can be made of concrete. A simple site-built sump can be made by digging a hole large enough to accommodate a 55-gallon drum (Fig. 5-77). Enough concrete is poured into the bottom so that a 35-gallon drum can be placed on the concrete at a point where the top rims of both drums will be about 1" below the future floor surface. The floor surface is later sloped toward the sump as a floor drain. The smaller drum is centered in the larger one and filled to a point where the drain tile enters. The drain pipe is inserted through precut holes in the drums until it protrudes into the inner drum about 1/2" or less. More concrete is poured into the double drum form until it reaches the rims. Smaller sumps can be purchased from companies that handle clay tile, chimney flue liners, and other ceramic building supplies. One simple expedient is a large-diameter

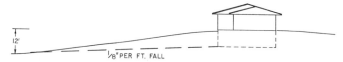

FIGURE 5-76 A basement floor drain and footing drain can be ground spilled where adequate elevation exists.

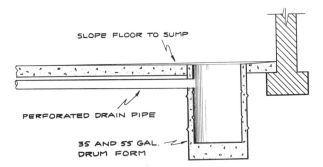

FIGURE 5-77 Drain sump made with two steel drums permanently left in place. Vitreous clay sumps are available in some localities.

belled sewer or storm drain tile with a precast entry hole in the side. This sump tile is placed on end with the belled end up. The belled top provides a shoulder into which a custom-fit lid can be placed which will not protrude above the floor surface. Where small children and little animals are frequent visitors or inhabitants, a lid is a good safety protection against a potential drowning hazard. The discharge pipe which exits vertically will be placed close to or against the side of the sump. A U-shaped cutout in the lid will accommodate the discharge. The discharge is piped into the top side of a sewer pipe or to an independent drain source at a higher level.

The sump pump will require an electrical source nearby. It is poor practice to use extension cords around any water-involved facility. Your electrical code may require armored cable or thin-wall conduit for the electrical feeder. Exceptionally good grounding with a GFI (ground-fault interrupter) is warranted for the sump pump.

WATERPROOFING THE BASEMENT

A basement should be made watertight on the outside as effectively as a swimming pool is made watertight on the inside. Making it watertight is another of those construction jobs where the name of the game is conscientiousness. No step can be slighted, no accidental damage left unattended, and no inadequate material used.

The traditional method was and is basically first to parge a block wall so that it is, in effect, like the surface of a poured concrete wall without any exposed bonds. This is done with waterproof portland cement. Regular cement, and especially mortar, will not produce the required results. Parging is done with two separate coatings of at least 1/4" depth each. Here again it is important not to shortcut. One coat 1/2" thick cannot be installed reliably. The weight is too great to cling to a vertical surface and it is impossible to gauge the depth reliably at 1/2". By contrast, if a 1/4" coat dips in a little here and there, the second coat passing of the trowel will usually fill it to a full depth. The first coat should be striated or roughened with a plasterer's scarifier so that the second coat will cling well. The second coat should be troweled smoothly but without overworking or undue delay. Start at a corner and work from the bottom to grade level around the foundation. Keep the full leading edge moist at all times to prevent incontinuity of bonding. Do not stop until a corner is reached or the whole perimeter is covered (the latter is preferred).

The curing time should be as long as can be tolerated. Actually, the parge does not completely cure until the twenty-eighth day. On the day after being plastered, by contrast, it is very chalky and easily damaged. Some compromise between the extremes is feasible. The parge is

coved onto the footing at the bottom. At the top it is usually discontinued an inch or so above the finish grade level.

Tarring is the next step. On a blueprint section view it may be called out as a "bituminous coating." A proven method is to scrub on the coating with a stiff brush. Sometimes this can be accomplished with a long-handled scrub brush from ground level. With minimum clearance around the wall this method will be less messy; however, it is more difficult to see pock marks and bubbles that later pop, leaving pinholes. Sprayed-on black coatings are seldom completely satisfactory. There simply is not enough body to form a "membrane."

Since the coming of plastic (e.g., Visqueen) in 100' rolls and various widths a last step is proving to be highly successful. Black plastic in full rolls is wrapped completely around the wall. Where a joint has to be made, tar is spread on a couple of running feet of the tail end of the sheet and a new sheet is pressed into it. Start the rolls by pressing the ends into the fresh tar coating. Roll out the roll a few feet ahead before touching the wall with it so that the bottom can go down over the cove. A second person follows along and presses all the plastic into the tar. Black plastic of 6-mil thickness is believed to have a longer life span than clear plastic in the earthen environment.

Next comes the exterior perforated tile. From this time forward every form of material or apparatus that goes into the excavation must be lowered with great care. The slightest contact of a ladder leg or the end of a pipe can tear a hole in the plastic. Any hole that goes unnoticed or unrepaired is like a hole in a boat. Any and all holes should be patched with tar for an adhesive and overlaid with a pressed-on plastic patch.

Lay the perforated pipe with the holes down. Start at the drain tee or Y and work your way around the building. Remember to connect any crossover pipes that go to the inside (Fig. 5-78). These may be elbowed under the

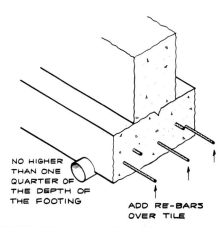

NO HIGHER THAN ONE QUARTER OF THE DEPTH OF THE FOOTING

ADD RE-BARS OVER TILE

FIGURE 5-78 Cross-under drain pipe and extra reinforcing.

footing or may have been formed partially in the footing provided that the reinforcing is not severed.

A covering of washed gravel is placed over the tile to a height that accommodates the severity of the water problem. A depth of 1′ takes care of single exterior pipe system, whereas 18″ is not too much for heavy drainage. The gravel must be spooned in by hand or very gently nudged over the edge with a small dozer such as the garden tractor snow blade, 40″ size. Gravel that is dumped from a truck or carelessly allowed to cascade into the pit will damage the plastic irrevocably and render it useless. A safety measure is found in using a sheet of plywood as a progressive movable guard over the plastic.

Bank sand comes next. It is hauled in. Do not use yard rubble or heavy dirt, as the veins of water that are at various levels above the drain fields cannot penetrate some hard-packed soils. Fill the excavation with the loose sand to a point about 1′ to 18″ below the finish grade. The sand need only stand out from the wall about 6″; however, it cannot be dumped in that formation. There is a team way to accomplish this zoning of materials as they are pushed in. A baffle (a plywood sheet with two handles) is pulled from the bottom up as dirt fill is dozed in on the outer side and sand is shoveled in by hand on the inner side. The system takes time and patience and a willingness to do some hand work. The results are gratifying and of long-term benefit (Fig. 5-79). After all, a damp basement has few uses, whereas a dry one doubles the usable square footage of the home and provides many potential uses.

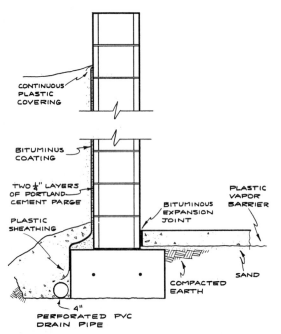

FIGURE 5-79 Waterproofing a foundation wall involves several possible materials.

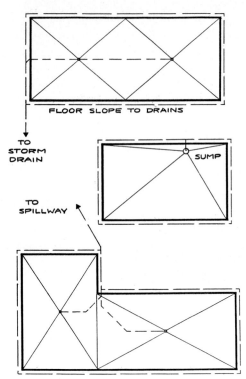

FIGURE 5-80 Typical layouts of drain pipe to carry off water from the foundation area.

The basement floor is the next waterproofing consideration. Should the soil base under the floor be of a type that resists the penetration of water, such as clay, a full bed of gravel or cinders throughout the surface will be beneficial. A bed of 3 to 4″ will provide a transit area through which the ground water can reach the drain pipes. A severe condition will require a system of perforated pipes under the floor to collect and run off the water to a disposal point. Where a sump is used the pipes will be directed to the sump. Thought is given to a distribution arrangement that equalizes segments of the floor area (Fig. 5-80). The exterior perimeter drain will cross over at several points, at least one per side and be coordinated with the interior system. A floor drain with a floating ball to prevent reversing may also be incorporated into the system. Enough drop (pitch) in the whole system is required to prevent any spot in the 4″ pipes from becoming a water storage sump on its own.

A thin layer of sand on top the gravel bed will provide a smooth, soft surface and cushion the concrete slab. With a soil bed that permits water to move adequately, the sand bed may be sufficient without an extensive gravel bed. A small gravel bed trench for the pipes, however, is usually advisable.

Next, plastic sheathing is laid over the sand. Workers should wear tennis shoes or soft sponge-soled shoes whenever it is necessary to walk on the plastic. Attempt to buy a plastic roll that is wide enough to cover the opening completely. Failing this, lap any necessary joint with a full 4′ lap or more and be certain that each layer is flat and without folds. Suspend a ladder from the stairwell with a couple of sturdy dimension boards run through under an upper rung which rests on the floor above. The ladder legs should be well above the floor so that the laying of the plastic and later the concrete finishing can proceed without the escape ladder touching. During the placement of the plastic, be exceptionally careful not to puncture it. Lay the plastic over column footings. If adjustable columns are in place, put a temporary screwjack ahead of each column (one at a time). Unscrew the permanent column and pull the plastic under it, then replace it. Columns that cannot be moved will be adapted to by running a separate sheet of plastic down each side of the basement. Provide the wide overlap. Slit the plastic at a column and let it be tucked up around the column. Tape it to the column. Make the slits in each sheet on opposite sides of the column so that there is a continuous piece underneath. Remember that any access to the sand layer below may, and probably will, permit an infiltration of moisture to the slab and be seen as a damp area on the surface.

After all piping, drain fields, sump pit, and floor work is accomplished, there will be one final finishing touch to the waterproofing detail. Following the closing in of the house above, the foundation walls may be painted with penetrating waterproofing liquid especially designed to seek out minute holes. In accordance with the instructions, a crack or area suspected of possible leaking may be wetted first. The waterproofing solution will then follow the moisture into the crack and seal it. It will subsequently be a source of satisfaction to hear water trickling or running into your sump while all about you is a perfectly dry basement.

BLOCK FOUNDATION DEPTH

There are recommendations in rule-of-thumb form and regulations in code form regarding the height and depth limits of masonry foundations (Fig. 5-81). Although hollow blocks are a convenient means of assembling a foundation, certain rules should be followed to avoid failure. The rules that refer to backfilling have an obvious relationship to excavation depth and to the foundation exposure between the grade level and the siding. Where full coverage with stone or brick veneer exists, there will still be a dramatic effect from grade to roof eave. To interrupt this effect, one might phrase a rule of thumb as follows for houses with basement foundations:

- An 8″ block foundation will net a high-profile house.
- A wider or thicker foundation will produce a lower-profile house.

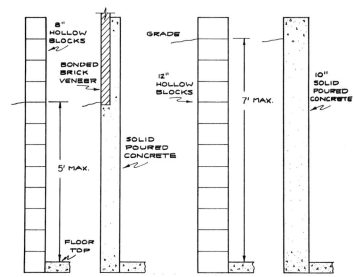

FIGURE 5-81   Backfill regulations for foundation walls.

This truism is a serious consideration to be dealt with during the design stage. It affects all the foundation components, from the footing bed up. It affects all the entry provisions into and onto the first-floor level. Step and porch heights, patio and/or deck requirements, and even the contour of the yard and slope of the driveway are directly related. The order of planning in this instance should be to establish the desires with regard to the aesthetics and living practicalities and then design the foundation to accommodate their specified requirements.

REINFORCING HOLLOW-BLOCK FOUNDATIONS

Most block producers of considerable volume will lend a hand with specific recommendations to meet the individual plan. Figure 5-82 shows some samples that are usually available. Other sources are the Portland Cement Association, Skokie, Illinois, and the National Concrete Masonry Association, Arlington, Virginia.

PILASTERS

For residential use a pilaster is usually formed in poured concrete or assembled with blocks to aid in supporting long side walls or to support the ends of a girder on end walls. Each type is constructed integrally with the foundation wall. In commercial construction a pilaster is sometimes used as a principal support column above ground joined by masonry curtain walls. The two components are joined against the elements but separated structurally by a mastic control joint.

Residential pilasters for basement wall support may

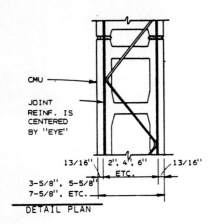

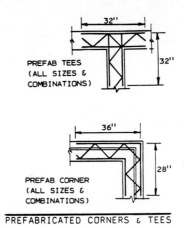

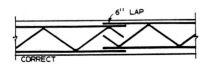

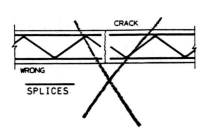

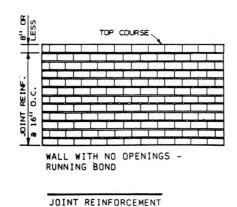

FIGURE 5-82 Lateral reinforcing in the bonded joints adds greatly to the strength of a block wall. (Courtesy of Arkola Sand and Gravel Company, Fort Smith, Arkansas.)

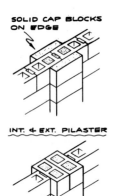

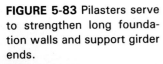

FIGURE 5-83 Pilasters serve to strengthen long foundation walls and support girder ends.

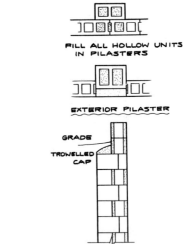

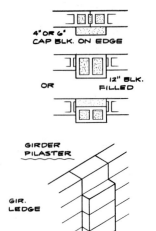

be designed and assembled by several combinations of blocks by facing them differently in alternate courses. Some examples are shown in Fig. 5-83.

Pilasters that project on the exterior side of a foundation wall are discontinued in the course that ends just below grade level. The top block of a hollow pilaster is filled. A slanted surface cap is formed on top to shed moisture.

A pilaster that juts out into the interior of the basement gives superior resistance to the lateral ground and hydraulic pressures from without. Such a series of projections along a wall are sometimes objectionable to the consumer for the use to which the space will be put. In an active recreation or rumpus room, for example, the protruding corners may present a safety hazard even though rounded "bullnose" blocks are used.

The shape and location of the added blocks in a pilaster can be altered to accommodate the foregoing objective. Basically, a pilaster is twice the width of the wall. In practice this rule can apply with 50% extensions on each side, 100% extended on the exterior, or all of the extension on the interior. The latter is most effective against ground pressures that want to push in the foundation wall; however, the all-exterior pilaster will serve well when properly bonded and reinforced.

Filling a pilaster with concrete after placing vertical reinforcing rods in the cavities and having truss joint reinforcing (e.g., Durawall) in the horizontal bonds will produce the ultimate strength obtainable. Most foundations with 8″ block walls will benefit significantly from pilasters placed at intervals of 12′ or less. Thicker block walls will also be sturdier with pilaster support, especially in deeper excavations and where the surrounding soil is of a shifty character or water laden.

REVIEW TOPICS

1. List the three general types of foundation beds in order of their supportive quality (the best first).

2. Sketch a section view of an inverted T footing. Place the minimum formula (not sizes) on the sketch.

3. Explain what is meant by pouring concrete "monolithically."

4. Explain, as though your listener knows nothing about the subject, how to square the first corner of a foundation layout on a lot.

5. You have just recorded the diagonal distances on a rectangular foundation layout and find that the two figures are not the same. Explain exactly what must be done to make the layout square in each corner.

6. Explain how batter boards are used to establish a foundation baseline below ground level (crawl space or basement).

7. Explain what a plinth is and does.

8. Explain how to build foundation footing forms in such a way that the form lumber can later be used in a girder or for floor joists.

9. Explain how to begin the placement of rebar in a footing form so that the ends of all bars to come will be staggered at least 4′ apart from each other.

10. Explain how, when, and where to use a V-grooving sled runner board.

11. Explain the basic difference between a monolithic slab floor and a conventional slab and foundation.

12. Discuss the pros and cons of an upflow and a counterflow (downflow) furnace for a slab-floor house.

13. Explain why concrete made from crushed and screened gravel is usually more uniform in strength than concrete made from pit-run aggregate.

14. Compute the volume of a footing that is 12″ deep, 2′ wide, and for a foundation wall 12″ thick. The building line is for a house 26′ × 60′. Find the volume by each of the following methods: the centerline method, the superimposed surface-area method, and the running-foot method. Show all your mathematics for each method, whether done by hand or calculator.

15. Calculate the volume in a concrete foundation wall that is 24′ × 48′ at the building line and is 8″ thick.

16. Determine and indicate the quantity of full block modules (units) in a foundation wall that is 8′ high for a building 28′ × 52′. No openings.

Chapter 6
WOOD FLOOR CONSTRUCTION_____

PURPOSE OF A GIRDER

A *girder*, sometimes called a *beam*, is a structural member of the floor system. Made of wood or steel, its purpose is to provide support under floor joists. Most houses are too deep from front to rear for a single board to span. A framework of dimension lumber (nominal-2″ boards) is laid in parallel rows from one end of the foundation to the other. These boards, which stand on edge, are called *joists*. It usually takes a set of two laid end to end to span the distance across the floor. A girder is used to support the ends of the joists which are at or near the center of the span. There are columns (posts) in a basement to support the girder. There are piers to support the girder in a crawl space foundation design.

GIRDER TYPES

Most houses today are built with steel I-beams or built-up wood girders (Fig. 6-1) to support the floor frame. A third type, the solid wood beam, is not widely used because of its high cost, limited length, and tendency to warp.

Steel Girders

Steel girders are I-beams made in two shapes, *standard* and *wide flange*. The wide-flange beam provides the advantage of a wider surface for the joists to bear upon. This is significant when joist ends are butted and strapped. The min-

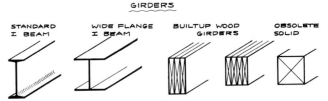

FIGURE 6-1 Typical steel and wood girders used under residential floors.

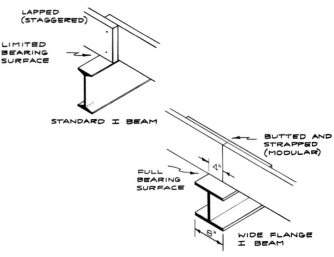

FIGURE 6-2 The standard I-beam usually limits joist placement to the less modular lap formation. The wide-flange I-beam usually provides adequate bearing for the modular in-line system of joist placement or for pocketing of joists to give clear ceiling below.

imum bearing rule in most codes is 4″. This means that at least 4″ of the joist end should rest on the girder. Since frame walls with 2 × 4 plates are actually 3 1/2″ deep, and they are accepted under the bearing rule for ceiling joists, most inspectors accept 3 1/2″ as a nominal 4″ of bearing. The standard I-beam usually does not have adequate surface to provide full bearing for joist ends that are butted. Therefore, it dictates the lapped joist system of placement (Fig. 6-2).

Advantages.   An advantage of the steel I-beam is its strength-to-size proportion. Fewer supporting posts are required. This nets larger unobstructed areas in a basement, an advantage for recreational or shop use. The exact column spacing for the load requirements should be obtained from an engineering source. Another advantage of steel is stability. The expansion ratio is minimal. Expansion of the steel will have little effect on the building except at the ends. The ends of a steel beam should have 1/2″ clearance all around. A tightly cemented-in beam can crack the end walls of a foundation.

Disadvantages.   Disadvantages of a steel girder are the high cost and difficult handling. Delivery is expensive. A steel girder beam is often fabricated in one piece. Massive equipment is required to handle it in transportation and installation. Few builders on a medium- or small-scale mode of operation will use steel when they must pay for the trucking and crane operation. The large-scale developer

of a housing complex may own and operate his own steel hoisting and transporting equipment. Steel is feasible for this builder.

Built-up Girders

The most common girder in use is the built-up girder (Fig. 6-3). It can be assembled into a single unit and hoisted by a crew, or it can be assembled directly on columns or piers by one or two workers. This design calls for planks to be laminated together with ends staggered to form a single long, stiff girder. Each board should be placed so that no weakness is built in. Every end joint should be placed directly over a column (Fig. 6-4). When assembling a three-piece girder at least one of the members (the center one or both outer ones) should run through over the column. This formation will alternate, as seen in Fig. 6-5. Because of this code-regulated practice, column spacing is important to both economy and weight-bearing ability. Refer to modular column spacing in Chapter 2.

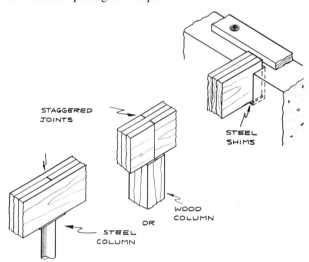

FIGURE 6-4   Each end joint of a board in a built-up girder should be centered over a column. At least one or two pieces should run through to the next column.

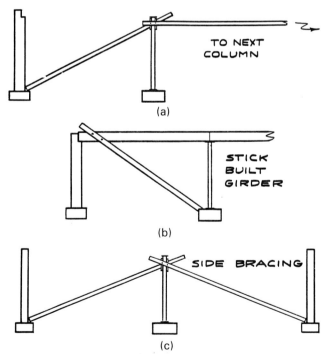

FIGURE 6-3   (a) How to temporarily brace all columns in place at once; use this technique when a full-length girder will be lowered into place. (b) How to brace while building a girder in place one piece at a time. (c) Side bracing.

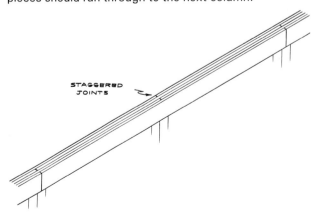

FIGURE 6-5   In the four-piece girder, two alternating pieces pass over each column to tie the girder into a single unit.

Correcting Crooked Girder Lumber. Individual boards that have more than 1/8″ crook (a curved edge) should be held out for some other purpose, such as joists, or should be chalk lined on the convex edge and sawed straight. Once a girder is assembled and nailed, it will not flex enough under the floor weight to be straightened. Such a convex curve will hump the floor. The curves should be removed before assembly. When studs of identical length (precuts) are used in a partition, a hump over a crooked beam will be paralleled in the ceiling. When trusses are used, the hump is carried into the roof. Errors of this type, starting at foundation level, usually compound and magnify the problem as the structure rises. A straight, level girder will add to the integrity of the structure.

SHIMMING A GIRDER

Any shimming under the ends of a beam (wood or steel) should be done with steel flats or solid masonry. Wood shims are forbidden because of their compressability. Shims of rectangular shape in thicknesses of 1/16, 1/8, and 1/4″ are ideal to make up any combination of height. These shims can be obtained from scrap bins at most steel works. They are needed to raise the girder so that the top surface lines up level with either the top of the foundation or the top of the sill. Putting a sill on a wood girder is a waste of material. Putting a wood sill on a steel girder may be desirable as a means of providing a surface to which joists can be secured with nails. Where a wood sill is used on a steel girder, the top surface of the girder must be leveled with the top of the foundation. Where a wood girder is used, it will be placed level with the top of the wood sill on the foundation. This is usually 1 1/2″ higher than the top of the foundation.

PLANNING THE GIRDERS

Location of Girders

Girders are usually parallel with the long sides of a floor. On a square foundation, a beam could run either way if there were no openings to be considered. The objective with any shape of foundation is to arrange the shortest clear span for the joists.

Column Location Relates to Girder Size

Appendix 4 provides adequate information for the builder or drafter to specify proper column spacing (the girder span between columns) and the girth of the girder. Girder size is stated in nominal figures which apply to both solid or built-up girders. A 6 × 10 built-up girder is made of three

2 × 10s. The actual size is 4 1/2″ × 9 1/4″. An 8 × 10 girder is actually 6″ × 9 1/4″ since four 2″ planks, each 1 1/2″ thick, are combined.

Material Size Affects Cost

On a long span (greater than 28′), the designer should consider the comparative cost of having two girders combined with sets of three smaller joists against the cost of one girder with sets of two larger joists. Part of the cost of a double-girder system will be in the additional columns and pads. The shape of the floor is the key factor in economy planning. A long, narrow floor is generally more economical than other shapes. Under normal market conditions, lumber cost, per board foot, compounds as unit lengths and widths increase. For example, a 2 × 10 = 20′ long costs considerably more than the sum of two boards half as long. From 18 to 24′, the cost jumps dramatically. To the planner, the significance of this can mean either economy or high cost. The planner must not use lumber board feet as the criterion for estimating cost. He or she must consider the price per piece (unit) of material.

Choosing Joist Direction

There are structural considerations when choosing girder and joist direction. For example, if a stairwell is specified, it is more economical for the well to run parallel to the joists. The usual procedure for providing a structurally sound opening is to double the joists at each side of the opening and use headers across the ends of the opening. In Fig. 6-6 note the amount of extra material required where the joists do not parallel the well. Additional labor time is

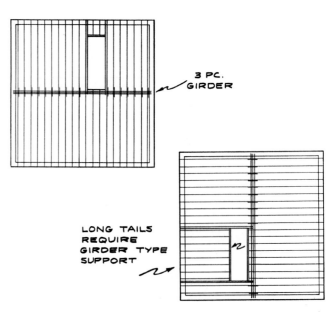

FIGURE 6-6 Choosing a girder direction can have an effect on economy where there are large openings such as a stairwell.

also involved. Long tail headers are comparable to a girder. This means that support is needed for them in the form of posts or a bearing partition underneath. Such supporting members require additional footing under the basement floor. Refer to Chapter 2, for more specific information on cost saving through modular planning when designing a floor.

Girder Span

Before the lumber lengths for the girder can be chosen, the spacing of the columns must be determined. This designing should take place as part of the foundation planning. The foundation pads for the columns will be formed and poured at the time the foundation wall footings are poured. The pad locations are precise. They reflect a coordinated plan that involves the girder span between columns and the unit lengths of the boards in the built-up girder. The most common space modules between columns are 7, 8, 9, and 10'. Eleven and twelve feet are possible but are extremely expensive, as they require 22 and 24' lumber lengths at premium cost. To achieve economy, spacing should be held at even feet. For example, a space of 8' between columns will net a built-up beam made with 16' lengths (Fig. 6-7). To stagger the butt joints over the first column, two of the pieces will run from the bearing point by the foundation wall to the center of the second column. In a three-piece girder, the third piece will span from the wall to the center of the first column. This sets up a staggered joint system. Each column will have one or two pieces of the girder passing over it onto the next column. With the exception of those pieces in the end spaces that are approximate half lengths, all the other members will be twice as long as the column spacing. When any figure other than a full foot is used for this spacing, there will be short scraps left over. For example, if a span of 7'6" were chosen, it would still be necessary to buy a 16' unit and waste a linear foot of lumber from each board (a linear foot of 2 × 12 is 2 board feet of loss). A common construction error is to simply divide the length of a basement or crawl space into equal parts. This practice guarantees waste. The spaces should be in full feet with the exception of the end ones, which will be shorter by the allowance for the thickness of the foundation wall or the back of a girder pocket. Nonmodular house lengths will always have an odd space at one end or the other in addition to the subtraction of the wall thickness.

Determining Girder Size

Girder size is dependent on two conditions, the width (depth) of the house and the type of roof framing (Table 6-1). The depth limits are classed in two categories: house floor and roof spans under 26' and those that are 26' and over. The second factor is whether or not there are interior bearing partitions. An interior partition is considered *bearing* when it runs at right angles to the ceiling joists and supports them. The weight of the ceiling is transported to the floor joists and to the girder. Where a trussed roof frame is used, none of the partitions are classed as bearing. The correct girder size and the limit of the span between columns can be determined from the table by cross-matching the horizontal and vertical columns that apply to the floor plan.

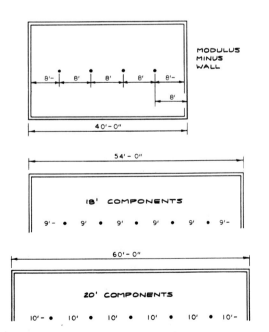

FIGURE 6-7 Sample house lengths with modularly spaced columns that will accommodate full-length girder components.

TABLE 6-1

FHA–MPS Maximum girder spans

Width of Structure	Girder Size	Supporting Bearing Partition		Nonbearing Partition
		1 Story	1 1/2 or 2 story	
Up to 26' wide	6 × 8	7'-0"	6'-0"	9'-0"
	8 × 8	9'-0"	7'-6"	11'-6"
	6 × 10	9'-0"	7'-6"	11'-6"
	8 × 10	10'-6"	9'-0"	12'-0"
	6 × 12	10'-6"	9'-0"	12'-0"
26–32' wide	6 × 8	6'-6"	5'-6"	8'-6"
	8 × 8	8'-0"	7'-0"	10'-6"
	6 × 10	8'-0"	7'-0"	10'-6"
	8 × 10	10'-0"	8'-0"	11'-6"
	6 × 12	10'-0"	8'-0"	11'-6"

Specifications

1. A one-story house
2. 26'-8" × 60'
3. No greater than 10" nominal girder desired
4. Widest span possible between columns desired
5. Full trussed roof (nonbearing partitions)

Problem

1. Find the girder size (girth).
2. Find the quantity of spaces and columns.
3. Find the centering span for the columns.

Answers

1. 8' × 8' or 6' × 10'
2. Six spaces (five columns)
3. 10'

Example. In this problem, the length of the house relates only to making economical choices of lumber units in the girder. If a span of 8' is chosen, there will be seven and one-half spaces and six columns. If 10' is chosen, there will be six spaces and five columns. For greatest economy, the span between columns should be in whole numbers with the nonmodular plan as well as the modular plan.

BALLOON FLOOR (OBSOLETE)

In the United States, there are two principal wood floor designs. Some older homes have the balloon framing system (Fig. 6-8). The modern carpenter is not likely to become involved in balloon framing, as the method is rarely used today. It may be encountered when remodeling is undertaken. A brief description of balloon framing will help the remodeler visualize what is hidden behind the walls and under the flooring. The main feature was the attachment of the wall studs, face to face, to the floor joists at a vertical angle. Stiffness of the walls and floors was achieved by using a beam-sized sill to support the studs and joists. The system was well adapted to pier foundations. As large timbers for sills became more expensive and more houses were built with full basement walls of blocks or concrete, the box design replaced the balloon.

The balloon design did not adapt well to standardized material sizes such as the precut stud and the 8 and 9' plywood siding and fiberboard sheathing units. In its day, it was suited to two-story construction. The studs were one-piece units going from the sill to the second-story upper

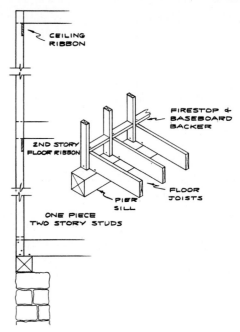

FIGURE 6-8   The obsolete balloon frame of yesteryear is found in old homes undergoing restoration or upgrading.

plates. In some designs there were top ribbons (no plates). Horizontal ribbons were cut into the studs on which the second floor joists rested.

BOXED PLATFORM FLOOR FRAME

As the one-story ranch style home gained in popularity, the two-story balloon frame became less prevalent. Builders soon realized the safety and added convenience of stacking one story on another. The system places a second box floor on top of the first-story wall frame. This box is dual purpose. It serves as the ceiling for the first story and the floor for the second story. During construction, the second-story subfloor provides a safe working surface upon which to frame the second-story walls and partitions. In time, most builders changed to the platform system.

Constructing the Boxed Platform

As the name implies, the boxed platform is constructed by building a perimeter box. Sill plates are laid flat and bolted to the foundation. Header bands are placed on edge and toenailed to the sills. Joists are placed inside this box parallel to each other (Fig. 6-9). The joists usually run across the shorter dimension of the floor rectangle. They are spaced apart equally. Sheathing is nailed over this framework to form a working surface—hence the term "platform."

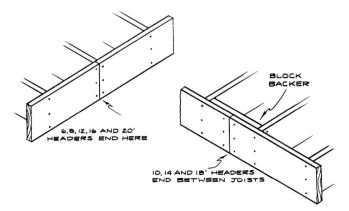

FIGURE 6-9 Header band joining methods are characterized by linear lengths of boards.

Wood Sill Plates

The first wood member on top of the foundation is called a sill plate. There was a time when these boards were called mud sills because they were set in wet mortar. The mortar system has been replaced by other forms of insulating sealers, such as fiberboard and fiberglass.

Using the Federal Housing Administration regulation of maximum 8' OC as an example, it is found that certain sill unit lengths are more economical in terms of bolt savings. The 18' sill board allows for maximum bolt spacing under this code. 16, 14, or 12' boards will still require three bolts each since a bolt is required within 1' of each end. The distance between these end bolts exceeds 8' with the boards above.

Preplanning of Sill Units and Anchor Bolt Locations. The size and position of each sill board should be planned before the foundation wall is constructed. Anchor bolts must be in specific places to meet codes. It saves money to match the bolt locations with the length of each sill board.

Building codes tell what the maximum spacing can be and the minimum quantity of bolts to use. For example, the FHA–MPS rules are (Fig. 6-10):

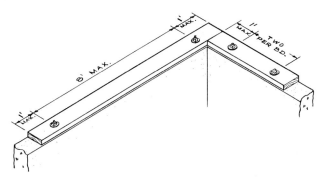

FIGURE 6-10 FHA–MPS rules for sill anchorage.

- A maximum of 8' apart
- Not more than 12" from the end of a board
- No fewer than two bolts per board

The first rule will vary according to geographic location. Local codes should be consulted. For example, the Southern Building Code Congress International (SBCCI) requires anchors not more than 6' apart.

Advantage of the 18' Sill Units. There is an advantage to 18' sill units when placing anchor bolts under the 8' maximum spread rule (Fig. 6-11). When the front and rear sill boards are started at the building line (the corner from which joist spacing will begin), the first bolt will be placed 1' in from the corner. The second bolt will be 9' and the third 17'. All these locations fall between the joists' bearing points. This pattern will continue throughout the remainder of the wall. Using 18s results in an odd-length piece at the end of each run except with a 36, 54, and 72' foundation (or any other even multiple of 18).

Advantage of the 14' Sill Units. Some localities require no greater than a 6' spread of bolts. For this module the 14' sill unit works with the same efficiency as described for the 18'.

Headers and Bands

Headers serve two purposes: to keep the joists in alignment and to provide a part of the support under the wall frame.

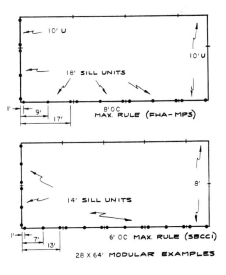

FIGURE 6-11 Anchor bolt spacing and sill board lengths should be coordinated in accordance with the maximum bolt spacing rule in your local code.

The support function is secondary when wall studs are properly lined up to bear directly over the floor joists. There are other headers in the floor, such as those which cross the ends of tail joists where an opening exists. In a floor frame, the word *header* is a general term referring to members that cross the ends of other uniformly spaced boards. The perimeter header is the header to which the joists ends are nailed. The bands are the outer joists on the ends of the floor box. The term "bands" is sometimes used to mean all surrounding perimeter members of the box frame. The headers and bands stand on edge to match the joists.

Select Straight Boards.   The builder should select the straightest boards for the headers and bands. Crooked boards (pronounced "crookt") should not be considered for the headers. A crook is an edge curve. Such a curve will not flex downward after sheathing is nailed to the walls. The floor and wall will remain undesirably humped.

Header Band Sizes.   The lengths of band headers are optional, as there is no modular significance. When lengths divisible by 4 are used, and joists are on 16" centers, the butt joint of the ends of the headers will be at the end of a joist. Lengths divisible by 2 (but not by 4), such as 10, 14, and 18', will cause a butt joint to fall between the joists. This latter joint should be backed up by a solid wood block to keep the header stiff, in alignment, and to prevent infiltration of air. End joints of headers should be staggered from sill joints. Bands on the ends of the floor box are the same size as the joists next to them. They may be ordered as joists on the bill of materials.

DETERMINING JOIST SIZE

The load-supporting capacity of a joist is dependent on:

- *Clear span:* distance across the unsupported space.
- *Species:* type of wood: pine, fir, spruce, etc.
- *Grade:* how good or strong the wood is for its purpose.
- *Load:* dead- and live-weight loads to be imposed on the floor. Dead weight is the weight of materials and permanent fixtures Live weight is people, furniture, and readily movable items.

The size of joist that may be used is dependent, in most areas, on prescribed code minimums set by a civil agency or lending agency involved. To design a plan or interpret one for specifications and cost analysis, the lengths and widths of the joists must be determined. To make a uniform floor surface, the height of all joists (board width)

should be the same throughout the floor. In some instances, such as small landings or alcoves, it may effect a saving to use smaller joists and shim them up. Wings off the main section of floor may have smaller joists. When a uniform joist height is to be used throughout the floor, its height requirement must conform to the greatest single joist span that is found in the floor. Some old timers use rule-of-thumb definitions such as "a 2 × 8 × 12 will go 12', a 2 × 10 × 14 for 14', and a 2 × 12 × 16 for 16'." Such generalizations were adequate years ago when only the better grades of lumber were considered. It is not adequate information for today's variety of quality and types of wood. The designer or builder today should use a recognized stress table from a reliable source such as the *National Forest Products Association*, the *Federal Housing Administration Minimum Property Standards*, or local codes obtained from municipalities. See Appendices 4 through 7 for span tables.

LUMBER GRADING

A word of caution to the prudent builder. Lumber grading is not universally consistent. Even the terminology fluctuates from words to numbers and combinations. When a responsible builder sees an obvious defect, such as a large knot in the central area of a 2 × 10 joist (Fig. 6-12), regardless of grade, he will set it aside. It may possibly be worked in later as a double (trimmer) under a partition, or it may be cut into usable lengths for headers. To ignore such inferior material is to encourage a "callback" at a later date to repair a breakdown.

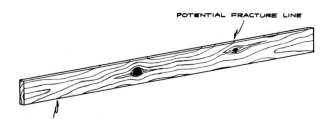

FIGURE 6-12   This board is a poor choice for use as a floor joist.

JOIST SPAN DEFINITIONS

Span is designated by two definitions. *Nominal joist span* refers to the total distance from the exterior of the foundation (the building line) to the center of the girder. A 24 × 40 house with a center girder running the long way has a nominal joist span of 12'. A house depth of 26'-8" will have a nominal joist span of 13'-4" when the girder is centered.

Clear span is the nominal length minus whatever total amount of the joist and header is resting (bearing) on

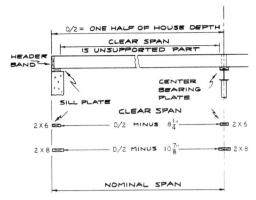

FIGURE 6-13 Joist span tables refer to "clear span," which is altered by the subtraction of varying amounts of sill plate width.

supporting surfaces (Fig. 6-13). Clear span is that length of the joist that is between supports.

Floor Joist Span Tables

The more detailed span tables may include load columns. These will show pounds per square foot of floor area that can be supported when a particular grade and species of lumber is used.

Lapped versus Strapped Joists

Before modular materials dominated the building scene, the spacing of structural framing members was not critical. The rule then was simply to have enough members for structural support and a no-sag appearance. Now that uniform sheets are most frequently used for sheathing the floor, walls, and roof, an understanding of precise spacing is essential to economy. When board sheathing was installed diagonally years ago, it did not matter that joists were lapped over a girder or whether a bowed joist was pulled into alignment before nailing down the sheathing boards. Random sheathing took up the slack for all the inconsistencies. The lapped joist technique is still used today by some builders, but certain adaptations must be made to cover such a frame with sheet materials (see Chapter 2).

MODULAR JOIST SYSTEM

The butted and strapped (tied) system of installing joists simplifies the spacing concept in a design. For that reason it has become known as the modular system. Tests have proven that the in-line characteristic of the butted joist generates a saving in the labor cost of a floor. The simplicity of layout helps maintain parallelism. The controlled length of the butted pair of joists prevents undersized or oversized

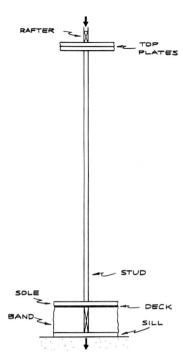

FIGURE 6-14 The optimum framing alignment is a straight vertical line through the structural members that bear the roof.

depth of the box frame. This simplifies straightening the front and rear floor lines. When the front is made straight by checking with a string line, the back will be straight because it is parallel. By contrast, the lapped joist system requires both front and rear headers to be put into a straight position before the lapped ends of the joists are nailed together over the girder.

Joist Spacing in the Modular Floor

The butted and strapped set of joists lines up across the floor with a common centerline as though it were one piece. All the offset considerations associated with the lapped joist system are eliminated. A notable feature is that a total vertical, structural alignment from foundation to roof can be made. The rafters, studs, and floor joists will bear in a common vertical plane onto the foundation (Fig. 6-14).

Joist Tie Strap

A nominal 1″ tie strap, 24″ long and the same width as the joist is used to hold the joists together (Fig. 6-15). With a pair of joists lying flat, the strap is centered over the butt joint and nailed to the faces of the joist. Nails should be slanted slightly toward the butt joint. This angling of the nails will resist the tendency of the joint to open up when the unit is moved into postion.

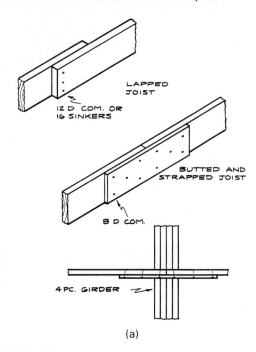

(a)

(b)

FIGURE 6-15 (a) Strapped joists accommodate sheathing sheets better. A four-piece girder provides greater bearing for a strapped joist. (b) Butted and strapped in-line joists.

LAPPED JOISTS

Should the designer choose to use the lapped joist system, the first realization of importance is that one-half of the floor frame will have joists on consistent "centers" measured from a starting point. The starting point will be the building line at the point of a corner. This datum is called the zero point or POB (point of beginning). The builder must consistently start all measurements from the same end of the house. Failure to do this will cause the spacing to be misaligned from front to rear on any length house other than those divisible by 16".

Spacing the Lapped Joists

All joists except the end ones will straddle a specified centering location. A joist is placed every 16" along the header band. This is the most common on-center (OC) spacing which fits modular-sized sheathing. The end joists are not on centers, as this would leave half of the thickness (3/4")

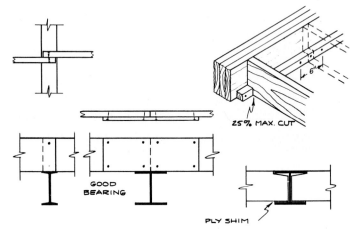

FIGURE 6-16 Pocketed joists and those on ledgers can always be aligned modularly on a common OC centerline.

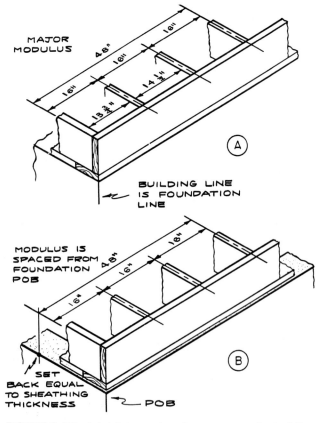

FIGURE 6-17 (a) Joist spacing that starts on the building line. The header band joist is not on-center. (b) Where sheathing is designed to be flush with the building line, the framework is inset.

overhanging the foundation. The outer edges of the first and last joists (the bands) are flush with the building line (Fig. 6-17). In the lapped joist system the joists on the opposite side of the girder will be offset 1 1/2″, the thickness of a joist (Fig. 6-16). They must be in parallel relation to the bands and the joists that they lap. It should be kept in mind throughout all the construction that this offset exists, as it will effect the placement of openings, such as stairways, chimneys, furnace plenums, and the drains for bathtubs, showers, and water closets (toilets). The offset also affects the sheathing placement, as described later in this chapter.

TYPES OF LOADS

Some areas of the floor will carry more weight after the house is completed. Load stress on a floor is classified as live load or dead load. *Live load* refers to things that are not permanently attached, such as people, furniture, and portable equipment. *Dead load* means the weight of the structural materials and anything else that is attached. When planning an area to house a heavy item, such as a grand piano or a slate-topped pool table, a designer should give special attention to the under-floor structure. It should be designed for a specific load, with some strength to spare.

Tables for Average Loads

Earlier in this chapter, reference was made to the two things that determine the size of a joist. Many simplified span and stress tables omit the load factor. Such a table recognizes an ''average'' load. Since the tables represent minimum standards of acceptability (maximum span), the chances are good that most designs will be adequately strong. It is poor practice to push the design to the limits of clear span. Any factor of weakness such as a wood defect will set up a potential breakdown.

Effect of a Conventional Roof on the Floor

The first consideration in floor reinforcement is the type of roof framing that will be used. There are two general classifications of roof frames. One classification is called the *conventional rafter system*. The conventional roof has rafters that are installed one at a time (''stick-built''). The lower ends rest on the outer walls of the house. The upper ends are nailed to a ridge board. The ridge board runs the long way of the roof. The ceiling joists are parallel to the rafters. They are cross-nailed to the rafters and toenailed to the upper plate of the outer walls. The ceiling joists form a tie across the building and keep the rafters and outer walls from spreading. Conventional rafters may have no connection whatever with the ceiling joists except at their outer ends. In this design, approximately half of the weight of the ceiling is transferred through partitions to the girder under the floor. The other half is borne by the outer walls. The floor joist span table and the girder table that take the roof frame design into account will usually indicate larger floor components for the conventional rafter system than for a trussed roof.

Effect of a Trussed Roof on the Floor

A roof truss is a ridged triangle. It is assembled before erection. The rafters are called *upper chords*. The ceiling joists forming the lower part of the triangle are called *lower chords*. *Webs* join the upper and lower chords together. Theoretically, a roof truss transfers all the roof load to the two bearing points of the truss, the outer walls. The lower chord of the truss takes the place of conventional ceiling joists. Any material attached to these chords, such as wallboard or ceiling tiles, is part of the truss load and is transferred to the exterior walls. The interior partitions do not support the truss or the ceiling. Under actual conditions, there is a little weight transferred to partitions that are perpendicular to the trusses as the partitions shore up the downward flex stress caused by the weight of sheathing and roofing.

REINFORCING THE FLOOR FRAME

Some reinforcements are required by code. Others are optional. A common requirement is to double a joist that is under a partition that runs parallel with the joist. Another example is any headed opening in the floor that exceeds two spaces. The joists on each side of the opening are doubled. Reinforcing options that denote good construction are: doubling under the front edge of a cast-iron bathtub, under the front edge of long built-in cabinets that are parallel to the joists, and any other points of known overload.

Full-Floor Reinforcement

In the case of an anticipated live load, such as a pool table or three-legged grand piano, the points of bearing can be so easily changed by moving the object that doubling under specific bearing points (legs) is ill advised. Doubling the joist strengthens only the immediate area. In the case of the fluctuating live load, better practice would be to narrow the spacing of all joists from 16″ down to 12″ throughout the critical area.

Methods of Reinforcing

There are four doubling techniques under a partition. Where any part of the partition sole is above an on-center joist, an extra joist may be nailed to the face of the joist. Where the partition is not over the joist, one of three types of block spacers can be used. The spacers make it possible to have the extra joist trimmer under the partition and still be attached to the closest on-center joist to gain extra stiffness. The size of spacer to use under a partition depends on the location of the partition in relation to the closest on-center joist.

Doubler.   An extra joist nailed directly to the face of an on-center joist is called a *trimmer*. This joist and trimmer set is sometimes called a *doubler*. An extra joist will add additional load-bearing capacity. This capacity is greatest when the trimmer joist is nailed directly to the adjoining joist. The simplest method of reinforcement is to nail alternatively from side to side in an approved pattern. This turns the two joists into a two-piece built-up beam. It gains additional strength as well as stiffness (rigidity) when nailed in this manner. It is important that this set of joists have a top surface that is straight. When an on-center joist is completely under a partition but not centered beneath the sole, the trimmer should be nailed to the side of the on-center joist, which will give the greatest support to the partition above.

Block-Spaced Trimmer and Joist.   The extra joist trimmer may be spaced apart from the joist by the use of blocks (Fig. 6-18). The blocked joist and trimmer is used when a partition is not over an OC joist. The blocking method adds the strength gained from the trimmer and shares the load with the closest joist. There are three blocking techniques for the purpose of positioning the trimmer.

1.   Where an on-center joist is situated partly under one edge of the partition sole or very close to it, the trimmer should be placed so that the sole is completely supported. This will be done by using scrap nominal-2″ stock blocks placed with their grain vertically between the joist and trimmer. The flat surfaces of the blocks will be adjacent to the joists, thus spacing the trimmer and joist apart 1 1/2″. The blocks will be placed from 24 to 36″ apart, depending on the total joist length. The spacing should be approximately equal. The blocks are cut a fraction of an inch shorter than the joist height (material width) so that the lineup for nailing is not as critical. A 9″ block would

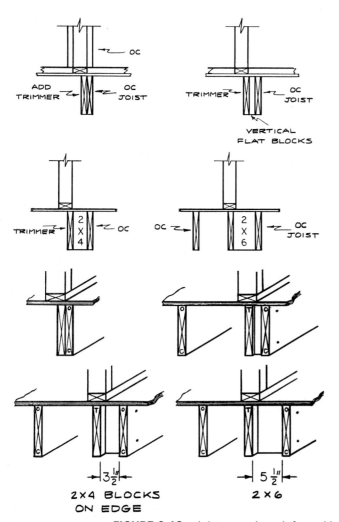

FIGURE 6-18   Joists may be reinforced by adding a trimmer joist and spacer blocks.

fit a 2 × 10 joist nicely, as the actual height of a 2 × 10 is 9 1/4″.

2. As the partition is found farther away from the on-center joist, the 2 × 4 blocks will be placed with *edges* against the joist and nailed from each side. This will position the trimmer 3 1/2″ away from the on-center joist and directly under some part of the partition sole.

3. The third position is made by using 2 × 6 blocks to space the trimmer and joist 5 1/2″ apart. Never is any size larger than 2 × 6 needed, as that would simply position the trimmer closer to the other side of the space and within range of being attached to another OC joist.

Spacer Blocks under Rigid Insulation. Some builders insulate under the floor with sheet Styrofoam laid on 1 × 1 ledgers (Fig. 6-19). The styrofoam is placed with its upper surface flush with the top of the joists. When insulating in this manner, it saves much cutting and fitting of the Styrofoam when the partition spacer blocks between the joist and trimmer are shortened at the top so that they do not protrude into the Styrofoam area. The ledger strips must be installed prior to assembly of the trimmer and blocks, as it is nearly impossible to nail them or power staple them after the blocked joist and trimmer have been assembled.

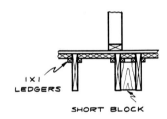

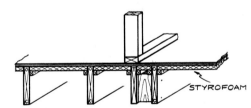

FIGURE 6-19 Install ledgers and spacer blocks before placing the reinforcing joist when Styrofoam is used for insulation.

Coordinating the Septic Vent with Joists. The size regulation on soil stacks (the waste vent drain from the toilet) varies regionally. A nominal-6″ wall frame may be required. This mandates a joist and trimmer combination using the 6″ block spacer. Placement of this partition is critical (Fig. 6-20). The sole of the partition should line up precisely over the space between the joist and trimmer. When the stack vent partition is parallel to the joists, it is good procedure to lay out its sole location on the floor first

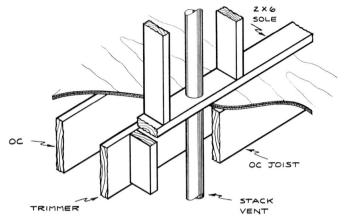

FIGURE 6-20 Modular alignment of a bathroom septic wall makes stack location simple.

to assure proper alignment with the components below. The other partition layouts may progress outward from this key location. After the floor frame is sheathed, there is little adjustment possible with partitions that are parallel to the joists. The builder is locked into the joist reinforcement locations that were specified, as the reinforcing trimmers and extra joists cannot be moved, and must not be cut away.

Block Bridging to Support the Subflooring. Block bridging spanning the 14 1/2″ space between 16″ centered joists should not be considered a means of adding load support. Blocks nailed in the space between two regular joists do not increase the bearing capacity of the joists. Blocks across a full space comprise a good technique for supporting short partitions that do not reach from one joist bearing point to another. 14 1/2″ blocks are useful when the roof is trussed and joist doubling is not required. They will help support a partition that is resting on

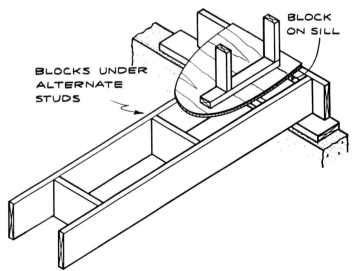

FIGURE 6-21 Bridge blocks may be used to support parallel partitions in place of a full-length trimmer where the roof is trussed (a categorical nonbearing ceiling).

a typical 1/2″ three-ply plywood subfloor. This common type of subfloor is so flexible that a partition above the space between joist sags the subfloor. An example adaptation would be as follows: a joist span of 14′, a partition 9′ long extending in from the exterior wall. Put a block under the nonbearing end and one or two spaced equally apart under the remainder of the partition (Fig. 6-21). Install the last block on the sill plate at a point under the partition end which joins the exterior wall. This last block transfers the bearing to the foundation wall, thereby relieving the subfloor of the strain.

Transferring Partition Weight.   After a partition has been covered with sheet materials such as drywall (gypsum board) or paneling, the partition is similar to a box beam. When such a partition is as long as the joist span, its weight can be transferred directly to the foundation on the exterior end and to the girder on the other end. For this reason, a partition located over the space between the joists should always have a block bridge under each of its ends in addition to those in intermediate positions (Fig. 6-22). This transfers the weight of the partition to the outer foundation wall on the one end and to the girder on the interior end. These two key places for block bridging are seldom recognized or considered. Without these end blocks on the bearing points, the weight will go partially onto the two adjoining joists. This is an avoidable strain on the two joists.

Surface Alignment of Blocks.   All blocks that span a full space between joists *must be flush* on the upper surface with the joists. Allowing a block to be even a small amount below the joist top will permit the partition to bend the subflooring down until it rests on the block (Fig. 6-23).

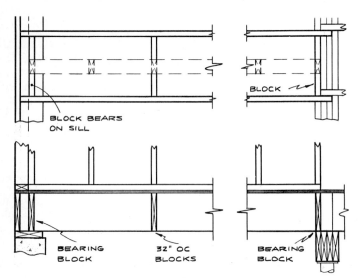

FIGURE 6-22   A block under each end of a partition which spans to solid bearing will turn the wall into a box beam and relieve most of its weight from the floor joists.

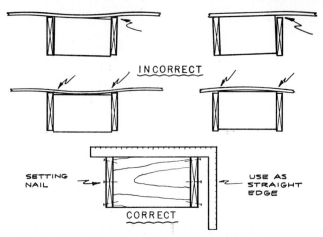

FIGURE 6-23   Improperly placed blocks cause dips and humps in a floor surface. Use a straightedge to align each end of the block while nailing it in place. Plane off a too-high top.

Allowing the block to be even a fraction of an inch *above* the joists will cause a humped partition.

OPENINGS IN THE FLOOR FRAME

A number of things that are larger than 14 1/2″ (the space width between 16″-centered joists) will extend vertically through the floor. More space is required by stairways, chimneys, fireplaces, and furnace plenums. The following are rules that apply to the construction of an opening to maintain load-bearing strength.

- The maximum length for a single header is 4′. Some codes state ''no more than two joist spaces'' (a better practice).
- Tail joists less than 6′ long may be supported on end nails of 20d size or larger.
- Tail joists longer than 6′ must be supported like joists to a girder: on top of a girder, on a ledger, in a metal hanger, or by angle irons.
- The maximum header length is 10′. An opening longer than this, at right angles to the joist, will be treated as a girder and the tails over 6′ long as regular joists (includes most stairwells).
- Wherever a double header is required, the joists to which the ends are nailed will be doubled.

These rules constitute good load-bearing transfer and good building practice.

Assembly Order of Floor Opening Parts

When the doubling of both headers and joists is specified, a specific assembly order is required to maintain adequate

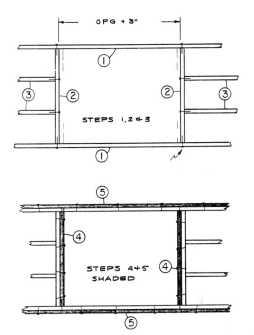

FIGURE 6-24 Headers and tails surrounding a floor opening which are supported only by nails must be assembled in a specific order.

nail penetration into the end grain of each part. It is important to *use nothing smaller than 20d common nail* for all joist nailing that anchors in end grain. The headers and tail joists are supported only on the sheer strength of the nails. A 16d framing nail is not adequate in either penetration or diameter. The assembling will proceed in this order (Fig. 6-24):

1. Joists adjacent to the opening.
2. First headers.

FIGURE 6-25 Styrofoam insulation being installed under floor sheathing. Note the little ledger boards and the double layering of the two 1″ thicknesses.

3. Tails.
4. Second headers.
5. Joist trimmers (the additional joists)

RIGID FLOOR INSULATION

Insulation under the floor is becoming more attractive for crawl space houses due to the high cost of heating fuel. Styrofoam in sheet form is suitable material (Fig. 6-25). It is impervious to dampness and moisture. It will not absorb condensation. It is easy to machine and fit between the joists. Some early forms of the liquid-expanding foam proved to be toxic when burned. The rigid styrene products manufactured for sheathing walls are considered suitable for floors under most building codes.

Ledger strips can be ripped from any form of less costly wood (Fig. 6-26). Economy precut studs, for example, are frequently the lowest cost per board foot. A precut stud can be ripped into four equal pieces that will be very close to 3/4″ thick by 1 1/2″. The ledger is nailed or power stapled to the face of the joists at a distance down from the top edge equal to the Styrofoam thickness.

To be fully effective, the Styrofoam should fit tightly at all points of contact. It is good practice to have the upper face a small fraction of an inch above the joist surface, 1/32″. The sheathing will then press it firmly against the ledgers, forming a tight seal.

The 14 1/2″-wide pieces may be ripped from 4 × 8′ sheets lengthways. The strip remaining is adequate to rip for insulating the partition posts on the exterior wall (described in Chapter 7).

Layering will increase the effectiveness by blocking infiltration cracks. One-inch layers are doubled or tripled in depth. The end joints are staggered with each succeeding layer.

Sheet Styrofoam is more costly than roll-batt insulation per R factor (resistence per inch depth per square foot). There are other factors to consider. Chicken wire or other forms of support are required with fiberglass, which can alter the cost picture considerably.

In the sequence of construction, the ledger strips for Styrofoam may come before or after diagonal bridging. When bridging is installed first, the Styrofoam will be carved to fit around the bridge tops. When ledgers are installed first, the bridges are cut shorter, to bear on the lower edge of the ledger board.

JOIST BRIDGING

A final method of making the floor stiff is to add bridging between the joists at the central point of the spans. Metal bridging can be purchased, or wood bridging can be made from a variety of wood sizes and shapes. 2 × 2s ripped from 2 × 4s, 1 × 3s ripped from 1 × 6s, or stock 1 × 4s

FIGURE 6-26 Ledger strips are most economical when ripped from economy studs. One stud will net eight strips.

will do well. The bridge is installed as a set of crossing diagonals. The ends of the boards are mitered. Finding the length and the angle of cut is done on a framing square. The square is laid on the edge of the wood and held with the body crossing the wood at the 14 1/2″ mark and the tongue at the figure that is the joist depth less 1/4″. Mark the board as shown in Fig. 6-27. Set up a stop block on the power miter box or radial saw. Remember that when one cut is made, the angle is made for the next board also. This saves much time and material. Never square cut the boards first. Bevel cut them to length from the outset. After the initial end of a long strip is beveled, each cut from then on nets a finished piece.

Installation of Wood Bridging

Wood bridging will be nailed onto the vertical face of each joist flush with the top edge just before sheathing is begun (Fig. 6-28). Some pieces will require custom cutting to fit into spaces that are narrower than the standard 14 1/2″ space. All bridges are made a little short purposely. This prevents them from hanging below the joist should it slip down while being nailed at the top. Toenailing always pushes a board in the direction of the hammer blow. A bridge that is a little short also provides some leeway. Joists are rarely perfectly straight. Slight variation in the 14 1/2″ space between joists may cause a maximum-length bridge to hang below.

Attaching the Bridging

Two nails are used at each end of a bridge member. When splitting occurs repeatedly, use a smaller nail or tap pilot holes. A split board is useless. *Nail only the tops of the bridges in the beginning.* After all flooring is completed on top of the joists, the dips and humps caused by the variety of crowns of the joists will be straightened to some extent and stabilized. At that time, the bottoms of the bridges will be nailed up. The bottoms should never be nailed at the initial installing time, as it freezes the joists in whatever position they are and the result is an uneven floor.

Metal Bridging

There are several types of metal bridging on the market. A cost analysis in your area may reveal the better choice.

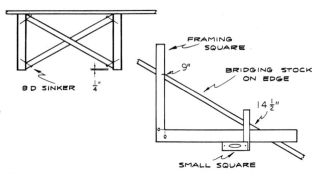

FIGURE 6-27 Lay out a bridge member with a framing square on the edge of the board. The example shown above is for 2 × 10 joists 16″ OC. For 2 × 8s the figures on the square are 7″ and 14 1/2″.

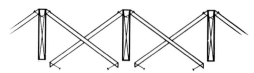

FIGURE 6-28 Attach tops of bridging flush with tops of joists. Leave bottoms hanging unattached until second layer of floor is installed (underlayment).

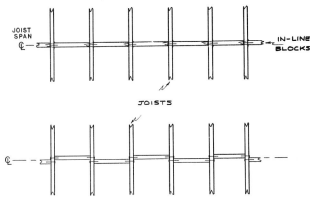

FIGURE 6-29 Where joists are very straight and block bridges are specified they may be installed by either the straight-line method progressively or by the staggered method working anywhere throughout the field.

Metal bridges that require nailing at the top end must be installed like wood. The type that stabs into the joist surface and is completed with one nail at the bottom is installed after completion of the floor surface. The most common floor today is the subfloor of lightweight plywood (usually 1/2″ thick) with a second layer of particle board for carpet underlayment. The flexible plywood does not equalize or level the joists, but the combination of the two materials does accomplish some flattening when properly installed. Put off completing the bridging until the top layer of flooring (underlayment or hardwood) is installed.

Block Bridging

This form of bridging (Fig. 6-29) is costly as a total system. It is also difficult to install properly. It can rarely be nailed on both ends prior to sheathing as the joists have varying crowns. When one end of the block is left unnailed, it will protrude above the joist when the one it is nailed to has a higher crown (upward curve). This protrusion hampers sheathing. When left unnailed on one end while waiting for the floor to self-level, it is difficult to complete the nailing after sheathing because part of the nails must be driven at the upper part of the space, where a full hammer swing is impossible. There is a specific role for the block bridge, as described earlier in the description of partition supports. Due to these factors, *blocks are undesirable as an overall system.*

SHEATHING LAYOUT

Sheathing of the sheet type can be laid, at no additional material cost, in certain formations, which will improve the strength of the building. Cyclone, hurricane, and explosion experience has given us evidence of good practice and poor. A few minutes of extra labor cost could mean

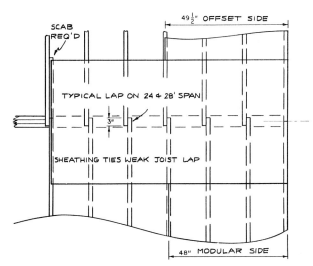

FIGURE 6-30 Lapping the center sheathing across the joist joint strengthens the weak tensile line down through the middle of a floor over a girder. Note that lapped joist ends require a scab to support the upper left corner. In-line butted and strapped joists do not require any scab.

the difference between a house that comes apart at the central seam and one that hangs together. Using plywood sheathing as a crossover tie at the central joist junction has proven to make a significant difference (Fig. 6-30). The FHA code recognizes this principle by waiving the joist tie requirement when the plywood sheathing crosses over the butt-joined joists. Another advantage of this strength addition is realized if the house is ever moved. In many floor plans, a central corridor divides the house. Few partitions that start on one side of a house pass over the centerline to the other side of the house. A central corridor combined with a sheathing seam down the centerline constitutes an area of weakness at the core of the house. All that exists to resist separation in case of movement are the floor joist straps and the ceiling joists (or truss lower chord) at the upper level.

Schematic Sheathing Diagramming

A girder may not always be at the centerline of the plan. A house of 26′ depth could have its girder 12′ from one side and 14′ from the other. Regardless of where the girder is, a schematic plan view of the sheathing position can be made which assures the feature of tying across the joist ends with the sheathing. The examples in Fig. 6-31 show correct and incorrect placements.

Methods of Diagramming the Sheathing Layout

The use of grid paper is an efficient way to begin sketching a proposed sheathing plan. If you are making your own drawings, the *overlay* system is simple and time saving.

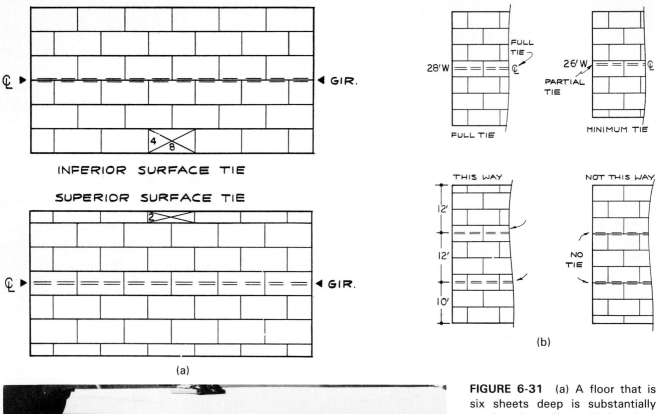

INFERIOR SURFACE TIE

SUPERIOR SURFACE TIE

GIR.

GIR.

CL

CL

4
8

2

(a)

FULL TIE

28'W

FULL TIE

CL

PARTIAL TIE

26'W

MINIMUM TIE

CL

THIS WAY

NOT THIS WAY

12'

12'

10'

NO TIE

(b)

(c)

FIGURE 6-31 (a) A floor that is six sheets deep is substantially weaker (top illustration) unless started and ended with a half-sheet course so that the center sheets bridge across the floor joists and tie them (lower illustration). (b) Other floor depths may be fully tied automatically (the seven-sheet 28' depth in the top illustration), while split modules such as the 26' depth provide automatic partial sheet tieover. Multiple girders or off-centered girders call for analysis to determine the best sheathing arrangement so that the joists benefit from surface tying. (c) A dadoed story pole spaces joists at their centers.

Put a new sheet of tracing paper over the floor plan. Trace the perimeter. Put the girder on with a pair of long dashed lines. Superimpose the sheathing formation.

Where possible, a full half-sheet *staggered* lap should be planned. If the first course is started with an 8' sheet, start the second course with a 4' piece. End joints that are close to those in an adjoining course will cause unnecessary stress on the joist(s) in that area. Two *adjacent sheets should never end on the same joist*.

The half-lap system of staggering the sheathing has another advantage. It is a guide to running a straight course. The edge of the first course laid down should line up on a chalk line snapped across the joists. Snap the line 4' in from the corners when starting with a full-width sheet.

When starting with less than a full-width sheet, the line will be in from the corners an amount equal to the width of the cut sheet. Put the factory-cut edge of the plywood on the chalk line. Do not use the edge of the building as a starting guide. Any little crook or bow there will get the first course off to a poor start.

Providing for Expansion

Plywood swells when it is rained on. It is wise to space it apart a little in areas where there is moisture during construction. A single 8d nail temporarily set in the joist between the ends and a pair of 16d common nails between edges will space the boards uniformly (Fig. 6-32). After

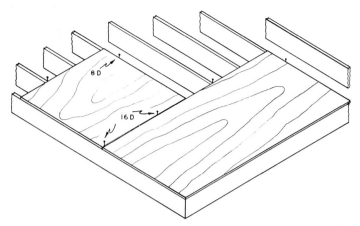

FIGURE 6-32 Temporary nails set in joists between the side and end of each new sheet will effectively space the sheets apart to accommodate the potential expansion due to moisture.

two or three sheets have been laid, it will be necessary to shorten a sheet in order to keep the ends on the joists (the sheets will run long by as much as the sum of the diameter of the spacing nails). Some uncertified ply sheathing on the market is not uniform in length. Your supply should be checked for actual width and length before beginning the job. Some manufacturers of plywood and waferboard print the recommended expansion spacing on each sheet.

Particle Board Overlap

There is another advantage to starting the sheathing with less than a full-width sheet on a floor depth that is divisible by 4'. The plywood sheathing joints, both at the sides and ends, should be lapped by as much of the particle board overlayment as possible. This will happen when sheathing

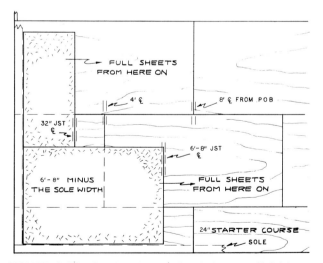

FIGURE 6-33 Partical board "underlayment" laid over the subfloor should be placed to lap the joints in the subfloor and still have the ends of each piece nailed through the subfloor into the joists.

is started with a 2'-wide course and overlaid with particle board of full-size sheets (Fig. 6-33). The full-width particle board, butting against a 2 × 4 sole, will lap the plywood joint by about 20 1/2″. This lapping creates desirable stiffness in the floor. The end joints should also be overlapped. Start with a custom-cut length that ends over a joist where the sheathing does not end. Save the cutoff for the end of the course. Carry on through the middle with full-length sheets. Fifteen-pound building paper or plastic film may be laid between the layers for a vapor barrier.

Effect of Lapped Joists on Sheathing Placement

The lapped joist system will affect the positioning of the plywood sheathing. Plywood is laid with its long direction at right angles to the joists. Floors that are 16, 24, and 32' across will have an even number of courses 4' wide. Starting at the building line with a full-width course results in a joint running the full length of the floor at the centerline. Where a girder is also centered, this sheathing joint will be over the lap joints of the joists. This is sometimes considered an undesirable weakness. It can be remedied by starting the sheathing in the middle (Fig. 6-34). Straddle the centerline with full sheets. To fit the offset joist half of the floor, the plywood is matched to the joists starting from the end that has the shorter space between the band and the first joist. If it happens to be a full sheet, it will hang over the starting point 1 1/2″. This 1 1/2″ piece is cut off the end of the sheet and used at the opposite end as a filler. A *scab* must be nailed alongside the band to support the last full sheet, as it will be 1 1/2″ short of the building line. The next course is started from POB with a half-sheet module. It will be slightly less than 46 1/2″ long. The saw cut removes about 1/8″ of material. The cutoff part of the sheet is slightly less than 49 1/2″ long. It is carried to the other end of the course, where it fits without cutting on a 4' mod-

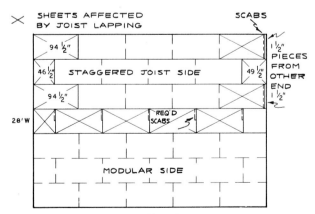

FIGURE 6-34 Lapped joist ends over the girder are the cause of much extra cutting and scabbing of the sheathing. This extra consideration is totally eliminated by the modular method of floor framing.

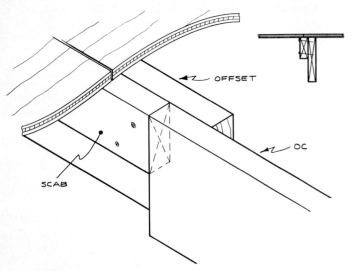

FIGURE 6-35 Scabs are required in several places to support the floor deck when joists are lapped over a girder. The nonsupported end of the sheathing occurs at the transition point of joist offset.

ulus floor. No backup scab is required for this half-sheet-plus module. There is no plywood waste when house widths and lengths are multiples of 4′.

Supporting Sheathing beyond the Lap-Joined Joist

On floors of unmodular widths, the sheathing joint nearest the girder may extend beyond the lap joint of the joists. It is necessary to scab the joist where the plywood sheet does not end completely on a staggered joist (Fig. 6-35). Some builders routinely prefer to place a course of sheathing straddle of the joist joint that is over the girder. For purposes of greater tying, this is especially effective on homes to be moved or those in potential cyclone, tornado, and earthquake regions. It reduces substantially the possibility of the floor frame stretching or pulling apart from tensile stresses along the joists. When the plywood course is started in the middle, for this purpose, about half of the end of each sheet will be unsupported on the offset joist side of the girder. It must be backed up (supported) by a 2 × 4 scab underneath.

ADVANTAGES TO THE FLOOR FROM OPEN WALL FRAMING

An open interior framing system has been used with great success in some areas of the country. It is significant in relation to floor strength. Reusable steel braces, with a turnbuckle action, are used for temporary bracing of the exterior walls. A trussed roof is installed. The house is closed in and roofed against the weather: No interior walls

are erected yet. Fifteen-pound building paper is laid out ahead of the underlayment particle board, which is put down over the subfloor wall to wall. This causes a full double-thick, uninterrupted floor, which provides greater overall strength and stiffness (Fig. 6-36). The labor time to install this top layer is a small fraction of what it is to fit and install it when all the interior partitions are in place (the conventional manner). Caution must be exercised when removing the braces (Fig. 6-37). Take down only one at a time. Reset it in reverse. Attach the lower end to a stud side and the upper end to a rafter or ceiling joist at about a

FIGURE 6-36 The open building system postpones erection of interior partitions until after closing. This system makes underlayment installation simple and fast.

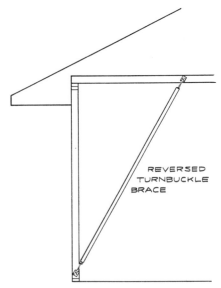

REVERSED TURNBUCKLE BRACE

FIGURE 6-37 Turnbuckle wall braces are removed from the floor-to-wall position and replaced from wall to lower chord one at a time as each is contacted by the underlayment being installed (open-concept construction).

60° angle to the floor. In this formation the entire floor is clear to be floored with the underlayment particle board.

The open interior framing system requires that all precut studs for partitions be shortened by an amount of the thickness of the underlayment floor material. There is more description of this system in Chapter 7.

The double overall floor surface that results from this system is made possible by the use of roof trusses. The unbroken double floor in conjunction with roof trusses eliminates the requirement for doubling of joists under partitions. Even so, it is still a good practice to stiffen the floor under parallel partitions by placing at least three blocks between the joists.

The conventional system of installing underlayment sheets involves custom fitting in and out and around all the partitions. It is a long, time-consuming task of cutting and fitting. Many edges of the cut sheets do not end over joists. Their nail base will be only the flexible sheathing.

CODING EXCEPTIONAL FEATURES

One of the time-consuming nuisances on a floor job comes later, when cuts for openings are required. It helps immensely where liberal use of a red carpenter's crayon has been made to mark and code joist locations. Mark boundaries of all corners of openings on the sheathing as it is being laid or make the necessary cuts immediately. Place a full or partial X from corner to corner. Outline joist spacing blocks, on the surface, in the immediate vicinity of future plumbing vents. Surface-mark double joists, crossing headers, and all exceptions to the common joist locations. Outline both protracted sides of the member so that there is no confusion as to which side of the line the hidden component is below. In general, remove as many mysteries as possible with graphics and bold notations. The job will then move along smoothly with minimum time loss and guessing.

REVIEW TOPICS

1. Of the two wooden classifications of floor girders, which is used by far the most today?

2. Of the two I-beam shapes of steel girders, which is the most versatile for residential floor construction?

3. Describe the advantages and disadvantages of a steel girder.

4. Explain the arrangement of the individual pieces of a built-up girder as if telling someone who is building a girder for the first time.

5. Explain what should be done to a board component of a built-up girder that has a noticeable crook.

6. Choose a floor plan, apply the girder table of maximum spans to the dimensions, and determine (a) the girder size, and (b) the distance between columns (in full feet—7, 8, 9, or 10). In a class situation the teacher may assign a specific problem for each student.

7. Make a bill of materials (an itemized list) of all the lumber needed for the girder in Topic 6.

8. Name the three basic component parts of a box or platform framework.

9. Explain why anchor bolt locations must be planned to coordinate with sill board lengths and joist locations before the foundation wall is constructed. Include in your explanation the rules for placement and the reason for not singly running down the wall with bolts on maximum spacing only.

10. Describe the difference between the nominal span of floor joists and clear span.

11. Explain why a conventional stick-built rafter system causes more bearing weight to be imposed on the floor girder.

12. Explain several methods of strengthening a floor under a parallel partition.

13. Explain the importance of placing a bridge block on top the sill between joists that straddle a partition above.

14. List the framing order of assembly for a floor opening that must be followed when headers and tails are supported by nails only.

15. Explain why "layering" of Styrofoam in a floor is preferred practice instead of installing a single thickness throughout.

16. Explain why wood bridging should be cut about a 1/4" shorter than the full diagonal distance between joists.

17. Why should the lower ends of bridging be left unattached when initially nailed on at the top?

18. How should underlayment sheets be started so that all the expansion cracks between the sheathing are covered?

19. Describe (a) the labor advantage and (b) the structural advantage of the open building concept (no partitions before close-in).

Chapter 7
WALL FRAMING

CONVENTIONAL WALL FRAMING

Wall-framing systems have not changed much in the past half century. The introduction of manufactured sheet materials for sheathing started the trend toward regulated spacing of floor joists, wall studs, and roof rafters. Prior to the 1930s, the need for uniform spacing of these structural components was not as important because most of the sheathing on the framework was boards of 1 × 6 to 1 × 12 size. These boards were put on the frame wall horizontally or diagonally. Each board was simply cut to length at the vertical centerline of the last stud over which it passed.

Sheet Modulus

Lamination and veneering had been in practice in the furniture industry for a long time. It was not until synthetic, water-resistant glues were developed that laminated sheets were mass produced for sheathing. When the techniques became perfected, a suitable material for house construction emerged. It was called plywood. Thin layers of wood are pared from logs as they turn on large lathes. Several layers are laid alternately with their grains crossing at 90°. Hugh presses and rollers make it possible for large sheets of this layered wood to be laminated by assembly-line methods. The basic size of a plywood sheet is standardized at 4′ × 8′. This plywood modulus set the standard for other materials that followed. The affect on floor, wall, and roof framing was to create a spacing technique that had to be followed if the builder intended to use plywood for shea-

thing. The motivation to use large sheet materials was keen because plywood was stronger (eliminated the need for some bracing), went on quicker, did not shrink a lot or leave many long exposed cracks, and was convenient to haul and store.

Soon, other sheet materials were developed. They were made from the fibers of plants such as cornstalks and other types of pulp. They were generally referred to as fiberboard, beaverboard, Celotex (a trade name), and blackboard. Early forms became noted for excess moisture absorption. The trapped dampness caused paint to peel from siding that was placed over it. When this problem was solved by asphalt impregnation, the use of fiberboard became common. "Blackboard" held the stage for many years as a suitable sheathing. It and other sheet materials firmly established the need for uniform stud spacing. Studs need to be placed so that the sheets will fit with little or no waste.

Studs

A *stud* is a vertical, structural (load-bearing) member of a frame wall. A group of studs held together with upper and lower horizontal plates make up the frame. The studs perform two functions. One is to support and transfer the weight of the ceilings and roof to the foundation. The other function is to provide a rigid skeleton to hold materials that will stand up to the wind and will shelter its occupants from undesirable weather. The most common stud module presently being used is the 2 × 4 "precut." It is a standardized

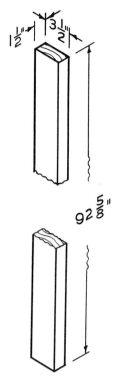

FIGURE 7-1 Actual dimensions of the modular uniform precut 2 × 4 stud.

size of 1 1/2″ × 3 1/2″ × 92 5/8″ (Fig. 7-1). The 2 × 6 stud wall, with its superior insulating capacity, is gaining favor. The 2 × 4 still accounts for the vast majority of sales. Other innovative exterior wall designs, such as the *double wall*, may be expected to gain in popularity as fuel costs continue to be a major consumer concern. These changes will not affect the basic spacing system, however, as the designs must adapt to available materials, and not the other way around. That is why study and comprehension of Part 1 are so important to the designer.

Plates

The term *plate* is a general name used to describe a component of a framework that lies flat, as compared to a header, which stands on edge. The novice builder is often confused by a variety of names and nicknames for parts of a house. Often the terminology is regional, having been handed down from one generation to the next. The old sailor called the forecastle of the ship the "focsle." In the construction business, the footing is sometimes the "footer," the sole plate is the "bottom" plate. It is better to know as many names as one can than to be limited to a so-called "correct" vocabulary. The important element in the construction business is to be able to communicate with the crew and the suppliers. There are several plate designations which tell us where these flat members are and what their function is (Fig. 7-2).

The sill plate is the lowest wood member of a frame structure. It rests on the foundation. The ends of the floor joists and the perimeter header bear on the sill. Its function and use are described in Chapter 6.

The sole plate is the bottom horizontal member of a frame wall. It performs several functions. The sole and the upper plate are the first members on which the stud spacing is laid out when wall framing begins. These two plates become the indexes for the placement of the studs, windows, and doors. The sole functions as a spacing board to which the studs can be attached. The sole is also a backup board to which finishing materials are secured after the frame is erected. Wallboard, paneling, and baseboard are solidly backed along the floor line by the sole plate.

Years ago, when balloon framing and wet plaster were the mode, a separate backer board or plaster ground served this purpose. A nominal-1″ board was nailed to the studs at floor level all around the rooms. The height (width) of the board was usually 1″ or so smaller than the anticipated baseboard height. For example, a 1 × 10 would be ripped in half to provide a nominal 5″ backup for a 6″ baseboard. The other function, called grounding, was to provide a solid guide for the plasterer to scrape off the excess undercoating and finish lime coating. The early wood lath and later, gypsum rock lath made up 3/8″ of the space, which left a space of about 3/8″ to be filled with plaster. The early 1″ board was sometimes a full 7/8″ thick. By midcentury it had declined to 13/16″ and then to 3/4″. In some of the more expensive woods, it continues to get thinner. Whatever the thickness used, the grounding board provided the standard of plaster depth throughout the house.

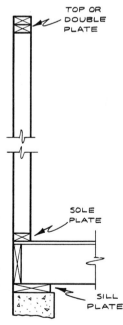

FIGURE 7-2 The term "plate" generally means a structural member lying flat which supports another part.

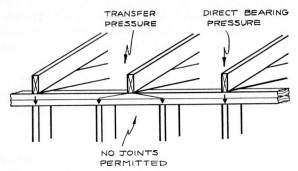

TRANSFER
PRESSURE

DIRECT BEARING
PRESSURE

NO JOINTS
PERMITTED

FIGURE 7-3 The double top plate transfers the roof weight to the studs. It must support every other truss when studs are on 16″ spacing and trusses on 24″ spacing.

The coming of the current technique of *box framing* covered with drywall materials has rendered the baseboard backer and plaster ground obsolete. The sole has taken over the nail-backing function.

For those students who are learning construction language for the first time, a suitable mental reference can be made. The sole of the wall is like the sole of your shoe. It is the first thing on top of the floor.

The top plate (Fig. 7-3) is sometimes called the *double plate* or the *upper plate*. The top plate forms the upper horizontal member of the frame wall. In positions of bearing stress, the top plate may be called upon to transfer a weight load to a stud location. This occurs when rafters and ceiling joists are not correctly placed over studs. This misalignment will occur on alternate roof trusses (every other one) when walls are framed on 16″ centers while the roof is framed on 24″-centered spacing. It may also occur when either the wall or the roof spacing is incorrect (one may be correct while the other is mismatched). The role of the upper plate is not intended as a bearing support. The wall stud is the main load supporter in a well-designed plan.

The top plate is actually a set of two plates, an upper and a lower piece. The system is designed to facilitate the locking together of corners and intersecting walls. The lower pieces of the top plate are all assembled to the various walls and partitions first. Then the walls are erected. The upper members of the top plate are then lapped over the butt joints of the lower top plate junctions. This forms a splice across the junction and holds it together. The top piece of the double plate may be installed prior to raising in those places that will not interfere with the erection. The effectiveness of the lapped joint is dependent on the quality of the nailing that takes place. This subject will be explained in detail in the sections that follow dealing with assembling and nailing.

The lower member of the top plate performs the same indexing function as the sole. The stud spacing marks will appear in the identical positions as those on the sole.

In foregoing paragraphs it was explained how to clamp or nail the lower member of the top plate to the sole temporarily for the purpose of indexing identical locations of studs and openings. Only with this perfect duplication of stud locations can a frame wall be made with parallel and plumb members.

The upper member of the top plate is of negligible structural utility. Its only intended function is to interlock the intersections. This can be achieved at much less expense with sheet metal gussets (nail plates). Building a frame wall with a single-piece top plate, however, requires rigid adherence to the in-line bearing concept. In some localities a double top plate is mandated. To sustain the present 97 1/8″ total height of the current wall design with only one plate would require a longer stud (94 1/8″) than the precut standard of 92 5/8″. This is not a serious obstacle, as the carpenter can jig cut many studs from 8′ stock in a few hours. Even when precut studs are used there is no great adaptation required. The bottom sheets of drywall will require shortening a little, as the total frame height will be 95 5/8″. A full-scale breakthrough is not likely to occur with the contract or track builder as long as the 2 × 4 framing modulus continues. The potential for saving gains rapidly as the trend toward the 6″ wall or the double 2 × 4 frame wall increases.

Stud Spacing Modulus

After the 4′ spacing modulus was established, it soon followed that 16″ would be the most used division for the placement of structural members. In terms of materials coordination, 24″ spacing works satisfactorily but it does cause some problems of surface flexibility of the materials that go on the framework. Siding, sheathing, drywall, and paneling are all apt to buckle and bow under certain stresses. Some 24″-spacing applications may be considered adequate. Unattached outbuildings such as garages and sheds are sometimes built with 24″-spaced studs as an economy measure.

Centering is the term used to indicate lumber components that are spaced equal distances apart. During the transition period from board sheathing to sheet materials, the girth of a milled stud was 1 5/8″ × 3 5/8″. The spacing modulus applies to all the studs in a wall except the corners at the end of the walls. The first and last space will be measured from the surface (outer edge) of the corner stud instead of its center (Fig. 7-4). The old-time carpenter would place the end of his tape or folding rule on the end of the plate and put a mark every 16″. He would then center the studs over the mark. Some carpenters seeking a little more accuracy would make the marks 13/16″ to the right or left of the 16″ modules. This indicated the edge of the stud. An X was then placed on the side of the line where the stud was to stand. This method provided a visible mark

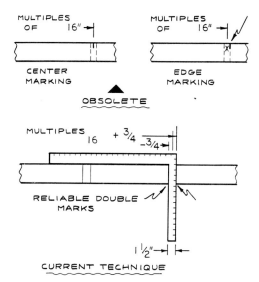

FIGURE 7-4 Old marking systems are improved on by marking along both sides of the coordinated tongue of the framing square.

for stud alignment. The edge-marking method was made easier in the late 1960s when stud thickness and width was revised to a standard of 1 1/2" × 3 1/2". The tongue on the framing square is 1 1/2" wide. By establishing a mark 3/4" (half the stud thickness) both left and right of the centering marks, the tongue of the square can be laid over the space between the marks and traced along both sides. This makes it a simple matter to place the stud between the two marks. Errors are minimized because there is never a question as to which side of a mark the stud should go. It goes between the two marks. Modulus figures are 16", 32", 48", and so on (adding 16" each time). Examples of where to mark are 15 1/4" and 16 3/4", 31 1/4" and 32 3/4", and 47 1/4" and 48 3/4", and so on.

The choice between 16 or 24" spacing of studs depends on several things. There is no choice in a construction zone where the building code dictates 16" as the maximum. The largest percentage of houses constructed in the past half-century in the United States have exterior walls and interior partitions with studs on 16" centers. In addition to the feasibility of the system, it is also regarded as a standard of minimum practice.

Studs spaced 24" OC, although they may be adequate for vertical bearing support, pose some other considerations. Flexibility of surface-covering materials is one. When drywall (gypsum wallboard) was first introduced, the common modulus was the same as the plywood sheet, 4 × 8. Most jobs were done with 3/8"-thick board placed vertically. In this position there were no joints that were not backed up by solid wood, studs, and plates. A few years later, the manufacturers began to offer longer lengths. Now gypsum panels can be had in 2' increments from 8' to, and including, 16'. This makes it possible to cover any wall

16' or less in length with a single sheet in the upper half and a single sheet in the lower half. This system of placement is standard practice by professionals today. On studs 16" OC, the 1/2"-thick drywall is stiff enough to bridge the 14 1/2" space between the studs along the single, horizontal joint without solid backing. It is not stiff enough to span the 22 1/2" space between studs 24" OC. On the wider 24" centering, one stud less is used in each 4' of linear wall. For an uncovered wall, such as a garage with exposed studs, this would amount to a saving. Where drywall is to be used, some backer system is needed to provide support behind the cupped joint. Pressure, such as merely leaning on the wall at a point above or below this taped and compounded joint, will flex the drywall edge and crack the joint. There are a number of ways to reinforce this joint. They are explained in Chapter 12. It may be found that the 16"-OC spacing system is no more costly than the 24" system when all factors are taken into consideration.

BEARING ALIGNMENT

The strongest arrangement of structural components—floor joists, studs, and rafters—is one that places all members in a single vertical bearing line. This means that a roof rafter will bear on the upper plates directly over a stud. The stud will be positioned on the sole plate directly over a floor joist. In the days of board sheathing and plywood-sheathed houses, the frame wall was strengthened by the wood sheathing. Support of the compression weight of the ceiling and roof was improved. The direct-bearing philosophy was not as important or critical when wood sheathing was used. When fiberboard sheathing became common, the need for direct bearing became more significant. The vertical supporting ability of fiberboard is inferior to that of plywood. Styrofoam sheathing has no supporting capacity. It makes a lot of sense under the variable material usage of today's construction to routinely design and frame all structures with the direct alignment system.

There may be some compromise with combined spacing systems. Where studs are placed on 16" centers and roof trusses are conventionally placed on 24" centers, every other truss should be arranged to bear directly over a stud. This is a maximum allowable bearing modulus of 4'. It should be kept in mind and adhered to as a bearing philosophy. In many codes it is a stated requirement.

Marking the Plates

Spacing of frame wall studs must start from the same end of the foundation as the floor joists if bearing continuity is to be maintained. In Chapter 6 we dealt with the spacing of floor joists. When floor joists are butted and tied, a complete bearing continuity can be achieved by spacing the front and rear wall studs exactly as the joists are spaced. The studs on the front and rear are then positioned directly above the joists. Where the lapped joist system is used, the rear joists are usually the ones that are offset 1 1/2″. The studs on the rear should not be offset. They should be directly opposite the front wall studs. They will not bear directly over the joists at the rear of the house. They will be positioned the same as the studs on the front wall so that sheathing materials will fit. Remember that the end spaces are the oddballs. They are always less than the modulus and will vary from house to house depending on the wall-to-foundation lineup system that is used.

Mismatched framing may occur from front to rear walls where the house length is of nonmodular or split-modular length (2′ multiples). Any dimension that is not evenly divisible by 16″ will require extra care to see that the layout of the studs is begun from the same end or same side of the house for the walls that are opposite each other. Consider the consequences should this principle be ignored. A house length is 42′. This is a midmodular dimension, divisible by 2′ but not by 16″. It is half of the basic 4′ modulus. The studs on 16″ centers will net 31 1/2 spaces in the 42′ wall. The boss says to start your stud spacing from the left and work to the right. The first wall is framed and erected. The layout carpenter turns around and lays out the opposite wall from left to right. The second wall is assembled and erected. Ceiling joists and conventional rafters are put in place before it is discovered that the second wall is totally misaligned with the first. Rafters and ceiling joists on that side bear in the middle of the plate span between the studs. What has happened to cause such a mishap? Several elements are involved. One of them is the reverse-side syndrome. When the layout carpenter turned around to face the second wall, the spacing reversed. This characteristic pops up many times in building. It occurs anytime a layout is transferred to the back side of a panel. It happens frequently when cutting out light boxes, duplex outlets, and switch box openings in drywall and paneling. It happens when measurements are transferred from a location to a piece of material. The instruction from the boss was neither adequate nor complete. Granted, the layout person should be more knowledgable. On the other hand, instructions were followed to the letter. The situation could have been avoided with better instructions that conveyed both knowledge and clarity. ''We want the studs in this house to be spaced exactly opposite each other from front to rear and end to end. Start your spacing for the front and rear bearing walls from the south end of the house the same as you did for the floor joist. When we get to the roof, we will line it up the same way so that it will bear directly on the studs. Our half-sized end space in this 42′ wall will be on the north end on the front as well as the rear. As for the end walls, this is a gable roof design, so they are nonbearing. You may start the spacing from either

corner but make the two walls match as you did the front and rear. Any questions?'' A few more words, a minute or two more time, but the result is the avoidance of tear-down and do-over work or having to settle for a poorly done structural frame. *It pays to explain it adequately and to do it right the first time.*

Marking Wall Openings

The manner in which window and door openings are marked on the plates will depend on the style of header that is used. Where cripple studs are to be used above a header stud, centering locations are marked the same as if a full stud would be there. A large capital C is placed between the stud lines to indicate that a cripple stud goes there (Fig. 7-5). A cripple stud is any stud that is less than full length positioned above or below an opening.

No stud marks will appear above a uniform header. A *uniform header* is one that fills the whole space from the opening to the plate. There is no reason to have stud spacing marks on the upper plate when the uniform header is used. In fact, such marks will cause confusion. Full studs

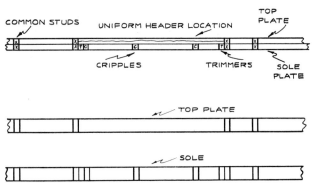

FIGURE 7-5 Cripples on top and bottom plates can be code marked with large letter Cs. Walls with uniform headers (2 × 12s) will have no stud marks on the top plate but will have cripple marks on the sole. Clamp or form nail the sole and lower top plate together face to face and mark across the edges. Transfer the location marks to the face of the plates.

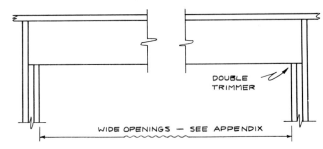

FIGURE 7-6 Exceptionally wide openings require double trimmers to provide 3″ of bearing for the weight placed on the header.

are apt to be thoughtlessly installed there and have to be removed. On each side of the opening, there will be a full stud and a shorter trimmer stud that supports the end of the header. The location of the trimmer may be indicated with a large T. Although there will be no nails applied in this space, the T mark serves to indicate that an opening will be left from that point on until a duplicate T mark is encountered farther along the plate. Some layout carpenters will draw a gently waved line along the middle of the plate from T to T to show that a window or door goes there. Others will print the word "window" or "door" in the space.

The rough-opening size (horizontal width) is the distance between the adjacent faces of the trimmers. The header length will be the opening distance plus 3". Each end of the header bears upon the 1 1/2" thickness of the trimmer, hence the 3" addition for the header length (Fig. 7-6). Exceptionally wide openings may demand double trimmers under each end of the header (check your applicable code). Garage door openings for 16 and 18' doors should always have double trimmers. The 3" bearing that this provides would never be adjudged excessive, especially where the weight of rafters and roof bear on the header by design. In these cases there will be two T-marked rectangles for the trimmers on each side of the opening.

Cripple stud spacing marks will usually be required on the sole plate below window openings. The exception would be windows that extend to the floor. These marks are needed in most cases because short cripple studs will be positioned there to support the rough sill. The rough sill forms the lower horizontal frame member of the rough opening. Some partnership and small-crew framers will omit the rough sill and lower cripples until the wall frame has been erected. This reduces the weight of the frame to be lifted and raised.

It is simpler and more accurate to transfer the rough window sill length by tracing than by measuring. Measuring always increases the probability of error. The sill board is held below the header location or on the sole after studs are nailed in place. The length mark is traced along the face of the trimmer onto the sill. *Never measure an opening between trimmer faces anywhere but at the sole or header* (Fig. 7-7). Confirm the spacing of the opening by checking the length of your sill board mark on the opposite end of the opening (sole or header location) from where it was traced. Bowed trimmer and stud assemblies will produce inaccurate measurements across an opening. These bowed members can be pulled in or pushed out by a rough sill of the correct length. On the other hand, a sill that is cut to fit its precise location will polarize the opening when nailed in place. When the distance between the trimmers is greater or smaller than it should be due to the bowed studs, the result will be a nonrectangular opening.

Omit stud location marks from the soleplate where a

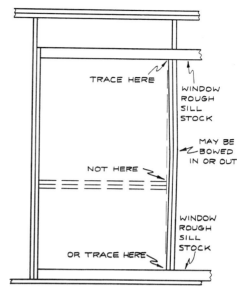

FIGURE 7-7 Trace a rough sill next to the header or sole, not where it will be installed.

door is to be. This portion of the sole will be sawed out after the wall frame has been erected and the soleplate has been nailed down. No stud marks are placed between the T marks where the trimmers will be for a door opening. The wavy line or the lettered word "door" on the sole between trimmers at a door location serves as a reminder that this portion of the sole should not be nailed to the floor after the frame is erected.

Partition posts (Ts) are marked with a large capital P (Fig. 7-8). The block located between the two stud components is marked with two diagonal lines from corner to corner or a large letter B. Where a partition is coordinated with a common stud location (the modular savings system) the block and extra stud will be adjacent to an existing stud location mark. The common stud mark is a component of the partition T post. In such a case, only the block and

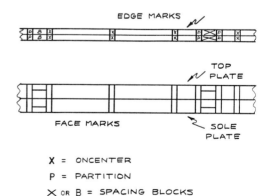

X = ONCENTER
P = PARTITION
X OR B = SPACING BLOCKS

FIGURE 7-8 Marking code for partition posts that are modularly placed and for those that are in between on-center studs.

extra stud are marked with the diagonals and the P. Where the partition intersects the wall between the common studs and touches neither, both stud components surrounding the block are marked with Ps between the lines.

Interior Stud Spacing

Basically, interior wall stud spacing follows the same routine as the exterior wall except for the starting points. The starting points will differ for those partitions which are parallel to the long outer walls from those which are parallel with the joist direction. Assume for the following example that all joists are running the same direction throughout the floor and ceiling.

Walls running parallel to the outer walls on the long sides of the house are said to be bearing walls. They are considered load bearing because the ends of the ceiling joists will place their weight on them. Because of this load, it is good practice to maintain the direct-bearing system by grouping the studs directly under the rafters or ceiling joists. To arrange this continuity, the starting place for spacing of the interior studs in this bearing wall (zero point on the tape measure) will be the building line at the same end of the house from which the floor joists and outer wall spacing began. In practice, the spacing marks can be made by transfer instead of measurement. The interior sole plate and upper plate are laid flat on the subfloor along side the exterior wall. The framing square is placed with its body (the 24″ side) along the edge of the new plates. The tongue of the square (the 16″ side) crosses the plates and touches the surface of the stud in the exterior wall. Mark both sides of each stud location. If the wall has already been sheathed, use a combination square. This method will assure duplicate stud locations.

Care must be taken not to duplicate errors. A misplaced or twisted stud can throw off the marks significantly. When it is noted that a stud is not perfectly aligned over the marks, the transfer should be made with the combination square (Fig. 7-9). Set the blade to extend only 7″,

just enough to cover the two interior indexing plates. Make the transfer from the stud mark instead of from the twisted stud. Why not use the combination square throughout the job? The adjustable part of the combination square only bears about 3 1/2″ on the edge surface of the plate. This is not enough for continual accuracy. Any small surface imperfection on the edge will throw off the accuracy of a square mark. For the most part, the framing square or a foot square will produce the most consistent accuracy wherever it can be used.

The transfer method of marking just described is particularly accurate where a centrally located interior bearing partition extends the full length of the house. It is equally accurate when the partition starts at one end but does not go the full length. An interior partition that touches neither end may still be marked by the transfer method. It is laid alongside the exterior wall sole starting at a point the same distance away from the end wall as it will be positioned when installed. Keep in mind that the objective is to have the ceiling joists bear over the studs, not in between them.

The interior frame wall will not have any openings in common with the window openings in the exterior wall. Since only the common stud locations are being transferred, it will be necessary to determine which of the two side-by-side studs is the OC stud at a window location. It could be either the full stud or the trimmer stud. To complicate the picture further, there may be a third member there, a cripple stud holding up the end of the rough sill. An experienced framer can usually tell by sight which piece is equidistant from the common studs to right and left. To be assured of an accurate transfer, the framing square blade (16″ long) can be held with one end in the center of the stud adjacent to the opening. The other end will be in the center of the OC member whose location is to be transferred.

Partitions that are parallel to floor and ceiling joists are laid out differently. There is no roof weight borne on partitions in this position. They are classed as nonbearing. From a load-bearing point of view, it is of little significance from which end the stud placement begins. Consistency of placement, however, is recommended. For example, when all parallel partitions begin their stud spacing from the inside surface of the exterior frame wall, a consistent pattern is established. After the wall-covering material is installed, the location of the studs is lost to sight. There are ways of finding a stud, such as tapping and listening for a solid sound or using a magnetic stud finder, which searches for hidden nails. This type of search usually ends with the necessity of punching several holes to pin down the stud location. Spacing all studs from the exterior wall toward the center of the house makes it a simple matter at a later date to locate a stud. One simply measures from the interior surface of the exterior wall along the par-

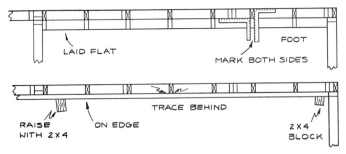

FIGURE 7-9 Transfer spacing marks from modular exterior walls to interior bearing partitions by using a combination square or foot square on top of the sole and partition.

tition. To establish any stud center after a wall is finished, it is necessary only to subtract the thickness of the wall covering from any of the OC figures (16, 32, 48″, etc.). Take, for example, an exterior wall covered with 1/2″ drywall. Measuring from this intersecting surface of the exterior wall it will be found that the centers of the studs are on 15 1/2, 31 1/2, 47 1/2, 63 1/2″, and so on. With this type of spacing consistency, many future problems and mysteries are solved. Picture-hanging nails can be placed with unerring accuracy. The nails along the top edge of baseboards will hit the stud every time.

POSTS

Corner Posts

When the use of wood plaster lath and wet plaster was common practice, it was not so important that a frame wall be perfectly flat and straight. The "brown" and "scratch coats" of plaster could be used as a universal straightener. With the coming of large sheet materials such as drywall and paneling, it became more important to have a straight frame wall. The quality of straightness is largely determined in the framing stage of building. Some of the old corner post designs did not line up precisely with the adjoining wall surfaces, a situation of minor significance with wet plaster. For this and other reasons, they are unsuited to modern framing, where dry materials hold the current stage. Figure 7-10 shows examples of obsolete corner post assemblies. These are nonfeasible from the standpoint of cost, warpage (the 4 × 4), or adaptability to drywall nailing and alignment.

A single system of forming a stud corner dominates today's construction practice (Fig. 7-11). The corner may be preassembled as a three-stud unit with spacer blocks, or it may be coordinated as two studs separated by blocks placed in one wall while the third member is placed at the end of the adjoining wall frame. The latter method is a little

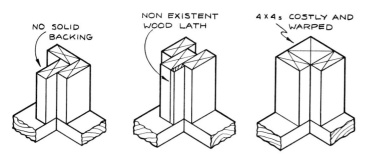

OBSOLETE CORNER POSTS

FIGURE 7-10 Obsolete corner post assemblies are no longer feasible.

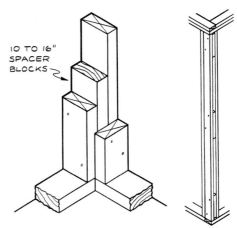

FIGURE 7-11 Most common corner post design currently in use.

simpler at erection time. The sole of the second wall does not have to be bumped under the end stud, which has been nailed to the corner of the first wall.

Studs in the corners should be straight. Many future complications will be avoided on the interior and exterior when the framer takes a little time to select straight studs for the corner assembly. Once the three studs in a corner are nailed together, there is no flexibility and no way to straighten them after erection. When culling the stud pile it may be worthwhile to label each stud with a large letter on the face near the center. A large grease crayon or felt marker is a handy instrument that fits in the tool belt. Capital letters will suffice to indicate the nature of the warpage: S for straight, C for crooked, B for bowed, T for twisted, and CB for crooked and bowed. Crooked, bowed, and twisted studs can be used in flat areas of the wall if their deformity is not too great (about 1/8″ of deflection is maximum). Only straight studs should be considered for corners and for trimmer studs next to door and window frames.

Assembling the corner post requires careful alignment of all the members. It is important that an attitude of perfection be present. Sloppy alignment will cause much difficult planing, chiseling, or hacking away with a hatchet to remove high surfaces that were not properly aligned. Should this remedial work be ignored, the problem will extend into the finishing stage of construction. Siding and corner trim will be affected and sometimes the eave soffit, frieze board, and other trim molds. It pays to do it right from the start. *The ends and edges must be perfectly aligned.*

10d common or box nails are adequate for nailing the studs to the spacer blocks. 16d nails are longer than necessary. They will go through two thicknesses of 2 × 4 and protrude, making it difficult to align the second stud on the blocks. The diameter is also objectionably large. There are usually four nails penetrating each block. The blocks split easily when the nail diameter is large or the nail is placed too close to the ends of the block. Remember the end-grain nailing rule. Stay back from the ends as much as the thickness of the board (1 1/2") or more. There are usually three block spacers in the corner post. A good nailing practice is to stay back away from the ends of the center block about 2". On the outer ends of the top and bottom block, it is wise to stay back about 2 1/2 to 3" for another reason. There will be 16d nails going through the sole plate and the upper plate into the ends of the studs. 16d nails are 3 1/2" long. They will penetrate the end grain of the studs a full 2" or slightly more. The horizontal nails through the face of the stud into the blocks should not be close to the nails from the plates. If these nails are driven close to each other, it adds to the probability of splitting the stud.

The blocks that are near the end should be recessed from the ends of the studs about 1/16 to 1/8". This will help prevent the possibility of the block slipping out beyond the end of the stud while hammering. Side alignment is accomplished by holding the thumb on one side and the fingers on the other side of the joint while driving the nail.

There are two mechanical ways to hold corner post components in place while nailing them together. One is done by using a wooden clamp called a handscrew. Handscrews are manufactured by two leading companies, Jorgensen and Hargrave. The builder should learn to operate this type of clamp the same way each time. Grasp the center screw handle in the left hand. Hold it still. Hold the outer screw handle in the right hand. Rotate it in a clockwise direction as you would close a faucet. The clamp closes. Rotate it counterclockwise and the clamp opens. To align the edges of the stud and block, the jaws of the handscrew must be parallel when the final pressure is applied to

the outer screw. There are many uses for the handscrew on a construction job. Traditionally, the handscrew has been thought of as a cabinetmaker's tool. One or two handscrews at the building site can sometimes be as useful as another set of hands.

Another alignment device is the corner post jig (Fig. 7-12). It can be quickly assembled at the site from available scraps. A 2 × 6 block is nailed to each edge of a stud about 1' from the end. Another block (2 × 4 or 2 × 6) is nailed inside this trough. It is placed on edge and nailed from the bottom of the trough. This block must have a square end facing the center of the stud. This forms a stop so that the two studs of the corner post will have their ends in precise alignment. This precision alignment of the stud ends is mandatory to avoid an assembled post that is longer than the other studs in the wall. Another pair of 2 × 6 blocks is nailed to the stud edges at a central point to form a guide for nailing the center spacer block. These guide blocks will straddle a point half the length of a precut stud (46 5/16"), or approximately 46" from the stop block. This jig may be used over and over again and taken from one project to another if 10d nails are used in the fabrication of the corner post.

Some builders standardize their framing nails in the wall and use only the 16d sinker. This nail is a compromise. It is coated with resin, which adds to the holding power. It is 1/4" shorter than the common 16d nail. At 3 1/4" long, 1/4" of the nail point will be exposed when squarely driven through two thicknesses of 2 × 4. The exposure can be avoided by angling the nail about 20°. The objectionable exposure can also be overcome by putting all three component layers in the jig at once. In this position 16d box nails may be used. Their length is the same as the common nail (3 1/2") but the diameter is smaller and less apt to cause splitting. With all three layers in the jig, the nail points of both sinkers and box 16d common nails penetrate the third layer, the lower stud in the assembly. The penetration is not deep enough to hold the lower member onto the blocks securely. Care must be taken when revolving the assembly in the form so that it does not fall apart. Lift under the bottom stud as you would carry a sack full of groceries.

Nailing pattern and consistency are important, to avoid driving one nail directly on top of another, causing a double-wedge affect. As you face the jig, stop block in front of you, place the two nails as you would write on a page. The first one will be in the upper left 2 1/2 to 3" down from the end. The second nail will be in the lower right about 2" away from the end grain of the block under the stud. When the post is rotated to nail the opposite stud, follow the same pattern (upper left, lower right). It will be noted that the nails thus applied go into opposite corners of the blocks, thereby minimizing the tendency to split the

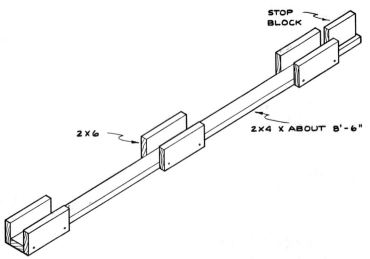

STOP
BLOCK

2 X 6

2X4 X ABOUT 8'-6"

FIGURE 7-12 Reusable jig for assembling corner posts in perfect alignment.

blocks. Nail all blocks before rotating the assembly. Then rotate the assembly and nail the other side. This nailing pattern places four nails into each block. The end part of each nail will occupy a corner of the block alone, thus avoiding split blocks with protruding edges.

Sometimes the framer is forced to use the oversized 16d common nail to assemble corner posts for one reason or another. When this is the case, the nailing routine will be the same for the first side. When the assembly is rotated, put just one nail through the stud into the center of each block underneath. This technique leaves the block with three nails through the block in a diagonal pattern. The assembly is put into the wall frame with the six-nailed side facing out and the three-nailed side facing in toward the next OC stud.

Partition Posts

The same changes that brought about the current corner post design affected the intersection post design. Spacer blocks used to be placed flat between two studs. This caused the post to be 4 7/8″ wide (3 pieces 1 5/8″). When the stud from the intersecting wall was nailed to the center of this assembly, it left a nailing surface of 5/8″ on each side. This was an adequate surface to which the wood lath could be nailed. The lath installer had to proceed in a sequence. Lath was nailed to the 5/8″ surface in the corner first. Nailing lath to the other wall first, where the 1 5/8″ stud surface existed, would fill up so much of the adjoining 5/8″ space that it was not possible to nail lath to the remainder satisfactorily. The same situation held true for the rock lath period of history (16″ × 48″ gypsum board lath). Then came the so-called ''Boston stud,'' with its 1 1/2″ × 3 1/2″ girth. This size reduced the lath bearing surface to 1/2″. All lath in use was now either metal or gypsum (rock lath). It became more difficult to place a lath nail in such a narrow space without crushing the gypsum. The standardization of the 1 1/2″ stud thickness rendered the flat block formation of the intersection post obsolete. The current design of the intersection corner post simply places the spacer blocks on edge (Fig. 7-13a). This variation of the former assembly nets a full 1 1/2″ nailing surface on all adjacent sides of the corners. It accommodates all types of wall-covering materials with no required assembly sequence. Since both surfaces at the corner are 1 1/2″ wide, a full inch of space remains after the gypsum wallboard is nailed to the first wall.

Assembly of the partition post is accomplished by standing the blocks on edge and nailing a stud to them. Balancing the stud on the edges of the blocks is made easier when a 2 × 4 is placed on edge crosswise under the stud. This procedure will prevent the stud from falling off the blocks while the nailing takes place. Nails should be stag-

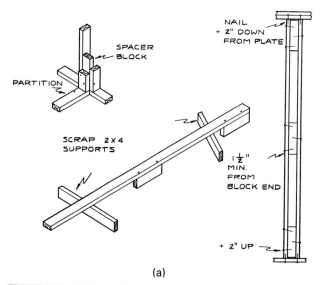

(a)

(b)

FIGURE 7-13 (a) The predominant intersection post design features a 1 1/2″ nailing surface throughout. A scrap block helps support the stud while nailing it to each spacer block. (b) The third layer of 1″ Styrofoam is installed from the interior side. Two layers have already been installed from the exterior side.

gered enough so that those coming from opposite sides will not be in the same place in the block. Remember to stay an adequate distance from the ends of the block so that splitting does not occur, and from the ends of the studs to avoid plate nails.

Insulating the Post Cavity

Insulation of walls is explained in a later chapter. It is important to break in here with a cautionary note. Using the intersection post just described in the exterior wall is frequently the vehicle to significant heat and cool loss. To avoid such a loss, it is imperative that the exterior side of the intersection post be fully insulated before sheathing is installed. This important detail is probably omitted more often than not. In this day and age of high fuel costs, few, if any, houses are being built without insulation, yet many, if not most, do not contain insulation in the cavities behind the corner posts and the partition posts. *It must be done before sheathing is installed.*

Several types of insulation may be used for this purpose. Batts or blankets may be cut and friction fit into the openings. When using these fiberglass wool types, the rain should be kept off. This mandates that the insulation be installed the same day that sheathing is installed. If for any reason the insulated cavities cannot be sheathed at once, the insulation should be covered with building paper or plastic film. Run the covering over the top of the plates so that the rain is shed.

When a wood floor has been insulated with Styrofoam cut from 4 × 8 sheets, there will be 8′ strips left over, which are ideal for insulating the posts (Fig. 7-13b). Floor joists on 16″ centers call for Styrofoam strips 14 1/2″ wide. Ripping three of these from a 4′ sheet leaves a piece that is a little over 4″ wide. For intersection post cavities rip these strips about 1/32 over 3 1/2″, the width of spacer blocks. Obviously, these strips may be cut from full sheets of Styrofoam. Custom fit a piece between the blocks in the upper and lower sections. Next cut two pieces (when using 1 ″-thick material) to a length of 92 3/4″. These are pressed in full length between the studs. The distance from the inside surface of the blocks to the exterior side of the 2 × 4 stud will be 2″, so the two layers will be flush with the underside of the sheathing. Make the Styrofoam strips just wide enough so that they can be pressed in snugly with a block of wood. Purposely make the strips about an 1/8″ longer than the precut stud. Press the ends in first, leaving the center bowed out. Press in the center with a 2 × 4 block held flat against the Styrofoam. This will cause the ends to press snugly against the plates and the sides against the studs. It creates a friction-fit, nearly airtight, seal. When done properly, no fastening will be required. Corner studs are custom plugged with 1 1/2″ Styrofoam strips in a similar manner. The three layers of

1″ Styrofoam net an R factor of about 16, which is greater than that of 3 1/2″ of fiberglass wool.

HEADERS

Wall Headers over Openings

An opening in a framed wall requires a structural beam across the top to take the place of the studs that would otherwise support the load. This member is called a *header*. Its function is to transfer the weight on it out to its ends and down the trimmers toward the foundation. The usual load is the roof, with all its materials that bear on the specific area. The size of the header that is required is in direct relation to the weight of the load that is imposed on it. This in turn relates to the specific width of each opening. One might think of it in this way. Each time an opening width is enough larger to require the removal of another stud, a structural supportive post, it may need a larger header to take over for the lost support. The most common frame wall depth is 3 1/2″. It is controlled by the stud width. Therefore, the only way to gain additional strength in a header is to advance the height of the board(s) as it is seen in position. The most common header in use is fabricated from two pieces of dimension stock. Each piece is 1 1/2″ thick. Headers may range in vertical size from 4″ stock up to, and including, 12″ stock. The actual sizes are 3 1/2, 5 1/2, 7 1/4, 9 1/4, and 11 1/4″.

Wall Header Designs

There are several header designs that are adequate for the purpose. Some of these styles have been in use for many years. Others are new, unnamed, and sometimes common to a particular region. Some are actually experimental, such as those being invented for the 2 × 6 wall and the double 2 × 4 wall. In the sections to follow, clear definitions will be presented. Some logic is cited for each design feature. Many building codes do not include any reference to new framing techniques. It becomes the architect's or the builder's role to convince the inspector of the feasibility of a design that does not appear in the written code.

A starting point for any design may be had by using a recognized header stress table such as the FHA-MPS model on page 129. Note that three columns are presented. Each qualifies a different load range category. Several elements affect the load. They are the amount of slope in the roof (lower-sloping roofs are subjected to greater live loads, such as deeper snow), the type and amount of trussing that transfers weight to or away from outer walls, and the presence of interior bearing walls, which share some of the load. An understanding of what imposes a load or relieves one will be helpful in gaining a sense for sound construction.

WINDOW AND DOOR HEADERS FOR EXTERIOR OPENINGS

Width of structure	Header size (on edge)	* Roof Construction		
		Roof joist with bearing partition, slope 3 in 12 or less / Brace rafters with bearing partition, Slope over 3 in 12	Rafters with bearing partition, Slope over 3 in 12 / Trussed rafters, Slope 3 in 12 or less	Trussed rafters slope over 3 in 12 / Rafters with bearing partition, Habitable space
		1 Story and Second Floor of 2 Story		
Up to 26 feet wide (span)	2 - 2x4s	3' 6"	3' 0"	2' 6"
	2 - 2x6s	6' 6"	5' 0"	4' 6"
	2 - 2x8s	8' 6"	7' 0"	6' 0
	2 - 2x10s	11' 0"	8' 6"	* 8' 0"
	2 - 2x12s	13' 6"	*10' 6"	* 9' 6"
		1½ or 2 Story		
	2 - 2x4s	2' 6"	------	------
	2 - 2x6s	4' 6"	4' 0"	3' 6"
	2 - 2x8s	6' 0"	5' 6"	5' 0"
	2 - 2x10s	7' 6"	* 6' 6"	* 6' 0"
	2 - 2x12s	9' 0"	* 8' 0"	* 7' 6"
		1 Story and Second Floor of 2 Story		
26 to 32 feet wide (span)	2 - 2x4s	3' 0"	2' 6"	------
	2 - 2x6s	6' 0"	4' 6"	4' 0"
	2 - 2x8s	8' 0"	6' 0"	5' 6"
	2 - 2x10s	*10' 0"	* 8' 0"	* 7' 0"
	2 - 2x12s	*12' 0"	* 9' 6"	* 8' 6"
		1½ or 2 Story		
	2 - 2x4s	------	------	------
	2 - 2x6s	4' 0"	3' 6"	3' 6"
	2 - 2x8s	5' 6"	5' 0"	4' 6"
	2 - 2x10s	* 7' 0"	* 6' 0"	* 5' 6"
	2 - 2x12s	* 8' 6"	* 7' 6"	* 7' 0"

Note: The above spans are based on allowable fiber stresses as follows: For 2 x 4s, 800 psi; for 2 x 6s and larger, 1,200 psi. These allowable stresses are average values taking into consideration upgrading for doubling of members. Where 2 x 4s having allowable fiber stress exceeding 800 are used, the spans for 2 x 4s may be increased by 20 percent. Where conditions vary from these assumptions, design the headers in accordance with standard engineering practice.

* Triple studs at jamb opening; headers to bear on two 2 x 4 trimmers on each side.

* The roof construction affects the bearing weight placed on a header. Read the header span maximum in the column under the roof type and pitch (slope). Crossmatch this column with the house width and story height categories.

Historic headers start with the *solid beam* header. The solid one-piece header has disappeared from most conventional building sites, for two reasons. The cost of timbers, as this size of lumber is sometimes called, has risen so dramatically that it is not an economically feasible unit to use. The second reason is that solid beams of the wood species generally used for headers warp so much that it is rarely possible to install them without a lot of remedial work during and after installation. The other historic header is still prevalent in many regions of the country. It is known as the built-up header, or the two-piece spaced header, or the cripple header (since it requires cripple studs above). A better name for it would be the *span* header because the size of its girth is dictated by the width of the opening over which it must span.

The span header (Fig. 7-14) is constructed by laying two header pieces face to face but separated by 1/2" or 3/8" spacers. The spacers are usually rectangles of plywood. There should be enough spacers to have one every 24 to 32" apart in addition to one at each end. The shape of the spacer is determined to some degree by the header height (board width). The smallest header (two 2 × 4s) will need rectangular spacers to keep the nails more widely separated. All spacers will be easier to install if they are a little narrower than the header. Spacer height for the 2 ×

4 (3 1/2" high) will be about 3 3/8". Length should exceed this by a few inches so that the surface nail nearest the end is at least 2 1/2" away from the header end and the next nail a couple of inches farther away. This signifies a spacer 3 3/8" by about 6". There will be nails coming through the stud horizontally into the end of each header piece. As with posts and plates it is inadvisable for nails to be running into each other inside the wood. The 4 × 4 built-up header is so small that two 16d box or sinker nails through each spacer will be adequate. Drive only one nail through the 2 × 4 into each spacer on one side (upper left). Rotate the header and again drive a nail through the 2 × 4 into the upper right half of the spacers (the first nail is now in the lower left). This staggers the nails from top to bottom and keeps them separated.

The best nail choices for holding the header ends to the studs are 16d common, 16d box, and 16d sinker. Deep penetration into the end grain of the header is an objective. By firmly fastening the two header boards together (even with the spacers), a certain increase of resistance to horizontal deflection is gained. The header will not bend down as easily. Therefore, on the header span tables the well-nailed built-up header is ranked the same as a solid beam of equal girth when the built-up members are positioned on edge.

The uniform header is one that fills the entire space above the window or door opening (Fig. 7-15). It is made of two 2 × 12s with sandwiched spacers or surface shims. It eliminates completely the need for cripple studs between the header and the upper plate. This design may be used over any opening that does not exceed the span limits of a 4 × 12 header. This usually accommodates all the typical openings in a house. For a number of years the design was slow to catch on. It was thought to be expensive. When a uniform header was seen over a narrow window or a door, it appeared to be overbuilt (excessively strong and costly). As labor costs increased it became evident that whenever the construction time element was a factor, the spanned header was more costly despite the greater quantity of wood involved in the uniform header over narrow openings. The uniform header soon became a universal system. Few houses are built with spanned headers today.

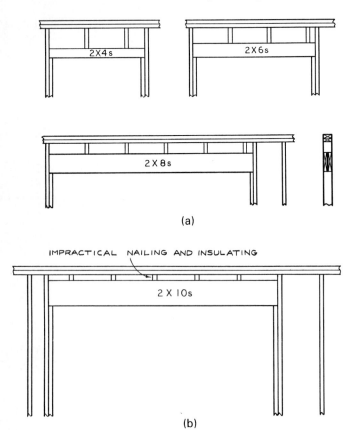

FIGURE 7-14 Traditional spanned headers are sized in accordance with the width of the opening.

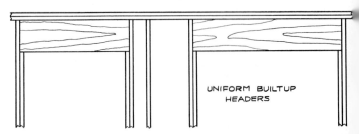

FIGURE 7-15 Uniform header: two 2 × 12s used in all openings up to the table limit.

A great advantage of the uniform built-up header (two 2 × 12s) is that it saves time for both the architect and carpenter in other places in the wall. By combining the uniform header with the precut stud, it is possible to frame the wall with much less use of the tape measure. These two uniform components control the height of the wall and the distance from the subfloor to the underside of window- and door-opening headers. There is no need to measure for the length of trimmer studs. The header is installed first. The upper plate is nailed to it so that it is firmly held in place. Nails are then driven through the face of the adjacent stud into the ends of the header components. Remember to stay down far enough from the top of the stud so that this nail does not intersect the nail that is holding the plate to the stud. With the header thus secured in place, the trimmer 2 × 4 is laid in the opening with one end (a corner) pressed against the bottom edge of the header. The other end is simply traced where it reaches the upper face of the sole plate. The tracing method is always superior to the method where measurements are lifted from an opening and transferred to a board. There is no way a gross error can result from tracing. Minor error can take place from dull pencils or improper reference contact with the materials. When tracing the trimmer the pencil mark will be inside the total length. The saw cut should be outside the line lest the trimmer be cut short.

The detail drawing is simplified for the architect when the uniform header is used. The drawing requires only a callout notation that specifies the uniform header and the precut stud. No dimensions are needed to indicate the ceiling height or the top of the window or door. Nor is a dimension required from the floor to the top of the rough sill. This location will be arrived at by measuring down from the underside of the header the amount specified as the rough-opening height, which is found in the window schedule. The architect is not likely to make a separate detail for every different-sized window. With the uniform component system the one drawing he makes will fit all typical openings rather than being a representation of only one in particular. His detail presentation is therefore more real than symbolic.

For the carpenter an added bonus is found in the elimination of the necessity of determining each header girth that is required for different-sized opening spans. He has only two things to check or guard against. One is to check the plan for an exceptionally wide picture window that might exceed the limits of a 4 × 12 header. Since the 12″ nominal high header is the greatest height that can actually be used, it is not likely that such an opening will be found on a residential plan unless intermediate mullion posts have been designed between multiple window units. The second element is the wood species and grade (quality). Where an opening approaches the maximum span, special attention should be given to the strength and density of the wood. For example, a board that meets the qualifications of both species and grade but which has an obvious structural weakness, such as an oversized loose knot, should be rejected for the long span. It can be sawed into short lengths and used satisfactorily where its girth far exceeds the span limits of smaller openings.

Another benefit is realized from the uniform header system. Because the header material that is ordered is all the same girth, the boards can be further graded for quality. The best ones are designated for the long spans. Those of lesser quality are set aside for short-span use.

The many advantages of the uniform header have made it the universal system. Although most textbooks have failed to point out the obsolescence of the spanned header, one seldom will see it anymore at building sites.

Plywood spacer shapes for headers may progress from horizontal rectangles for the 4 × 4 and 4 × 6 headers to squares for the 4 × 8 header. The spacer for the 4 × 10 and 4 × 12 header may be about the same as those for the 4 × 4 and 4 × 6 but placed vertically. The shape is of little significance if it is large enough to provide for adequate nailing. The nail pattern also changes. More nails are needed across the breadth of the header as the height increases. There is a unique objective when nailing built-up headers. In addition to polarizing the two dimension members into a single, stiff component, the nails must resist any warping tendency in the wood that will cause the two boards to spread apart. The header must not be deeper through than the wall frame depth. For a 2 × 4 frame this will be 3 1/2″. For the wider (higher) headers this means that a greater concentration of nails is needed vertically to resist cupping. Therefore, the spacer blocks do not need to be large or long horizontally. Spacers for a 4 × 12 built-up header could be as little as the 3 3/8″ width used on the 4 × 4 header. Their height would be 11 1/8″ (1/8″ less than the 11 1/4″ actual size of the 2 × 12s). This shape would accomodate four nails placed in a vertical stagger, two from each side. (Fig. 7-16). The quantity of nails in the 8, 10, and 12″ headers also depends on how flat and square the members are. If there is any sign of a cup in

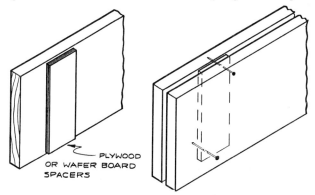

PLYWOOD OR WAFER BOARD SPACERS

FIGURE 7-16 Spacers between the built-up header boards.

either piece, it will help to concentrate the nails more closely in an area that will tend to counteract the direction of the warp (pull it together).

Removing a crook, bow, or twist in header components is nearly impossible. For the header to fit into the frame perfectly, each piece of the built-up header would have to be perfectly flat and true. This is not the nature of wood. The lengthwise fibers, particularly the hard, late summer growth layers, are constantly contracting and changing the surface character of a board. Soaking rains and blistering sunshine will alter the wood shape in a matter of minutes. It is rarely possible to reverse a change once it has occurred. In rare cases it may be possible to reverse a bow. A board lying on humid earth in the sunshine frequently curves up at the ends. Turning such a board over may cause the bow to start to reverse. When it reaches near straightness it can be moved into the shade and stacked off the ground. Dumping a baled stack of studs on the ground is a sure way to warp many of those on the bottom layers under some climatic conditions. Although cross-grain cupping is never as extreme as lengthways bowing, it nonetheless creates a serious problem in the construction of wide headers.

The headers *must not protrude* beyond either the exterior or the interior surfaces of the frame. When they are allowed to stick out it will be necessary to plane, chisel, or power sand away any portion that protrudes. This is a time-consuming and discouraging practice. It should be avoided by method and design.

There are a number of techniques that will prevent the protrusion problem. Two methods are: reduce the spacer thickness, or group the header boards in certain formations. Where the warpage of either board is as much as 1/8" the spacers may be made from 3/8" plywood. This system will work when the total warpage is not over 1/8". Cupped header boards are not easily lined up for nailing when the cups are laid parallel to each other (Fig. 7-17). When two edges are made flush, the opposite edges will be staggered. Neither of these edges will present a square surface contact for cripple studs or the upper plate to bear on. To assemble two boards and spacers in this parallel cupped formation it will be necessary to do it on the edge of the subfloor, or on sawhorses, or on a bench. The framing square is positioned across the width of the concave face of the upper board. The tongue hangs down, crossing the edges of the three pieces (two pieces and a spacer). The lower board is tapped toward the square tongue until its edge corner contacts the square. Nails should be preset and driven through the top board and mostly through the spacer. Final adjustments are made so that ends are flush, the spacer does not protrude, and the upper edges of the header are both in contact with the square tongue. With one heavy blow the preset nail is driven into the bottom board. The same procedure is then repeated on the opposite end, with

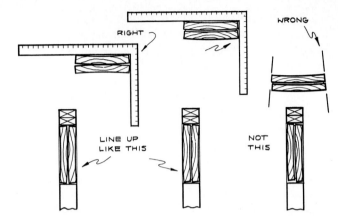

FIGURE 7-17   Cups of 1/4" in each board can be assembled by omitting spacers. Boards with less than a total of 1/2" deformation can be adapted to a maximum thickness of 3 1/2" by using thinner shims. Line up the edges with a square.

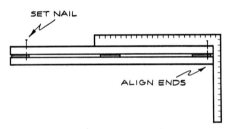

FIGURE 7-18   Hold a square over the ends of both boards to square the unit then set the nails.

the square tongue hanging over the same edge of the header. Before putting in the remaining nails, check the ends of the two header boards with the square to assure that one does not stick out beyond the other (Fig. 7-18). If it does, it probably will not be by much. It can usually be bumped back into position since there are only two nails in the whole assembly so far. Place the long end on a solid surface with the header in an upright position. Tilt it a little so that the short end is above the surface. Strike the piece that is off the surface a sharp blow on the top end with your hammer. Repeat until the ends check square across. Both ends should check square. If one checks square and the other does not, there is either a board that is too long or one that is too short. Possibly both are off. If the long board is the correct length and the other one is only a fraction short, there is nothing to be done. When the shorter of the two is the correct length (3" longer than the width of the specified rough opening), the longer one should be shortened to the correct length. Cut the excess from the end that protrudes.

A cupped header of the type just described may need remedial treatment even with the thinner 3/8" spacer. Parts of it may still protrude beyond the wall surface. The carpenter should proceed with the construction of a header using cupped boards only after assessing all the degrees of

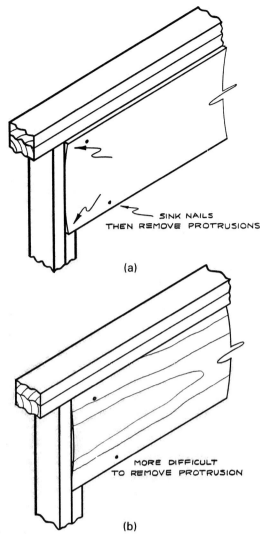

FIGURE 7-19 All protrusions should be removed before covering the wall: (a) easier type to remove; (b) much more difficult. Check the end grain to assure proper positioning to avoid the formation shown in part (b) should warpage occur after installation. All warpage is exaggerated for graphic clarity.

warpage that will affect his labor time. After determining that there will still be a little protrusion (Fig. 7-19), the least effort will be expended by planing any projecting corners of the concave side as compared to planing a large central surface from the convex side. To determine how much must be removed, the framing square is held on the concave side. The depth of the curve tells how much must be removed from the high corners. Any amount in excess of that gained by using a thinner spacer will have to come off from each protrusion. Any nails in the area must be driven below the surface and redriven every time a shaving cut of the plane comes close to the nailhead. There is a better way to use the cupped or warped board in a header. It is explained in the paragraphs that follow.

The uniform header gained in popularity and common usage when the cost of labor became a major item. The uniform header gets its name from the practice of using two 2 × 12s on edge for all openings in the exterior wall from small to large. It came into use when the 2 × 12 was 11 5/8″ wide. It worked well over doors and windows alike. It still does, even though the actual size is now 11 1/4″. Because the rough opening is now higher due to the smaller 2 × 12 size, some rough exterior door openings will require shimming down. This is done with a 3/4″ spacer when steel doors are specified. This information can be found in advance by studying the manufacturer's specifications. When one knows in advance that a shim spacer will be needed, it can be nailed on top of the header before installing the header. When one does not know ahead of time what type door will be used, the spacer can always be nailed on the bottom of the header if needed (Fig. 7-20).

There are several advantages of the uniform header system:

- Reference time saving. No time is expended in determining the span-size requirement of each opening (header height). No reference to plans or code tables for individual header girth is required.
- Construction time is less since no cripple studs are required.
- Making up a bill of materials is simplified, as is inventorying of the delivery.
- All measuring is eliminated after the header parts are cut.

One might think that the cost would be more because the board footage of lumber is greater. There are some hid-

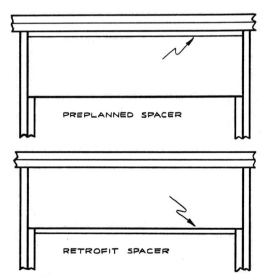

FIGURE 7-20 A 3/4″ spacer (1″ nominal) is needed for many prehung steel door casements, as this design does not top out as high as all-wood casements do.

den savings that help. The lengths of headers are never modular. There is a greater opportunity for economy, however, when using only 2 × 12s. More combinations of required lengths can be worked out to fit board lengths when the width is uniform. Less time will be lost looking for a specific-width piece of header stock. Occasionally, a header piece is mistakenly cut short. Sometimes, it can be used in a different location for a smaller opening, while a replacement is cut from a different board with no loss and no necessity to reorder. When some of these less obvious advantages are added to the recognized ones, it usually works out that the uniform system is less costly than the span system.

Header Design Variations

Assembly of the uniform header is basically the same as the built-up header when the dimension lumber size is a standardized set of 2 × 12s with ply spacers. The warpage problem seriously plagues the builder of the uniform header. The maximum-width pieces are particularly vulnerable to summer heat and sunshine. Variations of the uniform header have developed as a result of this problem.

One variation involves the omission of the spacer between the two header boards. The two pieces are nailed face to face. A 2 × 4 horizontal trimmer is nailed to the lower edges of the two assembled 2 × 12s. It is lined up flush with the face of the header that will face the exterior. When the face of the header is warped, be sure to nail this 2 × 4 on in such a position that no part of the header board protrudes beyond the edge of the 2 × 4 stud wall. The frame wall will be assembled on the subfloor. The exterior surface of the frame wall will be facing up as it lies flat on the floor. Therefore, the exterior face of the header will also be facing up. After the wall is erected it will be found that the inside 2 × 12 of the header is as much as 1/2″ below the surface of the wall. This provides an opportunity to better insulate the header area (the cavities between the spacers of the conventional built-up header frequently go uninsulated). With the space exposed on the surface, it is

a simple matter to fill it with a custom-fitted piece of 1/2″ Styrofoam sheathing (Fig. 7-21). If a solid backing is desired adjacent to the window or door jamb, it can be provided with a 1/2″ × 1 1/2″ filler strip ripped from scrap 2 × 4s. The advantage of the no-spacer system is that there are 3 1/2″ of space in which to sandwich a 3″ header. The header can be severely cupped or bowed and it will pose no problem. A crooked header can usually be adapted by ripping the crowned edge to a straight line provided that the crook is not overly excessive. Twisted headers should be avoided. Too much time is involved attempting to machine a flat, straight top and a square bearing edge on the underside.

What about size? If the 4 × 12 built-up header accommodated doors and windows without the 2 × 4 horizontal trimmer, will it work with the addition of this 1 1/2″ piece of material? The answer is a qualified "yes." As to the window openings, it will work for all windows. The standard rough-opening height for 6′–8″ exterior doors has been 82 1/2″ for many years. The rule given in many texts is "add 2 1/2″ to the width and height of an exterior door for the rough opening." This rule was needed when most, if not all, of the headers were the span type and cripples were used. The height was measured from the bottom of the sole. The uniform headers system eliminated the need to measure anything for height. The opening is built from the top down simply by assembling the components (another timesaving factor). The double plate nets 3″, the uniform built-up header nets 11 1/4″. This total of 14 1/4″, subtracted from the component frame height of 97 1/8″, leaves a door rough opening of 82 7/8″. The added 3/8″ above the old standardized 82 1/2″ has never posed a problem, as the molding framework around the exterior door jamb easily covers the space. To subtract another 1 1/2″ from the 82 7/8″ component-arrived opening, however, reduces it too much to accommodate either the traditional wood door casing or the current steel door casing with its aluminum threshold. To avoid lowering the opening by the 1 1/2″ of a horizontal trimmer under the doubled 2 × 12 header, the lower member of the top plate is omitted over the header. The header is set up under the top member of the double plate. By so doing the total height of the header, plate, and trimmer is maintained the same as that of the conventional built-up uniform header (Fig. 7-22).

If all this seems a bit confusing, let us explore some criteria to determine a choice of headers.

- When you have more time than money, the old-style span header will save a few dollars, due to the savings in board-feet cost.

- If saving construction time is important because you are paying rent or because you are building to sell, a uniform header system is the best choice.

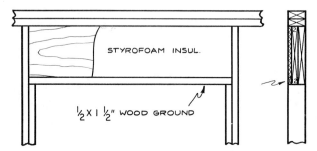

FIGURE 7-21   This design employs a wood spacer to form the solid surround and still takes advantage of the superior insulation characteristic.

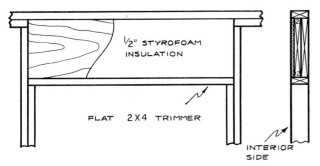

FIGURE 7-22 The header is raised into the top plate and the plate (trimmer) placed on the bottom to form a solid ground around the opening. Styrofoam insulates the cavity; a superior thermal characteristic over the plywood spacer method.

Which uniform system should you choose? Some of your openings require 12″ header height due to their long span. There are two choices open. One is the conventional uniform 4 × 12 header with its inherent warpage problems. The time of year, the climate, and the quality of the wood—all of these things will be taken into consideration. The second choice is the two-piece 4 × 12 header (no spacers) with the horizontal 2 × 4 trimmer placed on the bottom. This system may be the best choice when your header wood is mostly warped. The bottom line is that the determination should be thought out and made well in advance of the day of assembly. Once the materials are delivered, the system is more or less locked in.

Interior Header Designs

Interior headers are designated as bearing or nonbearing in accordance with the partition of which they are a part. Few, if any, building codes take this load factor into account or give it any attention. No header span tables are known to exist that differentiate any size difference for the two categories on the interior. Some builders state with pride that they use two 2 × 6 header components throughout the interior as a symbol of quality. Such a practice is actually wasteful and labor costly (Fig. 7-23). The most common interior door size, which accounts for the majority of header material, is the 30″ passage door. The 4 × 4 built-up header is adequate for this size of opening in bearing partitions. It follows that any size that is adequate in a bearing partition will be more than adequate in a nonbearing partition. Therefore, most authorities will expect the builder to use the exterior header span tables to determine the interior partition header requirements. In reality, a center or centrally located bearing partition is the only one that may bear a load that is even comparable to the exterior wall. Even though other intermediate partitions may be classed as bearing, the ceiling joist span is usually coordinated with the center bearing line (half the house span). Like the floor joists, the span must be considered on the basis of the longest member when all joists are to be the same girth.

For many years interior partition headers were constructed the same as exterior headers. When the uniform header became common, it was more obvious that overbuilding could get out of hand. To put a 4 × 12 header across a 32″ rough opening (for a 30″ passage door) in a nonbearing partition, for example, was neither necessary nor desirable.

Nonbearing partitions (those running parallel to floor and ceiling joists) support relatively little weight. When a door in the opening below the header swings on hinges attached to the vertical jamb, no weight from the door is placed on the header. In this case minimum-size headers are usually adequate. When an opening is quite wide, 6′ for example, and supports a pair of sliding doors on a track, there will be more weight on the header. In such a situation it is feasible to use a single-piece header, a 2 × 10, which is equal to the built-up double 2 × 6 header.

Single Header and Trimmer

Shortly after the coming of the uniform exterior header, the uniform interior header appeared. The interior design, however, utilizes only one dimension piece (a single 2 × 10; Fig. 7-24) placed on edge at or near the center of the surrounding components: the upper plate, the studs, and the horizontal trimmer. The logic behind this header design is compelling. Even so, many builders do not understand it and have been reluctant to abandon the old ways in favor of it. Rationale for the uniform interior header:

- It compares in supportive capability to a built-up 4 × 6 header (two 2 × 6s).
- It is usually adequate for all passage and closet door openings in a floor plan.
- Construction time is about one-third that of the built-up model, with its spacers and cripple studs.

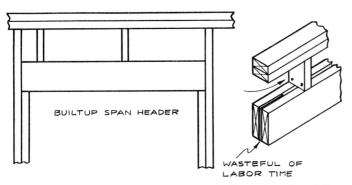

FIGURE 7-23 The traditional old built-up 2 × 4 and 2 × 6 interior partition header is outdated.

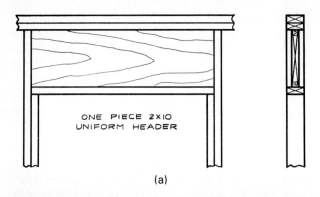

ONE PIECE 2×10
UNIFORM HEADER

(a)

(b)

FIGURE 7-24   (a) The single 2 × 10 with a lower plate trimmer has many advantages during and after construction. (b) Single 2 × 10 header and horizontal trimmer.

- The opening is component assembled. There is no need to measure any part of it after the opening width has been laid out on the plate.

- Surface quality, straightness, and flatness are not required. This is probably the only location in the framework of the house that warped boards can be used with no bad effects or remedial work (an off-centered crook is an exception—it should be sawed straight).

- The opening height is a little more than the old standard. This permits door jambs to be installed without end trimming.

- It permits the jambs to be installed high enough so that doors never have to be cut off at the bottom to clear deep pile carpeting. It is a good practice to set the jamb up off the floor 1/2″ or more in locations where it is known that wall-to-wall carpeting will be. This permits the carpet to be installed under the jamb. It eliminates the tucked-down recession that collects dust and dirt (a homemaker's frustration).

- All factors considered, the single uniform header is the most economical to use for the professional builder and the builder to whom time is important.

Constructing the header involves a simple technique. The 2 × 4 horizontal trimmer is centered by eye over the bottom edge of the 2 × 10. Line up one end. Place a 16d nail about 4″ back from the end. Reverse ends. Center the header again and nail. There should be a nail for about every 12 to 16″ of space throughout the remainder of the header. This assembly will take place with the parts in an upside-down position on the subfloor or a workbench.

Crooked header boards should be straightened on the convex edge before nailing the trimmer to the concave edge. This straightening is especially important on long header spans. Left unstraightened, the result will be a curved ceiling line.

A short header such as one over a 30″ passage door need not be straightened if the crook does not exceed an 1/8″ or so. Attention must be given to an adjustment in the installation, however, to accommodate the crown that exists (Fig. 7-25). For example, a header with an 1/8″ crown must be set 1/8″ below the plate at its ends. The top edge of the header will be nailed 1/8″ lower than the top of the studs on each side. The high point of its crown will then bear under the double plate at a central location in the span over the opening. By so doing a straight plate and ceiling line will be maintained.

The same system can be used with wider spans, but there will be a danger of ceiling joists bending the plate down to meet the header. To eliminate this problem, shims as thick as the gap should be placed between the plate and the top of the header directly under the ceiling joist position (Fig. 7-26). On partitions that run parallel to ceiling joists, place a shim for every 12 to 16″, being careful not to raise the plate by driving the shims in too tightly. On bearing partitions the shims are placed directly under each ceiling joist over the crooked header.

The plate is not always straight and level when it spans over a considerable space. When this appears to be the case, a string line should be put in place. A convenient reference place is the joint between the two upper plate boards. Place a nail in the crack over each end of the header location. Use a shim of the correct thickness to cause the top of the plate to be straight when it bears through the shim onto the header. If this straightening is undertaken after the frame has been erected, the lower member of the upper plate will already be nailed to the single header. If the plate is curved down, a small crowbar (a wonder bar) may be used to pry it up from the header. The shims are then placed and the header is driven back down with a heavy hammer.

A slight upward bow of the lower horizontal trimmer that results from using a crooked 2 × 10 is of no concern.

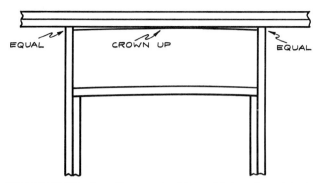

FIGURE 7-25 Install a crooked 2 × 10 header with the crown up.

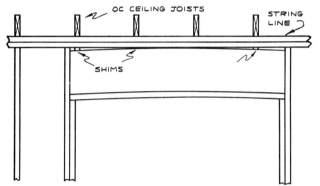

FIGURE 7-26 A long crooked 2 × 10 single header should be shimmed under ceiling joist centers to maintain a straight upper plate or at equal intervals on a parallel partition.

It is completely concealed after the casing is applied to the jamb. In fact, a slightly crowned board on edge is considered to be prestressed. It will resist vertically downward pressure, as an arch does.

ROUGH SILLS

A rough sill is the horizontal bottom member of a rough opening in a frame wall (Fig. 7-27). It may be a single-dimension board or it may be doubled. The option sometimes relates to concepts of quality. Double rough sills (Fig. 7-28) are considered by some builders to be a symbol of higher-grade construction. The advantages of a double rough sill are (1) stiffer resistance to lateral pressures where openings are wide, and (2) a higher nail backing surface, 3″ as compared to 1 1/2″, for nailing the casing under the window stool. *Window stool* is the finished interior windowsill. Since no load bearing takes place on the rough sill except at the ends, a single rough sill is considered adequate by some builders. Many of the windows in use today have some of their weight supported by the nails in the flanges that surround them. A double sill also furnishes a

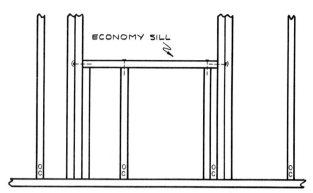

FIGURE 7-27 Economy rough sills are sometimes used in narrow openings. Cripples are frequently needed under both ends unless the OC cripple is very close (nonmodular planning).

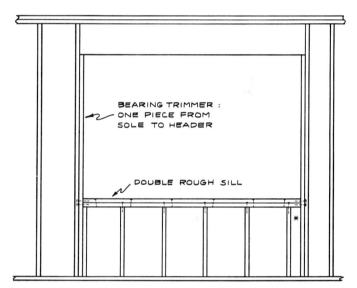

FIGURE 7-28 Double sills are sturdier and a mark of quality, especially in wider openings. The one-piece trimmer is superior to an interrupted trimmer and is required on walls that bear the roof weight (modularly planned opening). *Rule of thumb*: Less than half a space—no cripple required under end of rough sill.

sturdier nailing surface on the exterior where wood trim sills may be used.

TRIMMERS

In the wall frame, vertical trimmers are the support studs upon which the ends of the headers bear. There are two trimmer designs. One is suitable for any wall, whether bearing or nonbearing. It is a one-piece stud-sized member that fills the entire height from the top of the sole to the underside of the header. It carries the load imposed on the header to the sole without interruption. It may be called a *one-piece trimmer*, a *bearing trimmer*, an *uninterrupted trimmer*, or a *trimmer stud*. In some localities it is called a *scab trimmer* because it is scabbed onto a full-length stud.

The interrupted trimmer (Fig. 7-29) is one that extends from the underside of the header to the top of the rough sill. It is interrupted by the rough sill. The end of the rough sill butts against the face of the full-length stud. The bottom section of the trimmer extends from the underside of the rough sill to the top of the sole. In this formation the bottom trimmer piece is identical to the cripple studs under the rough sill. The only advantage of this design over the one-piece trimmer is that is occasionally saves an added cripple, which must be placed under the end of a rough sill. A good rule to follow to determine when this extra cripple stud is needed with the one-piece trimmer is: Add the cripple when the OC cripple adjacent to the trimmer is more than a half-space away.

The drawback to the use of the interrupted trimmer is that it is not permitted in bearing walls by most building codes. This means that it can only be used in walls over which a gable end of a roof exists. The gable end of a roof is a vertical triangular wall above the end wall of the house. No rafter ends bear on the gable end wall. A sheathed gable is considered much like a truss. It transfers most of its weight to the ends (the corners of the house). Therefore, the wall below is not considered to be a load-bearing wall. A hip roof, by comparison, is shaped something like a pyramid. All the exterior walls support the ends of the rafters, so all walls are of the bearing classification.

Few builders use both trimmer designs in the same house. One is apt to see all one-piece trimmers or all two-piece trimmers. Where the code exists, the latter technique

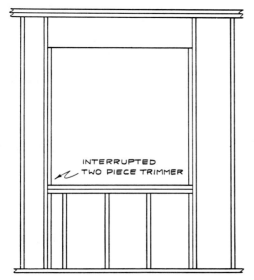

FIGURE 7-29 Interrupted two-piece trimmers can be used only on gable end walls that do not bear the weight of the roof. There are four precision fits to make instead of two with the one-piece trimmer.

will be in violation on the bearing sides of the house. Such a violation is usually a matter of ignorance of the code as well as the rationale.

There are several reasons why the single-piece trimmer is considered better for load carrying. A board is porous. It contains hard fibers from the summer and fall growth rings. The spring growth is soft, spongy, and crushable. In vertical position the tubular nature of a stud is strong. It bears weight effectively. Where the end of a rough sill is placed between the two-piece trimmer the porous grain of the sill is horizontal. This puts it in a crushable position. One has only to look at the edge corners of a load of steel-banded lumber to see what "crushability" means.

Shrinkage proportion is another factor. Shrinkage is greater when four ends of the vertical two-piece trimmer are exposed to the air than where two ends of the one-piece trimmer are present. Also, the shrink proportion will differ in flat-laid intercepting members of a rough sill from the same amount of vertical material. Add to this the doubled precision that is needed to accurately press-fit two trimmer pieces instead of one. In the final tally there will probably be no significant savings, if any, by using the interrupted trimmer technique.

ASSEMBLING FRAME WALLS

The primary fastener in the conventional frame wall is the nail with a full head. The larger contracting firms will make use of compressors and air hammers (nail guns and staplers). Smaller framing crews and the individual builder will drive nails by hand. Regardless of the tool that is used, there is much more to correct fastening than meets the eye. *Every nail in a house calls for a particular angle. Each angle serves a purpose.* There are only a few places where nails are intentionally driven perpendicular to a surface. Gypsum wallboard and asphalt roofing shingles are two examples that call for nailing at right angles to a surface. The heads must be parallel to the surface in these two cases. The carpenter should know and understand why a certain angle is superior to any other. Following this learning, he should gain a certain sense, a feeling, for the art of fastening with nails. His knowledge of the characteristics of the wood and the holding power of a particular nail, coupled with a sense for the direction of a nail, will cause him to produce a sturdy product.

Principles of Nailing

There are several principles of nailing that cannot be violated without suffering negative affects (poor joints). When these principles are learned at the beginning of training by the student or novice, and practiced conscientiously, the result will be well-assembled sturdy products. As principles, the philosophy of correct nailing can be established as rules of conduct and practice.

Principle 1. A board that is split by nails will form an inferior joint. *Rule:* Do not split boards with nails. That is an obvious rule to follow such a principle, isn't it? The question is: How is splitting avoided? Wood has grain running lengthwise of a board. The grain of construction lumber is made up of alternate layers of soft and hard fibers. A nail is, in reality, a steel pin with a four-sided wedge point. When driven into the board, the fibers of wood are fractured or pressed apart. When the grain is too hard, or it is not severed, or the nail is too large in diameter, the board may crack. When this occurs at the end of a board, the intended joint will be inferior, if not useless. It can even be a source of additional trouble. A split at the end of a board makes the board wider. The extra width will protrude beyond the uniform surface, with which it should be flush. If unattended, this will cause faulty exterior trim joints and unsquare interior corners. It can even result in unplumb walls when upper plate lengths have been referenced and traced from the soleplate. Splitting can be avoided by following one of three rules:

- When surface nailing at the end of a board, do not nail closer to the end than the thickness of the board (farther away when possible). Regard the end of a board as a vulnerable area (Fig. 7-30). With framing lumber of 1 1/2″ thickness, this means that the nail should be started at least 1 1/2″ away from the end.

  A plate will be nailed to the end of the corner post stud which is 1 1/2″ thick. This poses no problem. The nail is started 1 1/2″ back from the end. This places it directly over the *edge* of the stud. If driven straight it would penetrate between the stud and the spacer block. To get the nail into the stud, it is simply angled toward a point in the stud that is centered in the wood at the final resting place of the point of the nail (Fig. 7-31). About a 1/4″ tilt of the nail at its head will achieve this objective. Two nails are driven into the corner stud. In order that the stud cannot twist easily, the nails should be spaced apart as far as possible. About 1/2″ from the edges is good. A slight angle toward the center axis of the stud is also useful. It causes a gripping effect between the two nails.

- When the dropback rule is followed and the plate still splits, two alternatives remain. Use a smaller-diameter nail, preferably of the same full length. The customary 16d common nail, used for attaching the plates to studs, is frequently the cause of split plate ends. The prudent carpenter will carry

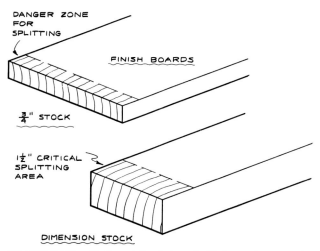

FIGURE 7-30 *Nailing rule of thumb:* Nail no closer to the end of a board than the thickness of the board, to avoid splitting the grain.

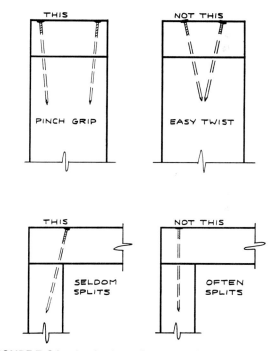

FIGURE 7-31 Angle the nails to grip, far enough apart so that the stud will not easily pivot or twist, and far enough from the end to avoid splitting.

a handful of 16d box nails in one of his nail pouch pockets. The 16d box is as long as the common 16d but enough smaller in diameter to prevent splitting. The box nail is reserved for those locations where splitting is a danger.

- When all else fails and the board still splits, a specialized remedy must be used. Splitting can be avoided completely by tapping a pilot hole for the nail. Tapping works well where a board is too hard, a knot exists where the nail must go, or the first nail caused a split. The nail that splits the board and causes a protrusion should be carefully removed. The crack will usually close. A pilot hole is then tapped in a new place. The drill bit should be just enough smaller in diameter than the nail so that friction will hold the nail in the tapped hole. Tapping is done only in the piece being attached. All the holding power available is needed in the end grain of the stud.

Modern tools have simplified the tapping routine. A small reciprocating drill can be conveniently carried in the tool belt. A variety of bits is stored in the handle. Recent developments in cordless drills have made this power drill a favorite on jobs where it would otherwise be a nuisance to string power cords among the framing. Holsters are available for convenient carrying. Care should be exercised in carrying the drill when a bit is left in the chuck, as a serious stab wound can result from carelessness. A resharpened broken bit of shorter length is a good choice, as it protrudes less. Of course, the bit can be removed from the chuck for complete safety between intermittent tapping jobs. Tapping to avoid splitting is another case in point where quality is an objective and future complications in the construction are undesirable.

Principle 2. Surface or edge grain (cross grain) has much greater nail-holding power than end grain. The end grain of a board is actually a lot of holes surrounded and connected by wood fibers. Driving a nail into this porous group of tunnels causes little or no fracturing of tissue. The nail seeks out a path of least resistance, usually the soft annual growth ring, and slides into it. Since little wood is displaced, the gripping effect is minimal. Gripping can be improved by only two means, penetration and adhesion. *Rule:* Use as long a nail as possible within the limits of its diameter (Fig. 7-32). The largest nail intended for nailing floor headers to joist ends is the 20d common. The longest and largest nail advisable for plate nailing to studs is the 16d common. A compromise nail that is widely used is the 16d sinker. The sinker is characterized by a slightly funnel shaped head. It is also coated with resin. Its diameter is between those of the common and box nails. It is actually possible to find sinkers in a variety of coatings, shapes, and sizes under the same designation. Much of this nonstandardization is occurring from foreign manufacture. The sinker is about a 1/4" shorter than the common nail of the same number. The lesser penetration is successfully offset by the adhesion effect of the resin. A resin-coated nail is much harder to extract than a smooth nail. Once pulled, it will not hold as well if reused because the resin is largely stripped away. Pulling a coated nail is at best a difficult task. The thinner, tapered head usually strips off, leaving a steel pin with little to grip.

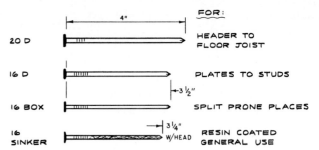

FIGURE 7-32 Each of these framing nails has a special role. The carpenter should recognize each nail by sight and know where to use it.

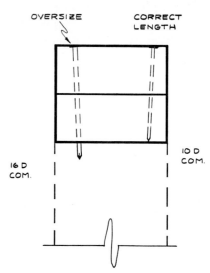

FIGURE 7-33 Overlong nails are wasteful for double-plate fastening. The protruding points may cause avoidable injury when raising the wall and later when installing insulation.

Cross-grain nailing does not require nails of any greater length than the total thickness of the two pieces being nailed together. The upper plates, for example, total 3" of vertical depth when nailed to each other. The nail length need not be over 3". It is preferable that it not be. A longer nail will protrude from the underside (Fig. 7-33). It presents a safety hazard throughout the remainder of construction. When the all-purpose 16d sinker nail is used to nail the top plate to the top under plate, it should be angled sufficiently so that it will not protrude out the underside. The function of the surface nails in the upper member of the top plate is primarily to hold the members in lateral alignment. It is not to hold down the plate. The weight of the ceiling and roof will do that job. Therefore, a 10d or 12d common nail will be adequate for top plate fastening of the upper piece.

Principle 3. End nailing is superior to toenailing (Fig. 7-34). Some builders lay out all the soleplates on the

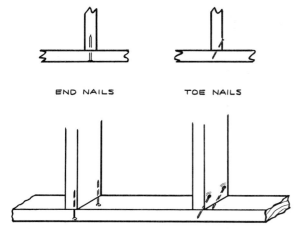

 END NAILS   TOE NAILS

FIGURE 7-34 End nails are superior for initial construction. Toenailing is sometimes required for inside butt joints and retrofitting.

subfloor and nail them to the floor permanently. The wall frame is then assembled by nailing the top plate to the studs. The frame is erected and braced. Each stud is then toenailed to the sole. A more universal system is to end nail both plates to the bottom and top of the studs before erection. The latter system has proven to be more accurate, quicker, and the frame is much easier to erect and brace. Since the roof weight presses down on the studs, the end-grain holding power is important only during erection. *Rule:* End-grain stud nailing is superior to toenailing. Lateral stress resulting from the nailing of surface materials such as sheathing, siding, and wallboard is absorbed better by the end-nailing system. The toenailed stud is more likely to split away from its nails. One small advantage exists for the toenail system. Should a stud have to be taken out or moved for any reason, the toenails are easier to get out, as they are exposed above the floor. On the other hand, it is possible in most stud locations with the end-nail system to saw between the stud and plate with a hacksaw blade to a

point where the nails are severed. The end-nailed system is the most universally practiced today.

Principle 4. More nails are not always better. In fact, a few well-placed nails of the correct size will produce a sturdier joint than more nails of an inferior size or type. Who has not seen an antique piece of furniture where the intended remedy for a loose joint is the addition of nails. Most often they are ill sized and driven in without tapping. There is usually evidence of a lack of understanding of the stress involved. The result is a multitude of cracks and splits and loose protruding nails. One correctly sized nail installed with understanding might have saved such a joint. *Rule:* Use correctly sized nails in reasonable quantity.

ORDER OF ASSEMBLY

There is a logical sequence to assembling a frame wall. Some small details may be altered. The size of the wall-raising crew will have a bearing on the method used. The most common method is to assemble a complete frame wall with all the parts lying horizontally on the floor. All the components that have been described are nailed into the wall frame. The frame is then raised, braced, and anchored to the floor (Fig. 7-35). The limitation of this system is that a wall frame may be too long or too heavy to be raised by a small crew. In this case the wall may be assembled in smaller segments. Each segment can be small enough that one or two workers can raise it.

Regardless of how many units there are in the full wall, they should all be constructed on the floor in a full-length assembly before any segment is raised. This is a control measure. The total length of the plates must not exceed the specified overall length. It is extremely easy when building segments of a wall to permit the upper plate to stretch laterally at the joints. The more segments, the

FIGURE 7-35 Raise the wall on command and keep it flat throughout its arc.

more joints, and the greater the error becomes. It is then impossible to plumb both exterior corner posts of the frame, as the wall is now a trapezoid instead of a rectangle. Even when the segmented upper plates match the sole length, it is common for the assembly to develop excess length when erected. Any lateral flexing opens up the butt joints. These seemingly insignificant cracks add up dramatically in proportion to the number of plate segments. When it occurs, the feasible alternative to an unplumb corner is to check the top plate overall length with a one-piece tape measure (one that will extend the entire distance). When the excess length is no more than about 1/4″, it can all be sawed off the interior end of the last plate segment. (The longer the segment, the lesser the quantity of unplumb studs.) If it is more than 1/4″, it will be advisable to go back toward the center of the wall and take off part or all of the excess from a centrally located plate. The out-of-plumb stud characteristic that will result from the expanded top plate can be minimized by erecting and bracing end sections of the wall first, then working toward the middle. The length adjustment is then made with the last, centrally located, section to go up.

A permanent way to prevent lateral stretch of the top plate while raising the wall is to nail the upper top member to the under top plate board while the frame is still on the floor. To avoid polarizing the double plate into an unstraight line before erection, the framer should choose the straightest possible boards for the top plate. The segments of wall must be lying flat on the floor or all parts blocked up from the surface with equal-thickness blocks. Any crooked characteristics that exist in the edge of the first upper plate member will be frozen in position when a second piece is nailed on top of it.

When two plate members both have a slight crook (up to a 1/4″) and one is to go on top the other, the position of the crowns should be reversed. On the floor this means that if the lower plate nailed to the stud tops is crowned up, the upper plate should be nailed onto it with its crown down while the edges are held in alignment. This is done in the hope that the spring pressure in each piece will counteract the other and produce a tolerably straight double plate. Should two crooked boards become assembled in parallel formation, one upon the other, the resulting stiffness will make it difficult, if not impossible, to bring the wall to a straight line on top and hold it there with temporary braces.

The first upper plate on the studs may have its individual pieces terminate (butt together) over a stud or between two studs. In each case special consideration is required to achieve a good joint. The ends of the first members of the upper plate that meet on top a single stud should bear equally on the stud (3/4″ each). This presents a nailing situation that is very sensitive to splitting. Two nails through each board makes four of them penetrating

the end of a single stud. The placement should be such that no two nails touch each other in the end of the stud. In regard to the plate ends, drilling tap holes is the safest practice from the start. The thinner 16d box nail or 16d sinker nail is preferred.

Joining the plates at a point between the studs can be done satisfactorily when the upper plate is nailed on top before erection. Care is taken to be certain that no gap is permitted between the two lower members where they butt while the nailing takes place. *A joint between studs should not be permitted to occur in a space over which a truss will bear* (Fig. 7-36). There is no danger of this happening when rafters and ceiling joists are both placed 16″ OC over the studs. However, if not kept in mind, this can happen automatically when roof trusses are positioned 24″ apart over studs that are 16″ apart. Every other truss bears directly over the center of the space between two studs. To avoid

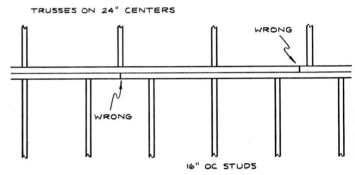

FIGURE 7-36 Incorrect location of either the top or lower member of the double plate results in inferior support to a roof truss.

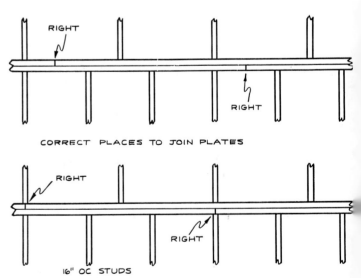

FIGURE 7-37 Two alternative correct ways to join plates under trusses where studs are on 16″ spacing and trusses on 24″ spacing. Joints should be in nonbearing spaces or on studs. Minimum distance apart is 4′.

a plate joint where a truss will bear, the first plate member must be shortened enough to throw the joint into a space to the right or left of the stud locations that are multiples of 4′ (Fig. 7-37). Suppose that 16′ boards will be used for the plate members. To get a pattern started correctly, the first plate board will be shortened 8″, to a length of 15′-4″. The truss to one side of this location will sit over the 14′ mark, which is centered between the 13′-4″ stud position and the 14′-8″ stud. The next truss sits on the 16′ stud location, the next one on 18′, and so on. In this manner the joint is made in a non-load-bearing space. By continuing with 16′ plate members the joint pattern will continue consistently to avoid the bearing space. Of course, the pattern ends as a partition overlapping plate is reached.

Most building codes require that no joint in the lower or upper members of the double plate be made closer than 4′ apart. The intent of this rule is to maintain stiffness to resist side pressure. It also provides adequate nailing surface to resist tensile stresses (lengthwise stretching).

Partition Intersections

When the second plate is nailed on before erection of the frame, provision must first be made for the partition intersections. A space precisely equal to the thickness of the partition is left open in the upper piece of the double plate. The first upper plate board is nailed to the corner stud. The second (top) plate will come from the adjacent wall. It will lap over the first plate, forming an interlocking corner joint. If these top boards are long enough to reach from the corner to the first partition, they will be accurately cut to end at the first edge of the partition. A mark already exists on the top of the plate which earlier located the partition post in

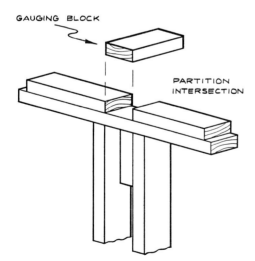

FIGURE 7-38 Use a scrap block to accurately space the ends of the top plates apart when the top plate is installed before the interior partition that will intersect it.

the frame. A short 2 × 4 block is placed crosswise at the end of each top plate in the place that will eventually be occupied by the upper partition plate (Fig. 7-38). The next top plate beyond the partition is butted against the block and nailed in place. Top plates should not be laid down the full length of a wall and then sawed out later over partition posts. This practice simply creates a lot of short plates with extra end joints within the same room length. Whenever possible it is preferred that the top plate be full length (one piece) between partition intersections, as this makes a much stiffer wall. Keeping this in mind, it then becomes important that *no joint in the lower half of the double plate end closer than within 4′ of a partition.* Such attention to detail and structural rules will require knowledge, alertness, and conscientiousness.

Nailing the Top Plate

The upper board of the double plate may be nailed with 16d common, box, or sinker nails, although all of these are oversize. Spacing is 16″ apart for these large nails. Plenty of angle is advisable so that the points do not protrude. To avoid the protruding-point problem completely, 10d common nails are preferred. The 10d nail is spaced 12 to 16″ apart. Whichever nail is used, follow three rules:

- *Do not put a nail on top of a stud location* (Fig. 7-39a). There are already two nails below this location. Also, the rafter and/or ceiling joist may take up a full 3″ of space at that location. There will be toenails in this area, as rafters or trusses will later be nailed there. Stay at least 4″ away from the stud.
- *Stagger the nails from side to side* (Fig. 7-39b). When a twist is encountered in a board, put more nails on the high sides that try to stand up. Start nailing from the center out on the twisted board. This reduces the spring pressure to half for each end.
- *Slant the nails lengthwise only.* Crosswise slanting tends to draw the sides out of vertical alignment.

Vertical lineup of the double plate edges is best achieved with clamps or jigs. All dressed dimension boards have rounded edges. This makes it difficult to line them up flush by feel or sight. A small Jorgensen handscrew is an excellent tool to put the edges into perfect alignment. A 4″ C clamp also works well. A wooden channel box similar to a wooden miter box can be put together quickly (Fig. 7-39c). It is simply slid ahead of the current nailing spot. All these tools work well when the top plate is put on after the frame is up and braced. The C clamp and the channel block can be used at floor level with some adaptation of raiser blocks to hold the top of the wall above the floor.

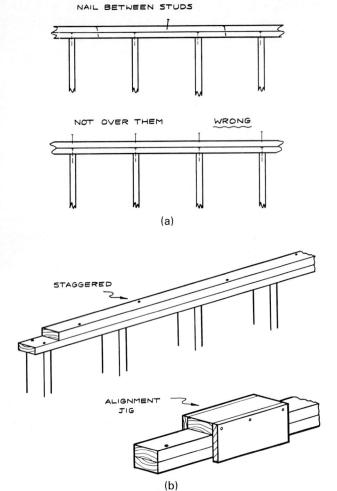

NAIL BETWEEN STUDS

NOT OVER THEM   WRONG

(a)

STAGGERED

ALIGNMENT JIG

(b)

FIGURE 7-39 (a) Nail the top plate between the studs, not over or near them. (b) Stagger the nails from side to side. An alignment jig, a C clamp, or a handscrew clamp helps line up the two plates until nailed.

ORDER OF WALL RAISING

The sequence of wall frame erection determines the order of construction of each wall. To keep the maximum working area available on the floor, each wall will be raised and braced as soon as it is assembled to the point desired. It is easier to raise small walls than long unwieldy ones. It is less precarious holding a small wall up while temporary braces are applied. For these reasons it is logical to *begin with the shorter end walls of a house*. The frame is assembled with the sole lying on edge a few inches in from the end of the floor. Both end walls are raised and braced.

Long exterior walls will be constructed and raised next. When each is ready it can be raised and immediately nailed to the corner of the end wall. This eliminates the necessity of a temporary brace at the corner. The diagonal braces supporting end walls prevent the long wall from falling over the exterior.

The longest interior partitions will be next in order (Fig. 7-40a). The centrally located bearing partition is usually constructed first. At this point the framer must pay particular attention to the floor plan with regard to room sizes and partition lengths. He should preplan the order of wall assembly from this point forward so that he does not box himself in and find it impossible to assemble a partition on the floor.

Following the bearing wall and other lengthwise walls will come the shorter crosswalls (Fig. 7-40b). Generally, the logical sequence is to work from the exterior toward the center of the house.

(a)

(b)

FIGURE 7-40 (a) The last section of a central partition being raised. (b) Shorter nonbearing partitions are constructed and raised last, working from the tight spots to the more spacious areas.

Should the carpenter omit a short wall and find that an assembled frame cannot be put in place, a different construction technique will be required. Each separate piece of the wall will be put in individually. The sole is nailed down first. The two end studs are toenailed to the top of the sole. When a stud is in place at each end, the first of the upper plates is nailed on top of them. The rest of the studs are end nailed through the upper plate, one at a time, and then toenailed to the sole. Finally, the upper plate is put on. If structurally permissible, the top plate should extend onto the adjoining partitions. This may require sawing out the top plate of the adjoining wall if it was installed before the problem was discovered.

Interlock Nail Patterns

Thoughtless nailing of the top piece of the double plate to the lower piece at a corner joint usually results in split ends. It is imperative that a mental picture of the location of the nails in the lower half of the double plate be visualized. Without this consciousness it is inevitable that nails will be driven on top of others. They will be driven in the same grain lines or close enough to cause the double-wedge effect, which splits a board.

Nail patterns for corner intersections are controlled on the lower board. There will be two nails at the end of each plate going into the stud. The heads will be between 1 1/4 and 1 1/2" back from the end (Fig. 7-41). Remember that these are slightly slanted so that their points end up in the middle of the thickness of the stud when they are fully seated. The objective now is to interlock this corner by lapping the top plate across the butt joint of the lower pieces. To make an effective joint, it must be nailed into new places without splitting. It can be done by imagining an x-ray vision of the nails below. To be sure, one may mark the hidden locations to make it very obvious.

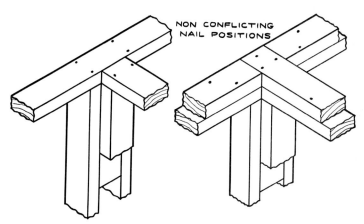

FIGURE 7-42 Nails through the pass-through plate may center over the studs, whereas those in the butting plate should be 1 1/2" away from the end and slanted toward the heart of the stud.

Two or three nails will be adequate when correctly placed. This is not a good place to use 16d common nails unless the wood is exceptionally soft. Two well-placed 16d box nails will be adequate. Three 10d common nails are also adequate. A triangular pattern will achieve the objectives. The nail closest to the end spearheads the triangle. It is placed about 1 1/2" from the end so as not to split the top board. A second nail may be placed to go between the two end nails in the board below. It is kept back away from the edge so as not to split the lower board in which it will anchor. A third nail may be put in position to complete an imperfect triangle. It is on the interior segment of the square corner but should not line up in the same grain line as the second nail. Move it back away from the end a little farther but keep its anchoring location about 3/4" from the interior edge of the lower board. Note that the invisible nails are shown with Xs.

Nail patterns for intersecting partitions are less critical (Fig. 7-42). On the lower board there is no end-grain splitting factor with which to be concerned. Unlike the corner joint, which is all nailed close to the ends, the intersection has members running through. The T joint completes its interlock with the one upper plate piece ending over the intersection. A spearhead pattern works well for this junction also. Follow the same logic as that given for the corner lock. The other two butting pieces may be nailed several inches back from the joint, thus avoiding the splitting potential entirely. Two nails are put in about 4 to 6" from the end of each board. These are staggered a few inches apart. From there on the plates are nailed on the staggered pattern 12 to 16" apart. *Avoid nailing over the studs.*

The only remaining intersection type is the cross. No special attention is required with this double intersection. One need only remember to stay away from the ends, whether they are visible or hidden below the top boards.

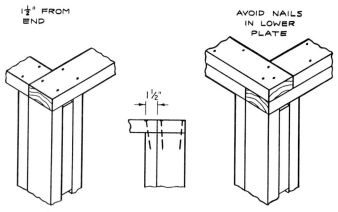

FIGURE 7-41 When nailing the first plate, stay back from the ends 1 1/2". When nailing the top plate, choose locations as far from the nails underneath as possible.

Wind Bracing

Permanent bracing of the frame walls against lateral pressures may be begun while the frame is still lying on the floor. It is not usually completed on the floor. There is too great a potential for polarizing the frame into an unsquare state while it is in the horizontal position. In such a rigid state it is usually impossible to *plumb* the wall lengthwise after erecting it. Plumbing of this type means making a surface vertical, parallel to the earth's gravitational forces.

Before plywood was common to the market, corners were braced with diagonal boards. It could be found in several forms. The simplest bracing form was to sheath the entire wall surface with boards placed at 45° angles. Another system involved inletting a 1 × 4 or 1 × 6 nominal-1″ board into the surface of the studs. This brace was run diagonally between 45 and 60° from the top of each exterior corner down to the subfloor or sill. There followed a phase where a sheet of plywood was nailed to the framework on each side of each corner. This technique is still widely practiced as a wholly acceptable method of wind bracing.

In recent years considerable attention has been directed to heat and cool conservation. A trend toward greater thermal saving has reversed the direction away from strong sheathing materials that double as bracing. In many areas it has turned the calendar back to the old inlet diagonal bracing method. Metal braces are also available (Fig. 7-43a). This technique is being used routinely under Styrofoam sheathing.

Dadoing a Corner Brace

To accommodate a diagonal wood brace, a dado is made in the sole, the lower half of the double plate, and in each stud that it crosses. This is called inletting the brace. Many illustrations in books show the brace running right into the top corner. *The dado should never but cut into the corner* (Fig. 7-43b). This practice destroys a substantial quantity of the interlocking joint of the upper plate. Start the first dado back from the corner at least 6″. This will clear all corner post materials. It will also eliminate the possibility of sawing into nails.

The optimum brace is one positioned at 45° (Fig. 7-44). When there are no door or window openings within about 8′ of the corner, a board of 12′ length will be used. Cut one end off at 45°. Square the frame wall on the floor as much as possible by making it parallel to the side and end of the floor. Lay the 45° cut end of the brace flush with the bottom of the sole. Position the lower edge of the other end of the brace on the plate about 6″ from the end of the wall frame. Temporarily tack the ends of the board to the sole and the upper plate. Trace a mark at all points where the brace board crosses studs and plates. *Do not cut off the*

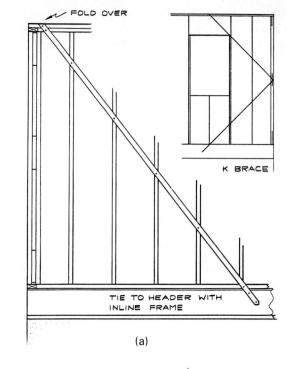

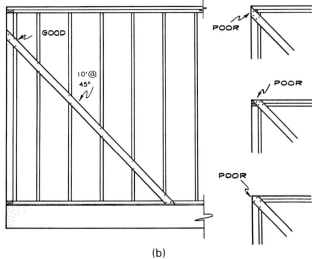

FIGURE 7-43 (a) Steel braces are effective under insul-board sheathing. (b) Diagonal braces should be let-in to the plate or the post but never cut into the corner lap joint. Optimum angle is 45°. Up to 60° is acceptable.

top of the brace yet (it will be cut off flush after the brace has been permanently nailed). Remove the brace. Set your portable circular saw to a depth equal to or slightly deeper (1/32 to 1/16″) than the thickness of the brace. Make a cut along each pencil mark on the plates taking out no more than the pencil lines. The stud cuts may be cut wider than the traced opening. Many studs are bowed. The wider gap will permit the stud to be pulled into vertical position (straight) before it is polarized by the brace nails. The dados can be cut out by routing with the saw or a router. They

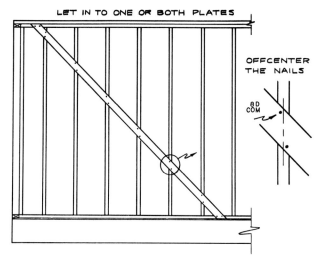

LET IN TO ONE OR BOTH PLATES

OFFCENTER THE NAILS

8D COM

FIGURE 7-44 An optimum brace at 45° is attached to the plate. It is cut from 12′ stock. Nails are placed to avoid being in the same grain line (annular ring) of the stud.

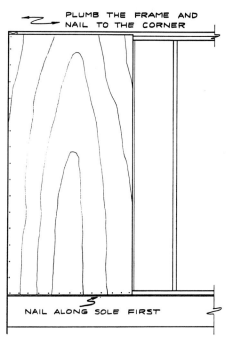

PLUMB THE FRAME AND NAIL TO THE CORNER

NAIL ALONG SOLE FIRST

FIGURE 7-45 Plywood corner bracing is fast and effective. Nail along the sole first. Hold the frame plumb and nail up the corner.

FIGURE 7-46 Raise the short wall frames first. Drag braces will follow along. Safety blocks will prevent the frame from sliding off the edge of the floor.

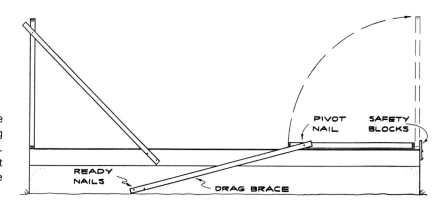

PIVOT NAIL   SAFETY BLOCKS

READY NAILS

DRAG BRACE

may also be removed with the power saw by cutting the two crossgrain end cuts first and then making a surface rip cut. The latter is best done in two stages. The two diagonal end cuts are made while the wall is lying on the floor. The surface cuts are more conveniently made later after the wall is in an upright position.

   Where plywood is used for corner bracing (Fig. 7-45) it is installed after the wall has been erected and braced. It is important to remember that no temporary braces from the upper part of the wall to the floor can project into the surface area where the plywood will be installed (between the studs). In practice it is possible to use the ply sheet as its own temporary as well as permanent brace. Enough nails should be started up the corner and across the sole so that one carpenter can drive them all in while a helper holds the wall in perfect plumb.

Plumbing, Bracing, and Anchoring

The first wall to be erected can have a set of temporary braces (Fig. 7-46), nailed to its ends before raising. A 16′ 2 × 4 is a good choice for these two braces. A 12 or 14′ length will work fairly well. Anything less than 12′ will net a brace that stands steeper than 45°. One form nail is placed in the center of the width of the 2 × 4 brace about 6″ from the upper end. Two form nails are placed on the other end. They are about 8″ apart and staggered. The first is about 6″ from the end. The end of the board with one nail is positioned close to the top of the frame. It is nailed to the corner post. The 2 × 4 is laid out in the opposite direction the wall will be raised. Such a brace is installed on each side of the house (each end of the wall). The ends of these braces are lying on the ground. The crew should

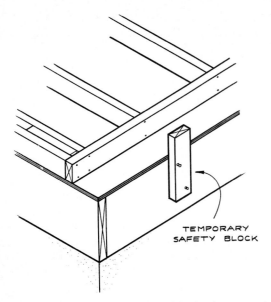

TEMPORARY
SAFETY BLOCK

FIGURE 7-47 Temporary safety blocks (two or three) may be nailed to the header to prevent the bottom of the frame from sliding over the edge of the floor while it is being raised.

act upon command and raise the wall uniformly. *The wall frame must maintain a flat plane throughout its trajectory while being raised.* If one part gets ahead of another, sharp snapping sounds will be heard. These are the sounds of nails pulling loose and joints coming apart. When this is allowed to happen, the uniformity of the wall height is destroyed. It will then be necessary to send a worker around the top plate with a sledge hammer to drive the plates back down before sheathing can be installed.

Set a few nails in the sole as soon as the frame is erect. Drive them partially into the subfloor and floor header. One person does this quickly with minimum concern for accuracy. The objective is to keep the bottom from falling off the floor. Where extra insurance is desired to prevent this possibility, a few blocks may be nailed to the face of the header (Fig. 7-47). A part of the block extends above the floor level to prevent the sole, and subsequently the entire wall, from sliding over the edge. Next, while the crew continues to steady the frame, the same person positions himself at the end of one of the temporary braces. The braces drag along automatically as the wall goes up. Each brace end now sticks in the ground and effectively prevents at least the corners of the frame from falling back. The danger in a small crew is usually that the wall may continue over and fall away from the crew if all members are not alert to stopping it as it reaches a vertical posture.

A worker is now needed at the corner with a long level (6′ preferred). His function is to push the corner into a vertical position while holding the level against it. First he will remove the temporary nails and place a permanent nail in the sole after tapping or pushing it into place. Then he holds the level vertically against the corner post. When

it indicates plumbness he will signal the person who is now holding the far end of the brace up against the floor header to nail it on.

Before long levels were common this plumbing job was done with string lines and plumb bobs. It is still a usable technique, especially when plumbing a two-story building. Its drawback is the time-consuming nature of setting up spacer blocks, shielding the line from wind, and waiting for the string to stop swaying. A 4′ level is a fair tool for one-story plumbing. A 6′ level is the most accurate. A 2′ or 28″ level is of little or no use for wall plumbing, as it picks up only the localized character of the surface it covers.

Even a good, long level should be routinely checked for accuracy. This is done simply and quickly by rotating the body of the level to its opposite edge while taking a reading. Regardless of the position of the bubble, it should be in the identical position for both readings in relation to the strata lines on the fluid tube. If it does not read the same when the level is rotated, it indicates a faulty relation between the tube and the body of the level. Some levels are adjustable. The dial is held with two or more screws. Such a level can be adjusted satisfactorily in the field. Others cannot. A nonadjustable, faulty level should be returned to the dealer or manufacturer, who will usually repair or replace the level without charge if the instrument does not show unusual abuse. As a temporary preventive measure, one should tape over or in some way render the defective window unreadable so that it is not used unwittingly. It is wise routinely to make a level or plumb check from both edges of a level. A seemingly minor accident to a level, such as falling over from a vertical stance, can jar a bubble tube out of alignment. When the first corner of the frame wall has been plumbed, the team moves to the opposite end of the wall and repeats the process.

Straightening the Sole Plate. A string line is stretched around the corners and hooked to a nail on each end of the sole. A uniform block of wood or a 16d nail is placed under the string at each corner. A third block or nail is used as a test gauge between the string and the edge of the sole. 16d nails are set in the sole, one in each space between the studs. Each nail should be positioned so that it will ultimately penetrate the header below the subfloor. Bump the sole in or out until the gauge block fits between the string and the sole. Then sink the nail where it checks out. 16d nails can be used as spacers and a gauge as well as blocks, however the string must be constantly monitored so it does not touch the sole.

Plumbing the Lengthwise Direction of the Wall. More resistance to movement in this direction is encountered due to the fact that pressure exerted is against the joints and nails of the assembly. It may take the push and weight of several people to hold the wall while a brace is installed. If steel turnbuckle braces are available, one may be used to bring the unsquare wall into plumb. The adjustable steel tension brace is placed at the end of the wall that leans out. The top of the brace is nailed to the corner stud near the top. The bottom is nailed through the subfloor into a joist. The brace is parallel to the wall or nearly so. The brace is adjusted by shortening while the level is held in place and the wall is plumbed. The temporary diagonal wood brace is now placed on the exterior side of this first wall. It must not be put on the inside of the wall, as it will interfere with the raising of adjoining walls. Generally, this means that the end walls which go up first are braced on the outside surface. As soon as an exterior diagonal brace is nailed in place on each end of the wall, the adjustable steel brace may be removed. Braces on the longer adjoining walls, usually the front and rear walls, may be placed on the interior side of the wall so that they can be left in place during the sheathing installation. The brace must not pass across a partition post if interior partition frames are to be installed before sheathing. Where permanent inlet braces are being used on the exterior corners, temporary bracing is not needed. The wall is plumbed and the permanent brace is nailed.

Before proceeding to brace the second end of a wall frame, the corner post on that end should be checked for plumbness. In theory it will be plumb when the sole and top plate are made of equal length. In practice, the top plate frequently stretches at the joints. Putting the second plate, the top piece, on while the frame is lying on the floor helps to eliminate this stretching problem. The corner that leans out must be rectified. Where the lack of plumbness does not exceed 1/8″, it is sometimes possible to drive the top of the corner post in with a blow from a heavy hammer. Use a wood block over the post to prevent damaging it. Saw off the excess, overhanging plate. More error than 1/8″ will mandate an inspection to locate the space discrepancy. Check out each stud spacing to locate the spread error. The top plate may have to be removed and the lower piece shortened at one of its joints.

Before nailing the permanent inlet brace or the plywood corner brace, attention must be given to making *each stud* vertical (straight). The same holds true for all studs not crossed by a brace. Many studs are bowed. They may have been straight when received, but a day in the sun or heat changes their shape. They may be twisted, bowed, or crooked. Looking closely at a frame wall, it will be seen that some studs curve to the right, some to the left (bowed). Some curve toward or away from the frame surface (crooked). Some look like propellers, their ends diagonal to the spacing marks (twisted). How can these irregularities be corrected? There are some ways to deal with them.

The objective is to produce a wall frame whose studs are uniformly straight, parallel, and vertical. The spacing is to be equal and modular for all common studs throughout their height. The vertical plane is to be as flat as it can be made.

Spacing the Studs. The ends of the common studs were uniformly spaced at the time of layout. After the frame is raised, attention is turned to the straightness of the individual studs. To ignore this detail is to court many future problems. Sheathing joints will not fit well. Insulation will have gaps. Drywall nails may near-miss a stud and later produce a "popout." A technique for straightening the studs is to place a temporary 1 × 2 or 1 × 4 across the inside of a room section of exterior wall. At its end it is nailed to the interior member of the corner post. It is marked to coincide with the stud locations on the sole and upper plate. Each bowed stud is pushed to the marks. A single nail is tacked through the stringer into the stud. Leave the nail head above the surface for easy removal or use an 8d form nail. Bring the studs into alignment one by one until all are straight. Apply the sheathing over this area on the exterior before removing the spacing stringer.

Reusable Spacer Boards

For the builder of many houses it will pay to make some dadoed "story pole" spacer boards (Fig. 7-48). Make them in different lengths to accommodate large and small rooms.

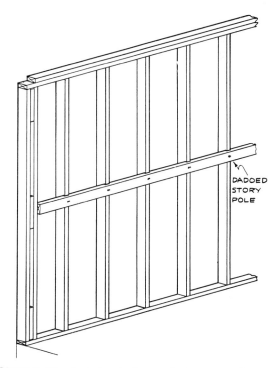

DADOED STORY POLE

FIGURE 7-48 A dadoed story pole is snapped over the studs to hold bowed ones in alignment while bracing and sheathing are nailed on.

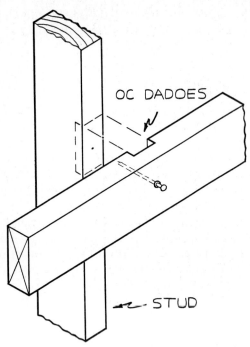

FIGURE 7-49 Dadoes are cut perfectly on stud spacing centers just loosely enough to be taken off easily.

A good combination is a set of three: a 4′, an 8′, and a 12′ spacer board. On the surface of a 2 × 4, mark dadoes 1/2″ deep by 1 1/2″ wide. Cut the dado precisely on 16″ centers. The first and last ones on the ends of the board will be half the width of the others (half the thickness of the stud, 3/4″). Now cut a dado at each 2′ centered position. These dadoes will be in the center of every other 16″ space. This board can be used to hold in proper alignment any group of structural members that is on either 16 or 24″ spacing. It may be snapped on the stud wall by successively pulling each stud into its slot. Those that do not want to stay put are tacked with an 8d form nail through the back of the dado (Fig. 7-49). The longest spacer board is started on the first stud away from the corner since the first space is always undersize (the spacing modulus having started from the exterior side of the corner post). If one wishes to carry on farther than the longest spacer board provides, another spacer board is lapped over the last space either just above or below the first spacer. This set of spacer boards can be used effectively on floor frames, ceiling frames, and roof frames as well as on all exterior and interior wall frames.

The crooked stud presents a different problem. Its direction of warp is crowned toward the interior or exterior. Either direction will tend to bow the entire wall surface out of true. Too many crooked studs in the same area of a wall will present a difficult problem. The type of sheathing has some bearing on the way the studs should be installed. When board sheathing or plywood is used, crooked studs that are not too far from straight and are not

too stiff may be used side by side on center. The crowns are alternated, one in, one out, and so on. This arrangement will cause a counteraction of stresses that helps to straighten the curves. A layer of drywall on the inside will add to the straightening process. Only straight studs should be used at the 4′ modulus positions with plywood sheathing. This is the location of the vertical joint of the ply-sheath. The pressure from plywood on the stud at this juncture is nil; therefore, a straight stud should be used there initially. *Fiberboard and Styrofoam sheathing have no straightening effect on crooked studs.*

The crooked stud that does not give promise of being straightened by the foregoing method should be placed with its crown toward the interior. When it is lying on the floor, this will be with the crown down. After sheathing is on, this maverick stud may need to be singled out for radical treatment. An extreme case, but not uncommon, would be a stud that curved into the room 1/2″. This is intolerable. It must be rectified. The stiff backbone of this unsatisfactory stud can be severed by sawing several kerfs into it (Fig. 7-50). These cuts must be made on the convex side of the stud in order to sustain its compression strength. That is the reason the crown was placed down—so that it would face the interior after the wall is raised. The outside cannot be reached as easily as the inside after sheathing is in place. When the stud is more or less uniformly curved, make the first cut in the center (halfway up the wall). Make two more cuts at quarter points (one-fourth up from the bottom and one-fourth down from the top). Cut about 1″ deep. Push on the crown of the stud. If it flexes readily, it will probably straighten out when the drywall is installed. If it con-

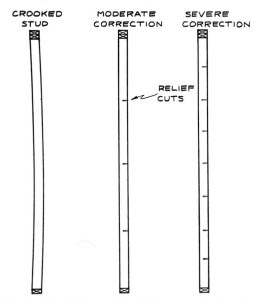

FIGURE 7-50 Make saw kerfs in a crooked stud at equal divisions or at the crest of the crooked area (saw kerfs exaggerated for graphic clarity).

tinues to resist pressure, saw the kerfs deeper; 2″ deep is considered the limit. These cuts should be made with a thin-bladed saw. When the stud is flexed to a straight posture, all the cuts should be closed on the crown side. If the three cuts close before the stud reaches straightness, make two more cuts, one between each of the initial three cuts. If all five cuts close too soon, make two more, one in the lower quarter and one in the upper quarter. This failing, open up the initial cut a very small amount, testing as you go until the stud will flex to a straight position with all kerf edges touching. Only with the kerfs tightly touching on the interior edge of the stud will its compression strength be maintained.

Some inspectors frown on this practice. Indeed, they should if it is practiced repeatedly and in close proximity. There comes a point where the too-imperfect stud should be rejected. It is downgraded, demoted to a lesser important role. It can usually be cut into short lengths for non-structural purposes.

The inspector may suggest, or order, that a sound stud be nailed alongside the kerfed one. Place the nails two to a kerfed section. Stay at least 3″ from the saw cuts. Nail from the cut stud into the whole stud. Reversing this direction may result in a section of the cut stud being broken out, in which case all of the salvage effort will have been for naught. Use 10d common or box nails.

The twisted stud does not pose a great challenge. Do not be deluded that the twist can be removed by nailing one end squarely on the marks and then twisting the other end onto the marks. It cannot be done. The problem is solved by compromising at the initial installation. Allow each end to straddle diagonally the central axis of the intended position (Fig. 7-51). Nail it in this canted attitude. This will cause one corner of the stud to protrude above the plate as it lies on the floor. The diagonally opposite corner will also protrude at the other end of the stud. On the other side of the wall, the alternate corners will protrude. This happens because the stud end is diagonal to the plate surface, which is a longer distance than when placed squarely across. *The protruding corner edges must be removed.* Use a hand plane to cut away all excess that protrudes beyond the wall faces. This is ascertained by laying a straightedge (a long level) at right angles across the offending stud and the studs on either side. As long as the edge protrudes, the level will rock on the high point. Slide the straightedge up and down the studs, planing a little at a time off the twisted stud until it no longer rocks at any point. Do this on the exterior surface while the wall is still lying horizontally on the floor. The other side will have to be done after the wall is raised.

A combination bow and crook is found in many studs. This type of board characteristic is usually beyond remedy, if at all severe. It is best to disqualify this board for stud use. About the only use that can be made of it is in the

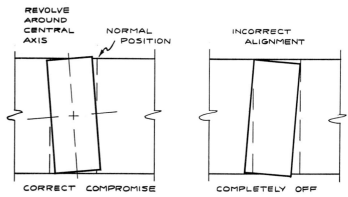

FIGURE 7-51 A twisted stud should be centered over the marks in accordance with its center axis, not by one facing edge.

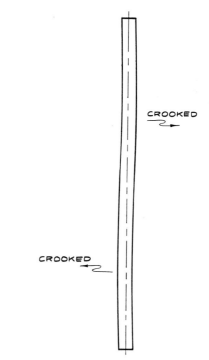

FIGURE 7-52 An elongated S-shaped stud should be cut into short usable lengths for other purposes where straight edges are not important.

brace role from wall to ground stake. There is such a need when frame walls are constructed on concrete slabs. An equally useless, malformed shape is the board that is S shaped. A part of it crooks in one direction, then reverses and crooks the other way (Fig. 7-52). This type of board can be cut into short lengths and used for blocks above ceiling nail backers.

Bracing between the Corners

Now that the corners have been braced and the soles nailed to the floor in straight lines, it is time to brace the walls at points between the corners. There are two objectives to coordinate:

1. Fix each frame wall in a plumb position throughout its length.
2. Hold the upper plate in a perfectly straight line until the ceiling and roof have been attached.

At the same time all components of the various walls should be perfectly parallel. The degree to which these objectives are attained depends on the accuracy and conscientiousness that is devoted to each step in the procedure. Partitions that intersect the exterior walls will form natural bracing potential. Therefore, a freeboard diagonal brace to the floor should not be placed near a partition post. A logical place for the first brace to be installed is toward the center of the exterior wall *between* any partition posts. Frequently, there is a window opening at this location. Such an opening provides a good place to nail the top end of the brace. The double stud provides a more solid backing against which to nail than a single stud. Nail against the trimmer stud under the header. Nailing against a single stud can easily result in the end of the stud being driven away from its location.

Adjustable Wall Braces

The one-time builder will use 2 × 4 material for braces. When the need for bracing is over, the 2 × 4s are consumed for other purposes in the house. There are, however, steel box tubing braces available that can be used repeatedly for many years (Fig. 7-53). These braces are advantagous because they can be adjusted without resetting nails. There are pivoting nail plates on each end fastened

to screw shafts. One screw is right threaded, the other is left threaded. After nailing the plates to the floor and near the top of the frame wall, a long level is held on the vertical edge of a straight stud. The tubular brace is rotated like a turnbuckle and the wall is brought into plumb. These braces function better as tension braces (pulling) than they do in the compression mode (pushing). The brace can be set up initially to work in the tension mode by first attaching the top of the brace to the side of the stud directly below the top plate. Do not nail the brace plate to the interior of the stud, as it will pull out the nails. The installer then leans on the wall, pushing it out a little beyond plumb. The bottom nail plate is then nailed while the wall is leaning out. The bottom end of the brace must be nailed through the sheathing into a joist. Sheathing alone is too flexible as a nail base. Now the turnbuckle brace is rotated in the direction that pulls (tension) the wall back to plumb. At that point a locknut is snugged up on the screw shaft. The location for the upper nail plate that will hold best is on the side of the stud. In this position the sheer stress is exerted on the two nails. When the nail plate is placed on the interior surface of the frame wall (edge of the stud), it will not hold as well under tension because it is pulling on the nails in the direction in which they come out. This is also true at the floor end of the brace. The nails at this location must be driven at as great an angle as the hole in the metal plate will permit in order to resist the pull on them. Slant the points toward the wall.

Floor Anchor Blocks for Wood Braces

When using a wood brace this same condition exists. It will improve holding power if a 2 × 4 block is nailed flat to the floor over a joist (Fig. 7-54). The end of the diagonal

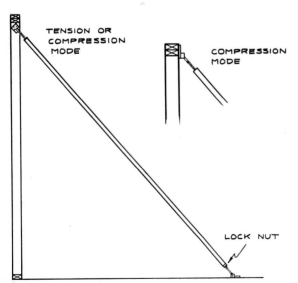

FIGURE 7-53 A fast, efficient way to brace frame walls temporarily is with adjustable steel braces.

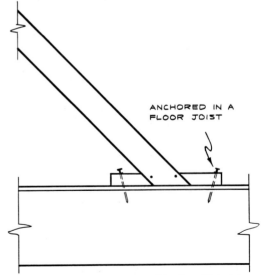

FIGURE 7-54 A wood anchor block will hold a wood brace more securely than toenailing a brace directly to the floor.

wood brace is angle cut so that two nails can be driven through the face into the edge of the block. This places sheer stress on the nails.

Brace Spacing

A brace is needed about every 8' along a wall. Rooms less than 16' long along the exterior wall will have only one brace somewhere near the center. As soon as an interior wall is erected and fastened to the partition post, a diagonal brace is placed on one face of the partition. This brace may be a 1 × 4, 1 × 6, or 2 × 4. One end of the brace is placed against the upper plate of the partition adjacent to the exterior plate. The brace is run diagonally to the sole toward the interior. This brace must not be removed until the opposite surface of the wall is covered with its skin (drywall, paneling, or whatever). For this reason the brace should be placed on whichever side will be covered last if there is a sequence. There may not be a choice. Sometimes only one side of the partition is clear of other intersections. Avoid running diagonal braces across door openings because it will result in traffic inconvenience later. The brace does not have to be adjacent to the outer wall to be effective. It does have to reach from the upper plate to the sole at an angle somewhere between 45 and 60°.

When a partition carries through in a straight line from one side of the house to the other, a single brace automatically controls the plumbness of both exterior walls at the two junctures. When soles and upper plates are made identical in length, both outer walls should be plumb and parallel when one side is made plumb. If this does not occur, look for a gap between a butt joint that has allowed the upper plate to become extended. Even the slightest difference should be corrected, as it will later affect the roof lines. Even though one brace has the potential of making both sides plumb a second brace on the other side of the house on this single partition is advisable to make the setup more rigid.

Straight Lining the Top Plate

The final objective of holding the upper plate in a straight line is accomplished in a manner similar to the way the sole was straightened. A string line is passed around the corners and tied to a nail. A block or a nail is placed under the string at each corner on the face of the plate to space it out (Fig. 7-55). A test block or nail is tried between the plate and the string while the plumbing process is going on. Hopefully, each place that is checked will reveal a stud below that checks plumb with a level. If there is more than a minor variance, an investigation should be made to locate the cause of the out-of-parallel source. Remember that the objective is to create parallelism in each rectangular framework cube. An error may be found in any of the plate line

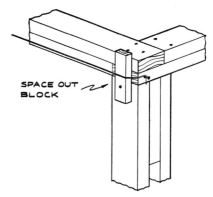

FIGURE 7-55 A string line is spaced out away from the frame with a scrap block attached at each end of the wall plate.

lengths. It must be corrected before continuing. Failure to accept this principle will cause untold problems throughout the remainder of the construction, particularly in the roof.

The central wall braces, those extending into the rooms, should not be removed until such a time as the roof decking has been installed. Only then will the upper plates be polarized in a permanent position. It is a great temptation to remove them earlier, as they are in the way. The temptation should be resisted. Without the sustaining support of these braces, the walls can move in or out under the influences of sun, wind, or construction pressures.

Sheathing

After the wall frames are secured and adequately braced, the exterior sheathing is installed. Sheathing material has gone through some evolutionary stages. Until the 1930s wood boards were the principal form. Wood was plentiful and inexpensive.

Wood Sheathing. Boards with rabbeted edges were an advancement over the square-edged boards. This molding design was called *shiplap.* Shiplap was used on top of floor joists, walls, and rafters. The rabbeted edges lapped over each other and formed a much tighter seal. With boards (S4S, surfaced four sides) and shiplap a little space had to be left between each board to accommodate expansion caused by moisture absorption. Shiplap is still a viable material wherever available at a comparable cost.

For a brief period plywood was used as an overall wall sheathing. It could be installed vertically or horizontally on walls. In the horizontal formation the sheets were staggered. A corner would be started with a full sheet on the bottom followed by a half sheet on the top. When placed vertically the plywood virtually sealed a wall. No cracks were exposed. When placed horizontally a joint existed 4' up the wall all around the house. Some builders would back up this joint with a 2 × 4 block called a firestop. The firestop block got its name from its original use in a balloon-framed wall, where a fire could start in a basement and quickly pass up the stud cavities. There was no sole to stop it. Firestop blocks were placed in the wall at various heights to stop the draft and impede the burning. Plywood has become too costly for sheathing, although it undoubtedly made the strongest wall in our history. It was also retired as a wall sheathing because products of superior insulating value appeared and at lesser cost per thickness.

A combination of sheet materials followed the all-plywood phase. A fiberboard was developed from vegetable products such as cornstalks. The trade name that became synonymous for fiberboard was Celotex. A common nickname is blackboard. Two thicknesses prevail, 1/2 and 25/32″. It comes in 8 or 9′ lengths. The 1/2″ size is still in common use. It is often used for the general sheathing where plywood forms the corner bracing. Blackboard is the least costly form of sheathing available. It requires 1 1/2″ galvanized roofing nails. The big heads are needed since the fiberboard is soft and compressible. Only blackboard that is fully asphalt treated should be used under painted or stained wood. Fiberboard, with only surface coating, absorbs moisture and causes paint to peel from siding installed over it.

Styrofoam Sheathing.   The most recent trend in sheathing is toward high-insulating sheet products such as Styrofoam. Standard sizes are available in 4′ × 8′ square edged and 2′ × 8′ edge matched (tongue and grooved or V grooved). Common thicknesses are 1/2″, 5/8″, 3/4″, and 1″. Custom sizes may be obtained from cutting plants. Styrofoam is exceptionally easy to cut at the plant. It is done on a large slicer composed of electrically heated wires. The wires melt the foam as it is pushed through the wire frame. The styrofoam is fed through in large blocks and emerges in as many sheets as the wires were set to "cut."

There are different types of foam. Some are dense and will hold a wet plaster coating. Others are course bead and not suitable for a plaster base. Some have a foil backing. The designer/builder should make a thorough study of the characteristics of the various forms and brands of Styrofoam so that a specific type can be specified. There is a large range of difference in heat and cool retention per thickness and also in cost.

Styrofoam sheathing has no practical structural strength. It must not be counted upon to aid the structural characteristics of a frame in any way. It therefore requires many less nails. Large sheet metal–headed nails called "simplex" are placed 12 or 16″ apart. Where Styrofoam is used as the only sheathing on a wall, special consideration must be given to wind bracing. The expanding use of Styrofoam under siding and brick veneer has regenerated the historical inlet diagonal corner brace. A newer form of brace is also in widespread use. It is the steel band diagonal brace. The steel brace is a flat galvanized band with holes about 1″ apart. It is intended to be surface mounted. However, the thickness of the metal is enough to interfere with drywall installation when the brace is installed on the interior face of the exterior wall. It bulges the gypsum board at each point where the brace crosses a stud. For this reason the steel brace should be inlet like the wood brace where it is used on the interior side of the exterior wall frame. This shallow dado is done much easier and quicker than the dado for a wood brace. The skill saw is set for an 1/8″-deep cut. It is held in both hands like a router. The guard is held back. The saw is passed back and forth over the desired spot. The wood is removed as it would be with a router. If there is a router in the tool inventory, it is the most suitable machine for this operation.

The steel brace may be put on the exterior side of the wall without inletting when Styrofoam will be over it. With brick veneer there is no need to inlet the brace since a slight bulge of the sheathing into the air space will be of no consequence. Under sheet siding, such as reverse-batt rough-sawn plywood, the bulging can be subdued. Before putting on the siding, place a scrap block of wood (2 × 4) on the surface of the Styrofoam sheathing over the brace at the point where it crosses the stud and plates. Rap the block a sharp blow with your hammer. This will compress the Styrofoam over the brace and help to dissipate the bulge. Under horizontal siding it is best to inlet the brace because the narrow individual boards will follow the contours of the brace. In certain angles of the sunlight a noticeable deviation from a straight shadow line will appear.

Walls are most often braced at the corners only. When Styrofoam is used, more bracing is needed in some places. Long walls, for example, with much space between the corner braces can use additional braces to advantage. Walls with windows or doors close to the corners may be braced with a K formation. The K brace is formed with two shorter diagonals reaching from the plates to a central location on the corner post. They are effective when a surface area is limited. The weakest part of a wall frame is at a door opening. When additional braces are desired, a good place to put one or two is adjacent to the door opening, especially if it is centrally located in the wall.

A general rule of thumb is to add additional bracing when Styrofoam sheathing is used. The typical 12′-nominal-length brace spans the hypotenuse of the triangle formed by the sole and the corner post at approximately a 45° angle. This means that the top end starts on the upper plate a few inches away from the corner post and extends downward to a point on the sole that is a few inches farther than 8′ from the corner. Counting the brace at the opposite end of the wall approximately 16′ of stud area is crossed by the two corner braces. Remember that Styrofoam has no resistance to pressures. It does not stiffen or pull studs into common surface alignment as some other sheathing types do.

A diagonal wood brace used with Styrofoam therefore takes on an additional role. It assists the studs that it crosses to resist lateral pressures. With this thought in mind it becomes feasible, practical, and in some situations, advisable to diagonally brace the entire wall expanse. Where studs of lesser quality are used, it is advisable. Where studs of superior quality are used, there should be no area greater than 8′ in horizontal linear distance left unbraced. The logical areas to brace are those where no partitions intersect and no openings interrupt the surface.

Nailing the Sheathing. Nailing to the studs and plates should follow the manufacturer's recommendations. Some fiberboard manufacturers print white or yellow dots on the blackboard; some provide indentations, to indicate the location of the studs as well as the quantity of nails to use. Generally there are one and one-half to two times as many nails prescribed around the edges as in the field. The exact nail desired is not always available locally. When one is forced to accept a smaller nail than desired, the deficiency may be overcome by using more nails spaced closer together. With wood sheathing a minimum penetration rule is to use a nail at least four times as long as the thickness of the sheathing. Three-fourths of the nail should anchor in the stud. For blackboard the length should be at least three times as long as the board thickness and have a large head (this mandates roofing nails or simplex-headed nails). Because blackboard has a small measure of structural value, the nail spacing is quite close. Styrofoam, by contrast, requires fewer nails because the only function of the fastener is to keep the sheet flat against the frame. Simplex nails have large sheet metal heads (about 1″) of either round or square shape. They are specifically designed for the soft, crushable forms of Styrofoam. The spacing need not be closer than 12″ both in field or on the edges of sheet Styrofoam when using the simplex fastener.

CODE-SPECIFIED FASTENERS

Most building codes will specify nails of a particular size and/or type for certain places in the building structure. In this text both general and specific recommendations are given to assist the builder in choosing the correct fastener. Excerpts from a typical code are presented in Appendix 1. Some principles bear repeating.

- If the board splits, the position of the nail is incorrect (usually too close to the end of the board) or the diameter of the nail is too large. Solutions: Move farther away from the end, use a smaller-diameter nail, or tap a pilot hole in the top board.
- Use longer nails when the anchor is end grain.

- When face nailing use nails only long enough to penetrate fully the two boards they hold together. Protruding excess is useless and dangerous.
- Angle all nails to gain holding advantage (except drywall, paneling, and roofing nails, or others where the heads must be flat with the surface).
- Drive nails in such a way that the material surface is not marred with needless half-moon hammer marks. Learn to dimple accurately.
- Remember that more is not necessarily better. Two well-placed and driven nails of a good size are more effective than several nails that split or do not anchor adequately.

WALL AND FOUNDATION ALIGNMENT

There are four ways to line up the exterior framework above the foundation wall.

1. The rough frame building line system places all the wood members on the floor and wall frame in vertical line flush with the foundation exterior. This vertical line coincides with the building line.
2. The inset sole system has the sole plate, and consequently the frame wall, set back from the building line an amount equal to the thickness of the sheathing.
3. The header inset system leaves only the sill plate extended flush with the building line.
4. The full inset system recesses all wood frame materials back from the building line an amount equal to the sheathing thickness.

Each system has some unique characteristics that may influence the choice of systems to be used. The explanations to follow relate the systems to modular length and width house plans whose dimensions are evenly divisible by 16, 24, or 48″.

Full Lineup Design

The full lineup design (Fig. 7-56) is perhaps the easiest to lay out. It does not confuse the first stud spacing with any type of dropback. The plates are laid flush with the corner of the subfloor, which is flush with the foundation. The point of beginning (POB) is the end of the plate. Corner post marks are put on the end of the plates. From there on two stud marks are made at each stud location. One is placed 3/4″ short of the module spacing number (16 or 24″). The second mark is placed 3/4″ beyond the module. This provides a 1 1/2″ set of parallel lines between which each stud is placed. The tongue of the framing square is

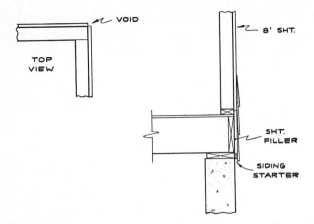

FIGURE 7-56 The frame lineup system places all wood framing above the foundation flush with the building lines, the vertical surface of the foundation.

exactly 1 1/2″ wide. It provides for perfect tracing of the spacing location.

When the frame walls at the ends of the house are raised first, the ends of the sole plates will be made flush with the front and rear building lines. The exterior surface of the frame wall is made flush with the building line. Each time an assembled component is put in place it should be put on straight regardless of the accuracy of other components that preceded. For example, the floor header may not be perfectly straight. If it bowed in 1/4″, the sole plate of the frame wall should still be nailed in a straight line above it. To accomplish a straight-line position with the full vertical lineup system, a chalk line is snapped where the interior edge of the sole should be. For a 2 × 4 stud wall the starting and ending points of the chalk line will be a point 3 1/2″ in from the corner of the foundation on the subfloor. The sole is brought to the line and nailed through the sheathing into the header band.

There are advantages and disadvantages to the rough-frame in-line system. Advantages include the fact that 9′ sheathing boards of Styrofoam or blackboard may be used. The 9′ length, placed vertically, covers the joint between the sole and the subfloor and seals it well against air infiltration. It gives a deep shadow line at the bottom of the siding. This is desirable when thin siding is used. Spacing of studs is simplified a little, as the carpenter does not constantly have to remind himself that spacing relates to a certain dropback or inset.

A couple of small disadvantages exist. Where the dimensions of the foundation are modular and terminate in 16″, 2′, or 4′ modules, the sheathing boards will end precisely at the corner of the corner post. This prevents lapping the sheathing at the corner. This little vertical square void makes it more difficult to nail the various patterns of lap and drop siding. It is more difficult to nail on the metal corners over bevel siding. Unless this void is filled with a

square strip of wood, it provides access for vermin and bugs.

Further protection against bugs is desirable. Around the bottom of soft sheathing types, a solid wood starter strip is needed. It performs as a solid backup for siding and a barrier to the vermin that delight in chewing away soft material. Custom ripping of the starting strip is usually required unless only 3/4″-thick sheathing is used.

Inset Wall Frame Design

The inset wall-frame system (Fig. 7-57) has the floor components lined up flush with the foundation building line. The outer face of the frame wall is then set back from the edge an amount equal to the thickness of the sheathing. The exterior face of the sheathing is on the building line. Sheets of sheathing are then purchased in 8′ lengths. The frame wall with the precut stud is 97 1/8″ high. The 8′ piece of sheathing rests on top of the subfloor. Its top edge is 1 1/8″ down from the top of the upper plate. With conventional roofs of 3-in-12 pitch or less, the birdsmouth seat cut will neatly fit just above the sheathing (see Chapter 8). Higher pitches will require making the plumb cut of the birdsmouths outside the sheathing. Trusses are not affected as they have no birdsmouth.

The principal advantage of the inset sole system is economy. A full band of sheathing materials, as high as the sill and band header combined, is saved. In regions where heat and cool conservation are objectives, the saving of a little material in this manner may turn out to be false economy in the long run. Unless the header area between the floor joists above the sill is well insulated, this area may account for significant heat loss, especially in a home with a basement.

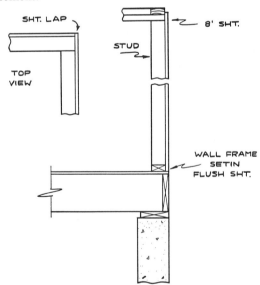

FIGURE 7-57 The inset frame eliminates the skirt filler and corner void.

The sole plate setback system just described permits a corner lap of the sheathing. The first sheathing board will run past the corner stud to the floor corner (zero point). The sheet that meets it around the corner will be reduced in width an amount equal to its thickness. The other edge of this sheet will then center on the stud 4' from the corner building line. From there on, each sheet will fit without cutting until the last sheet. The last sheet on the same side will be custom fitted to the remaining space.

Header Inset System

A third setback system provides for all wood materials to be set back except the sill (Fig. 7-58). The sill remains on the building line flush with the vertical face of the foundation. This indentation begins with the floor header bands which are set in on the sill the amount of the sheathing thickness. This system works well with soft sheathing types. The sill provides a solid wood band of 1 1/2" height around the foundation line, to which siding can be firmly nailed. It can even substitute as a starter strip for bevel siding. The sill is simply overhung as much as the starter strip thickness would be. Used in this role it is important that the facing edge of the sill be made perfectly straight. The bottom course of siding will mirror the straightness, or lack of it.

Another consideration with the header inset is the amount of joist bearing that remains. Most building codes call for a minimum bearing of 4". Where a header is lined up flush with the facing edge of the sill, this code rule mandates a 2 × 6 as the smallest sill that can be used. 1 1/2" of header thickness subtracted from 5 1/2" actual width of a 2 × 6 leaves exactly the minimum 4" of bearing surface. Therefore, when the header is set in, it will require a larger (wider) sill to maintain a minimum bearing surface for the ends of the floor joists.

Some builders of homes with basements prefer to use the 2 × 8 sill routinely. It provides an inner nailing surface that is close enough to the interior wall surface to be useful for nail backing of finishing materials on the interior of the basement wall.

To visualize the combination of stock materials, place a 9' sheet of sheathing on the frame which has a setback floor box. Use the most common floor joist, 2 × 10; the most common floor sheathing, 1/2" plywood; and a precut stud. The total height with plates from the top of the sill to the top of the upper plate is 106 7/8". This means that the 108"-high sheathing will protrude above the top plate 1 1/8". This necessitates cutting a notch for each rafter or truss tail or cutting off the excess all the way across the sheathing. Notching the sheathing makes the operation of hoisting and positioning a truss a little more precarious. It is easy to crush and break out chunks of the sheathing above the plate. With Styrofoam the breaking sometimes extends below the plate because there are few nails along the edge of the sheet. On the other hand, when a combination of 9' fiberboard sheathing and a 2 × 8 component floor is used, an auxiliary advantage can be gained. In this case the sheathing protrudes 3 1/8" above the plate. This is enough to act as an effective insulation stop between the roof sheathing and the top plate when 2 × 4 truss chords are used. For this role accurate notching and careful placement of the trusses are essential. Where a good wall bracing job exists, the trusses may be raised first followed by fitting of the sheathing.

Full-Frame Inset System

The full-frame inset method (Fig. 7-59) consists of dropping *all wood materials* back from the edge of the foundation an amount equal to the sheathing thickness. Of the inset methods, this one is probably the simplest. Starting with the sill, all framing is lined up vertically back from the edge of the foundation as much as the sheathing thick-

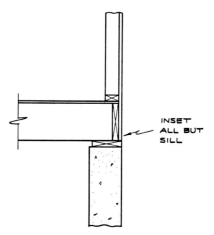

FIGURE 7-58 All but the sill is set back. The sill acts as a siding starter strip.

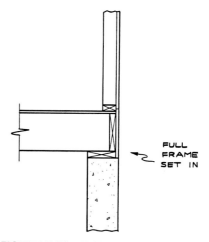

FIGURE 7-59 Full set-in of all framing.

ness. The basic consideration to remember is that stud spacing has its POB at the foundation line, *not at the corner of the floor*. This means that the first piece of wall sheathing at the corner will hang over the framework corner but its vertical edge will be flush with the foundation. The adjacent sheet around the corner will need to be reduced in width an amount equal to its thickness (the same amount as the setback). This arrangement provides a lapped corner. The outer surface of the sheathing will be flush with the foundation all around the building.

The height relationship with the top plate is again unique to the system. The sheathing is in contact with and resting on the foundation. With 2 × 10 joists the top of the 9' sheathing board is 3/8" down from the top of the plate. This is an ideal position in terms of full insulation coverage of the framework. With 2 × 8 joists the sheathing extends 1 5/8" above the top plate unless it is sawed off.

SLAB-FLOOR LINEUPS

With the slab floor there are two lineup choices, the flush and the setback. Many of the concrete slab floor houses are brick veneered. This poses some considerations. There are a variety of perimeter insulation methods and designs that may also affect the decision to setback.

Brick-veneer setbacks are affected by the brick size and the sheathing thickness. A standard brick ledge on which the bricks are laid is 4" deep. Brick of 4" nominal horizontal depth will take up the entire ledge when bonded.

The actual size of the brick is about 3 5/8". This allows for a 3/8" masonry bond of mortar behind the brick when the face of the brick lines up with the face of the foundation. This size of brick will have its back side only 3/8" beyond the building line. Masons prefer more space than this to lay the brick. About 1/2" is a minimum finger space for laying the brick. Some plans show an inch cavity. An inch is too much. Brickmold casing around windows and doors will not lap the brick enough for adequate sealing with caulking. With 4" brick veneer the frame wall should be set back a little more than the thickness of the sheathing to create a space between the brick veneer and the wall of 1/2 to 3/4" (Fig. 7-60).

Brick of 3" horizontal depth is the choice of many builders in localities where it is available. With this size brick a full inch is available beyond the building line (Fig. 7-61). 1/2" by 9' fiberboard or Styrofoam can be used on a frame that is flush with the building line. It is run below the sole level, which helps insulate at the slab level. There will be adequate finger room (1/2") to lay the brick.

Sheathing of greater than 1/2" thickness will require setting back (Fig. 7-62). A frame wall with 1"-thick styrofoam, for example, may be set back 1 1/4" with 4" nominal brick (actual 3 5/8"). This setback nets a cavity of 5/8". With 3" brick and 1" sheathing the frame could be set back only part of the thickness of the sheathing, so that a portion of the thickness filled the too-deep cavity.

Should the mason find too little space available with the face of the brick lined up with the ledge face, he has a limited option of corbeling (Fig. 7-63). Corbeling means

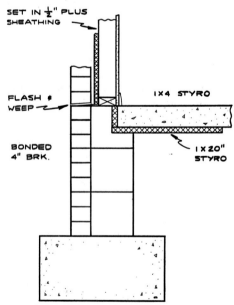

FIGURE 7-60 This illustration shows a typical frame setback to accommodate 3/4" soft sheathing and provide a 1/2" space. Note weep hole, flashing, and slab insulation details.

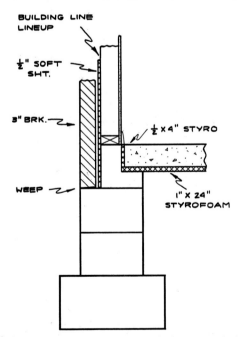

FIGURE 7-61 Preferred design to keep weep holes well below all wood parts. Twelve-inch foundation blocks are more economical than brick for deep foundations.

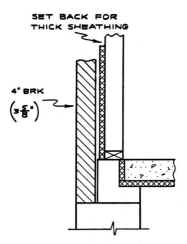

FIGURE 7-62 Thick wall sheathing and nominal-4″ brick require setting back the wall frame.

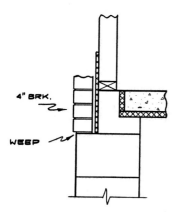

FIGURE 7-63 Corbeling (overhanging) the brick siding is an alternative for use with sheathing outside the building line or an irregular foundation line (outward bulges).

overhanging a masonry unit. Corbeling is permissible up to 25% of the depth of a unit on chimneys and fireplaces. This means that a 4″ brick could be laid with 1″ hanging over. This much overhang is not advisable with veneer siding. The siding is only one wythe deep (single brick depth) with no masonry backup. Corbeling on a ledge for brick veneer should be limited to about 10%. In inches the maximums would be about 1/2″ for 4″ brick and 3/8″ for 3″ brick. Despite the reduced bearing of the corbeled veneer the system provides an option that the mason can use under various conditions. A frame wall that bulges outward is one of the conditions which force the brick line to be set farther out from the frame wall.

Wood-, aluminum-, and vinyl-sided houses call for similar adaptations of the setback frame. It is practical to draw a section view of all the components that are anticipated to be assembled on the slab if one is not provided or if any material changes are made. Keep in mind that it is not practical to attempt to fasten any starter strips for siding to the concrete; also, that the edges of soft sheathing types must not be exposed on the lower edge even though they are adequately covered on the surface against the elements. Most siding types require a solid nail backer of some type around the bottom perimeter. Styrofoam will not fill this role. With these limitations in mind, a plan will evolve that determines the required amount of frame setback. Finally, remember to take the setback into account at the beginning and end of the stud spacing.

PARTITION LAYOUT AND ANCHORING

Parallelism and squareness are primary objectives when laying out the floor plan on the subfloor. There are different systems of dimensioning partition locations. Some plans will be dimensioned to the centerline of the partitions. Others will use a hypothetical wall thickness such as 4″ and dimension to the edge. The latter type requires adding 2″ to that end of the dimension to locate a centerline of the partition. The most common partition frame is made of 2 × 4s. The actual depth (thickness) of the frame is therefore 3 1/2″. The carpenter must also interpret the dimension in relation to its beginning at the exterior wall. The wall symbol may be drawn 5 or 6″ in depth. It may be 4″ inside the building line. These symbolic drawing techniques make it necessary for the carpenter to interpret the plan. He must not read such a plan literally. Rendering a floor plan with modular characteristics as recommended in Chapters 2 and 4 greatly simplifies the layout process. The dimensions may be taken literally instead of symbolically.

Transferring Plans to a Floor

After the dimensions are figured out, it becomes a task of transferring them to the floor. When the partition posts (the two blocked studs) have been built into the exterior wall, a starting point is established for rooms that have an exterior exposure. These points should nonetheless be rechecked for accuracy. If in error, it is easier to move the T than to move a whole partition or alter the plan. The intersection partitions are brought off the exterior wall at right angles unless purposely angled. This is accomplished by duplicating the distance on the opposite side of the room from the building line (Fig. 7-64). For example, when a T is 21′-8 1/2″ from the interior edge of the sole at the end of the house, that same measurement is made at the interior corner of the room. When a room is 12′ deep (in from the exterior wall), the corner of the room will be at an intersection point 12′ in and 21′-8 1/2″ from the end wall measured parallel to the exterior wall. The remaining interior corner is located in the same way. Theoretically, the room corners will now be square and the walls parallel. In reality, such will be the case only when the exterior soles have been perfectly placed with square corners, parallel sides,

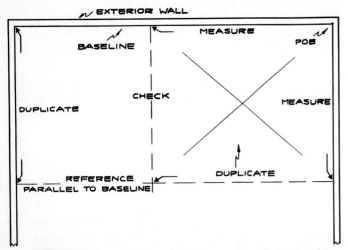

FIGURE 7-64 Lay out a corner room by referencing from a point of beginning (POB) and the opposite side of the house.

and with opposite sides of identical length. Rough carpentry seldom meets the ultimate of perfection, although it should constantly be attempted. When the interior corners of a room have tentatively been located, a diagonal checkout is made. If it is a little off, make an adjustment by moving both the interior wall corners an equal amount in the direction that will equalize the diagonal distances. This movement is made to right or left on a parallel line with the exterior walls.

Compromising squareness is occasionally forced on the carpenter. He must adapt to an undesirable absence of squareness or parallelism. It then becomes a decision of where to place the unsquare corner or wall. Some logical criteria exist. Large rooms may have less squareness or parallelism without it showing up so much. Kitchens where cabinets will be hung should be held to a rigid standard of parallelism, squareness, and plumbness. Any deviation will show up drastically in ill-fitted cabinets and trim. Floors where squares of linoleum tile or parquet flooring are specified will show off badly at the side edges when the room is not square. Compromise by placing the unsquareness in an area that will be carpeted wall to wall with a nonpatterned design. The goal is to make the structure so near perfect that few if any compromises will be required. Remember that *an irresponsible attitude in the rough construction phase leads to a compounding of problems* as the house progresses toward completion.

Points of beginning for partition layout relate to the type of construction technique practiced. The traditional stick-built house has all exterior and interior walls raised and secured before the roof is installed. Another technique, called *open framing,* has only the exterior walls built and erected followed by installation of the roof. The interior remains open (free of partitions) until the building is closed in against the weather. "Closed in" means that

all windows, doors, and roofing are installed. This system has many advantages, which are explained in Chapter 6, page 116.

Where the conventional stick-built technique is used, the location of partitions will start at floor level and rise to the ceiling. Partition starting points will be transcribed to a point on the floor below the corners of the spacer blocks at the bottom of the partition Ts that are found in the exterior walls. From these two points the interior sole lines are laid out on the subfloor. After confirming the corners, by paralleling and diagonal checking, chalk lines are snapped (Fig. 7-65). Some builders find it advantageous to set a nail in all the corner locations because marks on the floor can easily be lost or misread. When the partition is raised, the end stud, which completes the T at the intersection with the exterior wall, is carefully plumbed and surface nailed with two nails into each spacer block. 10d common nails are adequate. Since there are already three or four nails in this little block, any size larger than 10d runs the risk of splitting the block. The top piece of the double upper plate is then lapped over the exterior plate (lower member) and nailed. This completes the tie-in of the partition to the exterior wall.

Where the top member of the exterior wall upper plate has been preinstalled, a 3 1/2" gap is provided over the intersection post. This may be used as a point of beginning for partition locating. The plumbing process is simply reversed. A plumb line is projected down from the edge of this opening in the plate. This establishes the location of

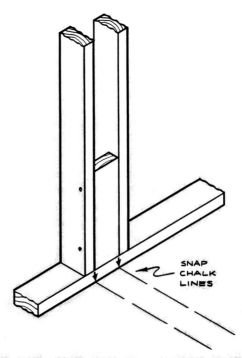

FIGURE 7-65 Chalk lines for a partition location are snapped directly below the block in the partition post.

the partition sole on the floor which it meets the exterior wall. The distance, which would usually be taken off the blueprint in the previous method, is now measured on the floor and duplicated on the other side of the room. It should be compared with the dimension on the plan. A variance of more than a fraction of an inch is cause to move the partition to a corrected location.

Either layout method may be used with equal success when all the elements of parallelism, plumbness, and squareness are met on the floor, the walls, and the ceiling. Even when the top plate of the exterior wall has been preinstalled, the partition can be plumbed from the bottom up. It may mean cutting the crossover opening a little larger should it not be precisely over the floor layout. If the misalignment amounts to more than a small fraction of an inch, an investigation should be made to determine whether the error lies with the original plate layout, the present partition layout, or the plumbness of the wall.

Anchoring Top Plates of Partitions

The way to hold an interior top plate in a desired position differs depending on whether the ceiling joists are parallel to a partition or cross over it perpendicularly. The anchoring technique is unique to each category. The objective remains the same, to secure the plate in a rigid, straight line. When the sole is straight, the end studs are plumb, and the top plate is straight and parallel with the sole, the potential exists for a vertically flat wall surface. The customary way to achieve this objective is to attach the top plate in some manner to the ceiling joists.

Long centrally located partition(s) are usually erected first. Consider the typical arrangement where the ceiling joists cross over such a partition. There are three ceiling joist alignment objectives.

1. The joists follow a consistent spacing pattern (16 or 24″ is the most common).

2. All joists should be parallel to each other throughout their length from exterior wall to exterior wall.

3. Regardless of how many pieces of wood or joints in the spanning set, it should be straight.

In theory, each joist will parallel the ends of the house. Attempting to make a joist parallel to the end wall plate by measuring in from the end wall anywhere but at the corners is a poor practice. Any little bow of the end wall top plate, in or out, will be reproduced throughout the whole ceiling frame of the house by this method (Fig. 7-66). Joists that are made parallel to a bowed end wall will be slightly diagonal to the ceiling rectangle. The problem created is that the ceiling framework in each room will then be running trapezoidally across the room. The attitude

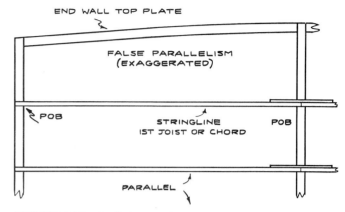

FIGURE 7-66 As little as 1/8″ of inward or outward bow in the end plate will set the stage for problems with the ceiling throughout the house. String line the first ceiling joist set to assure parallelism from there on. (The top plate is greatly exaggerated for graphic emphasis.)

that an 1/8 or 1/4″ error in this situation is inconsequential leads to much grief when it is time to install modular ceiling-covering materials. The ends of two butting sheets of gypsum board that meet on a joist will have just 3/4″ each of nail-backing surface. That is under optimum conditions of perfectly square and straight construction. Any deviation from joist straightness or parallelism will reduce this already minimum nail base. This problem is eliminated by seeing to it that the imperfection is contained in the area where it exists, in this case, the end wall.

The first full set of ceiling joists is string-lined completely across the house and then nailed to the bearing position. It is then used as a point of beginning to mark the spacing and location of all the remaining joists on the partition plate.

The partition sole of the centrally located initial partition is nailed to the floor using a chalked line as a guide. The two end studs are nailed plumb in their positions. A spaced-out string line is stretched alongside the top plate. The first ceiling joist is nailed to the top plate to be used as a POB. The remaining joists are ready to be nailed on their centers.

Fixing the top plate of a parallel partition to the ceiling joists is more difficult than to fix it to joists that are perpendicular to the plate. The partition ends are plumbed. After the string line is set out alongside the top plate, the plate is bumped into position. Inscribe a mark alongside both sides of the top plate on the underside of the joist. A pair of toenails is then started in the vertical surfaces of the joist over the plate. Place one nail on each side. Each will be 1″ inside the opposite edges of the plate so that they do not enter the plate in the same grain line. Bring the joist to a position of straightness using the pencil marks as your guide (Fig. 7-67).

It must be kept in mind that any offset caused by lapping of joists affects both the starting points and the center

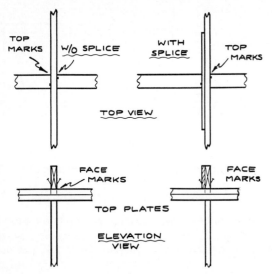

FIGURE 7-67   Mark along each side of the chord or joist and toenail it to the plate.

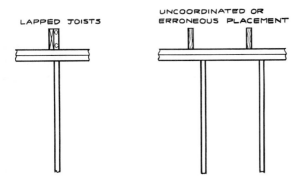

FIGURE 7-68   The on-center member of lapped joists is placed over the marks. Joists or chords placed elsewhere indicate nonmodular or uncoordinated placement of studs or misplaced ceiling joists.

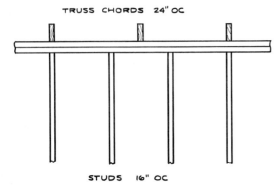

FIGURE 7-69   Two-foot-spaced trusses should coordinate over bearing wall studs in this manner. Every other stud will support a truss chord with direct bearing.

location (Fig. 7-68). Placing trusses in position, for example, is simpler than rafters and joists. The upper and lower chords of a truss are on the same 1 1/2″-thick plane. *Marks can be projected vertically from the stud marks* on both sides of the house.

With trusses there is no offset for lower chords as with lapped joists. Trusses are usually placed on 24″ spacing modules. Starting at the POB (point of beginning), this projecting method can be used to mark every other truss seat location when studs are on 16″ spacing centers (Fig. 7-69). This will be the positions over the 4′ modulus. The stud line up in the bearing partition will correspond to the studs in the exterior walls. The truss chords will then line up over the partition studs in the same relative places. The chalk line is held on the chord seat marks and snapped on the partition plate. Place the truss chord adjacent to the line and trace a second line on the opposite side of the chord. By so doing, there is never a question as to which side of the line the chord goes. It goes between the two lines. A string line may be preferred over the chalk line since a lot of chalk is needlessly wasted over the open rooms. The lines are drawn under the stringline with a pencil. To accomplish this final positioning efficiently requires the services of at least three workers, one each holding the string at the seat location and one to mark the partition. One worker can do the job by running the string around nails. Another efficient method of spacing the joists for nailing is to use the notched story pole on the joists after the first POB set has been nailed.

The chord or joist is now ready to be toenailed permanently. The toenails are struck alternate blows. By alternating the blows to the two nails that are on opposite sides, the toenails will not draw the joist away from the marks so much.

Backer Boards

A partition that is parallel to the ceiling framework is more difficult to hold in place rigidly. It is attached to the two nearest ceiling joists. These joists are flexible until the ceiling is attached. To freeze them in a straight formation, it is necessary to install temporary braces. A backer board is also needed on top of the plate to which the ceiling skin will be attached. This backer becomes an integral part of the plate-to-joist anchoring system.

The backer board is a full-length 1 × 6 nailed to the top of the partition plate (Fig. 7-70). It is placed so that 1″ hangs over each side of the plate, assuming that neither adjacent joist is within 1″ of the plate. 8d common nails are driven at an angle at about 6″ intervals staggered from side to side. This seems like a lot of nails, but remember that the ceiling gypsum board will be nailed to the underside of this 1″ overhanging edge. It must withstand substantial pounding from the underside. Fewer nails to hold

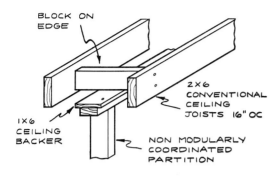

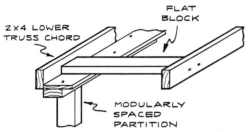

FIGURE 7-70 Ceiling backing board systems. Blocks may be flat or on edge, but there are implications involved with roll or batt insulation.

down the backer board will net a springy surface. It is difficult to nail into a springy backer. With nails on top staggered at 6″ intervals, they are actually 12″ apart on each side. This is usually adequate to keep the board from being driven up off the plate when the ceiling is nailed to it.

The backer board should be at least 7″ longer than the wall length. This will allow each end of the board to lap over onto the plates that cross each end. This lap will add significantly to the solidity of the backing at the room corners. It will also help prevent the backer overhang from splitting. The success of this end lap depends largely on whether it can be nailed split-free onto the intersecting plate.

Backer blocks (Fig. 7-71) are installed next. A backer block is usually made of 2 × 4 stock. It is nailed across the space between the two ceiling joists. A block is needed at each end just inside the room corner. These two blocks will help hold down the ends of the backer board. Another block is needed for each 32 to 48″ of linear space along the plate. The objective is to divide the length into equal spaces with the blocks. Examples: In a room 12′ long there will be four blocks and three 4′ spaces (blocks on 48″ centers with one at each end); a room 9′ long will have the same quantity of blocks but placed 3′ apart.

Do *not* measure the space between the joists at any point out in the room to ascertain the block length. A dimension must never be taken from a point where materials are flexible. For ceiling joists on 16″ centers, the blocks will be cut precisely 14 1/2″ long, the actual modulus distance between the joists. Truss chords on 24″ centers will require blocks precisely 22 1/2″ long. Do not compromise

this precision. It is an opportunity to use a control technique. Use the stop block method on the miter or radial saw to duplicate cut the blocks to length.

Blocks may be installed on edge or flat. The on-edge position causes a little more stiffness for the ceiling backup purpose. Where fiberglass blanket insulation is specified, the blanket must be cut and fit around each block. When the blocks are positioned flat, it is feasible to roll the insulation out over them. With blown or fill insulation it does not matter in which posture the block is placed.

Whichever position is chosen, the lower edge is lined up at a point above the bottom of the joist equal to the thickness of the backer board. With the 1 × 6 specified earlier, this is 3/4″, the actual thickness of the material. Since material varies a little in thickness, this distance should be the exact amount of the material used. The objective is to establish an equal level for the underside of the joists and the top of the plate. Nail through the joists into the ends of the blocks. Use two 16d nails per side. Angle each nail slightly downward.

Next the two ceiling joists between which the blocks are installed must be straightened and immobilized. This is a critical point in the procedure. It is another of those procedures which, when ignored, will cause future difficulties. The two rafters have been fixed together with the blocks. They are parallel but seldom straight and never rigid on a long partition. A string line is used to establish a straight face on one of the joists. A diagonal brace is then installed from a central point on the joist to a bearing partition or exterior wall.

This is a good time to space out the other joists. Most of them will be bowed to some extent. To make them parallel to each other and equidistant apart, a notched story pole may be used as a spacer. Another way is to nail a scrap board perpendicularly across the joists down the center of the span. Since the ceiling backer joists have been braced in a straight line, they may function as the point of beginning for the spacing of the others. On the ceiling that will be drywalled the first course of gypsum board will extend 4′ into the room. Therefore, a spacer strip should be placed beyond this point. The spacer board should stay on until a

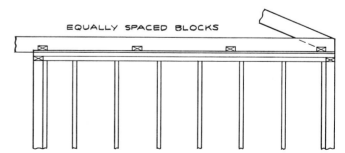

FIGURE 7-71 A block is positioned above each end of the ceiling backup board and equally spaced between 32 to 48″ apart.

course or two of gypsum board is in place. The ceiling wallboard then serves the spacing function.

Where trusses are used, it is not usually possible or practical to brace diagonally from above the ceiling chord. The truss webs get in the way. It must be done on the underside of the ceiling frame. Frequently, the spacing board is enough to solidify the two critical chord/joists over the partition. The temporary fixing of several joists together by the spacer board makes them more inflexible. It also has a self-aligning effect on the group. If the spacer board is attached first, it may not be necessary to diagonal brace the partition-holding pair of joists.

The next objective is to make the partition plate straight and consequently the partition plumb and flat. It is not practical to strike a chalkline across the blocks to align the edge of the ceiling backer board. The backer board is seldom straight. The backer's function is nonstructural, and therefore it can be of an inexpensive quality. This usually means nonstraight stock. To use such an alignment technique it would also be mandatory that the hangover of the backer board be parallel to the top plate. This is more effort than it is worth. Plumb the ends of the partition as described for bearing partitions. Place a string line along the vertical face of the top plate a couple of inches down from the backer. Use a spacer block under each end of the string. Start an 8d nail into the underside of the backer board at each point under the backer blocks except the end ones. Push the partition toward or away from the string line until the test block fits between the string and the plate. Mark a line along the edge of the ceiling backer on the backer block. Sink the backer board nail while holding the position on the line. Align each block and backer intersection in the same manner, and nail. When one side of the partition is secured, the opposite side may be nailed.

Other backer boards include those used behind wallboard joints, where a firm anchoring material is needed. Backers of this type are not always put in. They are a symbol of quality, however. They will, in the minds of knowledgeable consumers, symbolize a good-quality builder.

Backer boards of a third type serve a practical purpose at the top corners of window openings. In this position, curtain hangers can be screwed to the wall at uniform distances from the right and left sides of the window. Without the backer boards, the curtain rod bracket is customarily nailed or screwed to the window casing. This practice has never been a satisfactory method. The current universal moldings are 2 1/4″ wide. The upper corners are miter joined. Almost without exception, this molding will end up split from the rod bracket nails. Seldom do they hold for any length of time except perhaps with very light curtains.

Another factor in the positioning of a curtain rod is the quantity of light that is desired from the window. There is little logic in having a 3′ window to gain light and/or

ventilation if several inches will be lost on each side because the opened curtain is bunched over the glass. This kind of common sense leads the decorator to place the curtain rod brackets on the wall as many inches away from the glass as the accordioned curtain may be expected to cover. This distance usually falls at a point between the studs where no solid backing exists unless prearranged.

Backing material for curtain rod brackets (Fig. 7-72) can be fabricated from a variety of wood types. Solid blocks are practical. A 2″ nominal block may be held with nails through the stud from the field side and toenailed through the window post stud. Sheathing plywood is an excellent backing material. It requires inletting, or backer strips, or a combination. The plywood may be inletted into the field stud. Inletting is impractical on the window stud due to the trimmer and header materials, which contain nails. On this stud a 1 × 2 may be face nailed at a point back from the wall surface equal to the thickness of the backer boards. Nominal 1″ boards may also be installed as backers in the same manner.

Positioning the curtain backer depends somewhat on the type of curtains anticipated. A large draw drape with a wood valance, for example, may require some specialized backup to hold the ends of the valance as well as the curtain rod brackets. The average curtain rod will be positioned close to the top casing board centerline. A backer board of 6″ height will be well placed when it straddles this horizontal line.

The backer board will be installed before the wall is insulated. It is convenient *not* to permit a backer board to go up to the top plate. The insulation can be pulled up behind the backer board more successfully if a gap exists above the backer board. The insulation installer can reach

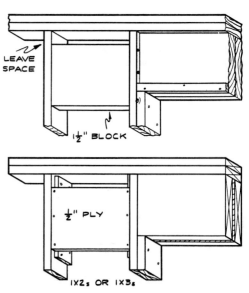

FIGURE 7-72 Curtain rod valance backing boards may be end nailed or cleated to studs.

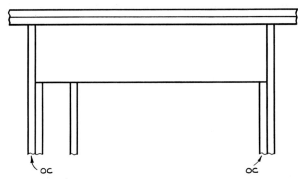

FIGURE 7-73 An opening that would have much waste header material may extend to the next OC stud to form an integrated backup for curtain rods or a valance.

down through this opening with one hand and pull the batt up while feeding it from the underside with the other hand.

Another form of backer can be arranged through the manner of framing the window opening. The uniform header is allowed to extend on one end or both to the next modularly spaced stud. This is economically feasible when the header length exceeds a 2′ modulus of dimension lumber length. An example is depicted in Fig. 7-73. Shown here is a rough window opening of 36 1/2″. The 4 × 12 uniform header minimum length required is 39 1/2″ (to bear on the two 1 1/2″ trimmer studs). An 8′ 2 × 12 will be required to make the two-piece header. The excess remaining is 17″. By extending the header beyond the trimmer to the next OC stud, a solid backer is formed by the header itself on one side of the window. Most of the 8′ board is used since this extended header is 46 1/2″ long. The scrap remaining is just 3″ instead of 17″ and a solid backing now exists on one side of the window opening.

Bathroom and kitchen backers (Fig. 7-74) are needed behind wall-hung items. Such items are towel bars, tissue holder (surface or recessed), soap dishes or dispensers, glass racks, shower curtain rods, can openers, bottle openers, and any other weight-supporting convenience. Without wooden backer boards, some of these items can only be mounted over a stud. Those that do not match stud spacing will not survive mounted only on plasterboard.

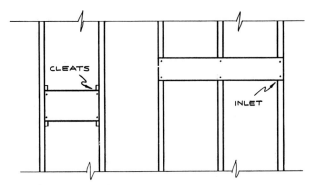

FIGURE 7-74 Bathroom and kitchen backers may be cleated or inletted. Half-inch plywood is usually adequate.

Without backer boards these room appendages can seldom be installed precisely where wanted.

The location of each backer board must be planned in advance with careful reasoning. A detailed map of the backer location must be kept for the final installation of the appliance. Once the backer board is covered by wallboard there will exist no obvious evidence as to its precise location except the dimensioned record on paper.

SIX-INCH WALLS

The 6″ exterior frame wall has been in existence in the cold belts of the United States for several decades. It did not account for a significant quantity of houses on the market in the United States until the energy crises became acute in the early 1980s. It then became a credible option for homeowners even into the temperate zones of the south. In addition to the desirability of saving heating costs, there is the need to save on cooling costs in the hot months of the year. More and more 6″-walled houses are being constructed as people become atuned to conservation principles. The additional 2″ of depth affords an additional 50 percent insulation capacity in the exterior walls.

Basically, the 6″ framed wall is similar to the conventional 2 × 4 wall. The sole, top plate, and common studs in the exterior wall may be constructed exactly the same as the 2 × 4 frame simply by substituting 2 × 6 components in place of 2 × 4s. Assemblies that are different or unique are the corner posts (Fig. 7-75), partition posts, and the window and door headers. Here a saving can be realized by using a combination of 2 × 4s and 2 × 6s.

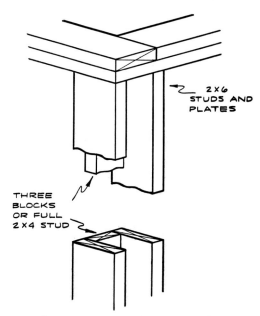

FIGURE 7-75 The optimum 6″ corner post employs full lumber units.

Spacing

Spacing is usually 24″ on center. The additional girth of the 6″ stud makes it more than adequate to support the compression stress placed on it by a roof. It is, however, more important with this wider spacing to unify the in-line bearing of all structural members. The trusses or rafters should be placed directly over the studs on exterior walls and interior bearing partitions. By the same reasoning it is preferred that the rafters be sized for 24″ spacing when a stick-built (conventional) roof is built. Trusses are commonly placed 24″ OC so that alignment is easily coordinated.

Different Component Designs

So little has been written or drawn in the detailing of 6″ components that fabrication has been and is being invented on the site by many framers. This kind of development results in trial and error. Unfortunately, in the construction business errors in structural component assembly are usually covered from sight by finish materials. A poorly conceived practice can perpetuate by habit. Such a practice may go along unnoticed and unidentified for a long time until an astute person recognizes the unseen causes of sags, cracks, and unsightly unlevel lines. The designs presented and illustrated on these pages have been field tested and approved in various localities under the auspices of different inspectors and building codes.

   The 6″ corner post (Fig. 7-76) fabricates well by using 2 × 4 block spacers placed on edge. The accumulative width is 6 1/2″, which leaves a full inch of nailing surface on one side of the interior corner surface. As with the 2 × 4 system, it should be remembered that it is important to insulate the hollow exterior side of this corner post before sheathing the wall. It will be inaccessible after sheathing. Another feature to remember is to start the drywalling on the 1″ side of the corner. The full stud on the adjoining side will then have a full inch of surface left for nailing (assuming the use of 1/2″-thick wallboard).

   It bears stressing that straight studs should always be chosen for the two corner post units that go into the wall that is erected first. If not enough straight boards can be

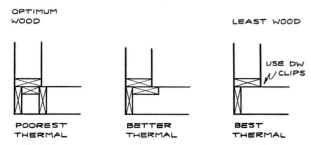

FIGURE 7-76   Top views of optional 6″ corner posts.

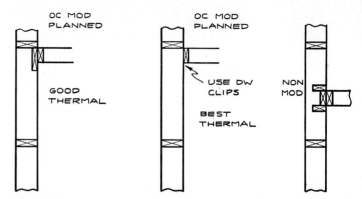

FIGURE 7-77   Top views of optional partition to-exterior wall junctions.

found for the purpose, a pair with slight crooks may serve. The crook should be removed by jointing or sawing off one edge only. In the post assembly the straightened edge of one of the studs will be *faced to the exterior corner position*. The second board will have its straightened edge facing the interior corner. The blocks will be aligned flush with the interior edge of the inboard stud. The other edge of the block in the center location will be permitted to overhang the corner stud by as much as was planed off the exterior edge of the straightened stud. By so doing both the inside and outside corners will be straight without loss of wall depth. The third stud component of the corner post will have its straightened edge facing the interior, thus completing a full set of four potentially straight and vertical adjoining surfaces at a corner. This procedure may sound like a lot of time and effort expended over a minor point. It is one of those preventive measures that will pay off later by eliminating the compounding of problems due to crookedness.

   Partition posts (Ts; Fig. 7-77) may be made of two 2 × 6 studs separated by three 2 × 4 blocks. A saving can be realized with no loss in utility when one or both studs are made of 2 × 4s. When the partition is modularly planned to utilize an on-center stud, that stud will be a 2 × 6. The one that is attached to it may be a 2 × 4. For one reason it should be a 2 × 4. Using the 2 × 4 will not only save money but will provide a 2″ space behind it so that insulation can be tucked in after the wall is sheathed. This permits the carpentry to progress uninhibited by the need to wait on insulating. Should the partition intersect the exterior wall at a point between the wall studs, both T studs may or should be 2 × 4s. By making them both of 2 × 4s the space behind them extends the full 22 1/2″. This permits a full piece of standard insulation to be placed behind the T. A vertical knife cut is made partway through the insulation along the T studs to permit the insulation to expand to its fullest in the cavities on each side of the T.

   Six-inch header designs have not been standardized to date. The following descriptions and illustrated assemblies will serve well. Regardless of shape or assembly the builder should abide by the same tables of span limitations that are in use for the 2 × 4 wall. There will be a small gain in bearing ability due to the double 2 × 6 top plate girth. As the window opening widens, this gain begins to drop off proportionately. As the window width passes the 4′ span category, the increased girth of the 2 × 6 top plate becomes less of a bearing asset to the compression forces on it and more of a liability due to weight.

The uniform header and trimmer (Fig. 7-78) is probably the most logical 2 × 6 header design. Its similarity to the nonspaced 4″ header system will make it a familiar design for the builder who alternates from 4 to 6″ framing. An orthographic front view of this design will appear exactly the same as the 2 × 4 wall version. A section view reveals the only difference to be the depth of the components.

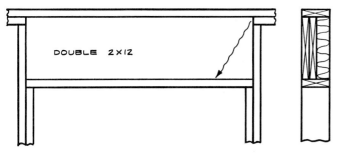

FIGURE 7-78 An excellent uniform header design for a 6″ wall that provides a 2″-deep cavity for insulation.

A distinct advantage of this design is its superior capacity for insulation. The cavity is formed to be on the interior side. It is 2 1/2″ deep, which is adequate to hold a 2″ fiberglass batt, a compressed 3 1/2″ batt, or a split 6″ batt. The lower horizontal trimmer maintains the common surface plane of the opening. In the building sequence the use of this design substitutes the horizontal trimmer on the underside of the header for the lower half of the top, double plate. This makes it necessary in all wall sections where openings occur to install the top piece of the double plate prior to raising the wall. It is needed to tie the assembly together since there is no lower unit of the double plate running through over the header. This header system should be considered a preferred method because of its superior strength (two 2 × 12s nailed face to face), its ease of insulating, and its minimum construction time.

A modified built-up header technique may be used by those framers who wish to stay with the more familiar system. This will require the substitution of 2 1/2″ spacers for the 1/2″ spacer used in the 4 × 12 built-up header. Only one spacer may be used horizontally between the bottoms of the two 2 × 12s, or vertical spacers may be placed along the length of the header. These spacer blocks are ripped from any scrap dimension lumber. When the single

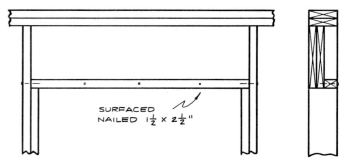

FIGURE 7-79 This uniform header for a 6″ wall has a 1 1/2″ × 2 1/2″ filler strip to complete the surround and provide an insulating cavity.

horizontal spacer is used, the cavity must be insulated before covering the top with the plate. This is a difficult thing to impress on independent framing crews, as they are not oriented to insulating. For this reason alone the builder may wish to reject the design.

Another design that works well and eliminates the insulating trap is to use the 2 1/2″ spacer horizontally on the interior face of the header (Fig. 7-79). This method exposes the insulating cavity so that it can be routinely filled when the rest of the wall is insulated.

The least complicated technique is seen in Fig. 7-80. Here the headers are not joined together. Each stands flush with the wall frame surface, leaving a 2 1/2″ cavity between. Because the cavity is open on the underside it is easily insulated at any time prior to being covered by window jambs or false jambs.

Obviously, the extra strength gained by nailing header pieces together is lost in this design. On the other hand, most of the windows in a house are overstrength headed when the uniform double 2 × 12 is used. All those openings on a window span table that require less than 4 × 12 (two 2 × 12s built up) headers will be adequately served by the unconnected set of 2 × 12s (spaced apart as shown). Generally, this will include all the openings under 8′ of clear span.

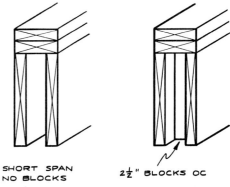

FIGURE 7-80 The simplest 6″ wall header for short spans employs no spacers. Longer spans can be controlled with 2 1/2″ vertical blocks on-center.

Openings larger than this will be served by an adaptation to this cavity design or one of the other previously described designs. To adapt the open cavity design, custom-ripped cripples of 2 1/2" size are sandwiched between the two 2 × 12s on spacing that coincides with the wall layout. This effectively ties them together. It provides the added unit strength of the conventional built-up header design while leaving open access to the underside for insulating.

Some other designs involving surface-mounted plywood on the sheathing level have been observed. "Surface mounted" means that the header supporting role is dependent on the sheer strength of nails. Sanction of this design is not likely to be found in code books, as there is no direct bearing on structural trimmers. The weight of the roof load over the header is born on the shear strength of the nails only. An adequate structural member (a trimmer post) should stand under the ends of any style of header to carry its load ultimately to the foundation.

It is possible to go backward in time and build a header for a 6" wall with cripples and the spanned header from the stress tables. The savings in materials would be even less than it was for the 2 × 4 header since the size of the cripples is greater in girth, whereas the 4 × 12 uniform header remains the same size.

Cost Comparison

One might logically jump to the conclusion that a 6" exterior wall would cost 50% more in materials than a 2 × 4 wall. Some attention to design features can make it come out on a par with a 2 × 4 wall, or nearly so. Discount the difference in insulation cost, as this is a fixed and unalterable cost on a square-foot basis. The additional initial cost of the insulation will pay back in fuel savings in a few

years. Consider some of the obvious things that make the 6" wall less costly by comparison than it would seem.

Cost saving is first realized by the wider spacing. Ignoring corners and partition posts, the 16" spaced 2 × 4 wall frame will contain three studs for every 4 linear feet plus one. For example, a 40'-long wall will have 30 spaces and 31 common studs. The extra stud closes in the last space. Hold your hand up with fingers outspread. There are four spaces—five fingers. The 3-for-4 technique, incidentally, is a quick figuring method of stud counting for ordering or estimating. Using the same example with 24" spacing, there is a stud for each 2' of linear space plus one. Therefore, the 40' wall with 2 × 6 studs, 24" OC, contains 21 common studs. This is nearly a third less in quantity of units than the 16" spaced wall of the same length. If 2 × 6s could be purchased at the same price as 2 × 4s per board foot, the wider spacing will net a comparable cost. In round numbers there are 165 board feet in 31 2 × 4 × 8s and 168 board feet in 21 2 × 6 × 8s.

Two elements cause this comparison to be a little less attractive than it appears. At this time 2 × 6s are not universally available in uniform stud length (92 5/8") as are 2 × 4 precuts. The 2 × 6 is available in an 8' length for studs. It is priced for that length. Extra labor time is required to machine the eight-footers to stud length. Later it is explained how this extra length can be used to advantage.

The second flaw in the board-foot comparison is that frequently the price of dimension lumber escalates disproportionately as the girth and length increase. The larger the board width, the greater the cost per board foot. Nevertheless, the cost of using 2 × 6 studs on 24" centers is comparable to using 2 × 4 studs on 16" centers.

2 × 6 soles and top plates will cost a minimum of 50% more than 2 × 4s since the same linear distance is being covered. This is true when the same system of construction is practiced as with 2 × 4s—a single sole and a double top plate. This extra cost can be eliminated by using only a single top plate. Many updated building codes permit a single top 2 × 6 plate in conjunction with rafters that bear directly over the studs. Many other codes ignore the technique, but an enlightened inspector will approve it. To join the corners and intersections of the single plate, galvanized sheet metal gussets are used (Fig. 7-81). This system of tying is frequently more effective than the common crosslap with its splitting characteristic. Since the 2 × 6 comes in a full 8' length (not 92 5/8" stud length), it may be shortened to accommodate one less plate member, instead of two, without sacrificing any room height. To coordinate with precut 2 × 4 studs which will be used on the interior walls, the 2 × 6 stud is duplicate cut to 94 1/8" (92 5/8" + 1 1/2"). To maintain a correct door and window header relationship, the double 2 × 12 header with a 2 × 6 horizontal trimmer under it is used.

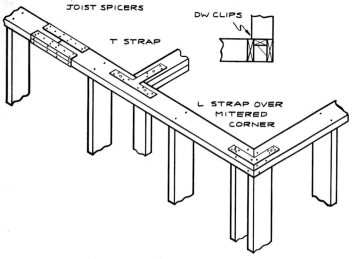

FIGURE 7-81   A single top plate on a 6" wall is joined with metal plates designed for the purpose.

Rough windowsills can be a source of a small saving. With the larger 2 × 6 there is little need to double the rough sill. In the nonbearing ends of a gable-roofed house, the interrupted trimmer system will support the ends. On the bearing sides where the cantilever rule indicates a need for support, a 2 × 4 cripple may be used. It is placed with its outer edge flush to the sheathing. In this way the cost of the rough sill assembly will actually be less than that of a double 2 × 4 sill.

Window and door jambs can inflate the relative cost with the 6″ wall. Wood jamb extensions, as required on some windows, are expensive. An alternative is to use a high-grade window that does not have an integral jamb. With this type of window the jambs are customarily made of wood and are piece built into the opening. A reasonable alternative is to drywall window openings where the wood jamb would normally exist on a 4″-deep wall. A metal corner bead is installed around the sides and top. A one-piece sill of wood or synthetic marble completes the opening. If casing is desired, it can be surface nailed to the opening. With curtains and drapes the casing at the sides of windows is rarely seen. Only the piece at the top may be visible when the drapes are open.

Another method of filling the extra 2″ of jamb space on windows where wood jambs are desired is to add a custom-cut strip of wood (Fig. 7-82). It would be very difficult to add a 2″ strip on edge and make it perfectly flush with the regular jamb. It can be done attractively by setting it back an 1/8″ all around, as is customary with window and door casing. This will look finished and intentional. It should be glued and nailed. Since the extension will be 2″ deep on edge, or a little less, it should be predrilled to accept long finish nails. Wood sash windows and doors frequently are available for two or more standard depths. One is intended for drywall, the other for wet plaster. When you plan to make your own jamb extensions, order the deepest jamb available at the standard price. This will save money, as the required jamb extensions can then be made smaller in depth and will be easier to install.

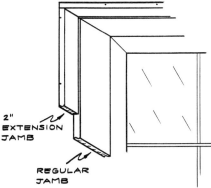

FIGURE 7-82 Two-inch extension jambs can be fabricated for windows with standard jamb windows used in 6″ walls.

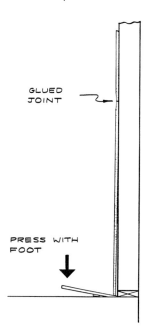

FIGURE 7-83 A foot raiser will hold the lower panel snugly against the upper panel while the nails are placed to hold it permanently.

An added drywall-related expense may be encountered with the 6″ wall due to the wider spacing, which is not common to the 2 × 4 wall. Plasterboard of 1/2″ thickness is by far the most popular current wall-covering material. It is installed horizontally on the majority of walls, the larger ones particularly. This means that there is a taped joint midway up the wall running horizontally all around the exterior walls. On 24″ spacing the 1/2″ gypsum board is too flexible between the studs to resist much pressure against this joint. Simply leaning against this taped joint can sometimes cause it to crack. It needs some type of support. There are two choices.

One technique is to **run a bead of polyvinyl resin glue** or panel adhesive along the top edge of the bottom sheet. The sheet must be quickly put in place and pressed firmly up against the bottom edge of the top sheet. Foot-operated raisers are used to hold it in place until enough nails can be put in to stabilize it (Fig. 7-83). The homebuilder who does not have raisers can place some small shims on the floor at right angles to the wall. The top edge of the wallboard is placed in position. The bottom is pushed in toward the wall. This causes a wedging effect. The top half of the board is nailed. The shims are pulled out and the bottom half is nailed. Any wallboard edges that do not line up flush between studs must be aligned by holding in place until the glue sets. Obviously, the glue will serve no purpose unless the edges of the boards are in contact throughout their length.

Wood backing boards present another alternative to eliminate the joint-breaking potential. There are two common methods. 2 × 4 blocks 22 1/2″ long are nailed be-

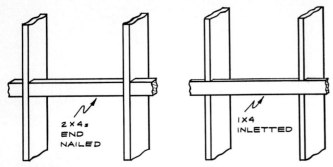

FIGURE 7-84 Backup systems for the horizontal drywall joint on a 6″ wall.

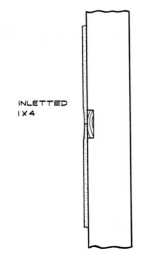

FIGURE 7-85 Section view of the drywall backup.

tween the studs. The face of the block is placed flush with the interior frame surface. The horizontal centerline of this block is 48″ down from the ceiling surface. When the ceiling is also 1/2″ wallboard, this distance will be 48 1/2″ down from the ceiling joist or plate top. Measure it at each corner of the room. Snap a chalk line across the studs. Straddle the line with the blocks. End nail the block where the stud surface is open. On the closed end start the nail in the crack above and below the previous block. Drive it at an angle into the end of the new block.

Another backing option is to **inlet a 1 × 4** into the studs (Fig. 7-84). This is done in the same manner as the diagonal corner brace was installed. More precision is needed, however, to assure that the surface of the 1 × 4 is perfectly flush with the stud frame surface. Should it fall below the surface, an excessive amount of drywall compound will be required to bring the finished wallboard surface into alignment. The inletting system may prove quicker and less frustrating since no individual fitting and precise alignment of block ends are encountered (Fig. 7-85). Once a good mechanical system of inletting has been worked out, the carpenter may prefer this technique. Batt

insulation also fits better behind the 1 × 4 than behind the 2 × 4, as it will be less compressed.

With a backer board of one kind or another in place, the wallboard is nailed to the backer board between the studs. The joint will now be safe from the danger of cracking under pressure.

Six-Inch-Wall Conclusions

The 2 × 6 exterior wall system is a cost-feasible design for any size residence or wood-structured building. Assuming that the day of cheap and plentiful fuel is gone forever, the 2 × 4 skinny wall will be rendered obsolete by more efficient designs and concepts. In Chapter 14 there is a discussion pertaining to the double-wall design, earth homes, and solar-assisted structures. Until these advanced concepts become more popular, the 6″ wall offers an attractive and feasible interim alternative. Over only a few years of operational accounting it will prove to be a cost-saving investment well worth the slight additional initial cost. Its popularity will increase with consumer understanding and interest.

ROUGHING-IN PLUMBING PARTITIONS

Many communities now permit the use of 3″ pipe for the main vent stack, compared to a traditional 4″ regulation. The vent usually runs vertically through one of the interior partitions that surrounds the bathroom. In other localities, a 4″ vent is still required. Plastic vent pipe is now widely accepted in the various diameters required. The bell-hub cast-iron pipe of yesteryear is obsolete in residential plumbing.

The 3″ plastic pipe can be installed in a 2 × 4 stud wall when the pipe is perfectly centered and contains no joints. The thickness of the pipe wall is about 1/4″, so the outside diameter is as great as the width of the sole and top plate. Most builders will opt for a 6″ partition so that clearances are not as critical. The 2 × 6 wall nets a plate width of 5 1/2″. There is adequate clearance for either 3 or 4″ plastic pipe in the 5 1/2″ space.

Construction Features of the Six-Inch Plumbing Partition

There are three variations of the 6″ partition in common practice. One technique is to use 2 × 6 studs and plates throughout. The framing is the same as for the 2 × 4 interior partitions.

An alternative to the use of 2 × 6s is to rip 2 × 4s in half and use the halves as shims. A regular 2 × 4 partition is framed. The shims are nailed to the studs and plates. These half studs will measure 1 1/2″ by approximately 1 11/16″ in girth. The 1 11/16″ dimension will vary according to the thickness of the saw blade that is used to rip them. The ripped shims are also likely to vary in dimension. This occurs because the saw cut is not often perfectly centered in the board or the board cannot be held firmly against the fence because it is warped. Because of this variance it is best to place the "2 × 2" with its 1 1/2″-uniform-thickness side against the studs. This will net a uniform depth partition of 5″ (the 3 1/2″ stud plus the 1 1/2″ shim), which is adequate for all 4″ or less plumbing stack variations. The soles and top plates must also be ripped or shimmed to conform to the 5″-depth module.

Notching the shimmed partition is a simple process (Fig. 7-86). A drain or a vent from a lavatory will run through notches in the shimmed partition. The location of this pipe can be plotted before the shims are nailed on. It is a simple operation to cut out the notches from the bathroom face of the studs. The 2 × 2 shims are installed on the soleplate and the top plate and all the unnotched studs. They are omitted from the notched studs until after the crossover vents have been plumbed in. Why not omit all the shims until the plumbing rough-in is done? Because the plumber needs to know exactly where the final frame wall line will be in order to set the tub and watercloset drains at the correct spot in the floor.

The sole and upper plates are usually drilled with a hole saw. The pipe can be dropped through the roof and fed through the upper plate to the location of the T or Y joint that receives the crossover vent. To locate the hole in

MOVE UNTIL OVER HOLE CENTER THEN MARK

FIGURE 7-87 Move the top of the plumb line around until the bob is over the center of the sole mark, then mark the location on the underside of the top plate.

the top plate, a plumb line and bob is manipulated back and forth on the underside of the upper plate (Fig. 7-87). When the string settles down and is in the center of the hole in the sole, the spot is marked by driving a nail or marking with a pencil. A short piece of pipe can be used as a template to trace the hole location. Hole saws with center piloting drills will require only the center mark to show where to drill. Safety glasses are called for when drilling overhead in this manner. It is difficult to drill straight through 3 3/4″ of top plate and backer board. Where there is room above to operate the drill, it will be prudent to counterbore halfway from the underside and halfway down from the top. The center mark on top can be located by projecting lines from the mark on the underside of the plate with a square.

The hole in the roof is located in the same manner, by dropping a plumb line and bob through the plate hole to the sole. When the center of the hole position is found on the underside of the sheathing, a nail is driven at the point. Drive it through all the materials. The protruding nail is then located on the surface of the roof. The shingles are carefully cut away so they can be flashed correctly after the pipe is in place. This technique is explained in Chapter 10.

The hole may be cut with any of several tools. It is possible to maintain vertical sides in the hole by using the compass saw (a hand tool frequently referred to as a keyhole saw) or its counterpart power tool, the tiger saw (reciprocal saw). A saber saw may also be used if one is not

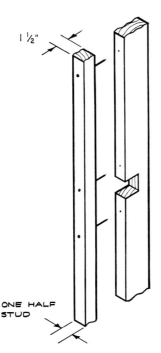

1 ½″

ONE HALF STUD

FIGURE 7-86 Plumbing partitions with horizontal drains and vents and a large vertical vent may be notched and shimmed to net a 5″ wall.

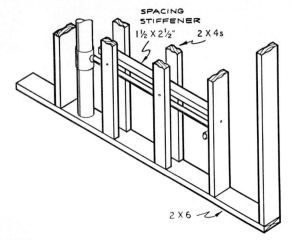

FIGURE 7-88 Flat stud method of providing for horizontal drain and vent pipes.

concerned about vertical edges. Any of these tools will require a pilot hole in which to insert the blade to get started.

The double flat stud wall (Fig. 7-88) is a third option that may be used as a plumbing partition. For this design, 2 × 6 plates are used. 2 × 4 studs are positioned with their 3 1/2″ surfaces flush with the partition surfaces. They are set directly opposite each other on 16″ centers. This arrangement provides a 2″ corridor between the stud surfaces through which both supply and vent pipes can be run horizontally without drilling or notching. 2 × 6 studs are used in the normal position elsewhere in this wall where a cavity is not needed for pipes since there is about a 25% saving in material over the double-stud setup.

The double studs in this back-to-back position are quite flexible. After the plumbing is installed, they should be made rigid by blocking them.

A flat rigid partition can be made by using a horizontal spacer full length between the double studs. Rip a 2 × 4 down to 2″ for the 5″ shimmed wall or 2 1/2″ for a full 6″ nominal wall. Its length should bring it in contact with the full-size stud on the one end and within a few inches beyond the double studs adjacent to the main stack. This horizontal spacer is placed a few inches above the crossover dry vent that frequently comes from the lavatory.

Making this double-stud section of the wall rigid is important. A flexible wall is undesirable. Ceramic tile must have a stiff backing. Even drywall can sustain cracks, separated joints, and nail pops if the frame behind is flexible. The flexible wall surface may pull away from cabinetry (the vanity) and tub and shower edges.

Plates with vent holes cut in them need to be restrengthened. One of the disadvantages of the minimum-clearance 2 × 4 plumbing partition is that the pipe holes completely sever the sole and the upper plate. The problem is not as acute with the shimmed 5″ wall or the 5 1/2″ 2 × 6 wall. Nonetheless, some reinforcing to sustain the

original tensile strength of the upper plate is desirable. This is accomplished with a one-piece plywood gusset or a one- or two-piece solid splice. Plywood with a drilled vent hole is ideal (Fig. 7-89). Since this gusset is directly above the ceiling skin, it may extend sideways as far as desired up to the adjacent ceiling joists. For example, a 1/2″-ply gusset could be as much as 14 1/2″ wide where joists are on 16″ centers. The minimum width should be at least twice the width of the plate surface. A length of 16 to 24″ will provide adequate surface on the plate for effective nailing. The board is held over the hole in the plate and traced from inside the hole. The plug is then drilled or sawed out and the gusset is nailed in place.

Solid dimension stock of 2 × 8 or larger girth may be fitted and installed in the same manner. Where 2 × 4s are the only available material, two pieces may be clamped together edge to edge and drilled with the center of the hole on the crack (Fig. 7-90). In the absence of a hole saw a saber saw will do well. If these tools are not at hand, a double V cut can be made with a hand saw or a power circular saw (skill saw). The saw base table is set at 45°. Most circle saws will cut deep enough in each board to form a V cut, which is adequate for a 2″ vent. For a 3 or

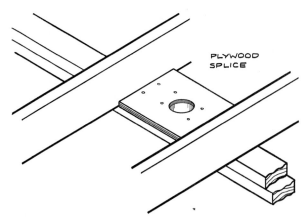

FIGURE 7-89 A 2 × 4 top plate which is largely severed by a 3″ pipe hole can be spliced on top the plate with a solid 2″ board or a piece of plywood.

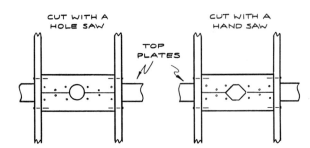

FIGURE 7-90 Two by fours are sandwiched around a pipe to form splices over 2 × 4 plates.

4" vent pipe, the cuts are made a few inches apart. This will create half of a hexagon pattern. The resulting half plug can be broken out with a sharp hammer blow. The cuts and the cracked edges have now formed a hexagonal pattern around the tracing. The two boards are placed together edge to edge over the plate and nailed down with 16d box nails (Fig. 7-90). The latter system is particularly adaptable when the splicing has been overlooked until after the plumbing is installed. The two-piece design can be put around the pipe. The one-piece design must be installed before the pipe is put in.

Face guarding against nails is necessary when the pipe is close to the wall-frame surface. Nails holding the wall skin to the wall plates must not be permitted to puncture the pipe. The old-style cast-iron pipe would turn aside a lath nail, or if not, the nail would give warning by bending or resisting in an obvious manner. Such is not the case with polyvinyl pipe. A nail will easily puncture the pipe with little resistance. To prevent this problem, a metal guard strip is nailed on the vertical surface of the sole and upper plate (Fig. 7-91). Any type of metal that will turn back or stop a lath nail is suitable. It needs to be 1 1/2" wide for the sole and 2 1/2 or 3" for the upper plate. 1 1/2" plates may be stocked routinely. In such a case, two pieces are used to cover the double top plate. The length of the metal need only be enough to accommodate one nail in each end. This can be as little as 1" on each side beyond the pipe diameter (a 6" strap for a 4" pipe, a 5" strap for a 3" vent). Nail holes are bored about 1/2" from the end of the strap. The plates are dadoed to a depth a little more than the thickness of the metal (1/8"-thick metal is quite adequate) so that the wall skin passes smoothly over them. A little extra depth will accommodate nailheads that protrude on the surface of the metal. Drywall nails are good to use here because their heads are relatively thin. A pair of carpenter crayon marks extending out onto the floor deck will indicate where the metal protector plates

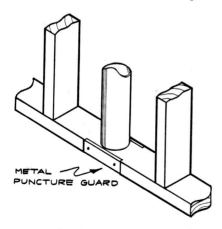

METAL PUNCTURE GUARD

FIGURE 7-91 Metal guards of about 1/8" × 1 1/2" are inletted in front of pipes and vents to prevent puncture from drywall or baseboard nails.

are so that the area is recognized as an off-limits place to drive a drywall mounting nail. The protector plates are needed on both sides of the partition wherever a vent pipe could be reached by a drywall or baseboard nail.

Framing around the Bathtub

There are several types of tubs and showers from which to choose when building a new house. The technique of framing around each type may differ. Some thought must be given to the type of tub or shower stall that is desired before the bathroom partitions are completely framed. The contracted house that has a full set of plans and a specifications manual will have entries referring to the tub type. Most plans and specs will call for a 5'-long enclosure for a tub. This is the most common tub length. Other lengths and shapes are available, but the 30" × 60" tub accounts for the greatest number of sales. In the absence of specific directives, the carpenter will frame the tub enclosure at precisely 5' from the face of the studs. On the floor plan the tub symbol measures 1 1/4" (5' at a scale of 1/4" = 1'). When the tub is 5'-6" or 4', there will usually be a dimension to indicate it. In such a case the choice of tub options is somewhat limited. A cast-iron tub will fit. A flanged steel tub requires a little adaptation because of a surrounding lip on top. Some fiberglass tubs will fit. Some kit-type wall enclosures that lock into tubs will fit. The one-piece tub and shower made of fiberglass cannot be taken through the door and put in place. *This unit, called a module, must be placed in the room before the framing of walls is begun.* In practice, it is prudent to put the tub in place and frame around it. Many floor plans make it impossible to negotiate the turns through corridors and doorways with the fiberglass tub/shower module.

Preparing to Set the Tub

There are some preparatory steps to take before setting any tub. The closed-in area under a tub that is against an exterior wall is prone to the collection of condensation. To guard against this, a conscientious job of insulating and vapor blocking is essential. This will minimize the temperature variable under the tub when it is exposed to hot water. The insulation should be tight to all surfaces and fluffed out to its full depth between the studs. Never fill the void around the tub or let the insulation touch the tub. A continuous covering of 4- or 6-mil plastic film is stapled onto the studs over the insulation from floor to ceiling. This is good practice even where the insulation is paper backed. There is no wallboard on top of the studs behind the tub to seal down the paper or foil vapor barriers. This area behind the tub can suffer from infiltration. The addition of the plastic sheet will help to eliminate the penetration of cold air.

Blocking the Tub

Cast-iron and steel tubs require blocking to support the back edge. The blocking is done with 2 × 4s or 2 × 6s. The blocks are positioned like short cripple studs but are permitted to stand out away from the studs under the tub rim (Fig. 7-92). In this position they form a post ledge to support a portion of the weight of the tub. The tub weight imposed on blocks in an exterior wall is transferred to the wall sole and ultimately to the foundation. Without the blocks most of the weight of the tub is placed on the floor joists. Each block is nailed to an OC stud. The height of each block is critical. The underedge of a cast tub is seldom uniform in height above the floor. An individual measurement is taken to the floor from each point that the tub will touch a block top. Each block is custom cut to the dimension required. After the tub is set in place, an inspection under the tub should be made to be sure that all blocks are being touched. Any that are not touching should be shimmed up. Place a little carpenter's glue between the shim and the block so that the shim will not vibrate out later.

  The back corner supports of the tub itself should not quite touch the floor. To check this, slip a piece of paper under each of these two locations. Such an amount of clearance will net a firm bearing on the rim blocks that are placed between. The tub will soon settle in as the blocks shrink and the tub bears down. At that time the tub will stabilize all around. The chances will be good for a wall-to-tub junction around the upper edge, which is not a constant source of opening and closing, causing the ugly crack that is so characteristic above cast-iron tubs.

  A good bearing arrangement exists when the tub is blocked at the back and is sitting at right angles to the floor joists, across them. A plan that has a cast-iron tub placed parallel to the joist direction will have only two common joists under it. A third trimmer joist should be nailed to the common joist on the side that will most closely position it under the room-side edge of the tub (Fig. 7-92). On a modular house with studs 16″ OC, this will place the trimmer under the edge of the tub, assuming that the partition behind the tub has been extended out from an OC stud in the exterior wall frame.

  On a 2 × 6 or double-wall designed house where a tub is parallel to the joists and the exterior wall, the trimmer joist should be spaced out with one of the blocking options so that it falls directly under the tub edge. There are tub designs which are 30″ at the ends while the center is flared to a wider depth. This design should be accommodated by placing the trimmer at a line that will net the greatest support.

  The placement of the extra joist to support the outer-edge side of a cast-iron tub is a critical factor. Where properly done, the support will help to prevent a sagging

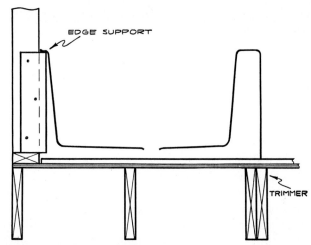

FIGURE 7-92 A cast-iron tub needs to be supported along its back edge by cripple studs.

floor, which, in turn, reduces the potential for cracks around the tub edges. Such accurate locating and placing of the support joist is dependent on a firmly committed floor plan. When the floor frame is completed and sheathed, no changes in partition location should be made lest the support features below are voided.

  The steel tub has a flange about 3/4″ high above the ends and back. This flange is a thorn in the side of the carpenter. If not dealt with during the framing stage, it gets worse at wall-covering time. Wall materials brought down over this flange usually tilt out into the room, destroying the vertical nature of the wall. The straightness of the flange seldom meets and touches every stud (studs are rarely that uniform). To eliminate this problem, the studs can be notched individually just deep enough to permit the flange to be flush or below the surface of the frame wall (Fig. 7-93). Where studs do not form a uniform surface, the ones at the corner of the tub will be used as gauges. Notch all the studs deep enough so that the flange will be flush with the surface of the corner studs. A stud that is behind the

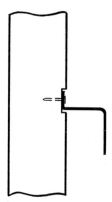

FIGURE 7-93 Notch the studs around a steel tub to recess the top flange below the surface.

surface line of its neighbors may be cut on the opposite side to permit it to flex into position (see the earlier explanation of crooked stud straightening).

To deal with the ends of the steel tub in a full 5′ opening, it will be necessary to notch the studs on one end and shim out the ones on the other end. Pick the shortest wall for the shimming, as the entire wall will have to be shimmed: all studs, the sole, and top plate. When it is known in advance that a steel tub will be used, the length of the enclosure can be framed about 1/4″ shorter (59 3/4″). This will accommodate notching on both ends and eliminate the necessity of shimming completely. This system, however, may require building the tub in at the time of framing.

Junction of the Wall Covering

The cast-iron tub has a small upward flare around its three enclosure sides. Waterproof enclosures above the tub include such finished materials as vinyl-covered hardboard, Formica, plastic tile, ceramic tile, and fiberglass panels (modular kits). All require some kind of backup skin.

Although gypsum wallboard would appear to be an obviously poor material to place in a damp and vulnerable position such as this, it is frequently used. The unknowledgeable builder or novice is apt to unwittingly use regular drywall, with disastrous results. Only the type of moisture-resistant gypsum board that is specified for moisture-prone localities should be used. It is also applied differently. A detailed explanation of the differences is presented in Chapter 12.

In other rooms the wallboard is nailed to the top half

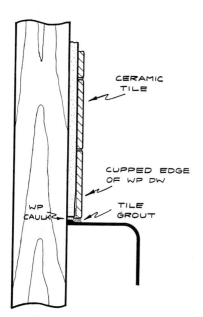

FIGURE 7-94 Water-resistant drywall is installed with its paper-sealed edge next to the tub edge.

of the walls first. Then the lower sheet is put on. In a bathroom this procedure would cause an exposed gypsum edge where the board was cut around the top edge of the tub. Even though it is grouted or sealed, it is still vulnerable to moisture. The correct way to avoid this obvious vulnerability is to put the sealed edge of the gypsum board next to the tub rim. It should be held above the tub surface about 1/8″ so that a waterproof (butyl or latex) caulking sealant can be squeezed in between the tub and wallboard edge. The remainder of the tub stall is covered simply by filling in the area above the sheet with a custom-cut piece. The top of this filler piece should be cut accurately, as the cut edge will be up against the ceiling board.

The tub enclosure material is brought down to the tub surface and sealed (Fig. 7-94). Ceramic tile is grouted to a watertight seal. Full-sheet-type coverings are set in a J channel which is preset in a bead of sealant. Much care must be taken to assure that no voids exist. Any leakage behind the edge of a tub will be the beginning of the breakdown of the inner materials. It usually results in a costly renovation job.

Setting the Module

The one-piece molded fiberglass tub and shower enclosure is called a module. The module may be installed in a 5′ space. In the 5′ space it will be necessary to shim all three walls above and surrounding the module. Instructions that come with the module usually describe the shimming technique. When it is known in advance that a module will be used, a technique can be practiced which eliminates the shimming requirement (Fig. 7-95).

The module has a flange that extends about 1 1/2″ around all wall contact edges. To eliminate shimming, the enclosure area is framed 1/2″ smaller than the module size (59 1/2″ for a 5′ tub/shower and 35 1/2″ for a 3′ shower). The module is put in its place in the bathroom area with its back against one wall and one end against the adjacent partition (the other partition is not yet erected). A pencil mark is traced across the top of the flange on each stud. A narrowed backup stud is installed behind each of the vertical flanges at the front of the module. These studs are ripped to 3 1/4″ depth. These two studs form the recess for the vertical edges of the module flanges. If an OC stud happens to be at the flange location, it is recessed (ripped) from the sole to the top flange mark. The soles must also be notched with a chisel to accept the flange at the front of the module. The module is backed out of the space. The notches are then cut out and the extra vertical flange backing stud put in. It is then put back into place with its flanges recessed in the notches (Fig. 7-96). The remaining partition is erected in place but not installed. It is marked for notches, the extra stud location, and the sole cutout. It is backed away or laid back down on the floor to complete

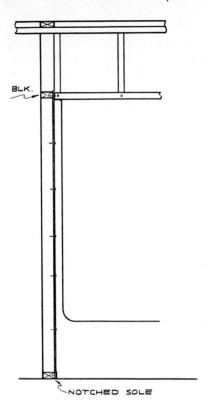

BLK.

NOTCHED SOLE

FIGURE 7-95   Shimming three walls surrounding a tub or shower module can be avoided when the flange is recessed. Notch a stud full height for the vertical flanges of the module.

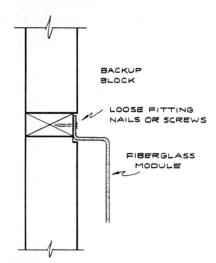

BACKUP BLOCK

LOOSE FITTING NAILS OR SCREWS

FIBERGLASS MODULE

FIGURE 7-96   Horizontal flanges around the top are recessed into localized notches.

the notch cutting and the installing of the recessed stud. It is then installed permanently. The entire module is now recessed. No shimming of surrounding walls is required. This system is especially desirable where a window exists adjacent to the tub module. It eliminates the necessity of custom-sized extension jambs where wood jambs are specified.

Blocking behind the upper flange is recommended by some manufacturers. A 2 × 4 flat block is installed between each joist to back up the top flanges. An alternative method is to inlet a 1 × 4 ribbon with its face recessed. The blocking method has one advantage. Each block can be snuggled right up to the back of the flange. By comparison, the ribbon is fixed as a unit to the studs and may be varied in its backup of the flange. Regardless of which technique is practiced, the installer should not place pressure on the module at any point by pulling in the flange with a nail. Such a condition of stress can lead to a cracked module.

Securing the module in place is done with nails through the fiberglass flange. This is a touchy procedure unless understood. Never nail through an untapped flange. Drill holes through the flange over each stud. Over the vertical trimmer studs place a hole at about 12″ intervals. Stay back from the corners and bottom about 2 to 3″. Use a drill

whose diameter is larger than the nail shank. Galvanized roofing nails make good flange nails, as the big heads will cover a larger part of the fiberglass. Internal rusting is retarded. The large hole provides some clearance, so there is a little room for the fiberglass to self-align after all nails are started. For that reason the nails should not be driven in tight to the surface. Also, the nail should be set in the center of the hole so that there is room for the fiberglass to move. This can be achieved by first punching a centered depression in the wood behind the hole. Then drill a little way into the stud with a 1/16″ bit. The nail will follow the pilot hole and stay centered. Later, when applying wallboard, care must be taken not to nail through the flange. Drywall nails should go into the full-depth stud only, none through the flange into the backup stud.

Underlayment in the Bathroom

Particle board over plywood sheathing has become a common and universal flooring system under wall-to-wall carpeted wood floors. Particle board is not suitable for a bathroom floor, which may receive frequent or even intermittent soakings. To illustrate the vulnerability of particle board to water, leave a small board half submerged in water overnight. In a few hours it will be found that the particle board has swelled in thickness about 20%. Unlike solid wood, it never returns to its original thickness. Ultimately, the particles and glue totally disintegrate. This characteristic can play havoc with a floor that is penetrated by water. A better underlayment for linoleum or a carpeted bath floor is tongue-and-grooved plywood in a waterproof-glue grade. The added expense is greatly offset by the superior durability. The standard 3/4″ thickness of the T&G ply puts it an 1/8″ above the customary 5/8″-thick particle board in an adjoining room or corridor. Added to the thickness of linoleum or ceramic tile this difference becomes an asset in that a carpeted meeting place (usually under the door) is more nearly on the same level. A metal joiner strip will not present such a hump.

Where tongue-and-grooved 3/4″ plywood is not readily available or affordable, an AC grade of regular square-edged plywood is an acceptable alternative. Waferboard is another alternative. During the laying of these sheets the edges are glued. The fit is made accurately so that the edges are in full contact. The glue will prevent any edge from flexing away from another under the weight of a human body. The joints will support floor coverings such as linoleum.

Any type of wood underlayment can be adversely affected by constant soaking. Some preventive techniques will minimize the potential breakdown. There are three systems of joining a tub and floor. One is good, one is fair, the last is poor (Fig. 7-97).

The good system is devised to prevent water from reaching the wood where the tub meets the floor. The underlayment wood is put down under the tub before the tub is installed. The sheet is run the long way of the tub. It is started from the tub side of the room. This places the first joint well out beyond the edge of the tub. No joints will then exist close to or at right angles to the tub edge. The floor covering is then laid at least part way or all the way under the tub. The tub is installed on top of the linoleum or tile. A bead of latex or butyl sealant is placed under the edge of the tub before it is lowered in place.

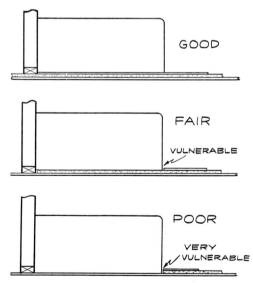

FIGURE 7-97 The top method of sealing between tub and floor eliminates most leak potential. Caulk failure in the ''fair'' example exposes underlayment surface to water. Caulk failure in the ''poor'' example exposes the end grain of the underlayment as well as the sheathing, which can cause a major breakdown.

With the module or steel flanged tub, the notches are cut a little higher. The tub is not nailed to the studs until after the flooring is down. While linoelum is being laid, the tub is propped up off the floor. The linoleum is scooted under the tub (tile must be laid in advance). As soon as the linoleum is in place, the tub is let down. This must be done before the wall skin is put on either side of the partitions that surround the tub. It is a simple matter to run a board over the sole at each end of the tub. The sole becomes a fulcrum. Stepping on each board raises the tub enough to slip the linoleum under. When working alone a heavy object can be laid on these wood levers to hold the tub up unassisted. The longer the lever, the less weight will be needed to hold the tub up off the floor.

The next best system is to floor under the tub as described, then set the tub in caulking directly on the plywood. Linoleum or tile is then carefully fitted around the tub to form the best possible contact. After the adhesive is set, any excess squeeze-out is cleaned from the tub and the linoleum surface. A coved bead of latex or butyl is run into the corner along the joint between the linoleum and the tub. Most tubs curve back under, with about an 1/8″ radius along the bottom edge. This is beneficial, as it provides a little recess to hold the bead. Butyl and latex can both be coved smoothly by wetting a finger and smoothing it out. The grout will be used with ceramic tile. There is a mistaken notion that a caulk tube should be pulled. It should be pushed so that the bead is visibly pressed into the opening. In the pulled position it is impossible to tell whether a crevice is being filled or just bridged over.

The third and least satisfactory system is to set the tub on the subfloor. The underlayment then has to be fitted around the tub curvatures. No matter how perfectly done, the junction of the tub face with the edge grain provides a potential cavity into which water will eventually find a path. It is only a matter of time before a breakdown occurs. This is an inferior system. There is no reason to practice it when it is known in advance how to avoid it simply by following the first or second choices.

During the remainder of construction the finished floor must be zealously protected against damage. A heavy layer of resin paper may be used to cover it. The joints are taped. The ends of the paper are folded tightly into the corners and run 2 or 3″ up the wall frames. The drywall is nailed over the paper. During the drywalling and cabinet installing, every dropped nail should be picked up immediately lest it be stepped on and the head imprinted in the soft linoleum, or a scratch made in the tile.

Tubs must also be protected zealously. Cast-iron and steel tubs are covered with a heavy layer of papier-mache. It is a sad day when a tool is dropped in an uncovered tub and the porcelain is chipped. A fiberglass module can be protected on the horizontal surfaces with cardboard attached with nylon tape.

Plumbing Access

Wherever possible it is prudent to build in an access door or removable panel to the hidden plumbing connections behind a tub or shower stall. Frequently, the plumbing end of a tub is opposite a closet or utility room. Such a location makes it possible to frame a simple opening in the wall through which the water supply pipes and connections can be reached. In a crawl space or slab-floor house, a drum trap can be inverted under the end of the tub. This system is also practical for a second-story bathtub trap. Its drain cap can be reached through the access. Valves are placed on the hot and cold water supply pipes within easy reach. This makes it possible to shut off a hot or cold supply to the tap in the tub to replace a faucet washer without shutting down all the water in the house at a main valve.

The location and visibility of the access panel will determine how fancy or finished to make it. Where it is exposed to constant view, it may be framed and cased like a flush door. One might choose to use a narrow casing of coved door stop and paint or paper the door panel to match the wall. On a paneled wall the access can be made virtually invisible except for a half dozen small oval-headed screws painted to match the paneling. In a closet a single piece of 1/4" plywood may be screwed over the opening. Such an access will likely be opened infrequently; therefore, no hinges or latches are required. The simplest removable fasteners will do.

Framing the Plumbing Access

One method of framing an access is to cut off the stud that stands in the way of the plumbing (Fig. 7-98). A flat header is placed under it a couple of inches above the point where the mixer faucet will go through the wall. Inlet a 3/4" board on the tub side that is high enough to mount the mixer. The board should go down low enough to back up the tub rim, or a separate board may be inletted. It is inletted flush with the stud surface.

The supply pipe to the shower head will pass through a bored hole in the header board. The pipe is attached to the face of the stud with a U clamp. Two cripple studs are placed below the 2 × 4 flat header to confine the width of the opening to whatever is desired.

Grounding strips as deep as the wall skin thickness, 3/4"-wide, may be nailed to the face edge of the studs. Nail them flush to the opening side of the cripples and header. This will leave half of the stud and header edge open for nailing the surface skin. The depth of these little casing strips will coincide with the wall covering depth. With 1/2" wallboard, for example, the strips will be 1/2" deep by 3/4" wide. Place a miniature casing of coved door stop over this fabricated jamb, or simply screw the ply-

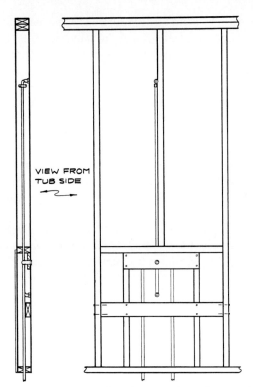

FIGURE 7-98 Access framing section view and view from the tub side.

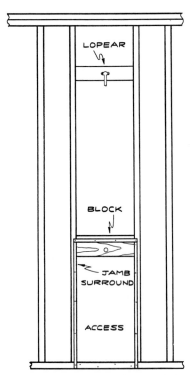

FIGURE 7-99 Access framing with straddle studs as seen from the access side of the wall.

wood panel on top of it using a panel size large enough to cover the junction of the strip and the gypsum board.

Another access framing method is to straddle the plumbing fixture end of the tub with two studs (Fig. 7-99). Place them far enough apart to allow room on both sides of the mixer valve. This will be 12″ of clear space or more. The same access header and fixture mounting board is installed. An additional block will be required at shower head height to mount the lop-eared elbow for the shower.

An access that will not be opened except for emergency breakdowns can be made of the drywall that is cut out for the access (Fig. 7-100). Carefully make the cut directly over the center of the 2 × 4 frame. To avoid tearing the paper or cracking the gypsum, scribe two cut lines around the centerlined location. Make these cut lines as far apart as the saw kerf of a fine-toothed hand saw or your saber saw blade. At the corners of the scribed opening, drill a 1/16″ hole straight through the surface. This will accurately locate the corners on the back side. Trace the two cut lines on the back and cut through the paper on that side also. Turn the board back over. Saw between the lines. Support the rectangle that is going to fall out so that it does not break away before the cut is complete. Install the full sheet. Install the baseboard. Cut off a strip from the bottom of the cutout that will fill the gap behind the baseboard up to about a 1/2″ below the top edge. Drop this strip down behind the baseboard. Drop the cutout down behind the

baseboard on top of the strip. The access is now closed and the cutout is held in at the bottom. Fit some molding strips over the joint of the wall board and the cutout. Miter the upper corners. The molding can be screwed on for easier detachment for that possible breakdown takeoff. The whole frame can be painted to match the wall for an unobtrusive cover.

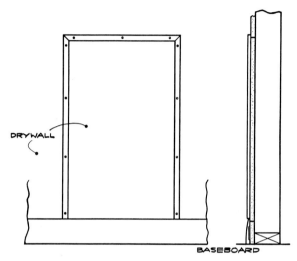

FIGURE 7-100 Simple access made of drywall. Cracks are covered with door stop or thin strips. Screws go between the cracks. Glue the strips to the door panel.

REVIEW TOPICS

Stud Walls and Partitions

1. What development in the manufacture of sheathing increased the importance of spacing joists, studs, and rafters at uniform distance from each other?

2. Explain how a precut stud differs from a 2×4 8 long.

3. How many inches high will a conventional frame partition be when made with precut studs?

4. Explain the primary function of the top member of a double top plate on a wall frame.

5. Explain the reason for and the importance of spacing studs on 16 or 24″ centers.

6. Explain why it is better to mark the location of a stud with two lines, one for each edge, on a plate than to use only a center mark or one edge mark.

7. Explain the importance of aligning the structural components (rafters, ceiling joists, studs, and floor joists) to bear in a vertical line from the ridge to the foundation.

8. Explain why no stud marks should be placed on the top plate where a uniform header over a window will be.

9. Explain why the length of a rough sill should never be measured from its location but should be measured above the sole or under the header.

10. Two marks (lines) appear across the plate that are 1 1/2″ apart. There is a letter P between the lines. Two more lines appear 3 1/2″ away. In the space between there is a letter B. What do these four lines and three spaces indicate?

11. Explain the proper spacing of studs in a center-located bearing wall in relation to the outer parallel walls and the ceiling joists.

12. Describe the transfer method of marking the location of bearing partitions.

13. Explain a sensible system of spacing studs for partitions that are parallel to ceiling joists.

Corner Posts and Partition Ts

14. Describe in detail, as though telling someone, how to assemble or make an exterior corner in adjacent walls. Be brief and clear.

15. Describe some problems that will result if the ends of the studs in a corner post are not assembled flush and crooked boards are used.

16. Explain why the nails closest to the top and bottom of the post, those into the blocks, should not be closer than 2″ from the end and why those into the center block should not be closer than 1 1/2″ from the ends of the block.

17. What does a corner post jig do for you? Be specific.

18. Describe the appearance (size, shape, and anything else) of each of the following framing nails: (a) 16d common, (b) 16d box, and (c) 16d sinker.

19. Describe the unique feature for the use of each nail in Topic 18.

20. Explain why no nails are driven perpendicular to a surface when assembling posts or assembling walls.

21. Explain why the blocks in a partition T should be placed crosswise instead of sandwiched flatwise as they are in corners.

22. Why is it important to insulate exterior corner posts and partition Ts before sheathing begins?

Wall Headers over Openings

23. List three or more of the loads (live or dead) that a header is called upon to transfer to the trimmers and down to the foundation.

24. Describe the components and assembly positioning of a traditional uniform header.

25. How does a ''span'' built-up header differ from a uniform header?

26. Explain specifically why a trussed roof will require larger headers for certain openings.

27. What are the sources for finding out how large a header an opening will require?

28. Explain why a carpenter need not use his tape measure again in framing an opening after the uniform header boards are cut to length, and the rough sill height marked.

29. What adaptation can be made to a uniform header when the 2 × 12s are warped?

30. Describe how to assemble a double header to incorporate a 1/2″ filler of insulation and still attach the two 2 × 12s to each other.

31. Explain why 2 × 6 built-up headers over 30″ doors in *all* partitions are wasteful and unnecessary.

32. List five or more advantages of the single-piece 2 × 10 header.

Rough Sills and Trimmers

33. What positive points can you make for a double rough sill as compared to a single-piece rough sill?

34. Explain the structural purpose of a trimmer in a wall opening.

35. Explain where an interrupted (two-piece) trimmer may be used and why it is not approved elsewhere.

Nailing and Assembly of Frame Walls

36. When a nail splits a board near its end it is usually because the nail is too large or too close to the end. What can be done to prevent splitting? Describe three techniques.

37. What are the three different types of 16d nails for wall framing?

38. Explain why the ends of top plates should not be joined between certain studs when roof trusses will be used.

39. Both top plates are sometimes installed before raising a wall and spaces are left for intersecting partitions. Explain how this arrangement affects the layout routine for the partitions.

40. Explain where the nails in the uppermost plate should be placed and why other areas should be avoided.

41. List the order in which the outer walls and interior partitions should be erected and explain your rationale (reasons).

42. Describe where to inlet (dado) a corner brace, where not to inlet it, and the correct range of angular degrees within which it should be placed.

43. Relate the sequence (order) of installing a plywood sheet as a corner brace (nailing, plumbing, stud straightening, etc.).

44. Describe the use of a dadoed stud spacer board (a horizontal story pole) and tell why this stud spacing routine is important.

45. A simple string line is one of the most important tools when it is time to make the walls plumb and straight. *Describe* the technique of straightening the sole plate and the top plate to create a straight and plumb wall throughout its length.

Frame and Foundation Alignment and Sheathing

46. Describe the important characteristics of each of the following kinds of sheet sheathing: (a) plywood, (b) blackboard, and (c) Styrofoam:

47. Why does Styrofoam sheathing, regardless of thickness, usually require more attention to wall bracing than do other sheet forms of sheathing?

48. Explain why each of the four alignment techniques will have an influence at the starting point (POB) of stud placement.

49. Discuss the factors involved in positioning a frame wall on a slab floor where the siding will be brick veneer.

Partition Layout and Construction

50. Discuss the advantages of modularly coordinated partitions (ones that use a common OC stud as part of the intersection).

51. Describe the steps in laying out a corner room as parallel and squarely as possible.

52. Explain how to position ceiling joists over a bearing partition so that the joists are perpendicular and parallel and the partition is straight and plumb.

53. Describe the components required over a parallel partition that are necessary to back up the ceiling board and freeze the partition straight and plumb.

54. Name as many wall-hung items as you can think of that would benefit from a wood backing board.

Characteristics of a Six-Inch Wall

55. Explain why the use of 2 × 4s in a 6″ wall as part of a corner post or partition T is not only economical but also advantageous from a fuel conservation standpoint.

56. Sketch a section view of your choice of a uniform header design for a 6″ wall. Include the insulation symbol.

57. What is the objection to a surface-mounted plywood header?

58. What length would a carpenter cut the 8′ 2 × 6s for studs in an exterior wall that will have only one top plate and will match up with interior partitions with double plates and precut studs.

59. Explain what an extension jamb is and how it can be fabricated on site at a saving for a 6″ wall.

Plumbing Rough-in

60. Describe three ways (designs) to frame a deeper partition to accommodate the main vent and feed-in vent pipes in a bathroom.

61. Describe the method of locating the vent passage hole (a) through the double top plate, and (b) through the roof.

62. Describe before and after drilling methods of reinforcing the top plate where it has been largely cut away for a large vent pipe.

63. Describe how to guard against puncturing vents and drains with drywall or trim nails.

64. Explain how to support the back top edge of a cast-iron tub.

65. Explain how to provide extra support for the front side of a cast-iron tub whose long dimension is parallel to the floor joists.

66. Steel tubs and fiberglass modules have flanges to be lapped by the wall covering. Explain what provision can be made so that the wall studs will not require shimming on three sides of the enclosure.

67. Describe the best of the three alternative methods of joining the tub with the floor covering.

Chapter 8

CONVENTIONAL ROOF FRAMING

ROOF FUNCTIONS

The purpose of a roof is to protect the building and its contents from the elements that come from the sky. The roof sheds the rain and snow, which are harmful to building materials. The word "shed" indicates the nature of roof designs. The greater the capability to shed the elements, the better the roof works and the longer it will last. The shedding capability of a flat roof is poor. It will not have the life expectancy of a steep roof, whose capacity to shed is great.

There are other factors to consider before choosing a roof style. Low-pitched roofs will shed rain adequately. High wind, however, will sometimes drive the water far up under the shingles to a point where it finds its way into the house. Low-pitched roofs will sometimes hold snow for months until a thaw sets in to melt it away. The climatic conditions that are characteristic of an area should be taken into account when choosing a roof style and pitch.

Another factor to consider is the use that can be made of the area in the attic. Low-pitched roofs will be more economical to build but will offer limited use of the space in the attic. A high-pitched roof may have enough space to be used for storage or habitable rooms.

A third element that influences the choice of roof design is the neighborhood style. Many neighborhoods have a continuity of style. A house that does not adhere to the theme will be a misfit. The house may be beautiful and functional, but the possibility of selling it is diminished. The author remembers a newly constructed octagon-shaped house. It was innovative and attractive. Unfortunately, it was built between other houses of more conventional design. It stood vacant for five years while one realty firm after another tried to sell it. Finally, it went back to the creditors, who disposed of it at auction for a fraction of its value.

Some consideration should be given to the capabilities and knowledge of the builder who will be erecting the roof. The novice who attempts a difficult style on his first job will probably suffer delay and frustration. The probability of wasted material and unsound construction is ever present.

It is the purpose of this text to explain the basics of roof framing and to express fundamentals for decision making. The subject of roof framing is extensive enough to fill a book by itself. For the more advanced student, the author recommends the reading to be found in texts dealing specifically with roof construction and with the use of the framing square.

ROOF STYLES

There are three basic styles of roofs. They are the *shed*, the *gable*, and the *hip* roof. Other styles are variations of these three. Two popular variations are the *gambrel* and the *mansard*.

Flat Roof

The flat roof is not really a roof, as it does not qualify with the basic shedding principle. A flat roof on a house is a poor choice. It is sometimes chosen as a matter of economy. The economy is often defeated by leaks that destroy the interior finish and ultimately rot away structural members.

Shed Roof

The shed roof (Fig. 8-1) is a single surface that slants in one direction. It is man's earliest design to shed rain. Primitive models were called lean-tos. There are many forms of lean-tos which have evolved into contemporary design. A lean-to is the simplest add-on type of roof. Italian architecture is characterized by multistory shafts with individual shed roofs at terminal levels. The buildings on the University of Colorado campus at Boulder are built in the Italian motif.

Gable Roof

Two shed roofs joined together with their high sides forming a ridge create a design called a gable roof (Fig. 8-2). The gable style accounts for the greatest number of roofs in the United States. It is simple to build. It divides the water shed, directing it to different areas. The roof pitch (steepness) can be varied to suit climatic or attic space objectives. The equilateral triangle formed by the two sides of the roof at each end of the house is called a gable. Gables provide an ideal space to place ventilators through which the heat and humidity from an attic can be released.

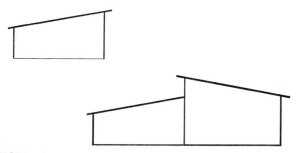

FIGURE 8-1 The shed roof may be a single cover or may be found in variations of multiple sheds.

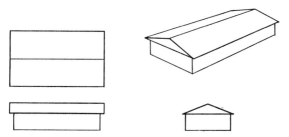

FIGURE 8-2 The gable roof is a set of shed roofs with a common ridge.

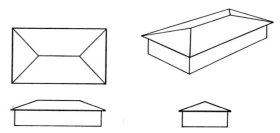

FIGURE 8-3 The hip roof slopes in all directions toward the top of the walls.

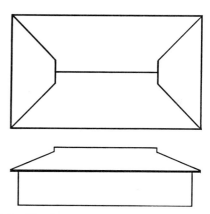

FIGURE 8-4 The Dutch hip is a hip roof with small gabled louvers at the ends of the ridge for ventilation.

Hip Roof

The hip roof (Fig. 8-3) slopes toward all four sides of a rectangular building. Hip rafters that start at the corners are seen in a top view to bisect the corners of the building (45° angles to the plates). The hip rafter is made to bisect the horizontal corner plane regardless of its pitch. When the house is a rectangle, it therefore will have a ridge board like the gable roof running through the central section of the house. Many designers feel that to be attractive this ridge should not be less than half the length of the house (longer is preferred).

The Dutch hip (Fig. 8-4) is a variation of the standard hip. It incorporates a small gable from the central ridge down to the hip rafters. This provides a place to install a vertical triangular ventilator.

Hip roof rafter cutting involves many compound miter cuts where rafters meet hips at two different angles. The layout presents no challenge to the experienced and knowledgeable builder but presents a formidable challenge to the beginner.

Mansard Roof

The mansard roof (Fig. 8-5) is a combination of two hipped surfaces. The lower rafters rise at a steep angle, usually

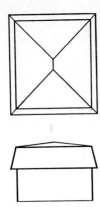

FIGURE 8-5   The mansard is a double-pitched design. The outer pitched sides are very steep. The top of the roof is a low-pitched hip or shed frequently hidden completely from view at ground level.

between 75 and 85°. On some buildings the steep part of the mansard doubles as the second-story wall. The second or top level is a low-pitched hip roof. The mansard is historically linked to France. A familiar American adaptation is seen on many fast-food restaurants. Where the back side of the building is not exposed to view, the mansard motif is used on three sides as a parapet. The actual rain-shedding roof, unseen from below, may be a simple shed from front to rear.

Gambrel Roof

The gambrel roof (Fig. 8-6) is most familiar to Americans as the classic barn shape. The roof consists of two pitches on each side with gable ends. In essence, the steep pitch of the lower sections serve as roofed walls. The roof style was popular for barns because of the large storage area afforded for hay. It is an attractive home style for a number of practical reasons. The space in the second story nearly

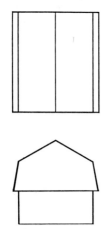

FIGURE 8-6   The gambrel is a familiar roof shape due to its heritage as a classic American barn roof style.

duplicates that on the first floor. Roofing is generally less costly than siding both initially and for maintenance. The large gable ends provide for both light and ventilation on the second-story level.

Butterfly Roof

The butterfly roof (Fig. 8-7) is a design affectation. Basically, it is an assemblage of two shed roofs joined at the lower edge. Common sense will tell us that this system opposes the basic principle of getting rid of the elements efficiently. The butterfly roof is infamous for collecting leaves, and snow, and general debris. It is, in effect, an open-ended trough. It is prone to leaking, with resultant interior damage. The practical house builder or designer will avoid this roof style.

CEILING FUNCTIONS

When a roof is "conventionally stick built" (a board at a time) the ceiling framework is an integral, structural part. In addition to providing a horizontal ceiling surface for the rooms, the framework functions as a tie across the top of the exterior walls. The tying function prevents the walls from spreading outward under the lateral compression stress of the rafters. The ceiling joists are the baseline of the roof triangle (Fig. 8-8).

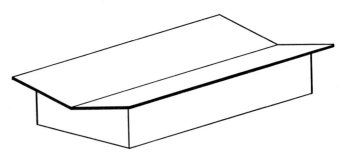

FIGURE 8-7   The butterfly roof, though simple to build, is not a practical roof for the homeowner.

JOIST IS BASELINE

FIGURE 8-8   The lower edge of the ceiling joist is the baseline of the roof triangle. The joist is a tie to hold the outer walls in alignment and keep the rafters from spreading.

CEILING STRUCTURE

Alignment and Fastening

Because of the structural role the ceiling joists play, they must be fastened to the plates and the rafters in an adequate manner. The tying function can be nullified to a large extent by a disregard for, or a lack of understanding of, the principle of sheer stress. A small amount of angle in the way a nail is driven can make it an effective hook. It will resist tension (pulling). Driven at right angles or slanted the wrong way, it is less effective.

Toenailing the joists to the plates is a traditional way of attaching them. When the toenail splits the corner of the joist, the hooking effect which resists the tension will be nullified. Persisent splitting nets a poor job. Where splitting occurs, pilot holes should be pretapped for the nails. Battery-operated drills are conveniently carried in a shoulder holster for this precautionary drilling.

The angle of the nail is important. The angle from horizontal should be somewhere around 60°. The point of entry should be at least as high up the side as the thickness of the ceiling joists. This will be about 1 1/2 to 1 3/4″ above the plate. The head of the nail is then tilted a few degrees (5 to 10°) toward the outer wall side of the plate (Fig. 8-9). The point is thereby directed slightly toward the interior. This position provides the hooking character that provides the desired resistance to the tensile stress.

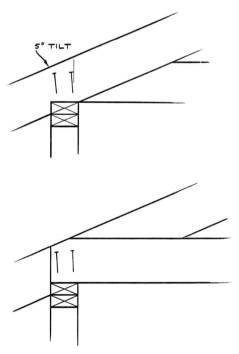

FIGURE 8-9 The angle of the anchor nails in the rafter and ceiling joist should counter the spreading tendency of the walls.

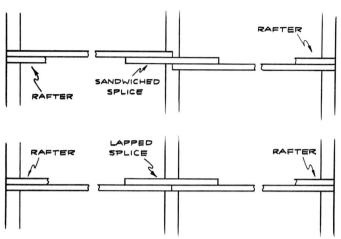

FIGURE 8-10 Ceiling joists must be in a parallel plane. The lower system shown here also keeps them on a common straight line.

Joist Placement

It will be noted in Fig. 8-10 that a block separates the joists over the bearing partition. Without this alignment block it is impossible to place the ceiling joists in parallel formation with the end walls. When the outer ends of the joists are affixed to the faces of the rafters, as they should be, and lapped at the center, they will run a diagonal course across the room. Each will start out next to the OC rafter seat and end up 3/4″ out parallel over the center bearing. It matters not whether the outer joist ends are placed on the same side of the rafter ends or on opposite sides. This misalignment was of no consequence when wood lath and plaster were the common ceiling covering materials. When modular materials entered the scene in the late 1930s, the diagonal characteristic immediately surfaced as a problem. 16 × 48″ rock lath did not fit all the way across a room. Gypsum board (drywall) end joints were not parallel to the joists. The joists can be positioned perfectly parallel with each other and the rafters by the addition of a spacer block sandwiched between their central ends. The block is positioned directly under the vertical plane of the rafters. Joists on one side of the house are lapped on one side of the rafter end. Joists on the other side are lapped on the opposite side of the rafters.

Another technique to maintain parallel joists is to put them on the same side of the rafters. A common joist line then exists across the house. This a good method to use when the house depth is a modular 24 or 28′ and the bearing wall is centered. The 12 or 14′ joists will butt over the center plate. With so little bearing a substantial 2″ nominal splice is needed. Even with the splice some codes will not permit the minimal 1 3/4″ bearing that results. A splice is required whenever joists are butted and serve as ties.

Frequently, a hallway or closet exists at the center of the house. Such a floor plan offers a convenient solution to

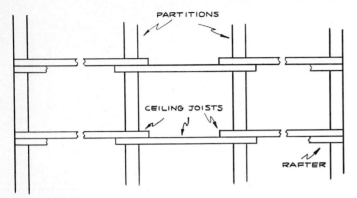

FIGURE 8-11 Where a closet or corridor exists perpendicular to the joists, short joists may be used like splices to maintain parallelism.

the parallel problem. The joists coming from the outer plates are terminated on the hall plates. When the stock length of the joist puts it no more than 1′ beyond the partition plate, it is left to hang over. The joist from the opposite wall is placed on the same side of the rafter set. Over the hallway a short joist is placed under the rafter plane. It provides the connector tie between the two room joists. It maintains the continuity to provide an antispreading component across the house (Fig. 8-11). Corridors 36 to 41″ wide can be spanned by a modular 4′ tie or one half of a precut stud. This length maintains a full 3 1/2″ actual bearing for the splice joist on each partition plate.

Modular consideration helps one to recognize designs that contain economical limits. For example, the next lumber modulus for a splice joist which affords no waste is 5′ (two 5′ joists can be cut from 10′ stock lengths). Subtracting two partition plate bearings from 5′ nets the next widest economical corridor size, 53″.

Where the floor plan has a nonmodular house depth there will always be a quantity of joist length left over. Unless this amount exceeds 12″ there is no point in cutting it off. The excess length is used to advantage by giving a greater lap surface on each side of the spacer block. In so doing, the nail positions are more widely spread out. Less splitting occurs and a stronger joint results.

Overceiling Beams

Many plans have a living room in one corner of the house and a dining room adjacent on the opposite side. Unless an arch or a header beam separates the two areas, the ceiling joists will be unsupported from beneath. Conventional ceiling joists must be supported from above (Fig. 8-12). There are several adequate designs. The first responsibility is to determine the size of a beam that is needed. There may be difficulty finding specific tables for this situation. There are two sources for reference. One is the floor girder table. It would be considered applicable when a livable room exists

above the span. The other source is the window header table. It will serve as a reference when the space above is a nonfunctional attic.

A space in the attic that is usable for storage or rooms will require a beam that is flush on both the lower and upper surfaces of the ceiling/floor joist. It is constructed the same as a floor girder with ledgers. The interior end must have a minimum 4″ bearing on top of a bearing partition. Two or more studs are required to support the ends of the beam. The exterior end of the beam bears on the exterior wall plate. A rule of thumb is to have one stud under each built-up beam member. The ceiling joists are attached to the beam on a ledger or in metal hangers. Because the ceiling joists function as lateral wall ties, they must be tied in some manner across the beam. *Toenailing* the ends to the beam and ledger will not accomplish the objective. Steel straps 1 1/2″ × 24″ may be used across the bottom of the beam. A strap on the bottom should be recessed into the joists and beam so that the ceiling skin will be level. Strapped in this manner, one tie per 4′ of beam length will perform adequately under most circumstances. Again, the nailing angle is important. The holes in the strap should be enough larger than the nail size so that the nails can be slanted (pointed) toward the beam (Fig. 8-12).

A **suspended joist beam** may be used in an attic where its protrusion is not objectionable. The joists can be

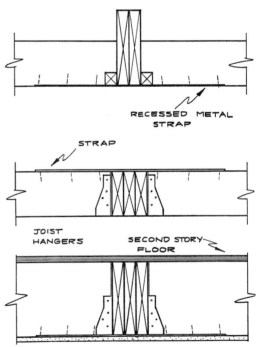

FIGURE 8-12 An adequate over-ceiling beam is needed where a flush ceiling between rooms on opposite sides of a house is desired. Note the angling of the nails in the metal tie, which helps resist outward stretching of the joists.

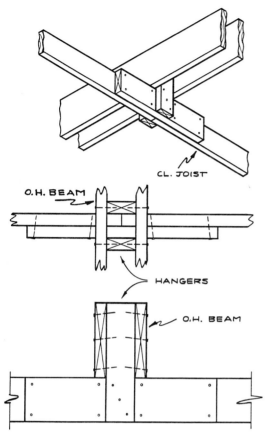

FIGURE 8-13 An overhead beam system for supporting ceiling joists all made of stock wood. Note the direction of the nail slant, which makes each nail a hook to resist the tensile stress placed on it.

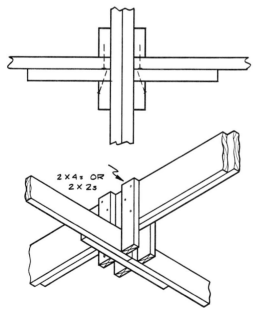

FIGURE 8-14 Another simple fabrication system for supporting flush ceiling joists over an opening. Note that joists must be nailed to hangers before applying the tie splice (top view).

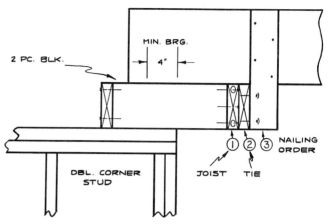

FIGURE 8-15 Interior bearing end of an overhead beam. Nail ends of the ceiling joist to the end of the bearing block before applying the splice and hanger.

suspended and supported with wood or steel straps (Fig. 8-13). A wood design of this type will resemble block-spaced double floor joists. The block suspenders extend down to the ceiling level. The joists are carefully nailed to them. Drilling is recommended for all of this nailing, as splitting the hanger will ruin its function. There are several joint combinations that can be made. The one shown in Fig. 8-14 achieves both the objectives of vertical support and lateral tensile resistance with the use of wood and nails only. Whatever the method practiced, it should meet the two criteria: to suspend rigidly and to tie the joist ends laterally.

The bearing ends of the suspension beam are on the level of the top side of the joists. The beam ends will be supported with a set of blocks made from short lengths of joist-sized wood (Fig. 8-15). One block is placed on, and parallel with, the outer wall plate. The other block will be mounted on the partition plate. This block should be cut as long as the space between joists so that it can be end nailed through the face of the joists.

Strongback

The strongback is a stiffening device used across the top of ceiling joists to hold them at a uniform level. Its function is to equalize the joist levels near the center of the span and to distribute the ceiling material weight among neighboring joists. The strongback acts secondarily as a convenient spacer board to maintain the correct spacing and parallelism of the joists.

A strongback is used to advantage where ceiling joists span wide rooms. In this circumstance the joists are usually flexible. No two are apt to have identical crowns (upward curvature). In fact, there may occasionally be a joist that was erroneously placed upside down. In the absence of any recognition or treatment of these conditions, the resulting ceiling surface will roll up and down across the room. With

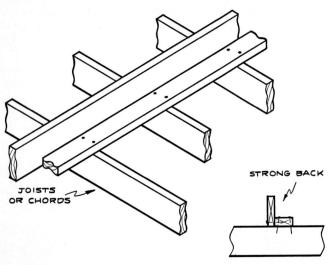

STRONG BACK

JOISTS
OR CHORDS

FIGURE 8-16   A strongback is used to support, stiffen, and align long ceiling joists.

a ceiling light on at night, the shadows created by the un-evenness will testify to the condition.

The strongback (Fig. 8-16) is shaped like a wooden angle iron. The smallest strongback size would be one made of two 2 × 4s. The assembly usually has to be done in the attic if the roof is already on and the gable ends have been closed in. When the strongback is installed during the rough-framing stage, it can be assembled on the floor and hoisted up into place as soon as the ceiling joists are in place and before the rafters are raised.

The two members are nailed together in the cross-section form of an L. The horizontal base of the L is a 2 × 4. The vertical member may be a 2 × 4, 2 × 6, or even a 2 × 8 in extreme cases of sag. Seldom is more than a 2 × 6 needed if correctly chosen. This is an ideal location in which to use a board with as much as a 1/2″ crook. By placing the crook in the "crown" position (up) the strong-back is prestressed. When in position and nailed it will ef-fectively counteract the increasing downward sag of a ceil-ing as it approaches the center of a large room.

Assembly into the L shape should take place before the unit is secured to the joists. The flat-lying 2 × 4 should not be nailed to the joists first, as it is not strong enough by itself to push down or pull up those extreme joists. The 2 × 4 is placed on edge on the floor while the upright member is nailed to its edge. A 16d common nail should be placed about every 10″ along the edge. Avoid an 8″ spacing module, as it might fall where the joist has to be nailed.

Put the strongback in position. It will be most effec-tive if it runs the full length of the room. In such an ar-rangement the ends should pass over the partition plates. A joist-sized block is toenailed to the partition under each end of the strongback to carry the bearing down to the par-tition. The parallel partition may already have its ceiling

nail backer installed (a flat 1 × 6), in which case the sup-porting block will need to be reduced in height 3/4″.

The flat 2 × 4 base of the strongback is nailed to the top edge of the joists. The first joist over which it passes should be string-lined from end to end and brought into a straight posture. It is marked at both edges on the strong-back at a place that can be seen while nailing. Nail the strongback to the aligned joist. After this first joist has been nailed, it is used as a point of beginning. The spacing is then laid out edge to edge (both edges) along the rest of the strongback. The joists are pulled into position between the marks and nailed from above.

Those joists that are low will place a lot of downward pressure on the nails. When joist flexibility is not too stiff, a pair of 16d nails may suffice. A stiffer joist may benefit from the greater penetration of 20d nails. The ideal nail for the joist that wants to pull away from the strongback is the annular pole barn nail.

The angle of the nails is probably more important in relation to stress under these circumstances than any other situation encountered so far. The joist is literally hanging from the nail shafts. A pair of nails angled to pinch the joist will hold much better than a pair driven straight down. Also, the two nails should be staggered a little so that they do not enter the same grain line of the joist. Start each nail at a point that will cause it to enter the top of the joist one-third of the way in from the edge. Head them for the cen-terline of the joist. Head the points away from each other a few degrees. Stagger the nails from side to side. A 16d *ring shank* nail is the best choice for this situation.

A short bar clamp is an excellent tool to take the pres-sure off while nailing the strongback to the joists. Fre-quently a joist is so stiff that it will not draw up tightly to the strongback. Heavy hammering only abuses the wood or loosens the side nails. The clamp is hooked over the vertical part of the strongback and under the joist. The joist and strongback are drawn together and nailed. If the nails fail to hold after the clamp is released, the last alternative

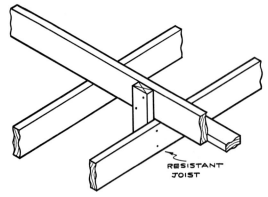

RESISTANT JOIST

FIGURE 8-17   A severely crooked ceiling joist that exerts great pressure on the nails holding the strongback to the joist can be held more firmly with a 2 × 4 hanger.

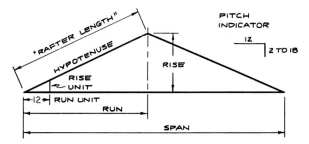

FIGURE 8-18 Rafter terms. Pitch is designated in 1″ units of rise per 12″ units of run (one unit).

is to put a wood or metal vertical tie on the junction (Fig. 8-17).

ROOF FRAMING TERMS

To frame the roof with a minimum of time and error, a knowledge of the terminology is essential (Fig. 8-18). It makes it possible to understand an explanation of the use of the framing square.

Span is the distance across the base of the triangle that is formed by the set of rafters and ceiling joists. Nominal span is measured from the outside edge of the top plates where they are in alignment with the building line (foundation line). Clear span, when there are no supportive partitions, is the open distance that is bridged between supports (the interior edge of the plates).

Run is half the distance across the nominal span. It is half the depth of the house.

Rise is the height from the top of the plate to the upper end of the rafter measuring line.

The measuring line is the hypotenuse of the run–rise triangle. It runs from the outer top corner of the plate to the top of the rise line (not to the top of the ridge).

A unit of run is a measure of 12″ along the horizontal baseline.

A unit of rise is 1″ of vertical height for each 12″ unit of run.

Pitch is the slope or angle of the roof. It is expressed as a proportion by the builder. It is sometimes expressed as a fraction. Example: a 4-unit rise is called "4-in-12 pitch." As a fraction it is called 1/6 pitch. The fractional designation is found by placing the rise number over the span number 24. For each 12″ across horizontally the pitch line rises 4″. The 4 is placed over 24′ (span being twice the run). 4/24 is 1/6 pitch. "Quarter pitch" is an expression to denote a rise of 6 units for each 12 units of run or 24 units of span. 6/24 is 1/4. Carpenters do not speak in fractional roof pitch, as it has no application to construction. The proportionate terminology, on the other hand, is directly applicable to the layout process through the use of the framing square.

The term *rake* is also associated with pitch. Parts that are placed up the roof angle, such as the trim molding under a gable overhang, are called rake parts.

Roof Parts

Ceiling joists form the ceiling frame over the rooms in a house. They perform another structural purpose. They tie the outer walls together so that they do not spread out under the compression weight of the rafters during construction.

Rafters are the individual boards that make up the framework of the roof. They are the pitched or sloped structural members.

Common rafter is a name applied to any rafter that reaches the full distance from the plate to the ridge.

End rafters are the rafters above the end walls.

Fly rafters are the rafters that form the ends of the roof when there is an overhang.

Lookouts are short rafter extensions running perpendicularly from the first or second common rafter over the gable to the fly rafter. They are parallel to the facia and the ridge. They support the fly rafter and the gable soffit.

Ladders are composed of a fly rafter and a soffit nailing backer held together with blocks (steps, hence the name "ladder"). The component is assembled at ground level and hoisted as a unit into position. The ladder technique limits the amount of overhang. It is supported at the bottom by the eave facia backer and at the top by the ridge. The current use of 1/2 and 5/8″ plywood sheathing does little to support the central area of the gable overhang.

The ridge board is a board on which the upper end of the rafter bears. It runs at right angles to the rafters at the peak of the roof. In roofs with pitches greater than 3 in 12, the ridge board must be one size larger (width, height) than the rafter to provide enough surface for the plumb-cut end of the rafter to be fully supported (100% bearing).

Webs are posts that brace up rafters and/or support ceiling joists. A web may be attached to a centrally located place under a rafter and run at an angle to the top of a bearing partition.

Purlins are long dimension boards used as full system supports under the rafters. They run continuously under and at right angles to all the rafters. The purlin is supported on webs or knee braces. Correctly designed, the purlin system may make it possible to use a size-smaller rafter because the actual span of the rafter is considered to be reduced.

Gable plates run up the slope from the wall plates. These plates are supported on gable studs, which in turn support the lookouts and fly rafter. They are rake plates.

Rafter tail is the lower end of a rafter that hangs beyond the plate to form an overhanging cornice.

Cornice is the whole overhanging system at the eave.

Collar beams are ties placed horizontally in the upper third of the roof triangle to keep a set of two rafters from spreading apart. Collar beams should be placed no more than 4' apart. They are usually made from 2 × 4s or 1 × 6s. The ends should be pitch cut to provide greater contact and nailing surface.

Rafter Cuts

The cuts made on rafters are named for their position or their function (Fig. 8-19). There are three cutting terms that relate to the position of the rafter after it is in position on the house. Other cuts are named for their location.

Position Cuts

- *Plumb cut:* any cut that is vertical
- *Level cut:* any cut that is horizontal
- *Square cut:* a cut that is at right angles to the rafter axis

Location Cuts

- *Ridge cut:* a plumb cut at the top end of a rafter
- *Tail cut:* the cut at the lower end of a rafter (either a plumb cut or a square cut)
- *Seat cut:* the double cut made where the rafter bears on the plate [the seat on a flush cut rafter (one with no tail) is a simple level cut]
- *Birdsmouth cut:* a level cut and a plumb cut made in a rafter with an overhanging tail

LAYING OUT A COMMON RAFTER

Rafter layout is similar to stair stringer layout. The framing square and a sharp pencil are the principal tools. A traditional method involves the *step-off technique*. As with the stair stringer, the step-off technique on a rafter is less accurate than the total measuring-line method. The measuring line is the hypotenuse of the run, rise, and rake triangle (one-half of the roof triangle). When beginning the layout,

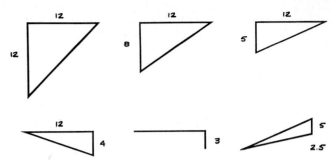

FIGURE 8-20   Pitch symbols used by architects vary, but all indicate the rise in inches per foot of run.

the run and the rise numbers are known. The measuring line is not yet known.

A pitch symbol is found somewhere on the working drawings. It may be on end elevation or on a section detail that includes a portion of the rafter. The traditional symbol is an inverted right triangle whose hypotenuse parallels the rake line of the roof. Recent blueprints show only the level and plumb line. The unit of run appears over the level line. It is always expressed as 12. The rise figure appears by the vertical leg of the symbol (Fig. 8-20).

Using the Framing Square

Not all grades of framing squares have rafter tables etched in the body. The carpenter needs this table. The measuring-line length can be worked out with the Pythagorean theorem as was done for the stair stringer. It is unnecessary to go through such an exercise when a square, with the figures upon it, is available.

Locate the table by holding the tongue in the right hand pointing toward your elbow and the body (24" side) in the left hand. The first line in the upper left corner of the body reads "*length of main rafters per foot run.*" A

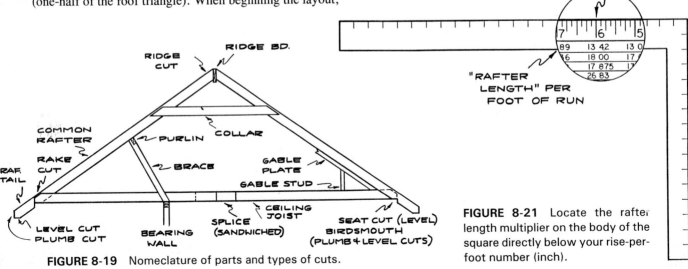

FIGURE 8-19   Nomeclature of parts and types of cuts.

FIGURE 8-21   Locate the rafter length multiplier on the body of the square directly below your rise-per-foot number (inch).

double figure appears under each of the inch marks from 2 to 18″. The first two digits are inches. The second two are hundredths of an inch. For example, the number under 6″ is 13 42. The number is read 13.42″. The numbers are the unit hypotenuse for each unit of run.

The inch figure on the outside edge of the square body represents the units of rise. In the example above, at a rise of 6″ per foot of run, the measuring line hypotenuse is 13.42″ (Fig. 8-21). On the square there is a range of rises and hypotenuse units from 2-in-12 pitch through 18-in-12 pitch. A 12-in-12 pitch ratio nets a 45° angle droof. An 18-in-12 pitch is very steep (67.5°). It is very common, however, to find the 18-in-12 pitch in chalet-style roofs.

Establishing the Rafter Board Size

Before beginning the actual layout of a conventional rafter it is necessary to know the girth and length requirements. Three specifications affect the size requirement. They are the run, the pitch of the roof, and the spacing between the rafters. It is a wise procedure to consult a rafter span table whether or not the structure falls within the jurisdiction of a building code. The table will have a column for 16″ spacing and a column for 24″ spacing. These two spacing modules fit the support requirements and the sheathing modules.

Finding the rafter length is accomplished by reading the rafter table on the framing square. The hypotenuse unit number found under the rise-in-inches number is multiplied by the units of run (half the span). The run units will vary for each different span. A span that ends in inches will have a fractional unit remainder. Examples are: a 24′ span = 12 units of run, a 28′ span = 14 units of run, a 26′-8″ span = 13.33 units. Apply these examples. The hypotenuse number of a 6-in-12 pitch is 13.42. 12 × 13.42 = 161.04″. 161.04″ ÷ 12″ = 13.42′ (13 42/100′). 42/100 × 12″ = 5.04″. Therefore, the measuring line length is 13′-5″+. From this example we can see that all roof runs of 12′ will net a measuring line in feet the same as the hypotenuse number on the square.

Apply the 14′ run example at the same 6-in-12 pitch. The hypotenuse unit is the same 13 42.

$$14 \text{ units} \times 13.42'' = 187.88''$$
$$187.88'' \div 12'' = 15.656666'$$
$$.656666 \times 12'' = 7.879992''$$

Total measuring-line length is 15′-7 7/8″. A 16′ board is needed.

This time take the span of 26′-8″ with a pitch of 4 in 12 to see how to accommodate the inch remainder. The hypotenuse number under 4″ on the square is 12 65. The run is 13′-4″.

$$13.333333 \text{ units} \times 12.65 = 168.66666''$$
$$168.66666 \div 12'' = 14.055555'$$
$$.055555 \times 12'' = .66666''$$

Total measuring-line length is 14′-0 11/16″.

The examples above have been worked out by calculator for maximum accuracy. All figures can be rounded to hundredths when the problems are done by longhand.

The actual rafter length is a little more than the measuring line, due to the plumb cut at the ridge. This added amount, however, is offset by the fact that a horizontal amount equal to half the thickness of the ridgeboard is subtracted from the plumb cut (Fig. 8-22).

Such seemingly insignificant variables as these can have meaningful effect on cost. A case in point is the last example of a measuring line that is 14′-0 11/16″. Assuming a ridge board of 1 1/2″ thickness, 3/4″ is subtracted from the ridge cut. This would appear to be a rafter length that could be cut from a 14′ board. In reality it is not because the mitered end cut extends beyond the measuring line. As the pitch of the roof design increases, this amount at the top end of the rafter gets longer (Fig. 8-22). Therefore, on a 4-in-12 pitched roof on a house of a 26′-8″ span the rafter design that has no overhanging eave would theoretically have to be cut from 16′-length stock because it is a little in excess of 14′ long. On a Cape Code style house where there is no overhang, this design characteristic could account for significant waste. Fortunately, most roof designs today have some overhang. With an overhang the measuring line modulus is relatively unimportant. The length modulus is adjusted in the length of the rafter tails.

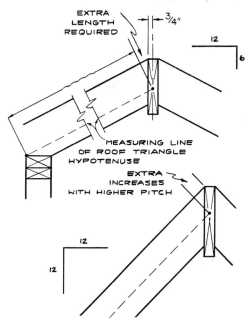

FIGURE 8-22 The measuring-line length is less than actual board length required.

Determining the Overhang

The quantity of overhang is dependent on many things. It is affected by:

- Desired shade in summer and winter
- Aesthetic qualities of the design
- Height of windows desired
- Pitch of the roof
- Initial cost of materials

Shade can be plotted on an elevation or section view of the eave side of the house. Consult the sun-angle chart (Appendix 12) to find the shade that will be provided on the longest day of summer by a certain length of eave for your latitude. Place this angle on the drawing with a line that passes under the lower corner of the rafter tail or facia (Fig. 8-23). An objective is to exclude the hot sunlight from entering windows in the summer while permitting it to enter in the winter. The height of the window (how low it goes on the wall) is regulated by the horizontal distance that the overhang extends. The top of the window is standardized to coordinate with door height.

Roof pitch has a basic effect on the extent of overhang. A high-pitched roof severely limits the horizontal overhang. The plancier return must not be lower than the top of the windows. When the usual trim is used around a

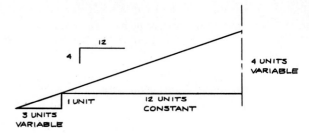

FIGURE 8-24 The overhang triangle is a scale miniature of the roof triangle.

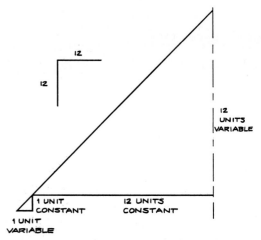

FIGURE 8-25 The roof pitch determines the horizontal depth of the overhang.

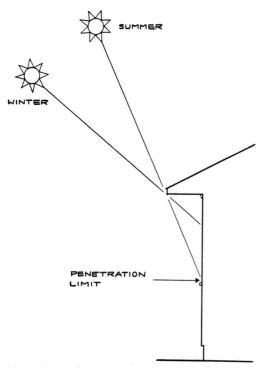

FIGURE 8-23 The length of the eave and the position of the windowsill affect the amount of direct sunlight that penetrates a house on different days of the year.

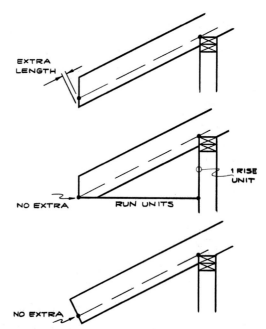

FIGURE 8-26 An exposed rafter tail and one boxed up the underside requires more length than the measuring line indicates.

window, this point is about 12 to 14″ below the top plate. The overhang profile is a miniature of the run, rise, and measuring line triangle. Using 12″ as its nominal rise the potential overhang can quickly be estimated. The 12″ is 1 unit of rise. The 1 is placed over the rise number. This is the fractional part of 12 units of run which will be permissible for a soffit return distance. It approximates the run of the overhang. Following are two examples, one low pitched and one high.

A 4-in-12 pitch gives a fraction of 1 over 4, or 1/4. Multiply this fraction times the 12 run units. The maximum horizontal overhang is 3′. (Fig. 8-24).

A steep pitch (45°) of 12-in-12 will have a fraction of 1/12. 1/12 × 12 = 1′. On this pitch only 1′ foot of horizontal overhang will be possible (Fig. 8-25). For more on this subject review Chapter 4, Figures 54, 55 and 56.

The cost of materials may affect the overhang choice. Obviously there will be more roof sheathing, building paper, nails, and shingles with the wider overhang. Hidden costs creep in when the overall length of the rafters is not matched to the soffit return distance.

The measuring-line length of the overhang is found in the same way as for the rafter. The measuring-line number on the square is multiplied by the run units of the horizontal return length, the run of the plancier triangle. The lower corner of the rafter tail will extend beyond the measuring-line point in the same way it did above the line at the ridge where rafter tails are open (no soffit; Fig. 8-26). A few inches of length must be reserved for this extra length. The square-cut tail requires no excess.

Plumb and Level Cut Layout

1. Find the crown. Check the rafter board for crook. Place the crown up, away from you.

2. Place the tongue of the square in the vertical position, by the right end of the board. Place the body in the horizontal position. The point of the square will face the underedge of the rafter (Fig. 8-27). For pitches up to 8-in-12 the greatest accuracy will be realized by doubling the rise and run figures on the square. The 8-in-12 pitch will take the full length of both the tongue and the body (16-in-24). 5-in-12 will be laid out as 10-in-24, 4-in-12, as 8-in-24, and so on. The rise number is placed at the upper corner of the rafter board. The run number is placed where it intersects the upper edge farther down the crown edge of the board. The rise and run numbers must be from the same side of the square, preferably the outside edge. Draw a pencil line along the outer edge of the tongue. This is the plumb-cut ridge line.

When using gauges they will be attached at the rise and run inch numbers. Pitches higher than 8-in-12 will be marked at the undoubled rise and run figures since the tongue is limited to a double of 8.

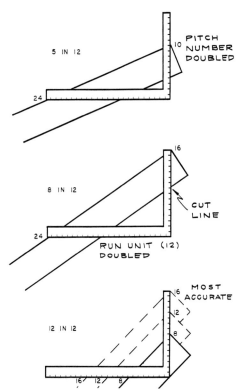

FIGURE 8-27   When scribing a plumb-cut line for the ridge cut, use doubled rise and run units up to 8-in-12 pitch for more accuracy. For 12-in-12 pitch any set of equal numbers may be used.

3. Locate the birdsmouth plumb cut. Measure down the lower edge (the underside) of the board the length of the measuring line. Slide the square to this point and draw a light plumb line from the underedge a couple of inches up onto the board. Move the square back up the board until another plumb line can be made 3/4″ away from the first mark (measured at right angles). The 3/4″ is half the thickness of the ridge board. By reducing the measuring-line length at the birdsmouth rather than cutting it at the ridge, the maximum length of the board is sustained.

4. Locate the seat cut. Move the square up the rafter. Stop at a point where the distance from the plumb line to the underedge of the rafter equals the width of the plate on which it will bear. Mark the level-cut line. For a 2 × 4 wall this level cut will be 3 1/2″. For a 2 × 6 wall it will be 5 1/2″. This provides a 100% bearing seat cut. The level cut should never be more than the plate width. Such a cut weakens the tail unnecessarily (Fig. 8-28).

5. Mark the tail cut. For a plumb-cut tail the position of the square is reversed. The body will be on top, the tongue pointing down. Mark the plumb cut along the tongue. The distance down the tail from the seat cut may be laid out on the measuring line or along the under edge of the tail. When a precise modular soffit depth is desired, such as 16, 24, or 32″, the soffit return line measurement should be reconnoitered for a more accurate result. Re-

member to subtract the thickness of materials such as wall sheathing and facia backer boards that will add to the horizontal overhang depth.

High pitches and deep girth rafters will usually require a level cut on the bottom end of the tail. Without such a height reduction of the plumb cut the facia will be oversize (Fig. 8-29). To accomplish this reduction a level cut is marked at right angles to the plumb-cut line at a desired point. Remember the roof sheathing thickness when deciding where to make this level cut. A boxed soffit must clear the top of the window casing. It lines up horizontally below the tail level cut, so the thickness of the soffit material must also be considered.

A wood facia board should hang below the soffit level 1/2 to 1″ so that dripping rain does not run back along the soffit. For example, with a 1/4″-thick soffit, a 3/4″ drip, and a 6″ nominal facia board (actual 5 1/2″ height) the end of the tail will be about 4 1/2″ high. It will vary according to the pitch of the roof and whether the sheathing is lapped over or behind the facia. Carpenters seldom bevel the top edge of the facia as they used to before metal drip edge became popular (Fig. 8-30). There-

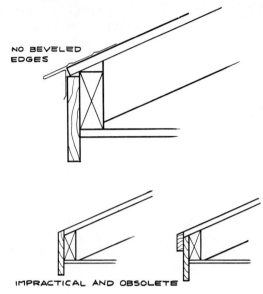

FIGURE 8-30 With metal drip edge there is no need for bevel matching the facia, facia backer, and the sheathing.

fore, it is efficient to figure out a tail cut that will accept a stock-size facia board (5 1/2″ or 7 1/4″).

RAISING CONVENTIONAL RAFTERS

It is a wise procedure for the novice to cut a pair of rafters and put them in place to check them out before cutting all of them. Some techniques can hold the test fitting or installation down to a one- or two-man job when necessity requires. Nail a long 2 × 4 onto the end of the gable-roofed house. Place it at or near the center. It must extend as high or a little higher than the ridge. Put up the first rafter and temporarily nail or C-clamp it to the brace. Tack a small 2 × 4 block to the top end of the rafter to fill the space that will be occupied by the ridge board. Toenail the seat cut onto the plate. The outer face of the rafter may be flush with the wall frame or it may be flush with the sheathing, depending on the design of the gable siding. Leave the nailhead exposed in case the rafter position must be altered or it must be recut. Raise the companion rafter and secure it temporarily. Check the two pilot rafters for fit of the seat cuts and the ridge joint. Check the tail cut to be sure that the bottom is not too low to clear the window and door top height. Use a level from the underside of the tail back to the wall to see where the soffit line will joint the wall.

Plumbing the Gables

For the rafters to be square and on a perpendicular axis with the plates and the ridge, the gables must be plumb. A long diagonal brace is nailed to the underside of the end rafter or to the first ridge board face. The brace is run to

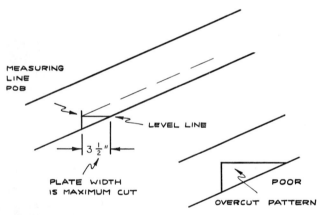

FIGURE 8-28 Lay out the birdsmouth with a constant level mark of the same length as the width of the top plate on the wall frame.

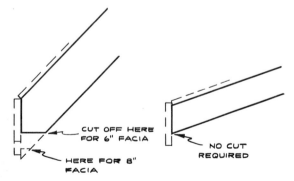

FIGURE 8-29 High-pitched conventional rafter tails usually require a level cut for 6 or 8″ facia. Low-pitched trusses seldom need a level cutoff.

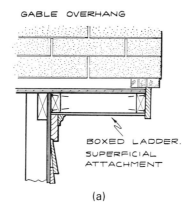

GABLE OVERHANG

BOXED LADDER. SUPERFICIAL ATTACHMENT

(a)

FIGURE 8-31 (a) Permit the ridge board to hang over to support the fly rafter of a superficial ladder. (b) A ridge board joined at the end of a pair of rafters needs a temporary strap to keep it from spreading until the sheathing is installed.

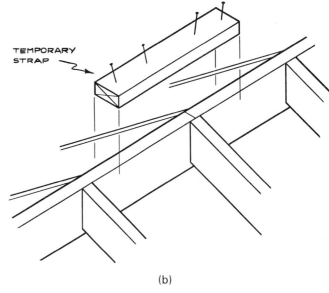

TEMPORARY STRAP

(b)

the floor or to a braced bearing partition. It is pushed out or pulled in until the gable rafters check plumb on a level or with a plumb line. The plumb line is spaced out from the end rafter at the peak with a block. A test block of the same thickness is used at the foundation level. When the string is the same distance out at the bottom as at the top and is parallel to the wall, the gable is plumb. The brace is nailed to the floor. Repeat this routine at the other end of the roof.

Surface bracing of the rafters is explained in detail in Chapter 9. The bracing technique is the same for trusses and conventional stick-built rafters.

Raising the Ridge Board

The ridge board segments are raised one at a time. It will be more convenient to mark out the spacing on the first board before raising it. Remember two items. Allow enough board for a gable overhang before beginning the spacing marks (Fig. 8-31a). Remember also that the first space will be less than a full module because the end rafters are not on center.

Brace up the interior end of the ridge board with a long 2 × 4. The height can be established quite closely by standing the brace up at the gable end and tracing the location of the ridge top on it. It is then clamped or nailed to the interior end of the ridge board. A pair of rafters is installed near this end of the ridge on the spacing marks. The ridge is now ready to receive the rest of the rafters between the two sets. The process is repeated with each new section of ridge that goes up.

Joining the Ridge Segments

Only a small building, a wing, or a dormer will have a one-piece ridge. The main ridge of a house will probably be made up of two to four pieces butted and tied at the ends. The butt joint can be made between the ends of a rafter set or at a central point between rafters.

The nailing situation is poor where the joint is made between the ends of the rafters. Only 3/4″ of the end of each ridge board is on the rafter ridge cut. This makes it

impossible to adhere to the rule that a nail should not be placed closer to the end than the thickness of the board. Therefore, the ridge should be predrilled to accommodate the nail so that splitting is avoided. Immediately after the adjacent set of rafters is installed, a temporary tie board must be nailed across the top of the ridge or across the rafters on either side of the joint (Fig. 8-31b). This temporary tie will prevent the ridge boards from pulling apart laterally. The tie is left on until the roof sheathing is in place. The sheathing will take over the tying function permanently.

Where the ridge boards meet between adjacent rafters, a permanent tie block is nailed to the face of the ridge boards. The top of this tie strap must be set down from the top of the ridge enough so that its outer edge does not protrude above the upper edge of the rafters. Allowing it to protrude will necessitate planing off the protrusion or removing the board and starting over.

With strapped ridge boards the joint should be made close to the center of the space between the rafters. This will allow adequate surface area on each end of the ridge boards to contain three or four nails. The nails are slanted toward the butt joint. In this formation they resist the tension stress and will more effectively hold the ends of the boards together.

The most effective strap material is nominal 1″ board of the same width as the ridge board. Place one on each side of the ridge, thereby sandwiching it. A dimension block may be used on one side only. It is thick enough and stiff enough. With a single block strap the joint will open up more easily if the ridge is accidentally swung toward the strap side. An advantage of the double strap over the single block is that both pieces can be nailed to the ridge tail that is already up and ready to receive the next ridge piece (Fig. 8-32). They then act as a socket into which the next ridge board is easily held and adjusted while nailing.

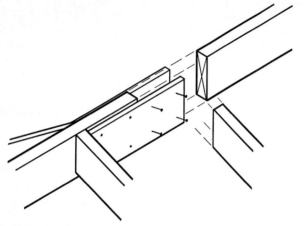

FIGURE 8-32 A double tie attached to the installed end of a ridge forms a handy socket for the next piece.

With the exception of the first ridge board, the rafter spacing marks are not put on any of the ridge boards before raising. This is because any lengthening out or stretching of the joints will render the marks inaccurate. Similarly, your tape measure should not be hooked to the last rafter installed to mark the second ridge board. Any discrepancy, no matter how seemingly small, will be perpetuated in all the rafters to come. Measurements should be made for all spacing marks, with the end of the tape on the point of beginning, the zero point. Should the gable rafters be set out for any reason, the tape may be hooked on the next rafter (the first one to be on a true center). When the last set of rafters is placed, the total distance across the length of the ridge should be identical to the distance across the rafters at the plate level.

Leveling the Ridge

In theory the ridge will be level when (1) all rafters are cut to identical duplicates of each other, and (2) the top plates of the front and rear walls are perfectly level, straight, and parallel. To be certain of this and to produce a straight ridge, use a string line. Place a nail on each end of the ridge. Stretch the line very taut. Most builders prefer to raise the end rafters first. Next a set of rafters is put up adjacent to the first joint in the ridge. This provides a bipod support for the full-length ridge. Place a 3/4" block under each end of the string on top of the ridge board. Check out all the bipod and joint locations with a 3/4" test block. It goes without saying that each individual ridge board should be straight on its upper edge. If any is crooked, cut the crowned edge to a straight line before raising.

GABLES

Gable Studs

Gable studes may be placed flat or edgewise. The choice may depend on the roof pitch. Higher pitches will benefit

from having the gable studs on edge like the studs below (Fig. 8-33). In this position they will be stiffer. When placed edgewise, the studs are attached to the rafters at the top by notching. The lower cut of the notch is on a pitch line. One nail is driven through the back side of the notch tail or through the rafter face into the tail. This nail holds the stud in the correct place. A toenail is driven under the rake cut to penetrate the under edge of the rafter.

Flat-placed gable studs (Fig. 8-34) are pitch cut on the top end. They are toenailed through the long end of the miter cut. Another toenail is placed on the front or rear face, or both, at the low side of the rake cut.

Gable Ventilators

Gable ventilators are readily available from your building material supplier. They come prefabricated and ready to install. Available shapes are square, rectangular, and triangular. The least costly type is the aluminum or galvanized sheet metal and screen design. Specialty designs, such as hexagonal and octogonal shapes prefabbed of wood, can be ordered.

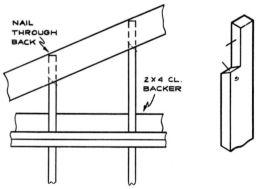

FIGURE 8-33 Rake notched stud for the left side of a gable. A 2 × 4 ceiling backer is placed on edge and nailed to the interior face of the studs.

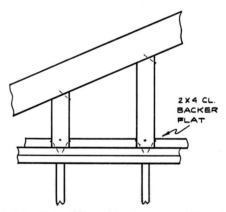

FIGURE 8-34 Flat gable studs are toenailed to the plate and rafter. A nail may also be driven into the flat 2 × 4 ceiling backer behind the studs.

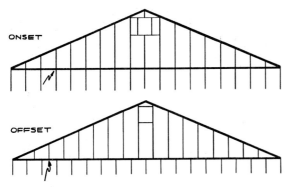

FIGURE 8-35 Two framing arrangements where rectangular vents will be installed (modular wall).

Purpose of Gable Vents. The gable vent provides a sheltered opening through which hot air and condensation can escape from an attic. There is very little movement of air from an attic unless a vent is installed in *each* gable. Even then the movement is severely impeded by the exposed rafters, which act as baffles to slow down the drafts. Wherever an adequate eave overhang permits, the same square-inch capacity of venting, or greater, should be provided in the tail soffits. This will set up a circulation pattern that tends to exhaust the hot air from the gables. Keep in mind that the minimum required net free venting area should be 1/150 of the square-foot area of the attic floor space. Even the screen in a vent slows down the exiting of air, so it is good practice to exceed the minimum, especially in warmer areas of the country. One-half of the square-inch venting capacity may be in the eaves or cornice. See Chapter 4 for more detailed information on venting an attic.

Framing a Gable Vent. Square and rectangular vents are available in widths that fit neatly between 16- or 24"-spaced gable studs. A one-piece rough sill and header completes the required framework. Consideration should be given to the stud spacing in advance when a rectangular vent is prescribed (Fig. 8-35). Studs should be placed to leave a space at the centerline. On modular spans such as 24 and 28', a stud in the wall below will be at the centerline point, 12 and 14'. In the gable the centering should be started and ended with a half module, which will place a space at the centerline location to accommodate the vent opening.

Should this detail be overlooked and the gable studs are spaced and aligned over the wall studs, it will pose no problem, only a little more time and material. It will be necessary to cut out the center stud and insert longer top and bottom frame boards, which will be end nailed to the studs to the left and right of the center one. Two trimmers are then end nailed in position to complete the centered vent space.

There is one situation in which the vertical continuity of the wall and gable studs should be sustained. When reverse board-and-batten plywood siding is used on the wall and the gables, the gable studs should line up directly above the wall studs. Without this alignment the 12"-spaced striated grooves (the reverse-batten effect) will not line up with those in the wall below. A strange mismatched effect will result.

Triangular vents (Fig. 8-36) pose no modular consideration, although they may require a top backup surround.

ROOF OPENINGS

Openings through the roof are needed for chimneys and dormers. Many openings will require cutting a rafter. The severed rafter will be supported by a header. The heading technique is similar to that described for floor headers in Chapter 6.

Chimney Openings

There are two clearance rules for chimney openings. There should be a minimum of 2" of clearance between a chimney surface and any structural wood members (ceiling joists, rafters, and ridge board). There should be a minimum clearance of 3/4" between the wood roof sheathing and the chimney.

Header Positioning

The opening for a furnace chimney is usually located directly above the opening in the floor. Four plumb lines are

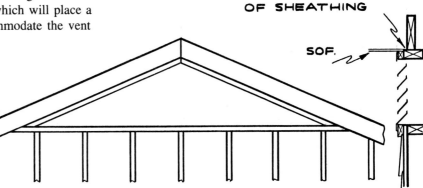

FIGURE 8-36 Framing for a triangular gable vent usually requires a setout 2 × 4 along the top edges.

dropped from the rafter level to the corners of the floor opening. Each corner of the roof opening can be located progressively with one plumb bob. The corner points usually fall between the rafters. The horizontal headers are installed parallel to the ridge, perpendicular to the rafters, in most cases. Occasionally, a fireplace is angled in the floor plan. Some builders will put all common rafters through a chimney area and cut out the opening afterward. Others will frame the opening as the raftering progresses.

Upper Header Positioning

The upper header is positioned to function more effectively for deck nailing and clearance when the severed rafter is square cut. The lower header must be positioned plumb (Fig. 8-37). If placed on a square cut below the chimney with 2″ clearance at the bottom edge of the header, the top edge of the header will be too far from the chimney. The sheathing will hang over so far that it is springy when shingles and flashing are nailed to it. On the plumb placed lower header the sheathing will touch only the edge of the corner of the board. Sheathing nails should be driven perpendicular to the sheathing directly over this corner so that they do not jump through space or slide down the surface of the header.

Header Size and Sequence

A practical rule of thumb for determining the need of a single or double header is to copy what exists in the floor below (assuming that the floor heading follows the good practice code). The girth of the header is usually the same as the rafters. An exception to this rule would exist where a fireplace chimney was exceptionally long and cuts through several rafters. In such a design the header would need to be doubled *and* of a larger size than the common rafters. The rafters at the ends of the long opening will require

trimmer rafters of a larger size also. The design is similar and comparable to a stairwell opening in a floor.

The order of assembly is the same as a floor opening. It must be followed unerringly so that nails will have adequate end-grain penetration. Nail size is 20d common.

FACIA BACKERS

A facia backer is sometimes called a false facia. It is a board nailed across the ends of the rafter tails which performs several functions. It backs up the finished facia, which may be wood, aluminum, or vinyl. The bottom edge of the facia backing board provides a nailing surface for soffit material. The top edge provides a stiff-edged support and nailing surface for the roof sheathing. Current plywood sheathing is flexible and needs backing between rafter tails. A secondary function of the backer is the role it plays in helping to align the ends of long, flexible rafter tails. 2 × 4 rafter tails that extend 3 to 4′ rarely line up. The backer of 2 × 6 girth is stiff enough that out-of-line tails can be pulled into place and nailed. Too much of this kind of rectification, however, can turn the backer into a gentle roller-coaster and defeat the purpose.

Backer size is related to finish facia size and type. For a wood facia the backer will be one width-size smaller. A 1 × 6 facia will take a 2 × 4 backer (Fig. 8-38). This

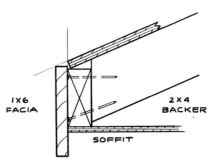

FIGURE 8-38 A 2 × 4 backer is used to back up a 1 × 6. A 2 × 6 would be used behind a 1 × 8 facia.

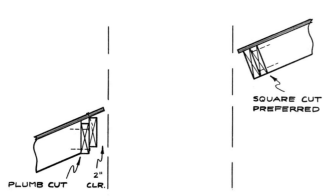

FIGURE 8-37 Square-cut headers provide better bearing above a chimney. Plumb cuts are necessary below a chimney.

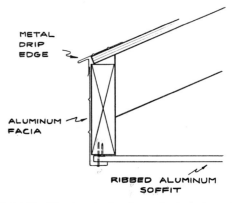

FIGURE 8-39 Vinyl and aluminum facia is installed on a backup (false facia) of the same designated height.

permits enough of the facia to hang below the soffit to prevent rainwater from running back along the soffit. It permits a choice at the top edge. The facia can be lapped over the edge grain of the ply sheath to give it added protection.

Facia installation sequence is dependent on the facia material. Wood facia must be installed before roofing begins. Vinyl and aluminum may be installed after the roofing is completed. The thin aluminum and vinyl facias can be pressed up behind the metal drip edge.

False facia used behind aluminum or vinyl will be the same height (width) as the unit size of the facia (Fig. 8-39). A 6″ facia of aluminum will take a 2 × 6 backer, an 8″ facia will take a 2 × 8.

Positioning the Facia Backer

The practice of beveling the top edge of backers and facias on a pitch line has disappeared in practice, although it is still shown in many texts. This was a common practice when wooden cedar shingles were the most commonly used roofing. When composition shingles became popular, cedar shingles were used under the first course as a drip-edge stiffener for the flexible asphalt shingles. A few years later the metal drip-edge unit was introduced and continues to hold the stage. The metal drip edge covers enough of the facia and sheathing junction so that beveling is no longer needed.

Imperfect rafter tails should be corrected before attaching the backer. A straight and true facia is the mark of a fine craftsman. An initial check can be made by sighting down the lines of the tail ends. Do it at the level of the tail cut. Any sign of misalignment is cause to set up a string line. Place it along the lower corner of the two end tails.

It must be pulled extremely taut. Block the line out at each end of the roof with a 16d nail under the string. If any tails touch the string, block it out with a 3/4″ wood block. Test for long or short tails. Do not shorten a lot of tails because a few others are short. Shim the short ones out. Thin shims are more successfully attached with staples across the grain than with nails, which usually split a thin shim.

Line up the facia backer by holding or temporarily nailing a short block on the top edge of the rafter tail (Fig. 8-40). Let it hang over a couple of inches. Bring the backer board up under the block until it makes contact and nail the backer. Do this at each end of the board. Start the nails for the in-between tails. Hold the block in one hand, push up on the backer with your shoulder, and drive the nail using your other hand.

Line up the sheathing in the same manner, except that the alignment block is nailed to the vertical face of the backer when the facia is to lap the sheathing. The sheathing is gently lowered to the blocks and nailed.

Positioning the Facia

Position a wood facia in the same manner as the backer board was aligned. Blocks are nailed on top of the sheathing at each end of the facia. Another block or combination square is held over the intermediate nailing points while each is nailed.

Finish boards such as facia should not be butted to each other to form a long piece of trim. The butt joint usu-

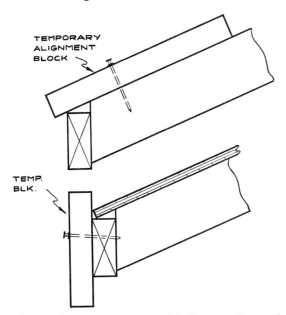

FIGURE 8-40 Use temporary blocks to align a facia backer, a false facia, and a wood finish facia.

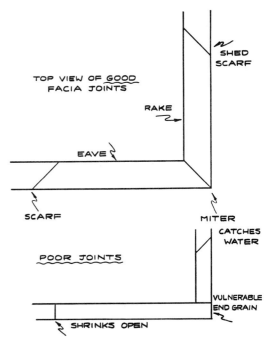

FIGURE 8-41 All exterior finish boards that require joining should be scarf joined. Those in a vertical or rake posture should be lapped in a rain shedding direction.

ally opens up when the boards shrink, leaving an unsightly crack. The wood facia boards should be mitered at the rake corner. At junction points along the eave backer a 45° miter joint is made. It is called a *scarf cut*. All trim boards that require joining should be scarf joined (Fig. 8-41). Those along the rake should be scarfed so that an upper piece always laps over the lower piece. This helps prevent water from running into any small separation that may occur.

SHEATHING THE ROOF FRAME

When a house has been modularly planned, there will be little or no waste of roof sheathing. To avoid waste, the overhangs at the gable ends will be coordinated to the rafter spacing and house length. A house length divisible by 4 can have eaves up to 2' on the ends. Rafters spaced on 16" centers can have 16, 24, or 32" overhang modules.

To conserve sheathing the roof length should be divisible by 4 or 8'. A roof length that is divisible by 4 but not by 8 is started with a full sheet. The last piece will be a half sheet. The next course is started with the remaining half sheet. It will end with a full sheet. This sets up a staggered end joint pattern from one course to the next. Staggering by a full half-sheet maintains the greatest possible strength in the rafters. Joints should never end directly above each other on the same rafter.

The roof length that is divisible by 8' will take a full-sheet starter. The second course starts with a half sheet and ends with a half sheet. All plywood sheathing is laid with its outer grain perpendicular to the rafters (crosswise).

Whether the roof frame is modular or not, the inside end of the first sheet of plywood to be laid is centered on a rafter. Its lower edge is brought to the vertical alignment blocks. The lower edge is nailed. Hook a tape measure on the inside end and place center spacing marks along the top surface at the edge. Pull each rafter to the mark and nail. It is particularly important to have the rafter that carries the sheathing joint in the course above perfectly spaced.

ALIGNING THE FLY RAFTER

Almost all fly rafters will be bowed in or out to some extent. When they are a part of a ladder overhang, they will have step blocks of uniform length. When hoisted and attached to the gable, the fly rafter will take on the contour of the gable rafter because the component is parallel. A gable rafter that is not straight can be straightened before sheathing or after about two-thirds of the sheathing is on.

To straighten the gable rafter before sheathing, a diagonal brace can be run from a point along the ridge to the halfway point up the rafter. If a single brace is not enough, two or more spaced out evenly will do the job until

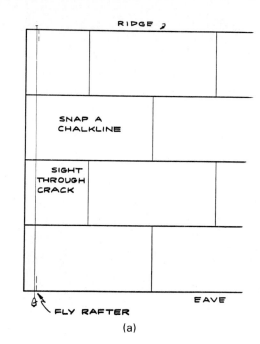

(a)

(b)

FIGURE 8-42 (a) Nonmodular overhang. Chalk line the position of the outer edge of the fly rafter. Push it into position and nail the sheathing ends. Structural lookouts support the fly rafter and roof.

the rafter can be held with the sheathing. To tell when it is straight, a string line is run over blocks at the tail and the ridge ends of the face of the rafter. This same procedure can be done after the ladder is secured in place. It may be much stiffer at the time, however, and present a more difficult task of pushing out or pulling in. Under great tension it is difficult to get a wood brace to hold with just one or two nails at each end. Therefore, it is more feasible to brace a bowed end rafter before attaching a ladder or any sheathing.

Another method of securing the overhang into a straight-line posture is to sheath the roof all or most of the way up without nailing any part of the sheathing to the end rafter or the fly rafter or any of the blocks (Fig. 8-42a). The entire ladder may be left on the ground until the sheathing is up on both sides. The sheathing is hung over the ends as much as is needed. After all of the sheathing is on, the exact intended location of the end of the roof frame is located on the bottom edge of the sheathing at the eave and at the top of the peak. A chalk line is struck between these points. The ladder is raised and nailed to the wall. The component is then pushed in or out until it lines up with the chalk line. There will be a small expansion crack left between the sheets of plywood. Sight through this crack to align the fly rafter. Nail it in place next to each crack. It is best to nail at about the center of the rafter first, as this will be the place of least tension. If there is excess sheathing hanging over to be cut off, it can be cut after all plywood corners have been nailed. The rest of the nailing is then completed (Fig. 8-42b).

Aligning a lookout overhang takes place by straightening the gable plate first with braces. The braces must stay in place until the sheathing is completed. The lookouts are then end nailed through the anchor rafter on their interior end (see details of cantilevering lookouts in Chapter 4.) The order is as follows:

1. Stabilize the gable plate with braces.
2. String line the anchor rafter.
3. Nail the lookouts to the anchor rafter on centers from the eave toward the peak. These centers will be 16 or 24″ from the eave. They will not be projected vertically above the gable studs. They are spaced to accept the plywood.
4. Nail the fly rafter to the eave facia backer, the lookout ends, and the ridge board.
5. Toenail the lookouts to the gable plate.

Temporary Bracing of Rafters

A complete description of the necessary bracing of rafters is given in Chapter 9. The technique for temporarily bracing is the same for both conventional and trussed roofs. An advantage of the conventional roof technique is found in the ceiling platform that exists. It provides a ready work surface by laying some sheathing or planks on it. Tack each end of the sheathing with one temporary nail.

SHEATHING

Plywood Clips

Plywood roof sheathing is automatically spaced apart between the edges when "ply clips" are used. A ply clip is H-shaped piece of aluminum about $9/16 \times 1\,1/8''$ (Fig. 8-43). Clips are available for $1/2''$- and $5/8''$-thickness

FIGURE 8-43 The flexibility at the edges of plywood or waferboard sheathing on a roof deck is stiffened by ply clips, which also serve to space the sheathing apart for expansion.

plywood. The purpose of the clip is to prevent the sheathing from flexing or sagging between the rafters along the edges of the sheets. For the small cost involved, ply clips used throughout the roof are a good investment. They eliminate the possiblility of breaking the building paper and cracking shingles while walking near the plywood edges. They prevent the dips and sags that are so noticeable when there is frost on the roof. Clips are advantageous with $1/2''$ ply sheath on both 16- and 24″-spaced rafters and with $5/8''$ ply sheath on 24″ rafter spacing. On 16″-spaced rafters, the $5/8''$ ply need for clips will depend on the plywood quality. Five-ply sheathing does not usually call for clips on the 16″-centered rafters. Four-ply, with its two inside plys running crosswise of the board, and three-ply $5/8''$ will both benefit from the clips.

Center the clips between the rafters. Gently tap them onto the lower sheet. The upper sheet is brought down into the grooves. Tap gently on the upper edge near the center of the board to set the clips firmly into both boards.

Sheathing Expansion Space

Sheathing swells under humid or wet conditions. Ply clips will cause a horizontal space between sheets to accommodate this swelling. A pair of temporary 8d nails driven at the end of each sheet will space the end joint adequately. After a couple of sheets have been spaced with nails, the next sheet will require shortening by about $3/8''$ to fit properly on the last rafter that it rests on.

Sheathing Cut at the Ridge

There is no need to bevel the sheathing at the ridge junction. In fact, it is preferred that this joint be kept in a low

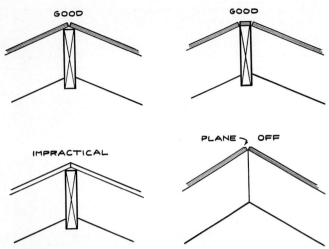

FIGURE 8-44 Sheathing need not be beveled at the ridge. The shingle cap rolls better over a less sharp ridge.

profile. It will have shingle caps bent over it later. The more gentle the curvature, the better. Composition shingle surface is easily cracked, especially in cool or cold weather. On roofs with ridge boards, the sheathing can be cut just above the edge of the ridge board. A filler of scrap plywood can be laid in the gap if desired, or the plywood can extend to the centerline of the ridge where the lower corners of the edge will touch (Fig. 8-44). Carpenters do not double-bevel ridges as seen in some illustrations. By the time shingles are lapped from each side and the caps are lapped, there are four layers of shingle over this joint. There is no need for a finish-type sheathing joint at the peak.

SOFFIT AND CORNICE RETURNS

The simplest form of eave soffit is the rake soffit. It requires no special framing. The soffit covering is nailed to the underside of the rafter tails and the gable returns. Because this surface is all on the same plane (pitch angle), the soffit will proceed around the corners and up the underside of the gable overhang without interruption. When it works out with the lengthwise modules, it is neat to carry an L-shaped piece of soffit covering around the corner and then continue the grain direction the same on up the gable. Three other optional corner joints are the perpendicular or horizontal butt joints and the mitered corner joint.

A mitered soffit corner is rarely a 45° angle. It would only be so when the return distance at the eave was identical to the gable overhang. The mitered corner is characteristic of aluminum and vinyl soffits. A diagonal return is nailed between the corner formed by the fly rafter and the false facia and the corner of the house. H strips or two back-to-back J channels are nailed to the diagonal return. The soffit pieces are custom cut on an angle to fit into the channels.

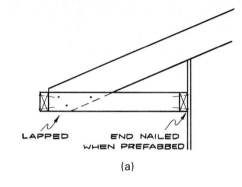

(a)

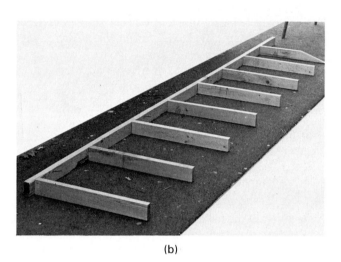

(b)

(c)

FIGURE 8-45 (a) Soffit returns may be prefabricated to the facia backer and the nailing ground at ground level and hoisted intact. (b) Eave overhang returns and soffit nailer assembled at ground level. (c) Soffit return section being installed.

A horizontal soffit requires structural framing. 2 × 4 returns are run back from the rafter tails to a nail backer on the wall. These returns may be nailed alongside the tails for some applications (Fig. 8-45a, b, and c). Modular spacing of plywood soffiting may require that the return be on the same plane as the tail. In this case the outer end of the return will be pitch cut and nailed from the underside to the tail (Fig. 8-46).

The soffit frame may be assembled at ground level and hoisted in segments. This permits end nailing through the backer into the returns. It is at least a two man job to hoist and secure the loose returns.

The other option is to stick build the frame. The wall is chalk lined at the intended location of the bottom edge of the nailer. Do not attempt to snap a line the full length of the building. It will sag in the middle, giving a false reading. Snap only 16 to 20′ at a time. The backer board can be made of a 1 × 4 or a 2 × 4. Nail through the sheathing into each stud. Point the nails up a little for a correct sheer angle, as the nail pounding for soffit installation will be against the lower edge in an upward direction. Toenail the returns to the face of the backer board.

Where the pitch cut is used on the lookout instead of lapping, it may be prudent to cut the return about 1/4″ long. Hold it in place with the pitch cut lapped behind the rafter tail. Trace along the underside of the tail. If the line is parallel to the pitch cut, the excess length can be more simply removed by shortening the square cut end the desired amount. Many times it is found that the traced line is not perfectly parallel. This provides the opportunity to cut precisely to the traced line. Now a perfectly custom-fit piece is ready for use.

Never cut all the returns into a common length with square ends first. Each time a pitch cut is made for one return, it is automatically made on the scrap side for the next one (Fig. 8-47). On low-pitched roofs, this practice will yield considerable savings.

The square-cut end of the return is toenailed to the backer board. Put a nail high on one side, low on the other. Mark the position for the lookout on the nail backer with two lines, one on each side of the location. Drive the two

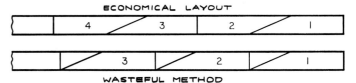

FIGURE 8-47 Labor time and much material is saved by cutting as patterned in this illustration.

nails with alternating blows. This will help hold the return between the lines.

Boxed Cornice Corner

The cornice corners have regional nicknames. Birdbox is one that has come down from early days when pigeons were housed in the structure. Framing the box is usually done by hanging a vertical member from the fly rafter and then connecting a pair of returns. One crosses over to the corner of the building. The other is a near duplicate of the eave lookout.

The birdbox is an attractive addition to the overhang. It is a natural extension of the horizontally boxed overhanging eave. This aesthetic feature is so common on the corners of a house that without it something seems skimpy and amiss.

Cornice Return Designs

There are three cornice return designs which come about logically from their size and substructure. Small returns, called ear boards, are characteristic of short overhangs and high pitches. This type of return involves little more than forming a small boxed triangle using trim materials.

An effective way of framing a low-pitched long return is to extend the soffit nail backer out beyond the end wall to a point where it will act as a support for the return and corner riser (Fig. 8-48). The soffit nailer forms the lower, horizontal corner at the house line. When the length of the eave overhang warrants a full framework, a 2 × 4 return (lookout) is attached to the fly rafter tail and facia backer on the outer end and to the soffit nailer on the inner end.

At this point, there is a choice of creating a single surface on the face of the return or one that has the rake facia standing out (the triangular box recessed). The flush face is common on smaller overhangs, where the triangular facia can be made from one piece of standard finish stock. This limits the upper end of the triangle (the rise) to 11 1/4″, as finish boards are only obtainable through 1 × 12 size. Larger triangles could be made from plywood, but the practice has not been widely accepted. A waterproof grade of plywood that would withstand the edge-grain exposure to rain is considered prohibitive in cost.

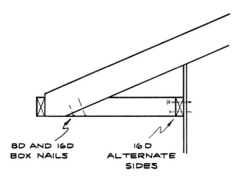

FIGURE 8-46 A truss-type return is aligned on a vertical plain with each rafter.

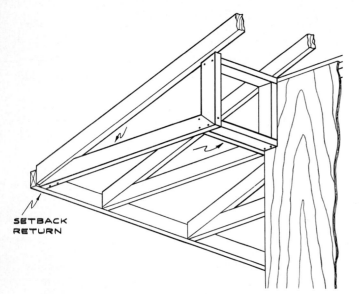

FIGURE 8-48 The soffit corner box frame is set back for a lapped facia arrangement and nailed to the end of an extended soffit nailer for support.

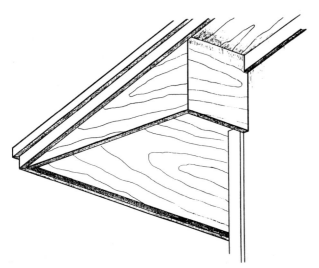

FIGURE 8-49 No joints to crack open and peel the paint in this birdbox design.

There is another objectionable feature of the flush-joined technique. The longer the joint between the lower edge of the rake facia and the upper edge of the triangular box facia, the more difficult it becomes to make a perfect joint. The joint must be perfect; otherwise, moisture gets in, paint peels, and wood rots. It is this type of problem that gave a boost to the aluminum and vinyl business.

Fortunately, an attractive alternative is to set the triangular box facia on the back side of the overhanging edge of the fly rafter facia. The lookout is rake cut on the end and nailed to the lower edge of the fly rafter tail. It is offset in this manner toward the house, leaving enough space for

the triangular facia to slide between it and the rake facia. Hardboard may be used for the material (Masonite of 7/16″ thickness in primed 4′ × 8′ sheets). It will leave 1 1/16″ of nailing surface on the underside of the fly rafter to which the lookout is nailed. Houses with rough-sawn characteristics, such as cedar board and batt, will usually have rough-sawn plywood soffits. This plywood is nominally called 3/8 RS. It is actually closer to 5/16″ thick. This material is a suitable covering for the birdbox frame (Fig. 8-49). The lookout and drop members of the frame are recessed behind the facia the exact amount of the thickness of the RS plywood. The triangular facia piece is mitered on its vertical end to match with a mitered vertical edge on the rectangular piece of facia that returns to the wall surface.

FIGURE 8-50 Birdbox framework supported structurally by an extended eave soffit nailer and an extended top plate.

FIGURE 8-51 Extending the top plate and blocking the extended soffit nailer provides some depth beyond the corner to provide a sense of support and stability.

Where the triangular box facia is to be covered with aluminum or vinyl, the lookout can be lapped inside the fly rafter. 3/4″ CD-grade plywood is used to form the triangular piece. The upper edge is butted under the edge of the fly rafter. This leaves 3/4″ of the edge of the fly rafter exposed beyond the plywood. This is exactly right for stock aluminum facia with a 3/4″ turnback U on the lower edge.

A third design incorporates an extended top plate as a support. As described in Chapter 7, the end walls of a gable-roofed house are framed and raised first. The front and rear walls, which will have the eaves, are raised last. This sequence permits the upper member of the top plate to be extended beyond the end of the house (Fig. 8-50). It is extended several inches more than the anticipated gable overhang. After the roof is framed, the plate tail will be precision cut to accommodate the birdbox framework. The vertical corner member of the cornice is face nailed into the end of the extended plate. Another return of the same length as the plate extension forms the bottom corner of the box. It lines up directly under the plate extension. Note that this system extends the cornice box onto the surface of the end wall an additional 3 1/2″ plus the wall sheathing thickness. This is even more attractive. With brick-veneer siding, it appears to be an 8″ corner surround (Fig. 8-51). The rectangular facia piece at the end of the cornice box should be nailed to the plate extension as well as the surrounding framework. This turns the structure into a miniature box beam.

REVIEW TOPICS

1. Explain as many relevent factors as you can think of when choosing a roof style.
2. Describe the difference in appearance between a gable roof and a hip roof.
3. State which type (gable or hip) puts the greatest weight strain on the front and rear footing of the foundation. Explain why this is true.
4. Describe the mansard roof and the gambrel. Compare the two graphically and structurally.
5. Explain what important function the ceiling joists perform and why it is so important to do a good nailing job to the rafters and to the top plates.
6. The rafters are placed on the plate directly above the wall studs. The ceiling joists attached to the same rafter set are nailed on the same side of the rafter and lapped at the center. Explain what the problem will be if left that way and how these ceiling joists should have been placed.
7. Describe with a graphic illustration and words how to utilize a central corridor or closet to maintain parallel ceiling joists in rooms on opposite sides of a house.
8. Describe how to support several pairs of ceiling joists where a flush ceiling is desired from one side of the house to the other (stick-built roof).
9. Explain where a strongback is most effective and describe the installation of one.
10. Describe the following cuts on a rafter: plumb cut, level cut, and square cut.
11. Describe the location and type of each of the following cuts: ridge cut, tail cut, seat cut, and a birdsmouth cut.
12. Explain in detail what it means to correlate overhang (eave length) with the sun's angles and how it effects windows.
13. Explain the method of installing, plumbing, and temporarily bracing the first set of rafters.
14. Explain all the factors that must be taken into account when the first ridge board is marked for rafter seating before raising it into place.
15. Describe all the essentials of making a ridge board level.
16. Conjecture as to what is wrong when you know the rafters have been cut to near-perfect duplicate length, and the gable rafters fit, but toward the middle the new rafters going up appear to be getting shorter with each set.
17. Discuss the pros and cons of gable studs that are installed flat compared to installing them edgewise.
18. Explain the significance of placing gable studs directly above wall studs in a modular wall as compared to situating them above and between the studs.
19. Diagram and explain the logic in the two header positions in a roof opening as described in this chapter.
20. Diagram and explain how to join the ends of facia boards at the corners, along the horizontal eave, and up the rake eave.
21. Describe how to start and how to continue installing sheet-type sheathing on the rafters. Include all knowledge about spacing, nailing, and overhangs. Include all pertinent knowledge about gable overhanging, spacing the sheathing, and nailing.

Chapter 9
*ROOF TRUSSES*_____

TRUSS DESCRIPTION

A roof truss is a component composed of a set of ceiling joists, rafters, and connecting webs. These parts are held together with metal or wood gussets. In a factory, the truss is assembled on a table-height jig. A sophisticated forming jig has hydraulically operated clamps to hold the members. Air hammers sink the metal gussets over the joints. Simpler jigs use angle irons or wood blocks to position the truss members (Fig. 9-1).

It is practical to build trusses on the site when a wood subfloor or a large flat concrete slab is available. Under certain circumstances, builders can afford to build their own trusses. The winter shutdown period is a good time if a closed shelter is available. Low-economy cycles, when no new contracts are waiting, is a good time for truss building. The homeowner/builder can save a substantial amount by building the trusses for his house. It requires the knowledge of correct design and component sizes to create a satisfactory truss.

THE TRUSS PRINCIPLE

Truss strength comes from the principle of triangular rigidity. Visualize a square or rectangular frame. The boards are lapped at each corner and held together by one nail. This frame can be pushed into a parallelogram shape by applying pressure in one of two directions at any corner (Fig. 9-2). Such is not the case with a triangular frame. It

FIGURE 9-1 Simple and effective truss jig.

206

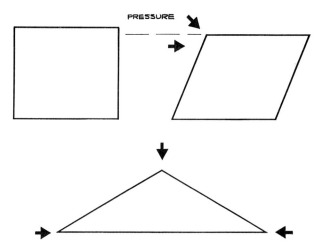

FIGURE 9-2 Pressures on a rectangle pivot the corners making it a parallelogram. A triangle sustains rigidity regardless of where pressure is applied.

is rigid. It effectively resists pressure in proportion to the size of the materials and the strength of the fasteners. Apply this principle to the roof triangle. A truss design results which is stronger, more uniform in shape, and will require less time to install than a conventional roof frame. A primary advantage of the truss is that greater distances can be spanned than with nontrussed roof frames.

TRUSS PARTS

The names of truss parts (Fig. 9-3a) differ from conventional roof members.

- *Lower chords:* ceiling joists; also serve as antispreader ties (collars)
- *Upper chords:* rafters
- *Webs:* connecting members that form the inner triangles within the outer roof triangle
- *King post:* vertical post that connects the lower chord with the peak of the upper chords
- *Queen post:* vertical web that connects the lower chord to the upper chords at a specific location along its length; usually at 1/4 points
- *Gussets:* plates of galvanized iron or plywood that are placed on each side of a joint in the truss to hold the pieces together
- *Tail chord:* end of the upper chord, which hangs over and beyond the top plate of the wall
- *Drop:* vertical member of the cornice assembly, which completes the soffit triangle
- *Return:* horizontal piece of an overhanging eave, called eave lookout on the end of a gable roof

There is a piece of a particular truss that may be called a *frieze drop.* It is a vertical "drop" from the top of the

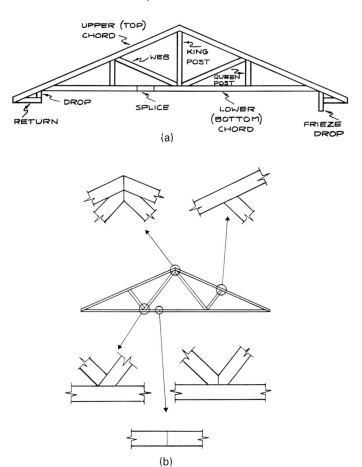

FIGURE 9-3 (a) Parts terminology of a roof truss. A frieze drop forms the pocket for brick-veneered walls. (b) Truss joints may vary depending on the type of fastener specified.

tail chord running down beyond the return along the face of the wall. For a brick-veneered house, this vertical piece will continue on down below the return to back up the frieze board. This drop forms a pocket for the soldier coarse of brick (the top vertical row).

TRUSS DESIGNS

Many truss designs have been handed down over the ages. They are seen in medieval history books and in existing architecture. Examples of the simple king post bridge are still found in the backwoods trails of the western states. Many old steel truss bridges still grace the countryside off the beaten path. They give silent testimony to the principle of the triangle.

Three truss designs are in common use by house builders. They are the Fink truss, more often called the W truss; the Howe truss, nicknamed the M truss; and the scissors truss (Fig. 9-3b). The W and M trusses derive their nicknames from the profile of the webs, which resemble

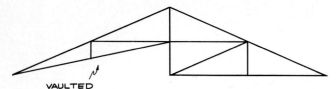

VAULTED

FIGURE 9-4 A vaulted ceiling usually refers to a ceiling that slants in one-half the span of a house. Half resembles a scissors truss, while the other half duplicates an M truss with a collar added.

the letters W and M. The scissors resembles an open pair of scissors.

W and M trusses have horizontal lower chords to provide a level ceiling. Either the W or M truss can be used on the same house plan. Scissors trusses are used where a cathedral ceiling is desired. Some house plans have a vaulted ceiling over the living room or family room. Vaulted refers to a ceiling that slants in one direction (Fig. 9-4).

W Fink Truss

W trusses are designed to span the depth of a house. The junctions of the lower and upper chords bear on the exterior walls. No intermediate bearing partitions are required; therefore, a truss is classed as self-supporting. This factor influences several other parts of the house. No partitions are considered "bearing" and as a result girder column or girder size may be affected positively. Conversely, all the

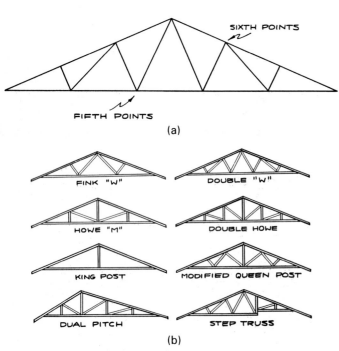

SIXTH POINTS

FIFTH POINTS

(a)

FINK "W"   DOUBLE "W"

HOWE "M"   DOUBLE HOWE

KING POST   MODIFIED QUEEN POST

DUAL PITCH   STEP TRUSS

(b)

FIGURE 9-5 (a) A multiple or compound Fink truss adds points to the divisions of the span by twos. (b) Other conventional roof truss designs built of wood.

weight of the ceiling is now borne by the outer walls (in theory), so that window and door headers are affected negatively (more compression on them).

Web Locations. The webs meet the chords at specific points. On the simple W truss, the points along the lower chord are called 1/3 points. The webs meet the upper chords at 1/4 points. These points are referred to as third and quarter points. On a double or multiple W truss, the points increase by twos. By adding a set of webs, one on each side of the truss, the division of the span increases by two. The smallest multiple W truss (the double W) has fifth points on the lower chords and sixth points on the upper chords (Fig. 9-5).

The number of points indicates the quantity of spaces that are evenly divided into the clear span. Clear span is the distance between the *inner edges* of the exterior walls. A 24'-deep house with 2 × 4 walls has a clear span of 23'-5" (two 3 1/2"-wide plates subtracted from 24'). It is a common *error* to divide the span by the points.

Computing Web Junctions. Finding the junction points of webs and chords may be done mathematically or by measurement. The measurement method is done accurately on site. The dimension should never be determined by scaling a drawing.

Third points along the lower chord are found by dividing the actual clear-span distance by 3 (Fig. 9-6). Some examples follow.

Example 1: 24' Modular Span

    24' minus two 2 × 4 bearing plate widths
    24' minus 3 1/2" minus 3 1/2" = 23'-5"
    288" minus 7" = 281" clear span
    281" divided by 3 = 93.6666" third point
    (actually 93 and 2/3")

Example 2: 26' Nominal Span

    26' minus 7" = 25'-5"
    312" minus 7" = 305" clear span
    305" divided by 3 = 101.6666" third point

Example 3: 26'-8" Nominal Span

    26'-8" minus 7" = 26'-1"
    320" minus 7" = 313" clear span
    313 divided by 3 = 104.3333" third point

Example 4: 28' Modular Span, 6" Wall Frame:

    (5 1/2" actual)
    28' minus 11" = 27'-1"
    336" minus 11" = 325" clear span
    325" divided by 3 = 108.3333" third point

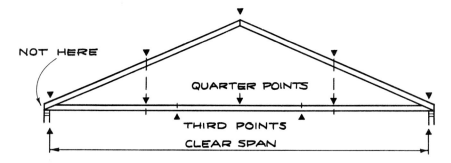

FIGURE 9-6 Third points are an equal division of the clear span. Quarter points are located on the baseline and projected to the top chord.

Multiple W truss divisions for fifth points are found the same way, using 5 as the divider. House spans are seldom great enough to require multiple W trussing. The multiple W is common to spans over 32′, such as those found in pole barns and other outbuildings, where column obstructions and girders at the floor level are undesirable.

Quarter points are effectively placed on the upper chord by measuring along the underedge. As soon as the upper and lower chords are placed in the jig, a line is projected vertically across the lower point of beginning, the interior face of the top plate. Measure in from the ends of the lower chord the amount of the top plate width. Lay the body of a framing square along the lower edge of the lower chord with the tongue on the mark. Draw a plumb line along the tongue. The intersection of this line with the under edge of the upper chord is the point from which the quarter point will be computed on the upper chord. Measure from this point to the lower side of the plumb cut at the peak, the rise point. Find the midpoint of this distance. Mark it. This is the quarter point on the upper chord.

Some designers locate the third and quarter points from a slightly different source. Instead of measuring from the clear-span point (the interior frame line), the beginning point is taken at the inside point of the heel cut on the lower chord. This is the junction point of the upper and lower chords. It is believed that this is the true clear-span point of the upper chord. This variance is of little consequence. It is a minor difference on high pitches and only slightly greater on lower pitches.

Note that both third points and quarter points are marked at the under edge of all chords. This is because the under edge of the lower chord is the baseline of the roof triangle on which all layout is founded. The upper chords are positioned above the roof triangle because there are no birdsmouth seat cuts. The lower edge of a top chord is the hypotenuse of the roof triangle. The lower edge of an upper chord is comparable to the measuring line of a conventional rafter. Thermal trusses are an exception (explained in Chapter 14).

A common error exists when ''third point'' is interpreted to mean one-third of the nominal span. Such an error will result in a larger center span between webs. This error combined with another, the use of equal-length lower-chord members, will usually result in a sag problem at the center

of the truss where no supporting partitions exist in that zone.

Eliminating a central sagging problem caused by this design or construction error is accomplished by proper design and assembly.

- Rule 1. Lay out the third or quarter points so that each section is an equal division of nothing greater than the *clear* span (not the nominal span.)
- Rule 2. Use lower-chord members of different lengths alternately. For example, members of a 24′ nominal span should be 10 and 14′, not 12 and 12′ long (12′ lengths are used only where a continuous partition system within 2′ of the centerline of the span exists). The splice location where the gusset is installed should not extend beyond the web junction more than 25% of the span distance between the webs.
- Rule 3. During construction of the trusses, stagger these lower chords so that the spliced joint alternates from one side to the other.

Index the tails of each truss so that each is placed on the house in the same relation that it came out of the jig. It is possible to make a perfectly symmetrical jig, but some inaccuracies may develop. By using the indexing system, each side of the roof will be uniform. This will assure straighter eave lines. It makes the installation of trim a more pleasant task. A simple way to index is to use an aerosol-spray paint of a bright color on the front tail as soon as the board is put in the jig. Installation can then be monitored easily by sight. Any truss that is inadvertantly reversed will be spotted.

Howe M Truss

An M truss is a larger combination of two simple king post trusses (Fig. 9-3a). The upper chords are extended to a meeting point. A king post is added at the centerline. The vertical webs in each half at quarter points are called queen posts. M trusses are self-supporting over the same spans as W trusses. Even so, they are especially effective where a centrally located bearing partition exists. The profile they present shows how each half of the truss is positioned like two separate roofs on each half of a house. This criterion provides a reason for making a choice between M trusses or W trusses for a specific floor plan.

Criteria for Choosing.   There is a little more linear lumber in the M truss than the W of the same span and pitch. On the other hand, there are some floor plans with bearing partitions that would make it possible to use 2 × 4 parts throughout an M truss, whereas the W truss might require chords of 2 × 6s. In general, W and M trusses up to and including 28' spans may be made with all 2 × 4 components. Therefore, W trusses are less costly over clear spans of the same length. M trusses may prove more feasible over long spans which have centrally located bearing partitions. Where there is any question or doubt about the required girth of components to fit specific conditions, the builder should avail himself of reliable engineered data.

M Truss Points.   M trusses are designed with quarter points throughout. The king post straddles the vertical centerline of a symmetrical M truss. Queen posts straddle the centerline of each half of the clear span. Lay out quarter points on the upper or lower chord in the same manner as prescribed for the W truss. Project the quarter-point locations with a framing square from the lower chord vertically through the upper chord.

Lower-chord splice joints will be located under the same rules as prescribed for the W truss except where a perfectly centered bearing wall extends full length of a building. In the latter case the joint may be made at the exact center (over the wall).

Scissors Truss

The scissors truss is designed to provide a sloped ceiling that gives an impression of spaciousness. It has been dubbed the "cathedral ceiling," a name that implies grandeur and elegance. To gain these aesthetic characteristics, the homeowner may elect to have the cathedral ceiling in spite of its extra initial cost and its sustaining additional costs generated by the extra cubic footage for heating and cooling. Like the M or W truss, the site construction of the scissors truss is within the capability of the house builder. There are certain criteria that apply only to the scissors truss.

Minimum Pitch of the Scissors Truss.   Practical pitches for M and W trusses generally range from 3 in 12 to 8 in 12. Above 8 in 12, the excess linear footage of web material and the lost use of potential attic space become compelling factors. With the scissors truss, it has been found through experience that a 5-in-12 pitch for the upper chord is the lowest practical pitch that should be attempted where no auxiliary support is used. The lower-chord pitch is usually one-half the pitch of the upper chord. Therefore, it follows that the lowest interior ceiling pitch to employ is

2 1/2 in 12 (Fig. 9-7). It has been found that scissors trusses of less than this combination have a tendency to spread at the heel and come apart at the apex of the lower chords.

Chord Design.   Some steeper-pitched scissors trusses have been known to fail for another reason. The strongest truss is achieved when the collar beam segment is a single, unjoined piece. Like the M truss, the scissors has two queen posts and one king post (Fig. 9-7). In addition, it has a horizontal collar beam at the midpoint of the rise. Some designs show a junction of the lower chords, the king post, and a two-piece collar at the center point. Such a design will put additional stress on the cross-tying function of the collar beam, especially at the lower pitches. The stress is directed almost entirely at the gussets which tie the lower chord apex together. From experience it has been found that a *two-piece collar* should be used only on a scissors truss whose upper chords are 12-in-12 pitch or steeper.

Point Locations on the Scissors Truss.   Point locations are found the same as for the M truss. The chords are quartered from the clear-span points. This locates the vertical position of the queen posts as well as the horizontal position of the ends of the collar. Since there is no lower chord from which to project a vertical quarter point, it can be found by measuring along the underside of the upper chord to the middle of the clear span of this chord. This point will represent a vertical centerline to be straddled by the queen post. The collar will be placed in the truss jig first. Each end of the collar (a pitch cut) will extend beyond the quarter point an amount equal to half the width of the queen post. The queen post straddles the quarter-point vertical line. This permits a square-cut end on the top of the queen post and reduces the sheer stress on the gusset (Fig. 9-7). A collar resting on 2 × 4 queen posts will be 3 1/2″ longer than the horizontal distance between the outer quarter points (1 3/4″, half a 2 × 4, beyond each quarter point).

Another design for a scissors truss employs the quarter points but differs in that the antispread function is achieved by extending one of the lower chords out to the top chord (Fig. 9-8). In this design the ceiling pitch will always be less than half the roof pitch.

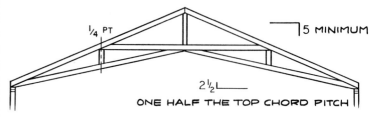

FIGURE 9-7 Sturdy scissors truss results from component intersections at quarter points.

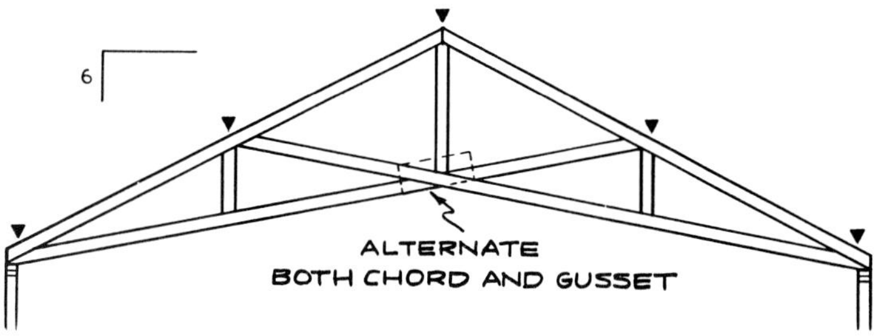

FIGURE 9-8 This scissors truss employs an extended lower chord in place of a collar to form the tying function. The lower pitch is more nearly one-third of the upper pitch.

CUTS AT JUNCTIONS OF TRUSS COMPONENTS

Webs will most closely follow the intended equal division of the span concept when they straddle their point locations. This philosphy will cause a number of different web cut possibilities. These differences can alter labor time and gusset size.

The size of the gusset will also have an influence on the cut design. A single-direction cut on a web, a miter on one side only, may be adequate when a large enough plywood gusset is used. The gusset should have about the same quantity of surface for gluing and nailing on each member that it fastens together. Figure 9-9 illustrates how the simple revolving of a gusset pattern can accomplish a nearly 50–50 surface contact compared to an approximate 40–60 contact.

Metal gussets, whether nailed or compressed on (the gang-nail type), are generally much smaller than wood gussets. This requires more precision in making the joint cuts because the nails or the press points of the gang nail plate are so close together. A sloppy joint or short web could result in a significant quantity of fasteners failing to penetrate sound wood.

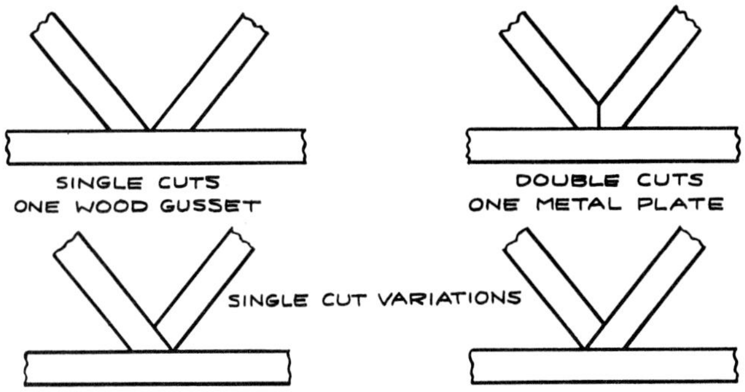

FIGURE 9-10 Single-cut webs will accommodate plywood gussets or require two metal plates. Double-cut webs may be held with a single metal plate of adequate size.

FIGURE 9-11 Top web cuts are also affected by single or double cuts.

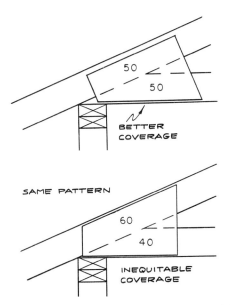

FIGURE 9-9 The same-size gusset can be positioned to provide more equitable coverage.

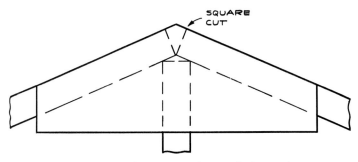

FIGURE 9-12 With a large enough set of plywood gussets, glued and nailed, the ends of upper chords and a king post may be assembled in square-cut formation.

The smaller metal gussets also require a tighter configuration of the joint. This necessitates double-cut ends on some web junctions, where a single cut may be adequate with plywood gussets. Figure 9-10 shows a comparison of the two types of cuts on a lower chord.

The upper junction of webs and chords is similarly affected, as shown in Fig. 9-11. Some truss designers, using plywood gussets, have further simplified this upper junction by assembling it with the mill cut square end. With an

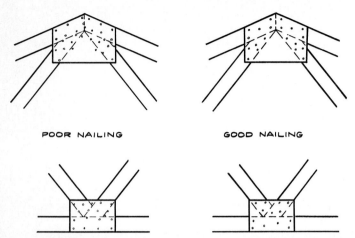

POOR NAILING   GOOD NAILING

FIGURE 9-13 Use x-ray vision and knowledge of wood to avoid splitting under a gusset.

adequately sized gusset, plenty of nails or staples, and a good glue job, such a pattern will pass the test. There is a potential weakness in the design. Figure 9-12 illustrates that the absence of a plumb cut on the upper chords removes the bearing factor that normally exists between the two top chords. Without the upper ends of the chords pressing against each other, the vertical load compression on the upper chords, which normally exerts lateral compression on the peak joint, transfers its force to shear stress on the glue and nails of the gusset. The labor time gained by using the mill-square cut end as is may be lost as the result of having to use larger gussets, more fasteners, and more glue.

The square-cut ends are not visible to the nailer when the gusset is being installed. Frequently, nails or staples from power guns are driven in the voids where the square cuts exist. Since there is no sensation (no feeling) telegraphed from the power gun to indicate the miss, the operator is unaware of the failure.

NAIL PATTERNS

The location of nails to secure a plywood gusset should follow some logic. First, it is important to recognize the principle that nails placed in the same grain line of a board, and close together, form a wedge effect and tend to split the board (Fig. 9-13). Nails driven close to the end of a board also tend to separate the fibers. Such fastening failures may not be visible to the naked eye at the time of nailing. They may develop into significant cracks later when drying shrinks the wood or when a stress load is placed on the truss (sheathing, shingles, snow, etc.).

METAL NAIL PLATE SIZE AND LOCATION

The location of a metal gang nail plate on the truss joint is critical. Much distrust of metal-gusseted trusses exists due

to the apparent small size of the plates for the job they are called on to do. The essence of strength is attained partially by the plate size and the quantity of effective nail points. The proportionate quantity of points that fasten each member of the joint is important. A single plate of adequate size could be rendered inadequate by carelessly being offset a small amount. One or more of the joined boards may not contain enough nail points, due to poor placement of the nail plate.

The size of the plate relates to its intended location and the size of the components as well as the design of the cuts in the joint. These elements being equal, an additional factor, longer span, may require larger plates.

Each manufacturer's plate design carries specific engineered and tested stress data. The builder who purchases gang nail plates should first obtain these specification data, from which an assessment of the needed sizes can be reached. Simply purchasing a quantity of plates out of the bin because they appear to be about the right size or price may be the prologue to a tragic collapse of a roof frame during or after construction. After construction, substandard plates may be the cause of stretched joints and a sagged ridge line. Cracked ceilings are not uncommon as a result of web joint failures on lower chords. Cracks in ceiling coverings are also common due to ignoring the staggered joint and/or the 25% spacing rule for the splice on the lower chord.

CONSTRUCTING THE FORM

The most convenient place for a house builder to make his trusses is on a wooden subfloor prior to wall framing. Trusses that do not require acute accuracy may be laid out on blacktop or concrete surfaces with chalk lines. On blacktop or concrete a single truss is made up with gussets on one side only (the other side is added later). It is turned over, gussets down, and used as an underlay pattern. Each successive truss is built on top of the original.

House trusses should be accurate. On a symmetrical truss, each half will be as identical as human hands and mind can make it. Ideally, all completed trusses will be duplicated, identical copies of the design. The attainment of this goal is dependent on the accuracy of the form and the conscientiousness of the truss builders. The author once attempted to use trusses purchased from a succession of suppliers. Each set purchased failed to be uniform, causing much alteration and adapting to achieve straight finish lines. Out of curiosity, he went to each firm and observed the assembling of the trusses. A variety of elements told the story. One company used forms on individual homemade tables which had suffered so many nail perforations that it was virtually impossible to hold a jig block securely in place. Third points were incorrectly located from the nominal span point. No staggering of the lower-chord splice was practiced. Workers were seen to place crooked chords into the form. When a web would consequently refuse to drop in the form, a hand-held maul was used to pound it in. The sheet metal gussets were power nailed. Many nails were driven indiscriminately without design or thought. Several nails per junction went between the joints. At another assembler's shop, a more sophisticated steel jig was in use. Here the junctions of webs and chords were more firmly held to tolerance. Nonetheless, a problem existed in continuity. The layout person went through the jig assembly procedure by measurement. Then a set of template pieces were cut out for one side. They were tried in *one half* of the jig but not in the other half. Satisfied with this half-tolerance test, the foreman ordered an assembly-line duplication of the parts. The first truss came out of the jig and was flipped over onto a flat table, where the nail plates for the second face were installed. There was the explanation for our job-site problem. The pilot truss had not been tested for symmetry by reversing it in the jig. Throughout the loading, unloading, and placement on the house, some reversing had occurred. The nonsymmetrical nature of the trusses caused tails and ridge lines to be erratic. Neither manufacturer adhered to the lower-chord-joint stagger system or to tail color coding as a means of eliminating some of the inherent problems with nonsymmetry. Visits to other plants revealed similar problems which were passed along to the builder and sometimes to the consumer. Fortunately, such practices are not characteristic of the truss industry as a whole. Many fine trusses come off assembly lines where sufficient care has been exercised to produce a symmetrical truss. The story is told to impress the reader and builder with the fact that quality and subsequent success are direct products of attention to detail and conscientious behavior.

CONSTRUCTING THE TRUSS JIG

Laying out a site-built jig on a subfloor begins by establishing a roof triangle with chalk lines. A truss that will be soffited on the underside of the overhanging tails or will have exposed tails may be laid out along the edge of the subfloor at the end of the house. There are some advantages in this case. The span of the floor is the same as the nominal span of the lower chord. Therefore, the lower-chord templates can be cut to length without measuring. The baseline of the roof triangle is the edge of the floor line.

The upper-chord lines of the triangle will start at the corners of the floor and will terminate at the rise point. These two legs of the triangle represent the underedge of the top chords. To create a perfectly symmetrical pattern on the floor, a junction of floor corners and the rise point is located. Make a line that is parallel to the baseline and at the height of the rise. Hook a tape measure to each of the corners of the floor. Stretch the tapes to the parallel rise

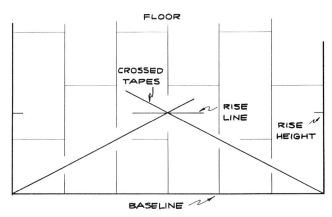

FIGURE 9-14 A truss without soffit returns may be laid out and jigged on the end of the floor deck.

line. Cross them and adjust right or left until the feet and fractional-inch marks are precisely equal on the rise height line (Fig. 9-14). This point of intersection will be on the vertical centerline of the peak at a point that creates an identical chord measuring-line length on each half of the truss. Place a small nail at this point. Stretch a chalk line from the floor corner and around the nail. Snap it. Repeat the chalk lining on the other side. The roof triangle is now established on the floor. The lower chords will be placed with their lower edge on the baseline, the edge of the floor. The upper chord is placed above the chalk line. Its lower edge will be flush with the chalk line.

TRUSSES WITH RETURNS AND DROPS

Trusses with returns and brick pocket drops will need to be laid out on a long side of the floor (Fig. 9-15). The baseline will be established and chalked far enough from the floor edge so that all of the chord tail is on the floor and a few more inches for forming blocks.

FIGURE 9-15 The following components of a gable truss are seen in this tail portion of a truss jig: the brick pocket drop, the lowered top chord, the tail chord, the soffit return, and the first gable stud.

Laying out the triangle proceeds the same as described for the open-tail truss except that the floor line cannot be used as a baseline. The baseline is laid out and chalked to a length equal to the span. It is convenient, but not essential, to make this line parallel to the floor edge. A very large truss, or one being constructed for a square building, can be laid out diagonally on the floor at an angle that will contain the tails on the floor surface.

The return layout will follow the plan. The overhang must be carefully planned, as described in Chapter 8, so that the return and soffit materials do not come below the top trim line of the windows. This point is approximately 12″ below the roof triangle baseline (the ceiling line). The return line of the jig should be made parallel with the triangle baseline. This parallelism is best assured by holding a chalk line all the way across the layout from one tail position to the other. Then hold the line down with a finger at the building line (the seat end of the lower chord) and snap the line in the lookout area. Do this on each side. By so doing, a chalk line will not appear below the triangle baseline at the lookout level. The two lines that do appear will be in a straight-line relationship with each other and, if correctly measured, will be parallel with the baseline. The soffits will then be assured of levelness.

Pocket drops are vertical 2 × 4s or 2 × 6s extending against the face of the wall sheathing below the soffit return. Their purpose is to provide a pocket for brick or stone veneer behind the frieze board. Pockets can be fabricated as a ladderwork and superficially toenailed in place after a roof is completed. This is the customary technique when ceiling joists and rafters have been ''stick built'' (installed one piece at a time). With truss construction, it is a simple task to coordinate this plancier framing into the truss form. It simplifies the completion of the trim by eliminating a significant share of overhead work.

The form layout person must bear in mind the wall covering design that will be used. If sheathing is to be flush with the building line on the exterior face, the truss span is the same as the floor span. In this instance, the pocket drops should be placed in the jig with about 1/16″ clearance per side. The distance between the inside edge of a set of drops on one truss will total an amount equal to the nominal span plus 1/8″. This small amount of excess will allow for minor imperfections in the wall frame. It is a small enough amount to permit nearly perfect plumbing of the walls.

The wall frame that is not inset for sheathing will require a longer-spanned truss. The distance between the two pocket drops will be greater by an amount of two thicknesses of sheathing plus 1/8″. The drops are moved out on the pattern to accommodate this added thickness of material. An example would be where 1/2″ fiberboard was to be used for sheathing over a flush frame. The house span is 24′. The distance between drops will be 24′-1 1/8″.

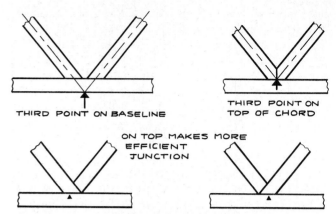

FIGURE 9-16 Web junctions on the lower chord may be centerlined from the baseline or from the top of the chord. Refer to Chapter 4 for more design information.

PROFILING WEB LOCATIONS

Web centerlines are chalked or drawn on the floor with a pencil. A 4 or 6′ level provides a suitable straightedge to trace along. After both sides have been centerlined (Fig. 9-16), comparative measurements should be made of the lengths of like pieces from side to side. Any difference that occurs should be reconciled by rechecking the third and quarter points and making corrections.

MAKING TEMPLATES

Making full-scale templates is next in order. The straightest wood is chosen for templates. Only one template is needed for each unique part of the truss, even though two or more components may be required. The perfection of the jig layout should be such that the template will fit on either side of the truss jig. Each wood piece is laid over the profile outline on the floor. End-cut marks are transferred to the templates. Plumb-cut marks such as the peak and tail should be checked with a framing square for accuracy. Where the pitch is 6 in 12 or less, the square can be positioned on double the rise and run numbers to produce more accuracy. With a 4-in-12 plumb cut, for example, line up the square on the outside edges of the chord template at 24″ on the body and 8″ on the tongue. For a 5-in-12 pitch, line up on 24″ on the body and 10″ on the tongue. Note that the full potential of the tongue is used by doubling the 12 to 24 on the body. The small triangular speed squares are convenient to carry but suffer from the same fault as the ruler compared to the tape measure. The framing square is the most accurate tool for rafter layout.

When a full set of templates has been machined, the set may be assembled on the floor with each piece in its proper location. Note that the webs usually straddle the centerlines. It facilitates the placement of blocks if the templates are temporarily nailed to the subfloor with form nails. Two nails are adequate in all webs and overhang components. Three nails are best for the long chords. Place the center nail in the chord opposite the web intersection.

SETTING THE BLOCKS

Enough form blocks are needed to immobilize each piece of the truss during the gusset fastening operation. Place the blocks at all joint intersections. Two-inch-thick nominal stock is best for these locations (2 × 4s, 2 × 6s, etc.). 1″ stock may be used around some of the smaller parts. Whenever possible, use 12d form nails through the 2″ blocks and place them to penetrate the floor joists below. 8d form nails will be adequate for the 1″ blocks or 2″ blocks over only subflooring.

As soon as one half of the jig is blocked (Fig. 9-17), the nails are pulled from the templates. The templates are reversed and nailed in place on the other half of the jig. The blocking procedure is repeated on that side. The jig is now complete.

LAYING OUT THE PARTS ON STOCK LUMBER

Before putting the templates to work, each should be marked on both sides with the word TEMPLATE after its name. Spread the letters out and make them large. Use a red carpenter's crayon or a large felt marker. The more obvious the labels, the less chance there will be of the piece being cut up or being prematurely made a part of a truss. The templates are used in the last truss. If several houses are planned with the same roof size and design, the templates may be kept for future use. The time saving will be worth the storage.

Finding the most economical layout of the templates on modular lumber is often worth the time spent. It is possible sometimes to conserve close to 2 linear feet of lumber from a single board simply by turning a pattern over so that the mitered ends are parallel instead of opposing. It is also possible to make combinations of webs to use most of a board. For example, two short webs and one long one may fit end to end to use most of a certain-length board. Efficiency and material gain are realized by butting web ends of the same-degree miter so that only one cut is made with the saw to accomplish two finished ends (Fig. 9-18a). An analysis of potential combinations can prevent a heap of scrap. Keep in mind that an excess piece may be multiplied by two or four times the quantity of trusses that are required. On a 60′ roof you could have as many as 240 unnecessary pieces of scrap.

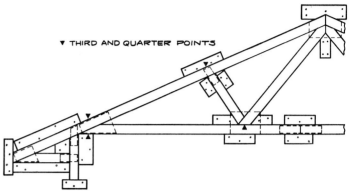

THIRD AND QUARTER POINTS

FIGURE 9-17 Half of a truss jig constructed of short blocks of 2 × 4s and 2 × 6s temporarily nailed to a subfloor deck. Dashed lines show plywood gusset shapes and positioning.

PLYWOOD GUSSETS

While the structural members of the trusses are being cut to pattern, the plywood gussets may be machined by other workers. The gusset cutting can be either a shop project or an on-site job.

Gusset Making

Gusset patterns are best laid out to scale on the drawing board or on 1/4″ grid paper. The plywood for gussets should have no less than five plies. This relegates the thickness minimum to 1/2″ and the grade minimum to AC. Waterproof glue is a must. Specifications of a particular design may require higher-grade or thicker wood. It is prudent to follow the design specifications to the letter unless a written variation is obtained from the design architect.

Plywood gussets for a house of 1200 to 1400 square feet will require 6 to 10 sheets of plywood, depending on the size and arrangement of the gussets on the sheets. Creating the pattern of each shape is done on the drawing board or on grid paper. A large-scale drawing of one half of the truss will make it easier to design the gussets to cover the joints. A scale of 1″ to 1′ makes a convenient size.

The direction of the surface grain, which represents three of the five grains in the board, is not a critical factor in the placement of the gusset. Some builders feel that a joint will be stronger when the major quantity of grains (three of the five) run across the joint perpendicularly. On the other hand, it is frequently more feasible to arrange the various shapes on a ply sheet in a lengthwise pattern. Three-ply plywood should not be considered for gussets.

Modularity of the gusset measurements is the first keynote to economy. Several sheets of plywood can be saved per roof frame by adhering to certain inch divisibles.

The numbers to use are 4, 6, 8, 12, 16, and 24. Any other number that will not divide evenly into 48 or 96 (the plywood sheet size) will result in costly waste.

Shape economy is created by arranging pitch angles of certain gussets to be matched on the ply board. For example, the large gusset covering the cantilevered chord, the drop, and the return can be laid out in pairs to coordinate with the peak gusset (A and C in Fig. 9-18a). This pattern is designed for the typical thermal truss design shown in Fig. 9-18b. One sheet of plywood nets 12 peak gussets and 24 tail gussets, which is enough for six trusses with no waste whatever but the sawdust from the saw kerfs.

Create sawing lines that go clear across a ply sheet and/or full length, by efficient design of the gusset. This type of layout is an operator's dream. The sheets are ripped lengthwise into thirds, sixths, and eighths, then each piece is cross cut as designed. Remember to halve (cut in two pieces) each segment first as compared to setting the saw fence and ripping from a common edge (the latter will net a last piece that is either oversize or undersize). When a sheet is cut in thirds, cut from the factory edge. The entire operation will proceed in record time with just two operators. The economy in time and material is generated on the drawing board and through a knowledge of the modularity of the materials.

The heel, tail, and upper web joints need not be adapted to the pitch-angle coordinate principle. Rectangles will suffice where equitable coverage can be obtained. The lower web and the lower chord splice joint are also covered with rectangular gussets. These are equally adaptable to an economical design and arrangement on a ply sheet. The peak gusset is the only exception when it is shaped like a roof top. There will be no waste where this design is coordinated as shown in Fig. 9-18b. The double-pitched pattern is not mandatory, although it appears more logical. A rectangle is equally feasible with low pitches, although it may have to be considerably larger to approach the role of equal coverage on each adjacent member of the joint.

TRUSS ASSEMBLY ORDER

The upper and lower chords are usually put into the jig first, followed by the smaller components. Any web that does not fit with only minor pressing should not be driven in under force. Boards with crooks occasionally cause the tracer to make an overlength piece. As a web the crooked edge will have no structural drawbacks. An adjustment should be made by trimming either or both ends to fit their intended location. *Do not alter the jig* unless a recheck reveals that it fails to fit the original templates. The problem is more likely to be with the single piece of the truss. Banging, pounding, and forcing on a jig will render it useless.

A stack of appropriate gussets will be placed next to each joint of the jig. To cut down on travel, when a crew is engaged, a plastic bottle of glue is placed within reach of each workstation. Place the gusset on its intended location, trace around it with a pencil, and turn it over. Spread a glue bead around the perimeter of the gusset. Stripe the remainder of the surface with beads about 3/4" apart. Run a bead of glue close to the pencil tracing on the truss. Stripe the interior of the pattern with glue beads spread in the opposite direction. Put the gusset back in place and nail as prescribed. It helps to pencil line the joint contact locations

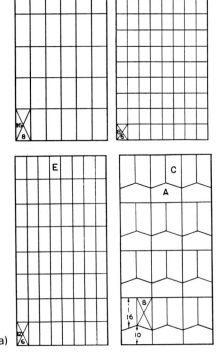

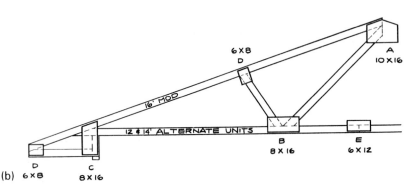

FIGURE 9-18 (a) A little planning on grid paper using modules in inches will provide efficient use of plywood for truss gussets and will simplify machining. (b) The gusset layout in part (a) is for this typical cantilevered thermal truss.

on the surface of the gusset before nailing. Some joints are difficult to visualize when covered by the gusset. The lines will help to prevent nailing in the no-nailing zones. If there is an excessive amount of glue squeezed out around the edges of the first gusset, reduce the size of the glue bead from then on.

Nailing Patterns

No specific pattern of nailing is advised or would likely be followed. Some principles, however, should be kept in mind.

1. Use nails that are barbed or hot-dipped galvanized. "Ring shank" annular or hot-dipped galvanized have excellent holding characteristics.
2. Use a length as close as possible to the combined thickness of one gusset and the chord. For example, with 1/2" plywood and 1 1/2" components a 2" nail is maximum.
3. Do not nail closer than 3/4" from the end grain of the web or chord. One must visualize the joint contacts by extending the invisible lines of the web and chord edges to their contact surfaces.
4. Do not nail closer than 1/2" from the edges of the webs and chords.
5. Slant the bordering nails slightly away from the board edge in a direction toward the body of the web or chord. Should the nail be closer than intended to an edge or end, it will then head toward sound wood.
6. Stagger the nails enough to prevent splitting an annual ring grain.
7. Place approximately the same quantity of nails into each equally covered web end.
8. Plan to use a nail for about every 4 square inches of grid surface on wood gussets.
9. Sink the heads flush with the surface but try not to fracture the surface grain of the plywood. This is accomplished better where it is possible to place the nail into the soft surface grain of fir plywood than into the darker hard grain.

NONMODULAR TRUSSES

Nonmodular nominal spans as well as overlength standard boards require cutting the lower chord to length. The cutting may be done on only one of the two lower-chord boards to save time. Trusses with lower chords of 20' length or less will probably use a single board chord. Where two boards are used, cut the rake angle on one end of each board first, then place both boards into the jig. Lap the longer board over the shorter one near the junction. Trace the end. Remove the lower short board and cut off the excess. Put the boards back in the jig and fasten the gussets. Alternate the long and short boards from right to left for each chord to follow. By cutting the excess off the short boards only, the staggered-butt joints will be off-centered as much as possible.

An excellent way to code the truss is to have an aerosol-spray can of bright-orange paint standing at either the right or left tail location. Spray each tail on that side only just before or as soon as the chord is placed in the jig. Later, at the erection phase, face the coded ends the same way on the house.

When all gussets are installed on one surface, the truss will be turned over onto a different place on the floor. The gussets are then installed on the remaining surface. With a crew of four workers it is efficient to start a new truss in the jig with two workers while the other two complete the first truss. On a one- or two-man project, it is advisable to complete each truss before starting a new one so that both sides are fixed before the glue sets up on the first surface.

Storing the completed trusses takes some space and some manpower. Each truss should be moved carefully so as not to put undue strain on any of the joints. A truss may be carried flat for a short distance. Care is necessary to keep the truss in a straight-line position. Neither the center nor the tails should be allowed to sag or flex. Over greater distances or rough terrain, the truss will carry less precariously if held between the webs and the heel in an inverted vertical position. Smaller trusses can be managed handily by two workers in this position. The lower chord rests on their shoulders.

Trusses should be laid flat and stacked directly on top of each other so that each gusset is in contact with the corresponding one below. Where there is no uniformly flat surface available, the gusset locations will need to be blocked up to make the first gusset level or straight. Concrete blocks are handy for this purpose.

Protect the gussets from the weather by covering them with a tarp or plastic sheet. The better grades of plywood gussets will withstand some moisture but are not impervious to continued or long-term wetting. For long-term outdoor storage, the plywood gussets should be painted, giving special attention to the edges, where the end grains are exposed. Voids in the end grains should be closed with caulking before painting.

ERECTING THE TRUSSES

A particular technique will make the erection of a truss quite simple. The house that has been framed without interior partitions, the open-concept system, makes it possi-

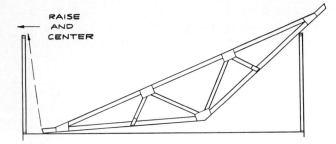

FIGURE 9-19 Within an open interior, the trusses can be raised from inside the walls. Start with the truss inverted, then rotate it into its upright posture.

ble to install the trusses from inside the house. The conventionally framed house will usually require placing the trusses on the top of the walls and partitions from the outside.

Trussing Over an Open Interior

Low-pitched trusses can usually be walked through a doorway or handed through a window opening. This is another benefit of the open-interior framing technique described earlier in the text. The truss is carried in the inverted position (Fig. 9-19). The lead framer runs the tail up and over the top plate near the location at which it will be fastened. It will be run past its seat point far enough so that the tail on the other end clears the wall below its ultimate location. The remaining tail is then raised above the plate and the truss is slid to a centered position. It is still inverted, with the peak pointed toward the centerline of the floor. One or two helpers with forked poles will rotate the peak or the web points in a 180° arc. The upper chord is now cradled in the fork and the lower chord braced against the pole. This position permits some control over the truss. Another worker will toenail the ends of the truss to the plates. A worker at the peak will secure the upper chords with lateral bracing.

Trussing Over a Partitioned Interior

Where interior partitions have already been installed, most, if not all of the trusses will have to be hoisted over the exterior wall. This constitutes a critical situation involving care and conscientiousness. The truss should not be bent along its flat surface, as the joint fastenings may fail. Gang-nailed trusses are especially vulnerable to this failure. Therefore, it behooves the workers to keep the truss as flat as possible, by any means available, while it is being passed over the plate. Once dragged across the top of the partitions, it is raised by one or two workers standing on top of

bearing plates of a convenient partition or a movable scaffold. These workers will grasp the upper chord and swing it through a 90° arc into position.

Installation Sequence

The first truss to install will be the gable truss on one end, followed by the one on the opposite end. Actually, these two are not trusses. They are prefabricated gables. These two gables will be of a different design than the common trusses. There is no need for webs in a gable truss, as the wall supports the lower chord. In fact, there is no need for a lower chord. Cripple studs, called gable studs, are needed to provide a backing for sheathing and/or siding. A ceiling backer board is needed on the inside at the bottom edge of the cripples. A soffit backer board is needed along the rake line for the overhang. These three components can be put together in the truss jig, thus eliminating a significant amount of scaffold and ladder work (see Fig. 9-20).

Another common gable truss is designed to have an upper chord in a lower position. Lookouts at rafter level will cross the lower end truss perpendicularly. These lookouts, as seen in Fig. 9-21a, should be used for all end overhangs that exceed 16″.

Lookouts are not placed directly over gable studs unless filler blocks are installed under the sheathing on top the chord. Without these blocks the lookouts should be spaced from the eave to support the sheathing edges, as shown in the top view of Fig. 9-21b.

Lookouts should not cantilever beyond the 50% point. This means that no more than half the length of the lookout rafter may hang beyond the supporting gable truss. With 24″-spaced common trusses on a modular house frame, this is a maximum overhang of 2′ without special treatment.

Two methods for overhangs in excess of the truss spacing module are satisfactory with some limitations.

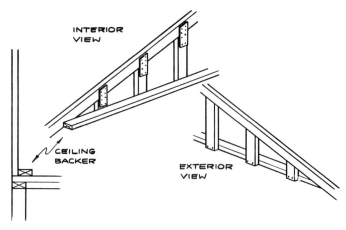

FIGURE 9-20 Lookouts require a specifically designed gable truss with a lowered top chord. This diagram is designed for the stressed skin principle.

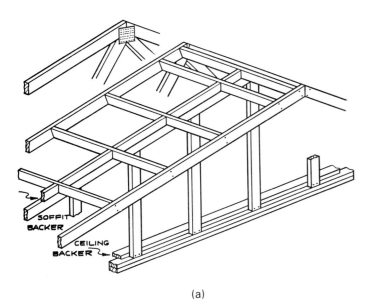

(a)

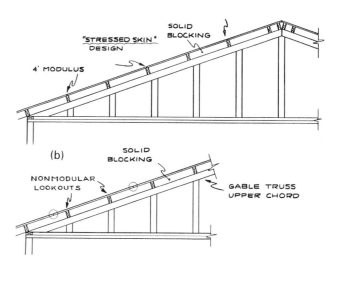

(b)

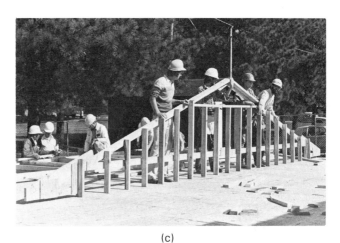

(c)

FIGURE 9-21 (a) Lookouts require a specifically designed gable truss with a lowered upper chord. This diagram is designed for the stressed skin principle. (b) Lookouts fall farther below direct bearing points as the stressed skin panels move up the rake. (c) A gable truss assembled in a regular W truss jig with a few adapting blocks. The gable studs extend below the lower chord to form a brick pocket framework.

Some rules of thumb have evolved from experience. Doubling the upper chords against which the lookouts are anchored is one method. Although marginal, this technique permits another 10 or 15% to be hung over without permitting noticeable eave sag or anchor chord raising. A preferred method is to omit the second truss and extend the lookouts to anchor on the third truss (Fig. 9-22). This advances the overhang cantilever potential to 4'. By passing through the position normally occupied by a truss, the lookouts consequently eliminate an entire truss, including the lower chord, which is the ceiling joist. There are a number of ways to replace this lost joist function. The simplest is to use a conventional joist setup provided that there are adequate interior bearing partitions for support. Another method is to place joist tails perpendicularly to the lower chord of the common truss and bear them on the end wall plate. The ends against the chord will be born in joist hangers. A trimmer the same size as would be required of a conventional joist is nailed along the interior side of the

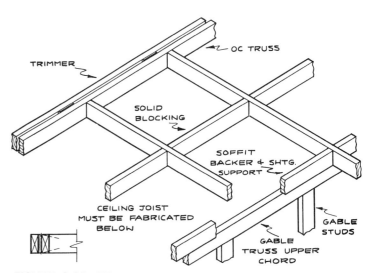

FIGURE 9-22 Where lookouts carry over to the third truss, the truss is reinforced by doubling all or top portions of it.

lower anchor chord to beef up its carrying capacity. Another alternative is to construct another set of custom trusses with lowered top chords—like the gable trusses but with webs. Where this technique is practiced, all need for doubling of components in the lookout anchor truss is eliminated. A 4′ overhang is excessive for 2 × 4 lookouts. Although not specifically delineated in most codes, the prudent designer/builder will opt for 2 × 6 lookouts to maintain the integrity of such a wide overhang. A rule of thumb evolves. Each common joist that is omitted, supplemented for by longer lookouts, will call for a size-larger lookout (girth). For example, when the next-to-the-end truss is omitted, 2 × 6 lookouts will be in order unless the overhang is minimally beyond 24″; when two trusses are omitted, 2 × 8s will be used.

In all these cases the anchor truss top chord will be doubled after the lookouts have been end nailed with 20d nails through the truss. The upper chord could also be increased in girth to match the lookout. Doubling can usually be done over metal gussets that are embedded nearly flush to the surface. Over a wooden gusset two or more nails will be placed to anchor the trimmer chord directly over the gussets. Additional nails should be placed at intervals between the gussets. Small plywood fillers, resembling window header spacers, are inserted between the common chord and the trimmer through which the attaching nails will pass. Should it be more desirable to attach the trimmer chord while the truss is in the jig on the floor, attention must be given to the left and right syndrome so that the trimmers end up on the interior side on the roof and the coded truss tail is in continuity with the other trusses (review the earlier section on continuity coding of the trusses). Where the latter technique of installing the trimmer before raising the truss is employed, it will still be possible to end nail the lookout by angling a nail in from each edge (see Fig. 9-22). Another alternative is to attach and support the ends of the lookouts in joist hangers.

Placement of the lookouts as they progress up the rake follows two alternative paths. An overhang of 2′ or less may have the lookouts spaced to receive the horizontal joints of the sheathing on the roof (Fig. 9-23). The POB is then the lower edge of the sheathing at the eave. When laying out the lookout locations one must pay attention to the exact edge position of the sheathing so that the upper edge will be straddled underneath by the lookout. Remember that there may be a backing board of 3/4 or 1 1/2″ depth added to the tails and that the sheathing may be lapped over the facia, adding some more distance. Also keep in mind that these dimensions are more than the material thicknesses because they are measured on the pitch line (rafter length line) as opposed to horizontally—and that line increases in length with higher pitches. A 2 × 4 backer and a 1 × 6 facia lapped by sheathing would net 2 1/4″ of depth (1 1/2″ plus 3/4″) horizontally. Diagonally on

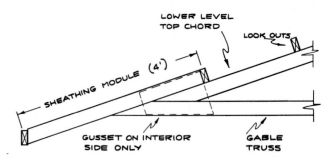

FIGURE 9-23 A gable truss with a matching tail is assembled in the common truss jig by repositioning a few blocks.

the rake angle it could easily be 2 1/2″ or more. This seemingly insignificant amount causes a problem when it comes time to nail the sheathing with an expansion space between.

Where the lookouts are spaced to back up the sheathing edge as just described, none of them will be positioned directly above a gable stud. It might occur accidentally with one stud, but regardless, the higher up the slant, the farther away from the stud each lookout will be. This is because the studs are spaced apart horizontally, whereas the lookouts must be spaced to receive a sheathing edge every 4′ up the diagonal hypotenuse. Therefore, the 4, 8, 12, and 16′ modules on the slant progressively fall farther behind the same spacing on the horizontal top plate.

A "stressed skin" panel is created where the foregoing technique is used. Blocks to back up the soffit are fitted between the lookouts on top of and overhanging into the soffit area. With 2′-OC lookouts each block will be 22 1/2″ long with the exception of the last one, next to the ridge. With the full-perimeter nailing and the intermediate nailing into the blocks, that portion of a sheet of sheathing that is over the lookout section can be classified as a stressed skin panel. If glue were added to the surface of the structural parts, the assembly would fully qualify. A stressed panel is superior to designs where panel edges are not in contact with the substructure. Its unified stiffness (antideflection) character largely eliminates any concern about individual lookouts not being positioned directly over gable studs. All elements considered, the stressed panel concept is superior, although seldom seen or explained in print.

Larger lookouts in both girth and length need to be supported in one of two ways. The top chord of the gable truss may be increased in size or each lookout may be aligned directly above each gable stud. In the latter case none of the lookouts will fall under the horizontal sheathing joints. In this situation the soffit backing blocks should be placed on edge so that the upper surface supports the sheathing in the same posture as the common trusses do. Lookouts over 4′ long that extend and anchor to the third truss must be additionally blocked at the exact position that

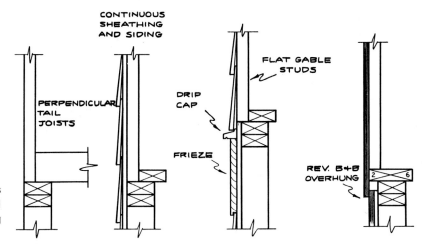

FIGURE 9-24 A gable truss is aligned with the frame wall according to the many siding variations available.

the second truss would have occupied. The grain direction of plywood sheathing and the nature of wafer board will induce a "soft" spot between the lookouts if not properly blocked on-center with the other truss spacing. This is particularly critical should this truss locality be the one on which alternating courses of sheathing butt at the ends.

As soon as the two gable trusses are in place, secured, and braced, the remaining trusses can be put up starting at either end or both ends simultaneously. The last two or three trusses on the open-interior house will have to be hoisted from an upright position unless several of the last trusses have been raised and stacked against the previously secured truss. For such a technique, care must be taken to brace the foregoing trusses adequately so that the weight of those being leaned on them will not collapse the entire roof. In like manner the conventionally partitioned house will necessitate raising the last two or three trusses in an upright position from outside the house frame.

Positioning the Trusses

The most common spacing for residential trusses is 24" OC. In conjunction with 16"-centered studs, every other truss will bear directly over a stud in the wall. The roof spacing is therefore laid out in the same manner as the floor joists and wall studs except on 2' centers. The first common truss in from the end will straddle a mark that is 24" from the building line POB.

The gable truss may be lined up flush with the building line, or it may overhang as much as the sheathing thickness below. Flushing the truss with the sheathing would be done to accommodate one of two designs. One design would have no sheathing on the gable. By making the gable framework line up with the wall sheathing, the siding can run from the wall continuously through into the gable. Where gable siding is specified to overhang the wall siding or a frieze board, the gable is sheathed. The upper sheathing then overhangs the wall sheathing and creates the correct relationship, as shown in Fig. 9-24.

Fastening a Truss

A truss is fastened to the top plate by toenailing. It may be further secured by the use of galvanized sheet metal ties. The ties are recommended in areas prone to high wind velocity and in tornado or cyclone belts. The cost of ties is nominal. Their use provides an element of quality as well as a selling point for the professional builder.

Toenailing is done with care and consideration. The lower chord has a long sharply tapered miter cut on the end. The pointed end of this miter sits on a 3 1/2"-wide top plate. With the lower pitches, this leaves very little wood body through which to drive a toenail. To complicate matters, a metal gusset covers part of the zone, leaving a limited choice of nailing locations. A feasible solution is to drill a clearance hole for each toenail that proposes to split the wood. If necessary, the hole can be placed through a gang-nail plate or a power-nailed plate. Toenails for a truss require length for penetration and small diameter, to minimize splitting. 16d box nails fill this need. The angle should not be lower than 60°; otherwise, the nail may simply glance out on top the plate.

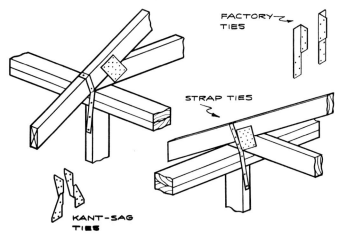

FIGURE 9-25 Metal ties provide protection against cyclone and tornado damage.

Metal ties are placed on the inside of the wall and on the face of the truss (Fig. 9-25). 1 1/2″ galvanized roofing nails are suitable for the tie. Their diameter is greater for their length, to provide the sheer strength needed. The head is large and thin, so a protrusion does not complicate drywalling over the tie. A metal tie should only be placed on the exterior of the wall frame before sheathing or where the wall is sheathed with wood.

BRACING THE TRUSSES

Temporary Bracing

The importance of adequate bracing during the erection phase of roofing cannot be overemphasized. There are three basic elements to accommodate in the bracing routine.

- Immobilize the gable ends with enough braces to fix the peak and the upper chords in the desired location (plumb and straight).
- Immobilize the center zone and the peak of each upper chord on the same centering (spacing) as the heel of each truss.
- Provide enough diagonals to prevent any movement of the total assembled roof frame.

End Bracing

A gable rafter frame may be braced primarily from inside the house when a wood floor exists. Most of the bracing must be done from the exterior with the concrete-slab-floor house, as it is not practical to nail into concrete in as many places as are needed.

The first brace to go up is a single 2 × 4 nailed to the outer face of the end wall (Fig. 9-26). It will extend as high or higher than the peak will be. Place the top of this brace off center if there will be a gable overhang so that it does not interfere with the peak lookouts to follow. Use a board that is long enough to extend down over the floor header. Place it over the stud in the wall that is nearest the center of the wall. The modular house will usually have a stud exactly on the center or a centered space. Should there be a stud at the precise center, the brace may be tilted slightly so that it diagonals across the stud enough to throw the top away from the peak. Nail the brace to the upper plate and the floor header, and put two or three nails into the stud. Form nails are best for ease of disassembly. Penetration must be adequate, as the nails will pass through sheathing before anchoring in wood. Two more braces of this vertical type are advisable for large or heavy gables. Each of these will go up at the midpoint of the rafters to provide intermediate support for each half of the gable

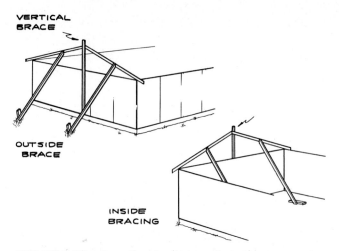

FIGURE 9-26 A vertical brace near the center prevents a gable truss from toppling over during installation.

frame. These braces are put in place before the frame is raised so that the truss will not topple over the end of the house while being put in position.

The truss is then moved back and forth across the end until the heels are in the exact transverse position desired. On a symmetrical roof, this will place the peak at dead center above the wall. It is plumbed and braced in the conventional manner. After the gable is fastened, the other end is positioned and secured. Next a string line is run from peak to peak to gauge the centering of all the other trusses. The string is tied around a small block at a point 1″ or so above the peak. By having it higher than the ridge line, the string will not touch any trusses if it sags in the middle.

Bracing on Top of the Rafters

Temporary bracing across the surface of the rafters (Fig. 9-27) is necessary whether a roof is trussed or stick framed conventionally. Done correctly, the bracing will serve two purposes. Diagonal boards will immobilize the roof skeleton against pressures from wind or weight that could collapse it at any time during or after the erection. Horizontal

FIGURE 9-27 Lateral and diagonal braces hold trusses in line while sheathing is installed.

braces give additional rigidity from one rafter to the next. Both brace types double as spacing gauges. Rafters are spaced under the braces with this in mind so that sheathing may progress later without additional attention to spacing. The perpendicular braces may include as many of the storypole dadoed-type spacers that are on hand. Remember to use just one 8d form nail at each dado so that boards can be removed easily without damage.

The perpendicular braces across the top chords are placed near the midpoint of the rafter span. Keep them at least 8' above the eave so that two courses of sheathing sheets can be installed before they have to be taken up. A single row is positioned near the top of the peak on one side only. At the outset the braces will hang over the few trusses so far that the ends will require support. Where a partition exists below, a vertical brace can be used. It is a temporary 2 × 4 post to support the loose end of the perpendicular roof brace. Where the open concept is practiced, a longer 2 × 4 pole can be run clear to the floor. With roof brace lengths of 8' or shorter, no vertical end support is required. Braces should be lapped side by side at the ends rather than butted. In the lapped position, 8 to 12″ of a standard board will hang over the rafter (depending on whether the spacing is 16 or 24″). The form nails will be in the field of the board instead of within the splitting zone at the end as they would be if the boards were butted (Fig. 9-27).

Measurement of each space between chord centers (or edges) should be taken from a single point of beginning. The initial step is to measure from the outer vertical surface of one gable truss to the outer edge of the one on the other end wall. The distance must duplicate the relative distance at the foundation line below. When it does not match, an inspection should follow to see where the discrepancy exists. It will be found at one or more of three locations on either or both ends of the house. The floor header may be bowed in or out from the building line. The top plate of an end wall may be bowed in or out. The end truss may be tilted in or out from plumb. It is too late to rectify the floor header misalignment. The top plate can be straightened in some cases. The rafter tilt can always be corrected, as it is only braced temporarily. In any case, the objective is to get the most vertical appearing profile possible. A plumb bob from a line set out on a 3/4″ block at the peak of the gable rafters extending to the foundation will be helpful. Remember to take into consideration any material thickness, such as sheathing, setbacks, and setouts, that are a part of the design. The ultimate horizontal distance from gable peak to peak exterior should match that at the seat of the trusses or rafters on the top plate.

Diagonal surface braces are run from the gable seat points and from the peak toward the center brace, as shown in Fig. 9-27. A pair of diagonals on each side and each end

will suffice for a small or a medium-sized roof frame. For a longer roof frame, approximately 60' or more, additional diagonals are a safeguard. In areas of high wind or when the sheathing will be delayed several days, it makes sense to add more diagonals in a zigzag bridgework pattern.

Plywood sheathing forms a most effective bracing for the roof. Therefore, the sheathing of the roof may proceed as soon as plumbness and straightness have been assured. Actually, the plywood sheet can perform a squaring function. With the bracing pattern described in the foregoing paragraph, the sheathing may begin one or one and one-half modules in from the fly rafter. In this position it will not require removal of the first diagonal temporary brace. For that matter, the sheets can be laid from the central area out toward the ends. Either of these techniques requires careful counting of the rafter spaces starting at POB (the fly rafter) to be certain that the first sheet on the end will be a full sheet or a half-sheet. An inadvertant situation must be averted. A sheathing end joint should not exist over the gable truss. Such a condition will eliminate all the potential support that the sheathing may provide to the fly rafter. *There should be no sheathing ends butted over the gable truss.* When perpendicular lookouts are used, the fault is less serious. Without the lookouts and without continuous sheathing across the gable truss, there will surely be a sagging overhang.

Sometimes a contractor finds himself in the situation where the roof framing is completed late in the day, perhaps on the day before the weekend. It is a temptation to pack it in and plan to start the new sheathing activity bright and early on Monday morning. The peace of mind that will be gained by putting up three or four sheets of ply sheath on each side of the roof are well worth the time, perhaps overtime, that it will take. One has but to witness or fantasize a full-trussed roof frame collapsed to form a mental attitude on this point of philosophy.

OPENINGS IN A TRUSSED ROOF

A small opening through a trussed roof frame is usually fabricated by placing headers between adjacent common trusses (Fig. 9-28). Larger openings will be cause for considerable retrofiting of headers and braces. An opening that cuts across more than one truss will in all likelihood require one or more specially designed trusses that are in the affected area. Some rules of thumb are pertinent to the maintenance of the strength of the trusses surrounding an opening. Most residential trusses are placed 2' apart, 24″ OC. A small chimney that would slip between the lower and upper chords will require only simple headers, a plumb header below the opening and a square-cut header above the opening (Fig. 9-29).

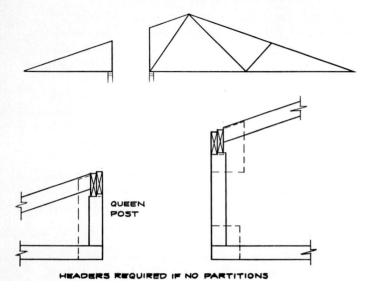

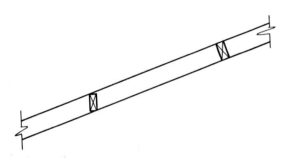

FIGURE 9-28 Custom-placed queen posts and repositioned webbing are designed to accommodate headers when an opening in a trussed roof is required.

FIGURE 9-29 A simple header setup between two trusses serves to provide a rigid support for the sheathing where an opening is 22 1/2″ or under.

Rules for Large Openings

An opening that requires cutting out a portion of the upper and lower chord should have:

- Double headers above and below the opening
- Double chords on each side of the opening or chords of a larger girth
- Additional replacement webs, preferably leading to a point of bearing such as a bearing partition

The cutting of one chord on one truss automatically causes the header span between the two trimmer trusses to be a nominal 4′. In a design where two or more trusses must be cut, the span increases by 2′ increments. Beyond the 4′ span limit a structural category is reached wherein adding size and bulk in the headers and trimmers presents a compounded weight problem. An average weight load on top of the roof frame using plywood sheathing, 15-lb underlayment building paper, and asphalt shingles averages

about 300 lb per square. "Square" is the term used to signify 100 square feet of laid shingles. To avoid the problem created by severed trusses, special consideration is given to the design of each truss. The objective is to distribute and carry the load of the severed truss to the nearest bearing point or to support it on headers. This consideration must not be left until it is time to raise the roof. The time to work out solutions is when the floor plan is being designed. It is then that the designer must visualize the skeletal framework of the structure and plan ahead for adequate roof support. The chain of support must ultimately reach the bed of the foundation footings. The most direct route will cause the least quantity of materials to be required. It will also prevent potential stresses that are so frequently responsible for sags, leaks, and cracks in the finished work of a house.

Code Treatment of Roof Openings

Some building code books deal specifically with roof openings in conventional ceilings and roofs. These rules follow much the same practice as required in floors. Unfortunately, there is a large void in the codes when it comes to trusses. Few or no specifics are found that will apply to a variety of situations. Nonetheless, it behooves the designer and/or builder to make adaptations that will bring the remaining portions of the severed truss back to its original strength. A typical on-site rewebbing is shown in Fig. 9-28. By keeping the principles of heading, trimming, and bracing in mind, one can usually design a satisfactory transfer of stresses.

SHEATHING WITH PLYWOOD

Sheathing the truss frame is basically the same as for a conventional frame. Since most trusses are placed at 24″ intervals as compared to 16″ for conventional rafters, it is more logical routinely to use the aluminum ply clip on the edge of the ply span between each upper chord. The automatic spacing apart of the sheets to negate swelling problems added to the superior stiffness that is gained make the practice well worth the small cost. Most upper chords, up to and including 28′ spans, will be 2 × 4 girth. The ply clips will tend to cause a flatter-appearing surface by spreading the stress over two adjacent sheets. This is especially true with the more flexible three-ply 1/2″ plywood.

Frame and Sheathing Consistency

Systematic consistency is a valid factor in choosing materials for both load-bearing capacity and ultimate appearance. Examine the following two inconsistent cases, which exemplify poor choices.

Case 1. The roof frame is conventionally built with 2 × 6 rafters at the maximum allowable span for this size. Thinking it will be advantageous, the builder puts on heavier ply sheathing. The heavier plywood acts negatively by adding preponderant weight. The added weight collects the greatest downward push at the least supportive place in the roof frame, the middle of the rafter. The result is a noticeable sag in this zone. The ridge, if unposted to a bearing point, will also tend to develop a sag. The moral is that thicker sheathing is not a means to support a minimum-sized framework. In this case lighter-weight sheathing will match more feasibly with the lightweight, maximum-spanned framework.

Case 2. Trusses placed on 32″ centers are used on an outbuilding. Although the stress tables allow for either 1/2″ or 5/8″ ply sheathing or 3/4″ (1″ nominal) boards on this wide-spaced module, the builder concludes that the 1/2″ plywood will be adequate. Wrong again. Even with ply clips between the rafters, the flexible three-ply sheets will show sag between each rafter when the weight of shingles is superimposed. 5/8″ five-ply (not four-ply) with clips is a choice more consistent with the wide spacing that exists. Nominal-1″ shiplap boards of 8, 10, or 12″ width will also be a good choice. The rabbeted edges of the shiplap design effectively spread the load stress among adjacent boards. Unfortunately, shiplap and tongue-and-groove sheathing have both been priced out of the market or have been made obsolete by the ready access of plywood in most areas of the country. Wherever available, shiplap or T&G is a good choice for the second case.

REVIEW TOPICS

1. What geometric figure produces rigidity in a truss?

2. Name the three most common roof trusses used in houses by inventor's name or by shape.

3. List the nine basic names for truss parts, not including gussets.

4. Explain how to locate the third points and quarter points of a W Fink truss.

5. (a) What is the minimum practical pitch of the top chord of a scissors truss? (b) The vaulted chord pitch of a collared scissors truss should not be less than the top chord pitch by what fraction? (c) At what points should the collar, king, and queen posts meet the chords?

6. When gluing and nailing a gusset to a truss joint, what skills and consideration must be practiced to avoid splitting the hidden wood?

7. Explain how to lay out a truss triangle in preparation for making a jig on the end of the floor deck.

8. Explain how to build a truss jig for a truss that will have tails, soffit returns, and a brick pocket drop.

9. Explain how to assemble a gable truss in the same jig after the common trusses have been completed.

10. Explain how to assemble a gable truss that will have lookouts running out over it.

11. Explain how to brace the trusses on the upper surface so that they are spaced correctly and are rigid enough to stay in place until the sheathing is installed.

12. Explain two alternative methods of positioning lookouts over the gable, and give the rationale (reason) for doing it one way or the other.

13. Explain why it is preferred to place soffit backing blocks on edge instead of flat on top of the gable top chord when lookouts are used.

Chapter 10

ROOFING, VENTILATING, AND WATER SHEDDING_____

ROOFING MATERIALS

There are many types of roofing materials. In the southwestern part of the United States, Mexico, Central and South America, and more distant countries, tile roofs are common. Some of the wooden buildings under these roofs have survived since the Middle Ages. There are shingles and roof coverings made of copper, aluminum, galvanized iron, asbestos, and fiberglass. Cedar shakes, both thick and thin, have recently enjoyed a resurgence in some areas in the United States. In other areas primarily municipalities, the cedar shakes have been outlawed due to their susceptibility to fire. In spite of the many innovations in roof-covering materials and designs, the most commmonly used covering is the asphalt composition shingle, which has been available since the 1930s. It has been marketed in many shapes, but the most common is the basic three-tab shingle. Since this text is intended to be a basic primer and not a bible of all things, the sections that follow will concentrate on the layment of the composition shingle. It is by far the preponderant roof covering in the United States today. Descriptions of other types of coverings are left to specialists in their fields.

ROOF-COVERING OBJECTIVE

It would seem simplistic to say that the objective of roofing is to shed rain. That, however, is precisely the reason for waterproof roofing, and believe it or not, there are roof coverings put on everyday that do not fully accomplish this objective. In a larger sense the roof should keep out the elements, protect the building material below it, provide shade, and in general, preserve the structure and its contents.

Basic Shedding Technique

To obtain the objective, the goal must be to cover the roof with a shedding system that will carry water away successfully. Since it is not usually possible to do this with a single piece of anything, it is accomplished with material units of a size that can be marketed and handled, if necessary, by one person. The three-tab shingle meets this requirement handily. Together with metal flashings, underlayment paper, and drip edges, the goal is to assemble these materials in such a way that no water will find its way into the woodwork under the roofing. At all times one principle must be kept in mind; *lap all parts from the lowest point up*. Keep the question in mind, "If I poured water over this, would it *all* run off?"

An immediate caution is that roof cement should not be thought of as a primary shedding agent. Its role, as its name implies, is to fasten layers together where nails are not usable. For example, caulking a joint or junction that has not been properly lapped, then trying to waterproof it by puttying it over with cement is not an approved technique. Another example is to attempt to surface mount a piece of flashing on a vertical wall and seal it with cement on its upper edge. It is just a matter of time until the cement shrinks, hardens, and cracks. The shedding principle must start at the bottom and continue all the way to the ridge.

DRIP EDGE AND BUILDING PAPER

Drip edge is a metal edge protector. It is available in several shapes. One is a simple angle-iron shape. This type does not support the overhang of composition shingles. Another, more universally used style has folds that create an angle iron and an overhanging lip. This type carries the water out a little farther away from the facia. During a light drizzling rain with no wind, the water draining from a roof will fall free of the facia. The drip edge comes in 10′ lengths in galvanized iron, aluminum, or painted steel. Drip edge provides a seal all around the edges of the roof. It will prevent rainwater from being blown in under the edge of the gable end shingles when it is coordinated with building paper.

Building paper is an asphalt-impregnated paper that comes in 36″ rolls. It is sometimes called felt and somtimes, erroneously, tar paper. There are two weights of building paper, 15 and 30 lb. The weight is designated per "square." A square in roofing terminology is 100 square feet. A full roll of 15-lb building paper is 450 square feet. It will not, however, cover 450 square feet, as it must be lapped a few inches. The 15-lb weight is used under composition shingles.

Drip edge and black building paper are installed simultaneously. The horizontal edges of the eave are covered with dripedge first. Start the first 10′ piece, with the end flush with the end of the sheathing and/or facia. Five nails are adequate on 30″ spacing. 4d galvanized nails are preferred over the big-headed roofing nail. The smaller number 4 splits wood less. The smaller head is adequate for sheet metal. Most brands of drip edge have two or three small raised V-shaped corrugations on the top flange. Place the nails between the upper pair. This should be high enough to avoid driving the nail into the crack between the sheathing and the facia board where the facia has been placed to cover the sheathing edge.

On the interior end of the first drip edge piece there will be a bit of rolled thickness where the overhanging lip doubles back to form the facia cover. Flatten about 1/4″ of this roll at the end (Fig. 10-1). This can be done with a hammer or a pair of pliers. Slip the next 10′ length of drip edge over this flattened portion. Gently tap it snugly together. Hold in place and nail. It is easier for some installers to keep a full-length piece of drip edge straight by putting in the middle nail first, followed by the nail next to the lap. Continue down the eave until the last piece hangs over. Lap it on its interior end. Trace it on the underside of the other end. Cut it from each of the three edges toward the

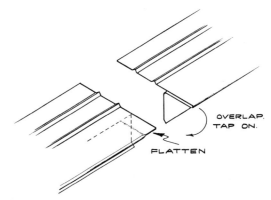

FIGURE 10-1 Metal drip edge is joined at the ends by pocketing and lapping the ends.

center. Bend and break it. Tin snips or straight-nosed aircraft shears work well. The latter are less bulky to carry.

The rules for sequence with paper and drip edge are:

1. Lap the paper over the lower horizontal drip edge.
2. Lap the drip edge over the paper on the gable ends, the rake.
3. Lap each course of paper over the previous course 2 to 6″.

When this procedure is carried out conscientiously, the underlayment for the roof will be leak-free.

Laying the building paper is a little exasperating. It constantly wants to slide down the roof, especially on the steeper pitches. The first course is with the lower edge flush with the drip edge (Fig. 10-2). A staple is placed about every 2′ along the lower edge about 3″ up to clear the metal drip edge underneath. Staple down the center

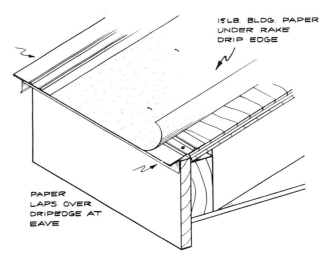

FIGURE 10-2 A conventional composition-shingled roof starts with 15-lb building paper laid over the drip edge at the bottom and under the drip edge up the rake.

staggered from the lower staples. For example, the lower staples will be spaced on even feet: 2, 4, 6, 8, and so on. The middle ones will be on odd feet: 1, 3, 5, 7, and so on. Do not staple the top edge yet unless there is so much wind that it is necessary.

Most brands of building paper have silver lines running parallel to the edges. These lines are reference points to help maintain parallelism. The first line is about 2″ from the edge. This is the minimum lap. Several more inches may be lapped if desired. The second course is rolled out and stapled over the top edge of the first course. Great effort must be taken not to permit the center of the course to sag. A sag will cause ripples and buckles in the upper edge, which in turn will cause the composition shingles to bulge up or roll. The paper can be stretched tightly by grasping the roll with the fingers in the holes in the ends and pulling. It must have several anchoring staples in the beginning end, or have a fellow worker stand on the end of the paper to withstand the jerking.

Immediate protection of the wood on the roof will mandate that the entire roof be papered as quickly as possible. As soon as several courses of paper are stapled, it is prudent to lay shingle bundles across the laps. This is especially important where wind is an element. The heavy bundles will help hold the paper in place. Care should be taken not to break or tear the paper package around the shingles lest the shingles blow away.

The starting end of the building paper may be hung over a little. After stapling it is pared off flush with the facia. When the other end is reached with the roll, grasp the roll with one hand in each end. Hold it down to the surface firmly and fold the roll over the edge. There will be a distinct crease or fold mark, indicating precisely where to cut.

The roll will ultimately run out somewhere in the middle of the roof. Lap the new roll a couple of feet over the tail end of the expended paper. Where a roll makes it to the end with a few feet left over, it is advisable to set the remainder aside and begin the next course with a new roll. End-lap joints are not desirable and should be held to a minimum. Scrap ends are usable later on in various places, such as over the subfloor.

When the ridge is reached, any excess up to a half sheet may be lapped over the top. Do not staple the lapover down until the other side reaches the top. There is sometimes a potential for saving quite a bit of paper by cutting it lengthwise into strips wide enough to cap the ridge and lap both sides. For example, if the ridge is 60′ long and only a 12″-wide strip is needed, a 21′ full-width piece of paper cut into three 12″ strips will cover the entire ridge.

Where the ridge is reached with just a few inches to roll over, it can be stapled down immediately. When the paper on the other side reaches the ridge it will probably have a similar overlap. It is lapped over the top to complete the job.

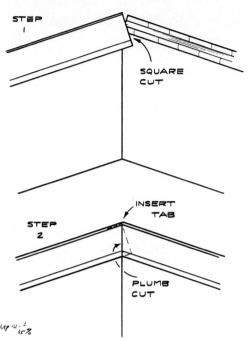

FIGURE 10-3 The first piece of drip edge to reach the ridge is square cut. The other side is plumb cut with a little tab left on top to fold and pocket into the first piece.

The drip edge is now ready to be completed on the gable end eaves. It can be started earlier and worked along with the paper. Remember that it goes on top of the paper up the rake. When the ridge is reached, make a right-angle cut in the first piece. The piece coming from the other side is plumb cut on the face at the centerline of the facia. The upper flange is cut so that a tab about 2″ long can be folded over and nailed through the flange on the other piece. This method effectively seals the point of the facia (Fig. 10-3). The roofing underlayment is now complete.

An alternative technique for starting the underlayment paper involves a double seal. It is a good system in localities that have lots of rain, frequent rain, or frost and ice buildup on the eaves. A half-width sheet of paper (18″ wide) is laid first (Fig. 10-4). The drip edge is placed on

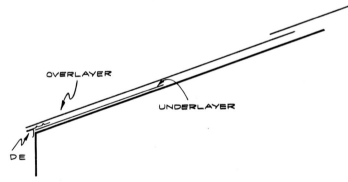

FIGURE 10-4 Good-quality underlay system for preventing damage from water or ice. In order of installation: (1) 18″ of paper, (2) metal drip edge, (3) 36″ of paper from bottom up lapped 2 to 6″.

top of it. Then a full-width sheet follows in the conventional manner. Water that may collect or be blown up under the starter course can run off rather than be dammed above the top edge of the drip edge. If the water freezes, it will later melt and run off without damaging the sheathing. It is an excellent insurance policy and well worth the minimum cost.

VALLEY PREPARATION

A house plan that is L- or T-shaped will usually have two or more valleys in the roof. Where the span of each segment is equal and the rafter pitch is the same, the valleys will meet at the ridge. The ridges are on the same level. Where an L addition is narrower than the main section of a house the valleys and ridge will meet at a lower point down the main roof. This is an important design consideration. It is contingent on a uniform and symmetrical pitch throughout the roof frame. Examine the following example. The main house section is 24' deep. An addition perpendicular to the main section is 18' wide. The uniform pitch is 4 in 12. The rise on the main roof is 4'. Since 18 is three-fourths of 24, the rise on the addition will be 3' $(3/4 \times 4 = 3)$. Therefore, the ridge of the addition is nominally 3' high, whereas the ridge of the main roof is 4' high above the top plate. The valleys will end 1' (vertically) down from the top of the main roof.

Valley Underlayment

Underlayment in the valley is accomplished in several ways. The specific technique will depend to some extent on the type of finished valley that is specified. Generally, there are two designs in practice, open valley and closed valley. The beginning step for either is the same. The 15-lb felt is rolled out from the starting edge of the roof toward the valley. Run the roll through the valley and up the adjoining roof about 3'. Cut the paper on a line parallel to the valley 2' beyond the valley. Turn the roll in a counterclockwise direction (assuming that the roll was run out from left to right). The angled cut will be parallel to the valley. Begin the next course with the 2' extension above the lower course by the valley. Roll back to the beginning.

Covering the adjacent side is done the same way. Lap over the valley and the previously laid felt 2' beyond the valley (a total paper lap of 4').

There is an exceptional condition that may demand treatment before the initial papering just described. Occasionally, the sheathing joint at the valley leaves something to be desired. A void due to misalignment of plywood edges that is large enough for the edge of a boot heel to sink into can be the cause of a valley failure. Such a void is cause to cover the valley initially with sheet metal so that there is support over the valley to ward off punctures from walking, dropped tools, or falling tree limbs. Lightweight galvanized iron of a 6" width is suitable for covering this type of valley. Strike a chalk line 3" away from and parallel to the centerline of the valley. Nail one edge of the sheet metal all the way from eave to ridge with galvanized 4d nails 1' apart. Use a long, straight, stiff board to press the metal down into the valley while nailing the opposite edge. Do not attempt to match the V contour of the valley. The felt and shingles to come will lay into the valley better if the contour of the valley bottom is a concave curve. Especially with the closed valley the crossover shingles will be laid with less danger of cracking in cold weather.

Open Valley

The open valley requires a layer of material that will be partially covered and partly exposed. The budget may dictate whether it is copper, galvanized iron, painted sheet metal, roll roofing, or tar paper.

The metal for an exposed metal valley will not likely be over 24" wide. An exposed valley 4 to 6" wide will leave 8 or 9" of the metal covered on each side of the valley. A 36"-wide piece of felt is laid up the valley on top of the shingle underlayment felt. Center it in the valley. Use a minimum number of staples to hold it in place. Place them only on the edge, three or four to a side. The valley is now protected 24" back with the first layer of lapped felt and 18" away from the valley, with the full-length piece running up the valley.

The metal valley is laid on in the same manner described for the backup metal valley. One side is chalk lined first and nailed. Only a few nails are needed to hold it in place. Later there will be nails holding the shingles penetrating through the metal valley in many places. If the valley is aluminum, it can easily be held with staples in the edge spaced about every 4'. Incidentally, aluminum is sometimes used with white and slate-colored shingles but rarely with dark shingles unless painted with roof tar. The glare from the sun is sometimes in a position to reflect objectionably.

Cementing the shingles to the metal valley is advisable for two reasons. The metal does not extend back under the shingles far enough to provide a positive seal. Its surface is too smooth to provide any resistance to rain being blown under the shingle tabs. The second reason for cementing the end of the tab is to minimize the closeness of nail punctures through the valley materials. A nail will not encourage a leak through the valley metal as long as the pressure of the nail holds the shingle material tightly down like a gasket. Occasionally, a nail shows no resistance to pounding. It has probably gone into the void between the sheathing edges. It should be removed and the hole plugged with roof cement from a caulking-gun nozzle. Otherwise, the nail is a candidate to vibrate loose and become the source of a leak.

The end of each adjacent shingle is cut parallel to the valley. A description of the method follows in the paragraphs on shingling. There are two techniques of cementing the singles onto the valley flashing. The simpler is to use the caulking gun. Roof cement is more costly purchased in tubes than in 1-gallon cans, but the cost is offset by a savings in time. A heavy bead is placed up the slant on the valley metal at a point that will contact the underside of the shingle 1 to 2″ away from the end. A doubly insured method is to place another bead on the underside of the shingle in the same relative location. When the shingle is pressed down, the beads contact each other, forming a positive seal.

Bulk cement, by the gallon, can be put on with a stick. This method is more time consuming but can be a more positive sealing method. Cement from a tube does not always adhere readily to metal. Laying the bead is simple and easy, but sometimes the contact is not adequate to cause adhesion. With a stick paddle, one actually rubs the cement on and it is obvious when and where contact is not being made. A wood-shingle shim or a paint-stirring stick with the end sharpened like a chisel makes a good applicator.

Whichever method is used, the seal must be continuous throughout the length of the valley. The vulnerable place is where one shingle laps another. An ⅛″ crack exists there. With the stick, an extra-thick dab is placed to fill the need.

Leftover asphalt roof cement can be stored indefinitely by the following method. Scrape excess cement away from the sides of the can back into the middle. Jounce the can down on a flat surface several times to settle the cement to a common level. Cover the cement with several inches of water. Close the lid tightly. Store the can in an upright position. The cement will remain usable as long as the waterseal exists.

The composition valley is formed in a manner similar to the metal valley. A problem may be encountered locating roll roofing of the same color blend as the tab shingles for this valley. There was a time when 9″ starter rolls and 36″ valley rolls were carried in coordinated quanitites by suppliers. Starter rolls are no longer routinely supplied. Roll roofing in coordinated colors is no longer universally stocked, largely as a result of another accepted method of starting with regular shingles.

Several systems have been used in various combinations to rainproof a valley. The following are probably the most important elements of a successful technique:

1. Adequately lap the first layer of underlayment paper.
2. Protect against sheathing edges that create voids or steps where roofing could be easily punctured.
3. Do not use a lot of fasteners in close vicinity to the valley.

The composition valley should have at least an equal quantity of layers as the rest of the roof. The conventional roof is double layered. There is a system of triple layment (explained later), but it exists only where weather is extraordinarily severe or where quality is king and budget unrestricted. A double-layered valley is made by using two composition strips of different widths. It is inadvisable to put down two layers of the same width, as the edges will build up a 1/4″ ledge. Such a ledge, running parallel to the valley but at a slant to the shingle tabs, will cause an unsightly ridge to exist under the shingles. Therefore, the first strip laid is cut to an 18″ width from a full-length piece.

An error in measurement occurs so frequently at this point that it warrants special emphasis. Do *not* take a length measurement down the centerline of the valley unless you intend to add to it (Fig. 10-5). The bottom of the valley strip will be shaped like a broad inverted V after it has been trimmed to the eave lines on either side of the valley bottom. In its square-cut form the bottom must hang over to an extent that the corners are at or beyond the eave. This amount of additional length can be determined by snapping the chalk lines for the edge location first. Hold a straightedge across from one chalk line to the other at the edge of the eave. Take a measurement from the ridge to the straightedge. This is the true length of the strip needed to reach the ridge.

The 36″ piece that has been cut down the center yields two 18″ pieces, one for each valley. This first valley layer is put on upside down, the granular surface against the felt underlayment. It is aligned to a chalk line 9″ from the valley and nailed along the edges (no nails closer to the valley).

It is important that all nails be driven squarely so that all heads are flush with the surface and smooth. No projection above the surface is tolerable.

The second layer is a full 36″-width piece. It will be several inches longer than the first strip, as its bottom corners are farther away from the valley. Lay it to a chalk line 18″ from the valley.

Both valley strips must bottom out in the valley. Unlike a sheet metal valley backer, a composition valley must

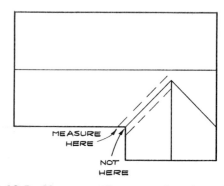

FIGURE 10-5 Measure valley paper length at the edge, not down the center of the valley.

not be allowed to bridge the valley with space underneath. Such a bridging situation is an invitation to a puncture at a future time.

SHINGLE STARTERS

The prevailing system for beginning the final stage of covering the roof is to install a starter course formed from regular shingles. A starter course is required to protect the exposed area between the shingle tabs of the first regular course. The slots that form the tab shape are called *rain gutters*. The three-tab shingles placed end to end form a continuous-appearing pattern of tabs of 12″ width. Each successive course of shingles covers the course below to the top of the gutters. The exposed part is expressed as so many ''inches to the weather.'' The shingles are staggered at each new course so that gutters from one course to the next do not line up.

   Starter rolls (no longer readily available) are 9″ wide by 50′ long. The 12″ × 36″ composition shingle on top the starter laps above the upper quarter of the 9″ starter by 3″ so that no double-deep ridge will exist at the upper edge of the first course. Innovative roofers from necessity have devised a 9″ shingle starter to substitute for the roll starter. It has become the standard of the industry. 3″ is cut from the end of each tab. A straight edge is used to maintain a straight cut. A variety of cutting tools are available. There are tinsnips, pocket knives, utility knives, and linoleum knives. Each has advantages and drawbacks. A knife must be used from the back side of the shingle, as the granular surface will destroy the cutting edge. The cut is made deep enough so that the tab can be cleanly broken but not deep enough to touch the granules on the face side and dull the knife. This is not a problem with tinsnips. The angle of the shear's cutting edge is so broad that it will survive thousands of cuts without sharpening. In hot weather the shingles are rubbery and sticky, which presents a problem for the shears.

   After the first starter shingle is cut, it may be used as a template to cut all the others. The rain gutters will now be just 2″ long. These gutters must be covered by the first course of regular shingles. The first starter shingle has a half tab cut from its beginning end (Fig. 10-6). This is called a *sixth cut*. Where the roofing is started from the left corner of the roof, one-sixth of the length of the shingle is cut off the left end. Where the roofing is started from the right side, the cutoff will be off the right end of the shingle.

Laying the Starters

The first starter is put in position so that no more than 1/2″ overhangs the metal drip edge. More than 1/2″ will render the overhanging part very susceptible to damage from ladders, falling branches, and high wind damage. The starter

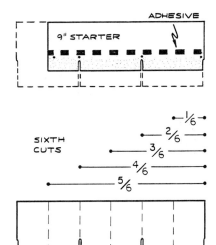

FIGURE 10-6 The first starter (lower left corner) is a ″5/6 cut″ with 3″ cut off the bottoms of the tabs. The starter is covered with the first full shingle and successively with one cut less each.

will overhang both the horizontal eave and the rake eave. Place one nail 3/4″ above each rain gutter. The nail at the cutoff end should center into the facia board edge below. Place your fingers under the drip edge with tips touching the vertical surface. Your extended thumb on top will indicate the edge of the hidden facia. Drop back a little more than half the thickness of the facia (3/8″ +) and drive the end nail. The nail on the other end will be 3/4″ above the half gutter cut and an equal amount from the end of the shingle. Only four nails are required, as there will be many more from the regular shingle course to follow.

   A simple way to gauge the nail spacing without measuring is to associate the space distance with something familiar. For example, place the nail above the gutter the width of your thumb or an amount equal to the diameter of your hammer head but no more.

   The straightness of the shingle courses on the remainder of the roof may have a direct relation to the starter course and first course. Chalk lines cannot be struck straight on a roof more than a distance of about 20′. The force of gravity whips the line downhill. It is not possible, for example, to strike a single straight line on a 60′ roof with a chalk line. The line will have a downward curve. The system on such roof length is to measure up from the eave at the corner and at a point about 20′ away from each end and strike three successive lines each about one-third the roof length. It is obvious that if the starter course and the first regular course of singles are not in a straight line, they will furnish an inaccurate and poor reference for the chalk lining of courses to come.

   When laying the starters, or any course to follow, the top edge of the shingle must not be used as a reference for straightlining the course. The shingles are not consistently 12″ high. The referencing is done to the lower edge of the exposed tab for all purposes of maintaining parallelism and straightness.

REGULAR COURSING

The first regular course will start with a full three-tab shingle. The gutters will be over the center of the starter tabs. This is called the sixth-cut system. It creates a 50% side lap over all the end joints of the course below. There are quarter- and third-lap systems. These systems are not advised, as they do not provide adequate coverage. The quarter-lap technique places the butt joint of the shingles only 3″ from the rain gutter, which is minimal protection against strong side winds during a rainstorm. There is no logical rationale for the third and quarter layment technique. It produces a noticeable herringbone pattern on a roof running diagonally. It is much more difficult to control the spacing so that the rain gutters show a consistent vertical relationship.

Sixth Cutting

The sixth-cut technique is begun by precutting at least five shingles to a specific length. The first course is started with a full 3′ shingle. The second course starts with a shingle that is 5/6 as long as a full one. Assume for the moment that the beginning point is the left side of the roof. Mark a point on the top edge of the second course beginning shingle 6″ away from the end of the back side. Remember the reversing syndrome problem when dealing with the back side. If you face the shingle as it will be laid on the roof, tabs toward you, and then turn it over vertically, the cut will be on the left side. On the other hand, if you roll the shingle over to the right, the cut is now on the right side. Do not measure the 6″ on the edge of the tab. The tab is less than 12″ wide by the amount of a gutter width. Measure across the top edge of the shingle. Use a framing square as a cutting guide.

Cut the remaining four shingles as follows. A 4/6 cut is made by centering the framing square blade edge over the gutter between the first and second tab. The 3/6 cut is measured 18″ from the left end of the shingle. The 2/6 cut has the square again lined up over the last gutter. The 1/6 last cut is 30″ from the left end or 6″ from the right end. Each of the cuts is made on a new, separate shingle.

As these first six course starters are being prepared, the remainder end of each shingle (the left-side piece) is carefully stacked in sequential order away from the work area. The stack is then taken to the other end of the roof. These pieces will be worked into the end of the courses. When kept in the correct sequence there will be a minimum of waste. Each piece will probably need trimming, but the

amount will always be less than 1/6 of a shingle once the coordination is begun. It begins by choosing the cutoff that exceeds the desired length by less than 6″ (1/6 length). Any cutoffs of less length than the first usable one are placed near the peak, as they will not be used in the sequence until the end of the capping. Hold rigidly to the system and the waste will be held to an absolute minimum.

Course Spacing

American composition shingles have gutter slots that are slightly in excess of 5″ long from the bottom of the tab. None of the shingle above the tab should be exposed. Metric shingles from Canada may expose about 5 1/2″ or less without violating this exposure rule. The standard exposure with American 12″ × 36″ three-tab shingles is 5″ to the weather.

Maintaining Straight Lines

Sustaining the standard exposure is maintained by consistent reference back to the first laid course. It is easy and efficient to work with the 5″ exposure module. Each succeeding course is laid on a multiple of 5. The figure on the tape measure from the first course to any other course will end in 5 or 0. For example the ninth course will be 45″, the twenty-fourth course on 120″, and so on.

Consistency in the system is totally a matter of attitude. The perfection to be gained takes a little more time. When practiced conscientiously there will be a modest saving. There will always be more waste when the system described below is not followed, as one or more extra courses of shingles will be required. It is humanly impossible to lay several courses of shingles perfectly straight and with consistent exposure. The closest one can come to the objective without guides is to use the tops of the gutter slots as alignment indexes for the course above. The pitfall inevitably comes as soon as just one shingle is allowed to slip down on one end. From then on, every shingle above it is misaligned. After several such common mishaps have occurred the entire job is out of control until a new straight baseline is established. The problem of the canted shingle frequently occurs with the first shingle or partial shingle at the start of the course. When this one is permitted to slip down on the interior end, ever so slightly, the stage is set for a downward curvature in the course. It takes only a few such curved courses to turn a straight roof into one that appears to sag.

Alignment Technique

There are few, if any, professional roofers who will follow the technique about to be described. This statement is not intended as a condemnation. The pro is always under pressure to make a compromising decision about time and money. When he can work to a tolerance of a little less perfection and maintain a salable reputation, that usually becomes his mode of operation because it pays more. If he can do three roofs to the trade standard in the time it takes to do two roofs with more perfection, the additional income is an enticing incentive.

The cost of the extra shingles is not usually a factor, as it is passed along to the consumer. In fact, this cost may even present an incentive to waste shingles when the job is contracted by the square. The more squares of shingles that can be invoiced, the higher the labor charge. This is one of the consumer traps in subcontracting that occurs in roofing, drywalling, paneling, and any other job where labor can be attached to a unit of material.

The homeowner/builder is not usually compelled by this type of profit motive. For those who tend more to perfection or simply like to do it the best quality way, the following technique is recommended.

Measurement and chalk lining are the keys to the system. Lay the starter course and first course as perfectly as possible. This double-thick drip edge will be the baseline for all reference measurements to follow.

Parallel coursing begins with the second course. The 5/6 second-course starter shingle is placed in position by measuring up from the eave of the first course. Measure at both ends to assure parallelism. Install all the rest of the 1/6 cut starters. Check each edge in the field. They should be precisely on steps 5, 10, 15, 20, and 25″ above the eave.

Move across the roof a distance that permits a chalk line to be used with accuracy. Think in modules of divisions of the total distance. Three chalkline resets would be adequate for any roof between 48 and 60′ long. From 60 to 80′ four divisions are adequate. The effective snapping distance on a slope is therefore about 16 to 20′. On very low pitches such as 2 1/2 in 12, or 3 or 3 1/2 in 12, under ideal conditions, it could be possible to go to 24 or 25′ with the chalk line and still get a straight mark. At the point of the division that is chosen, measure up from the eave exactly 5″. Hook the chalk line at the beginning and hold it on the 5″ mark. Draw the string up about 16″ and let go. Repeat this procedure over all the roof until a level is reached about 3′ down from the ridge.

Vertical gutter alignment is maintained with string lines attached from the eave to the ridge at modular intervals. A temporary nail can be pushed or nailed under the lower edge of the drip edge, leaving the head exposed. Place it directly below one of the gutter slots that is close to an even division of the total length of the roof. This distance works well if it is within a range of four to five shingle lengths (12 to 15′). Whatever length is chosen, it is best to divide the total length of the roof into nearly equal segments. A 36′ roof, for example, would have its first

vertical guideline placed at the end of the fourth shingle, 12′ from the starting edge. The next line is placed at the end of the eighth shingle, 24′ from the starting edge. In this manner there will be two vertical check points established at approximate third points across the roof's length.

The attachment point at the top of the roof for the string must take into consideration the fact that the drip edge and shingle overhang are not yet there at the gable eaves. The most accurate method of establishing this elusive point out in space is to hold or tack a scrap of drip edge against the facia. Place a shingle overhanging it to the exact duplicate amount as the first-course starter shingle. Duplicate, along the ridge, the distance taken from the string nail at the bottom course. Drive a nail at this point on the ridge. Stretch the tape measure on out to the second point and as many others as there may be on a longer roof. Do not measure from point to point. Always take the measurement from the point of beginning (POB).

The string lines for vertical alignment will remain in place until the last full shingle course is laid adjacent to the ridge. The string lines need not be cut for this purpose (Fig. 10-7). Make a loop in the end of the string and slip it over the bottom nail. Run the string up the roof to the ridge nail. Loop it around this nail once and proceed to the next ridge nail. Loop it around that nail and then down to the second eave nail. If the nail is driven into the facia, the string can be looped and taken horizontally to the next eave nail and up to the ridge again. One cannot put any side pressure on this nail unless it is firmly anchored. One can continue stringing the lines in this manner until all vertical lines are in place or until the string runs out.

Do not put too much tension on the lines. A lot of tension will cause the string to cut a slit in the bottom-course underlayment. Also, you may wish to detach the strings at the top temporarily by unlooping them. This facilitates lowering the lines while the 15-lb underlayment paper is rolled out progressively ahead of the roofing. In areas of high wind or with steep pitches it is prudent to stay

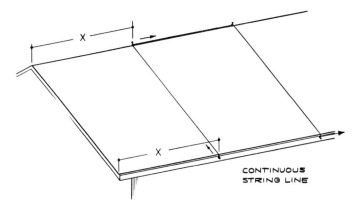

FIGURE 10-7 Perfect lineup of vertical gutters in the shingles can be maintained by stringing guidelines that start in a gutter and are parallel to each other.

only one course of underlayment paper ahead of the shingling operation. Slitting the lower shingle via string tension can be avoided completely by placing a small 2 × 2 block of wood under the string and on the face of the drip edge.

Adjusting the shingle placement may be necessary when the course reaches the vertical string-line check point. Remember that the objective is to cause the gutter lines to line up vertically on every other course. When the shingles ahead of the line are laid tighter than the base course, the one approaching the string will fall short of it a small amount. This should be checked out before nailing the last two or even three shingles ahead of the string. Lay them into position. Space them equally apart and nail them.

When the shingle extends beyond the string, a small amount (1/8 to 1/4″) of the end can be trimmed off. Trim the top portion of the shingle exactly the amount of the excess. The exposed lower 5″ tab must be trimmed back the same quantity as the top to recreate the half-gutter cut of the junction. When the gutter edge is not trimmed, the resulting gutter junction with the next shingle will be noticeably narrower than the standard. Any gross excess of either overlay or underlay is cause to recheck the accuracy of the parallelism of the vertical string lines. Such an inaccuracy compounds the error gradually and progressively as shingling progresses. It creates a horrendous problem when such an error goes undetected until after many courses have been laid.

When a large crew is involved in putting on shingles, the vertical check lines can be used as POBs within the segments. Whenever a course ends at the strings with a full shingle, a fresh start can be made from any string. The strings must be placed apart from each other a distance that is a multiple of several full-length shingles, such as 9, 12, and 15′. The system can be used on every sixth course, the ones that start with a full shingle. Nonetheless, with one person in charge and thorough coordination, a nearly perfect roof can be placed in minimum time.

Nailing Procedure

Nailing should be in accordance with the manufacturer's instructions. Failure to follow these instructions will nullify the guarantee. The instructions, including illustrations, are found on the shingle package. There may be minimum and optimum options. For example, a minimum option is four nails per full shingle. The optimum is six nails per shingle.

Wind and weather are factors to be taken into account. The shingle with six nails has a better chance of surviving the gales that are common to some locales. Roof pitch and quantity of rain are also factors. Very steep pitches benefit from the additional nails simply from the added support to counteract gravity. Low pitches do not exert this downward force on the single. On the other hand,

the low-pitched roof is more prone to leaking as a result of rain being blown up under the tabs. Here again, six nails hold the shingle down flatter and tighter. It can be seen why many contractors use the six-nail system routinely as a measure of quality.

Nailing Order

One of the two nails in the field should be placed first, preferably by the second gutter away from the butt joint. The shingle sometimes vibrates down at the open end from the pounding if the first nail is put in the closed end. By putting the first nail by the second gutter any movement is held to a minimum. If the end of the shingle slips down by the butt joint, it is easily seen and correctible before driving the second nail. The next nail to be driven may be placed by the butt joint or by the other gutter. The shingle is now immobilized. The remaining nails are placed in no specific order.

Butt Joining

The butt joints should be snug but not tight. The temperature will have some bearing on how the fit is made. Composition shingles swell in the first summer after layment much like the tar divider strips in a concrete highway. In hot summer temperatures, the shingles should be laid touching. In winter temperatures, about 50° or lower, a tiny gap should be left. About 1/16″ is adequate. The first hot season that follows the layment of a new roof will cause the shingles to swell. From then on they will dry out and shrink a little. Ignoring this principle may result in tabs that hump up in the middle. When shingles are laid tightly compressed at the ends in cold weather, there is no space to expand into when the first hot weather arrives. They have not yet begun to shrink from aging, so they hump and cause ripples. Unfortunately, the ripples do not always go away, as they are baked into shape. Sometimes, with a little luck, the shrinkage will cause them to lie back down. The wise and knowledgeable installer will not rely on luck.

Nail Angle

Roofing nails must be driven at right angles to the surface. The heads are flat and smooth when installed correctly. When a head is bent over on an edge, remove it before the final blow is struck. A turned-over edge will cut through the shingle, creating a spot that is vulnerable to tearing.

Nail driving is done efficiently by the following technique. Set the nail with a light touch, then sink it with one precise blow. With a little skill and some practice, one can drive roofing nails in this manner all day long.

Heavy hammers are not needed for roofing. The 20- or 22-oz framing hammer with its extra-long handle is out of place on the roof. The all-purpose 16-oz curved claw hammer is a good choice. If one is weight conscious, a 13-oz hammer is also adequate for the shingling job. A shake-shingle hatchet is usable. The hatchet blade can be used to scar the back side of a composition shingle in preparation for breaking it. The hatchet has a deficiency, however; it is a poor nail puller, at least one claw hammer is needed on the job for nail removing.

Positioning the Nails

Two elements of importance should be kept in mind when placing the nails. All nails must be covered by the next shingle. Each nail should be close enough to the top of the rain gutter to hold it down tightly. When a single nail is used above the gutters, place it no closer than 3/4″ and no farther than 1″ from the top of the gutter. It should be directly above the gutter. Use this same distance range for the six-nail system (Fig. 10-8). At the gutters and ends place the nails on an invisible line running up diagonally out of the top of the gutter. This will place the two field nails over each gutter apart from each other between 1 1/2 and 2″. It is important to restrict the horizontal spread to a 2″ maximum. A wider spread of nails may permit rain to be wind driven up under this vulnerable area.

Power stapling generally calls for the same spacing. The staples are driven so that the top of the staple runs horizontally. Where a single staple is used over the gutter, the legs of the staple will be equidistant on either side of the centerline emanating from the top of the gutter. Each staple straddles a centerline projected above each gutter.

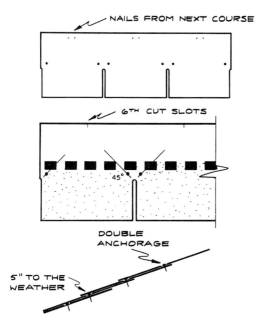

FIGURE 10-8 The six-nail system provides superior holding power, especially when combined with sealing adhesive.

Seal-down shingles dominate the composition shingle market. This shingle has an asphalt adhesive strip on the top side. It is intended to be clear of the nailing zone. Some brands have a continuous strip, while others have a dashed intermittent strip. Occasionally, an entire bundle will have the adhesive strip in line with the nailing zone. Wherever possible, avoid nailing through the adhesive. The well-driven nailhead craters the shingle surface slightly. When driven through the adhesive, a nail crater will result in the adhesive strip zone. This area will not be in contact with the underside of the next shingle tab. Offset the nail a little to avoid this condition. On the other hand, do not compromise the spacing rule more than 1/4″ or so. Nail through the adhesive when necessary.

Shingles are stacked in a bundle containing one-third of a square (three bundles to 100 square feet of coverage). There is a very thin plastic strip glued to each shingle to protect it from the adhesive strip on the adjoining shingle. Were it not for this protector strip, a bundle of shingles would be firmly bonded together after being exposed to the hot sunshine. The strip serves no other purpose. It may be left on each shingle and ignored at layment time.

Mastic Adhesion

There are several places on the roof where shingles will be secured solely with roof cement. Generally these zones involve metal flashing under a custom-cut shingle tab. A nail puncture through the flashing close to the water-runoff channel is never a good situation. Frequently, it becomes the cause of a leak. To eliminate such potential failures, small tabs or ends of shingles can be cemented to the flashing that runs under. Any cementing job works best when each contact surface is coated with adhesive. This is especially true with metal flashing and composition shingles. The roof cement must be rubbed onto the metal until one can feel it stick. It is then spread on the underside of the shingle. Outline the shingle in position first so that no cement is exposed after application. A wooden scrap is used for an applicator. Paint-stirring sticks are excellent in shape and size for cement applicators. Take pains to avoid getting the black adhesive on anything but the surfaces to be joined. On all but black roofs, any exposed adhesive will be unsightly. It is especially unnerving to step in a glob of black mastic and then walk across a new white-shingle job to discover that a trail of black spots has been laid. It is virtually impossible to remove such evidence. One should also avoid getting the tarlike substance on the hands, as it will be transferred to tools and clothing.

Specific places where adhesive is used are around chimneys and vertical walls that are butted by a sloping roof. A porch roof is a typical example. Flashing is laid on top of the last full or nearly full shingle course and up under the siding (Fig. 10-9). The lower edge of the flashing

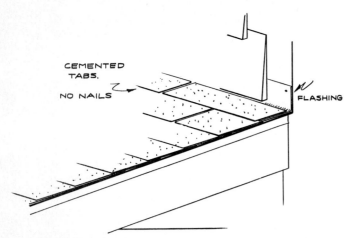

FIGURE 10-9 Surface tabs are cemented on top of flashing to avoid nail holes. Several courses are "crowded" to make the tabs near full size. Can you see where the transition started in this illustration?

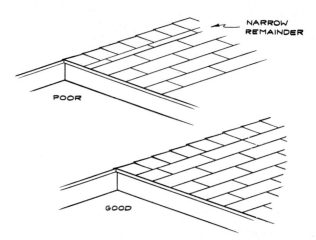

FIGURE 10-10 Advance planning and measuring before reaching the ridge permits slight shortening of the exposure, resulting in a more-normal-appearing final course below the ridge.

is nailed. There may be as much as 5″ of flashing exposed, in which case full tabs are cut horizontally at the top of the gutters. These tabs are cemented on top of the flashing, being careful to follow the vertical and horizontal spacing of the coursing below. Care is also taken not to place any nail in the flashing that will be exposed between the gutter space of each cemented tab that follows. This area can consciously be avoided. It is in the center of the shingle tab below.

Tabs to lay over flashing in the porch-type position will seldom be exactly 5″ in height. Usually, they are less as the distance from the eave overhang is not precisely divisible by the field shingle exposure (usually, 5″). There is a potential trap in this situation. Should the total distance from the lower edge of the first course to the top measure only 1″ (or less) more than a multiple of 5, it would present a problem if ignored. A cemented top course adjoining a vertical wall should be at least 2″ in width from lower to upper edge. More is preferred. How can it be arranged? Let us take a typical situation. Roofing is begun on a porch. A uniform 5″-to-the-weather layment procedure is used. When the last set or two of sixth-course starters is being placed, the roofer measures to the top and finds that the figure ends on 6″ or 11″ (1″ more than multiples of 5). He adjusts several of the last courses to a lower line (less exposure). For example, to gain an inch of width (height) for the last cemented tab he can lay each of the last four courses to an exposure of 4 3/4″. To gain 2″ the exposure of the last eight courses can be reduced by a 1/4″. Such minor adjustments go unnoticed from any vantage point.

CAPPING THE RIDGE

The approach to the ridge with the regular shingles is made in the same manner just described for the approach to the top of a porch roof where it joins a vertical wall. An ob-

jective is to avoid a narrow exposure of the last regular course of shingles. (Fig. 10-10). The edge of the ridge cap will be about 5 1/2″ down from the peak of the ridge. The ridge-cap pieces are cut from shingles. One shingle makes three caps. Each tab is cut off on a line perpendicular to the upper edge to the centerline of the shingle gutter. The tab is folded over the ridge. Since the tab end is about 11 5/8″ wide, the half that extends down each side reaches about 5 1/2″ (the curvature takes up the remainder). When the roofer has reached a point up the beginning side of the roof that is about 10 courses below the ridge, he should measure to the ridge and determine how much shortening of the remaining exposures may be needed. If the last full course would fall between 3 and 5″ of exposure, no adjustment is necessary. When it will be under 3″, if left unadjusted, an adjustment should be made at some point in the last set of sixth-cut starters. Remember to make the same adjustment throughout each course to maintain parallelism.

Laying the last full course of shingles on each side of the ridge will vary as to technique, depending on how much extends beyond the ridge and the condition of the ridge (Fig. 10-11). A ridge that has a sizable gap between the upper edges of the sheathing is strengthened to some extent by lapping the first shingle course to reach the top over onto the other side. The course coming up the other side is folded and lapped over the top so that it forms a double layer under the cap shingles. Both of these final courses should be cut so that no more than 2 to 3″ extends beyond the ridge. More than this amount will cause interference with the cap nailing. The ridge is now lapped with two layers of shingles, which provides a stiffer backing for the caps.

The ridge that is closed more tightly needs only one lapover of shingles. Cut the first course which extends beyond the ridge so that the top edge falls short of the ridge line about 1/4 to 1/2″. Lap and fold over the top course

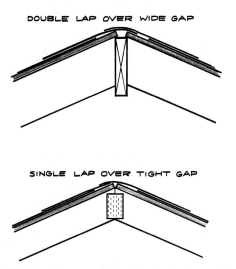

FIGURE 10-11   The motto for ridge covering with the top courses is: Double lap a wide gap; single lap a tight gap.

from the other side after cutting the lap quantity down to a size between 2 and 3″.

Cutting the Caps

The capping tabs are cut from full shingles and partial remnants which have one or two full tab sections. The shingle is laid face down on a board. Hold a square along the top edge with the tongue bisecting the gutter slot. Make a mark on the edge (Fig. 10-12). Hold the tongue of the square on the edge of the curve at the top of the gutter. Slant the tongue from this point to a point that is 3/4″ away from the top edge mark. Scratch a line between these two points. Reproduce another line on the other side of the edge mark opposite the first line. Reproduce these marks above each gutter. Scratch one slanted line on each end. With practice these lines can be scratched without measuring. With more practice and a skilled eye the cuts can be made without marks.

Cutting the caps is most successfully done with tinsnips. A knife applied to the back side is acceptable but has some drawbacks. When penetration is deep enough for a clean break, it frequently means that the point of the blade has penetrated to the stone-covered surface. The point is immediately dulled. It cuts poorly from then on. When penetration is not deep enough for a clean break, it is difficult to detach the sharp, pointed end of the triangular

scrap. Tinsnips, on the other hand, cut cleanly through the thin points of the scrap on all but the hottest days. A short pair of tinsnips (8 or 11″) will do well, as the composition shingle does not require a lot of leverage. The blunt shearing edges will endure the granules for thousands of cuts.

Computing the quantity of caps needed is a simple matter for scratch pad or calculator. The total length of the roof ridge in inches, including the drip edge and a couple of inches for overhang, is divided by 5 (the exposure) to net the quantity of caps. Knowing the quantity facilitates cutting the caps at a convenient location away from the roof, such as on a sawhorse table or the tailgate of a pickup truck.

Facing the Caps

There is a preferred direction toward which the open edge of the cap shingle should face. The edge of the cap that runs over the ridge is not wholly in a rain-shedding posture. A wind-driven rain will penetrate under this edge to some extent. For this reason the open end of the capping shingles should face away from the prevailing winds. In much of the United States the prevailing wind direction, the direction from which the wind usually comes, is southwest or northwest. In areas where this holds true, a roof ridge that runs east and west should have its cap shingles open ended toward the east, away from the wind. The roofer will begin the capping with a full-cap shingle on the east end of the ridge and lap toward the west (Fig. 10-13). There are many exceptions to the westerly wind direction rule which are caused by the surrounding terrain. Mountains, valleys, and seashores often cause a particular and prevalent wind direction. North and south ridges generally are faced south except in southern coastal regions where prevailing winds come from the ocean.

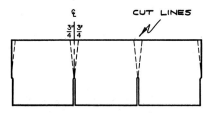

FIGURE 10-12   Cutting lines for making ridge cap shingles.

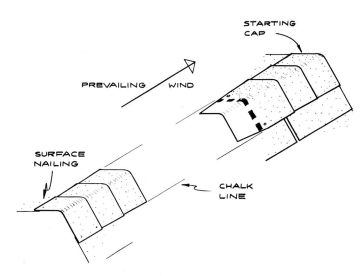

FIGURE 10-13   Lap the capping shingles with their open ends facing away from the prevailing wind.

The last cap shingle is a partial tab of 5″ or less. It is surface nailed and cemented. Like the last horizontal course, the last cap should not be permitted to be less than about 3″ wide. It requires this much width for appearance and nailing. At the minimum 3″ size only about half of it will be over wood in which to drive a nail. The rest is over the drip edge overhang and beyond. Spread cement on both contact surfaces and nail on the tab.

It is possible to arrange for a full 5″ exposed tab at the end by shortening the exposure length of several of the preceding caps. Done progressively, it will be undetectable from ground level. The roofer can start by shortening 1/16″ for two or three caps, then drop to 1/8″, then 3/16″, then finally 1/4″. Keep checking the distance to the end until it is determined that the 5″ or slightly less will be the last module.

Smaller-headed nails, such as 4d galvanized size, are preferred for the surface nailing. This size is also preferred for installing the drip edge. A tiny spot of cement covering nailhead completes the shingling job. The cement will deter rusting for many years.

FLASHING EXTRUSIONS

There are a number of things on a roof or passing through a roof that will require special flashing techniques to prevent the entry of water. One may encounter any or several of the following: plumbing vent pipes, an electrical entrance mast, skylights, roof vents (attic ventilators), solar water heat connections, TV aerials, chimneys, weather vanes, cupolas, and so on.

Pipe Flashing

Pipes are waterproofed with purchased flashing collars. Many old houses will have a lead collar and apron. The soft lead was peaned into the surface of the cast iron vent pipes to form a fair rain-shedding joint. Today's vent flash is made of galvanized or aluminum sheet metal with a synthetic rubber collar or is all synthetic.

Locating the hole for a pipe is accomplished by dropping a plumb line to the center of the vent pipe that will be coming through the roof. Move the string around on the underside of the roof sheathing until the plumb bob settles down in the center of the pipe. Mark the spot above the string on the sheathing. Drive a nail vertically through the roof. Proceed to the roof top with all the required tools and materials. Find the protruding nail. Hold a short piece of pipe of the correct diameter *vertically* and centered over the nail. Press a pencil vertically against the sides of the pipe. Pass it around the pipe, making a mark on the shingle. It will be noted that this pipe tracing is not round, it is elliptical. A round hole, the diameter of the pipe, will

not permit a pipe to pass through vertically. The higher the pitch of the roof, the greater will be the length of the ellipse from the bottom to the top.

Cutting the hole to fit entails two considerations. To have the least gap around the pipe, the edges of the hole will require plumb cutting all around the ellipse. Such finesse in hole cutting is seldom practiced by plumbers or roofers but may be an item of pride with a home builder. The hole should be at least 1/4″ larger than required to accommodate any minor error in location or angle. Cut away all shingle and paper along a scribed line about 1/2″ outside the tracing mark to expose the sheathing. Retrace the pipe as before. Drill a hole adjacent to the tracing (on the inside) that is large enough to accommodate a saw blade of the reciprocal type. A 1″ hole is a good size. A hand saw or a power saw may be used. A compass saw (frequently called a "keyhole" saw) will accomplish the job adequately. The drywaller's bayonette saw, which is compact to carry, is another choice. Start the saw in the hole and proceed around the ellipse, holding the saw in a vertical position throughout the cut. One must resist the inclination to saw at right angles to the sheathing. The cut should be straight up and down. Check the hole for size by inserting the tracing piece of pipe. Hold it vertically. Trim off any contact points that prevent proper positioning.

Removing nails from the shingle above the hole is usually required to permit insertion of the flash apron. Before placing the permanent pipe, put the flashing collar over the hole and adjust it by sighting through the hole. Trace the lower part of the flange up to a high point on each side, which will permit at least the upper half of the flange to be under the shingles. The top edge of the flange must not be exposed in a gutter slot. It must be up under the portion of the shingle above the gutters in order to shed water reliably. The rule of thumb is: top half under, lower half over.

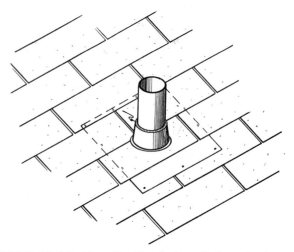

FIGURE 10-14 Vent flashing is installed to shed water and not depend on shingle cement.

Camouflaging the lower exposed part of the flange is possible in two steps (Fig. 10-14). The shingle tab that straddles the pipe wholly or partly is not removed. Instead, a circular cutout is made to accommodate the pipe. The tab below should not be nailed through the flange. Attach it with shingle cement only. The tabs are blended into the continuity of the regular shingles so that no break in the pattern exists.

Cementing the flange need be done only on the upper half, if at all. The shedding principle will exist when the flange is properly lapped with the shingles above and beside it. On some very low pitched roofs or those in areas of high wind it may be advisable to cement all the flange edges. Place cement on both contact surfaces. A border of cement about 1 1/2 to 2″ wide on the underside of the flange and matching area on the shingles will be adequate.

Nails are driven only along the edges of the flange. No more are needed than it takes to hold the edges down flat to the surface. Metal flanges stay flat much better than do synthetic ones. The synthetic apron should be nailed in the center of the edges first. Stretch each corner away from the center and at a slight diagonal away from the pipe. Then nail the corner. Without following this stretching technique the edges of the apron are sure to buckle upward, exposing a gap vulnerable to driven rain.

The last step is to spread a coating of cement around the pipe over the joint where the gasket contacts the pipe. Be certain that the gasket is not left in an inverted posture. Such a position frequently exists because the pipe has been pushed up from below to a point above its coupling and then pulled back down into the coupling. Pull the gasket up to its highest point and coat the joint with a cove of cement that sheds the water. Where the lower part of the flange apron is left exposed, the nailheads should be sealed and coated with a dab of cement. This will prolong their life by several years.

Electrical entrance masts that protrude through a roof are flashed in the same manner as plumbing vents.

Chimney Flashing

Chimney flashing varies a little depending on the location of a chimney on the roof. There are four common positions in which a chimney may emerge from the roof. It may sever the ridge. It may be external on a gable end or on the eave side. It may emerge from the roof at an intermediate point on the slope. Regardless of the chimney position, the order of flashing installation is the same as shingles. Each piece of flashing is placed starting at the lowest point and worked toward the highest point. Each individual piece of flashing laps the piece below, thereby achieving the shedding principle.

Flashing metal is most commonly found in 50′, or shorter, rolls of aluminum. Various widths are available.

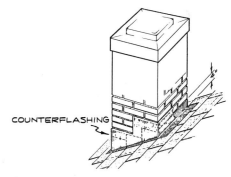

FIGURE 10-15 A chimney less than 30″ wide on the upper side may be flashed with a single piece (no saddle).

A 14″-wide roll is a convenient width which will net little waste. From it, 7″-wide pieces may be cut in lengths as needed. The 7″ width matches up well with 5″ of exposed shingle tabs. It is laid from the top of the shingle down to the top of the rain gutter, a distance of 7″. Its length will depend on how many courses it extends up the brickwork of the chimney. About 1″ of the metal is grouted into the mortar joint.

The lower and upper flashing on a chimney that exits somewhere on the slope may be a single piece when the chimney is small (FHA, under 30″ wide; Fig. 10-15). A chimney that is wider horizontally must have a saddle on the upper side to effectively shed water, melting snow, leaves, and debris.

The lower horizontal flashing may be grouted in on top of the first fully exposed course of brick. It is a continuous single piece of sheet metal several inches longer than the chimney width. The ends are folded around the corner much like one wraps a Christmas package. A dummy row of cut shingle tabs is cemented on top of the flashing where it laps the coursing below. This final layer covers and seals the exposed nailheads.

Flashing up the slope sides of the chimney is done in concert with the shingling (Fig. 10-16). There is no

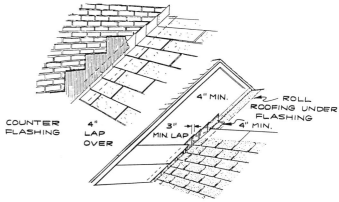

FIGURE 10-16 Counter flashing is another technique employed on chimneys and adjoining walls.

chimney there when the roofing is installed, only a hole. Therefore, it is necessary to anticipate the length of the flashing piece that will be required. Six inches or more should extend under the shingle. The part left hanging out will vary in length depending on whether it will be shingle flashed or counter flashed. The latter will require that uniform tabs be bent up. The chimney mason will then bond flashing pieces into the chimney joints which lap down over the shingle flashing. It is not feasible to advise a specific length of flashing that should be extended beyond the shingles. The builder should check his locality to see what the pattern is for that area. There may be a regulatory code to abide by, as well.

A saddled chimney is flashed in the same manner as the regular slope (Fig. 10-17). The saddle will be the same pitch as the roof. The saddle is simply a miniature wing (dormer roof) with its gable eave against the upper chimney face. It forms two valleys to shed the rain to the sides of the chimney. Although the majority of codes follow the 30″ FHA maximum-width rule, it is wise to have a saddle on all masonry chimneys that exit on the slope or the eave. Experience demonstrates that chimneys of any size without saddles are a major and almost inevitable cause of leakage. The result is usually rotted structural members, sometimes clear to the foundation, and water-damaged interiors.

The downside edge of a flashing piece against the chimney wall will be vertical when the forming is started with the bend for the grout joint. There is no necessity for it to be vertical. Each exposed edge will actually provide more protection if allowed to slant forward than it will if started on the shingle and bent at the upward chimney surface (Fig. 10-18). When the flashing piece is bent at the roof surface, its lower and upper edges will be at right angles to the pitch of the roof (Fig. 10-19). Therefore, the higher the pitch, the greater the forward tilt of the flashing on the chimney. Some designers of steep-pitched roofs prefer this flash lap to be vertical, for aesthetic reasons. It can be accomplished by holding the leading edge in a vertical position and bending the underlay portion on the pitch line. It can be done more precisely by laying out a bend line on the flashing in the same manner as one lays out a plumb cut on a rafter.

The vertical flash laps sometimes do not lie flat against each other and against the brick. To prevent this irritating condition, the builder must give attention to the curvature of the metal as it comes off the roll. The crown set of the metal is placed downward. By doing so, the metal has a gentle spring action against the chimney and will fit snugly. If one should forget and reverse this crown, all is not lost. The soft malleable aluminum can be recurved to reverse its original curvature. When these methods fail, a 4d galvanized nail can be driven through the aluminum into a mortar joint at a later date.

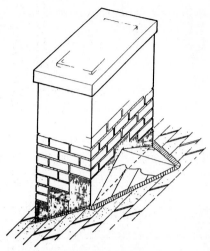

FIGURE 10-17 A chimney 30″ or wider on the upper side requires a saddle (sometimes called a cricket) and full flashing to dispose of water adequately.

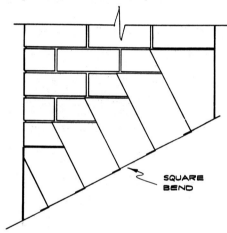

FIGURE 10-18 Flashing that begins on top the shingle (during roofing before chimney is built) will slant forward unless cut vertically on downside.

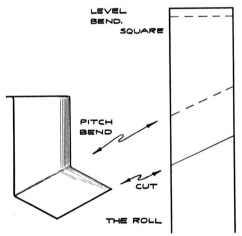

FIGURE 10-19 Pattern layout example for vertical flashing.

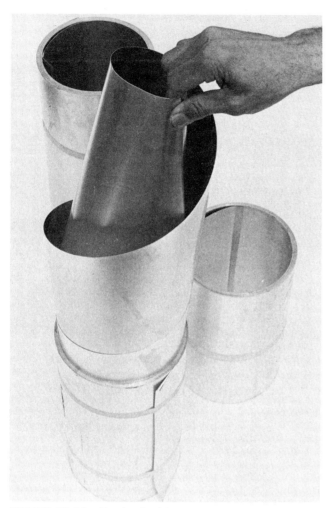

FIGURE 10-20 Feed a flashing roll out of the center like a corkscrew. Cut off what is needed and screw feed the remainder back into the center hole. Never cut the band.

An aluminum roll (Fig. 10-20) is most effectively handled by never cutting the baling band. Reach inside and tighten the end. Pull it up out of the center in a corkscrew. Cut off as much as desired. Screw the end back into the roll. This method will help prevent damage to the roll throughout its use. It is a safe method. An unsprung roll can easily cause a serious wound. A 50′ roll will unwind its full length when the band is cut, unless controlled. It need never be unrolled or rerolled with the corkscrew method.

ROOF VENTILATION

Roof ventilation is an important element in the design and construction of a house. In the United States there are probably many more homes that are underventilated than are adequately ventilated. After the invention of the blanket and the loose-fill forms of insulation, builders and homeowners became more conscious of the importance of circulating fresh air through the unused attics of a roof. Soaring fuel costs in the late 1970s and 1980s drew attention to the wastefulness of allowing heated air to escape into an attic area.

Tight sheathing on a roof is another factor that changed the concept of ventilating. The shake-shingle roofs of the pre-1930s era allowed an attic to ventilate freely. The shingles were laid on 1 × 4s that were spaced apart a distance equal to the board width. On a hot summer day one could go up into the darkness of the attic and see a universe of stars. The sunlight shone through the hundreds of gaps and cracks. When it rained families would rush up to the attic to place pots and pans under the leaks to catch the dripping water. After the shingles swelled, the leaking would subside. In a few years, the shingles would no longer swell enough to close. A new roof was required.

When composition shingles came into widespread use, roofs no longer ventilated freely. The system soon evolved to where asphalt-saturated building paper was installed as an underlayment to seal over the plywood sheathing. This design, which is still the most prevalent system today, makes a nearly airtight roof.

As a result, condensation problems began to plague the housing industry. When the temperature was considerably colder outside than it was under the roof, the heat in an attic caused the air to condense into moisture. In some recorded cases the effect was so extreme as to cause water to run out of light fixtures. Plaster became soaked and wallpaper peeled loose. The answer, of course, was to insulate the ceiling and ventilate the attic.

Ventilation Formula

A ventilation formula evolved which provided a standard for an adequate exchange of air. The formula, found in the early FHA-MPS manual, became the standard of the building industry. It is as follows:

- The ratio of total net free ventilating area to the area of the ceiling shall not be less than 1/150.
- The proportion can be dropped to 1/300 provided that a sealed vapor barrier exists between the ceiling and the attic.
- Fifty percent of the ventilators may be in the eaves. The other 50% must be toward the top of the roof (roof vents or gable vents).

This rule, or variations of it, is found in most recognized building codes in the United States.

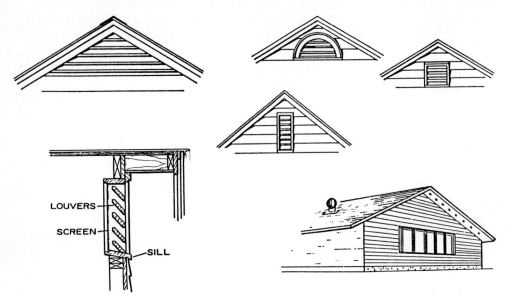

LOUVERS

SCREEN

SILL

FIGURE 10-21 There are many styles of ventilators. Some are functional and decorative; others are simply functional.

Forms of Ventilators

There are several forms and shapes of roof ventilators in use in the United States (Fig. 10-21). They vary in effectiveness. Premanufactured gable vents may be purchased in rectangular or triangular shape. There are several roof-type vents available. There are passive roof vents, turbines, power ventilators, and ridge vents. Of all these types the continuous ridge vent design is the most effective when used in conjunction with continuous eave venting. Each channel formed by the rafters acts as a bottomless duct. Air is drawn through the eave vents, rises up the underside of the entire roof, and is vented directly out the ridge vent. There is no crossing over from one rafter to another. No baffle effect exists to impede the air movement.

Installation of vents

The installation of a ventilator varies according to its location and the building materials that surround it.

Vertical vents (gable types) in most cases will require a surround. A *surround* is a surface-mounted casement. It forms a stop for horizontal siding. The surround can be nailed flat to the surface or on edge. For reasons of aesthetic continuity, one may choose to use a matching window casing to frame around a vent.

An aluminum vent is usually surface nailed with hot-dipped galvanized nails. It can be nailed over the sheathing into studs behind. Another technique is to frame the opening with a surround first, then nail the vent to the surrounding casement. Where horizontal siding is used, there must be solid wood behind the siding where it butts the casement; otherwise, there would be no nailing surface behind the ends of the siding. A double stud at each side of the opening will provide the necessary nail backing.

Roof vent installation is carried out in the same flashing manner as plumbing vents and mast heads. The various types of roof vents all have flanges (aprons). About half the flange will go under the shingles while the remainder of the lower part of the flange will lap on top of the shingles.

Constructing a Ridge Vent

Factory-made ridge vents are gaining acceptance in the United States. Those available are made of sheet metal. The continuity between sheet metal and wood is sometimes a drawback to acceptance. The high cost is another factor.

A simple ridge vent can be made of the same materials as the roof. It will blend well. It is an attractive added feature. The added cost is negligible. The cost is comparable to that of power vents, but there is no operational cost whatever.

The roof sheathing is stopped a couple of inches short of the peak. The size of the opening that results is not critical as long as it is equal to or greater than the sum of the openings under the eaves that feed air to it. Construct the vent in the following order (Fig. 10-22).

1. Cut the last sheathing boards to leave an opening of 4 to 6″ across the ridge. Where full-length 16′ rafters are used with a 1″ facia and a 2 × 4 facia backer, no cutting will be required. The four courses of plywood sheathing required will fall short of reaching the peak by an amount that is about right for an opening.
2. Cut a roll of regular window screen to a width adequate to cover the opening from one side to the other. Leave enough screen lapped onto the wood for stapling it to the sheathing. Trim the building-paper underlayment flush with the top of the sheathing. Fold the screen over

the peak and staple both edges. Lap the ends of the screen pieces 3 or 4″. This screen is an inner protector, a sort of second defense against any breakdown that may occur in the outer screen.

3. Cut as many short 2 × 4s as there are rafters (two per truss). Make them 12″ long. The blocks are nailed flat and centered over each rafter. Cut the upper end on a bevel (a flat plumb cut) the same angle as the pitch of the roof. On the framing square this is laid out as a plumb cut on the edge of the 2 × 4 (as compared to the face for a rafter). Make the same cut on the other end, except invert it. This will cause the end grain of the block to be sloped back under the drip edge. It will not be readily seen from the ground, and it will not be as susceptible to deterioration from rainwater or sunshine. Butt two blocks at the peak of each rafter set or truss. Nail them down with two 16d common nails. Stagger each nail to right and left. Slant each nail toward the rafter. Do not drive the nails all the way in until step 4 is started.

4. Cut some more screen strips to a width of 4″ or more. Tuck about an inch to an inch and a half of the edge of the screen under the lower end of the blocks. Let the remainder of the screen lie flat on the roof for the time being on the shingles below the blocks. Staple the screen in three or four places between the blocks at the start of the run where blocks are on 16″ spacing. Use five or six staples between 24″ spaced blocks and rafters. Space the staples evenly apart. Go to the far end of the screen piece and stretch it. Cut it off about 2″ past the last block. Staple it down while holding it tightly stretched. Lap 4 or 5″ of the next piece on top of the screen snugged up under the block. Staple it at its end over the end of the first piece. Move to the end and repeat the procedure. When the end of the vent is reached, all pieces will be taut. Go back and complete stapling between each block. There is no need to vent the overhang area at the ends of the ridge.

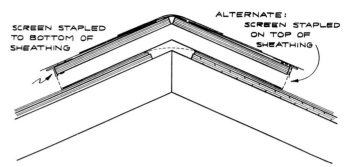

FIGURE 10-23 Section view of the ridge vent. Note the alternative method of attaching the outer screens, also the heavier sheathing.

Next, gently fold the screen up over the end of each block (Fig. 10-23). Do it progressively, moving down the length of the ridge. Keep the bend ahead of the stapling operation a couple of spaces to avoid rolls and puckers in the screen. A short board will be helpful in bending the bottom of the screen uniformly. Hold the board on top of the stapled area. Align it on a line between the lower corner of the blocks. Fold the screen up against the straightedge with the palm of the hand.

5. Block the ends over the unvented lookout with 1 1/2″ boards. Flat 2 × 4s butted against the vent blocks will close off the nonfunctional areas (Fig. 10-24). Do not stop the vent roof short of the ridge ends, as it will present a strange stepped effect and give the appearance of an uncoordinated add-on.

6. The decking for the little miniature roof must be thicker than sheathing. Use 3/4″ plywood or solid boards. Cut a sheet of plywood into four equal parts. *Do not* set a table saw for a 12″ cut. Such a setting will cause the last of the four pieces to be as much as 3/8 to 1/2″ less than 12″ wide. To net four equal near-1′-wide pieces from a sheet of plywood with a hand power saw (''skill saw''), a centerline is snapped down the center of the sheet with a chalk line. Straddle this line with the saw blade and cut.

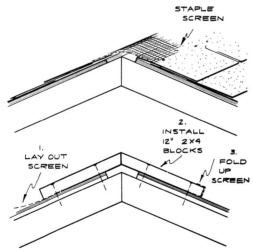

FIGURE 10-22 The first steps to making a very functional and attractive ridge vent on site.

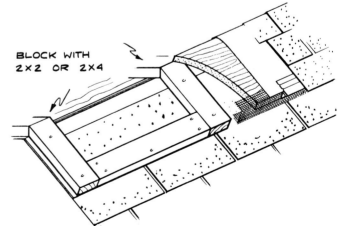

FIGURE 10-24 Extend the vent to the end of the roof. Close the sections over an overhang if the overhang is compartmented with lookouts and blocks.

Lay one half of this sheet on top the other half. Make the edges flush. Each board is now about 1/16″ less than 24″. Find the center on each end and snap another chalk line. The boards should be immobilized, one atop the other with clamps or a couple of partly sunken nails. Again, saw straddle of the line.

Install these sheathing boards on top of the vent blocks. Start one side of the ridge with a full-length sheet. Start the other side with a half-length sheet. Two of each four pieces cut from a sheet of plywood will still have perfectly straight edges. These are referred to as "factory edges." Place these edges on the lower side of the vent roof. Inspect both edges of the other two boards. Pick the straightest edge of each board and place it in the drip edge

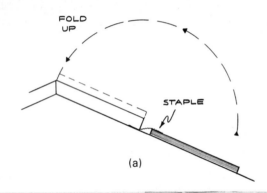

(a)

(b)

FIGURE 10-25   (a) Staple the screen to the underside of the vent deck pieces and carefully rotate them into position on the blocks. (b) Attractive site-built ridge vents.

position also. The lower edges of these boards should be aligned straight with each joint flush. The upper edge does not require perfect lineup.

Care must be taken to fold the screen, with each vent sheathing board, in such a way that no gaps will exist under the sheathing. It is possible to place the board on edge on a couple of 2 × 4 blocks, staple the screen to it, and then carefully pivot it down while maintaining a bearing against the lower end of the blocks (Fig. 10-25a). It is then pivoted back down into its final position and nailed (Fig. 10-25b).

Drip edge is installed next in the same manner as that at the eaves below. The ridge is subject to greater updrafts of wind than elsewhere. A good-quality roof will have a double layer of 15-lb underlayment paper. One will be installed under the drip edge; the second layer is installed over the drip edge. Both layers will pass over the sheathing junction at the ridge in one piece.

The underlayment starter course of shingles need *not* be cut to 9″ like those at the roof eave since each side of the vent will be only about 13″ wide (a 12″ board and 1″ of drip edge overhanging). The first underlayment will be a 5/6 cut shingle uninverted. The first overlay shingle will be a full three-tab shingle. Both the starter and first overlay course should overhang the drip edge about 1/2″. The second course will be laid 4″ above the bottom course. This exposure, if less than the 5″ common shingle exposure, will be approximately midway between the eave and the lower edge of the capping shingles on the vent roof. The third and final course is the cap. The cap on the ridge vent is identical to the cap on a ridge without a vent.

INSTALLING GABLE VENTS

There are several shapes and types of gable vents. Each type requires a particular framing and trimming technique. The prudent builder will determine just how a vent will be fitted into the gable before it is framed. Retrofitting a mistake is awkward and time consuming, as one must work from a ladder or a scaffold.

Centering a rectangular vent is most desirable from a design standpoint. This location poses early considerations in the spacing of the gable studs. An example of this is found when a rectangular vent is fitted between the studs. In this case the space between the studs should be centered under the peak. This will not happen automatically. In fact, it will seldom occur on house spans of even 4′ modules (24, 28′, etc.). The habitual marking off of stud locations starts at POB and progresses across the span. Whether on 16 or 24″ spacing, this means that there will be a stud centered directly under the peak. To provide a space straddling this location, one must consciously space from a centerline out toward the eaves one half space to the right and a half space to the left of center.

Failure to provide this centering of the space will not present a great problem. The gable with a centered stud may be framed with an upper header and a lower rough sill which extends to the studs right and left of the centered stud. Trimmer studs are then installed to close in the rough opening to the rough-opening size of the vent. This framing is the only place in the house frame where the header may be laid in flat. There is no structural load of consequence upon it. There will, however, be much more labor time and material consumption when a center stud must be removed (see Fig. 8-35).

When ordering gable trusses, one must specify whether there is to be a space or a stud at the center. The best tactical position to place oneself in is to furnish a scale drawing or diagram. There is little recourse when a mistake occurs following oral directives. A better method is to make the drawing, make a couple of photocopies, and furnish one to the truss builder at the time of ordering. Hold one for evidence. Date the drawing.

Triangular vents require an opening with only a rough sill (Fig. 10-26). The rafter forms the header. Where an overhang is to be boxed in with a soffit, it will usually be necessary to shim down from the rafters to provide a nail base for the ventilator along its upper rake sides. The shim thickness will be 1 1/2″ where 2 × 4s are used. Allowance must be made for this thickness when building or ordering the truss. The rough sill will need to be in a lower position as a result of the backer shim. When reliable rough-opening specifications are not verifiable, the surest way to get the correct opening size is to buy the vent before laying out the opening. Assemble the vent (the larger ones come in two pieces) and take the measurements from the real object or lay it into the truss jig assembly.

There is a site-built gable vent which is attractive and popular (Fig. 10-27a). It involves extending the gable out under the lookout eave. This overhanging vent is screened on the soffit bottom to provide a horizontal vent. Unfortunately, there is one great disadvantage to this design. It does not work well. Air will enter to some extent when wind is blowing against the gable. It does not exit well at all. The hot air will not move down from the peak and exhaust itself. From the formula standpoint this type of vent can be only rated along with eave vents. It is more a source of air entry than exhaust. Other exiting vents will surely be needed in the roof.

EAVE SOFFIT VENTING

The most effective system for exhausting hot air from an attic is to have a continuous eave vent for air to enter and a continuous ridge vent for the hot air to escape. The next most efficient venting system is to have eave vents in conjunction with other roof vents.

FIGURE 10-26 Triangular vents with flanges to mount them usually require a backing board under the chord or rafter.

(a)

FIGURE 10-27(a) This type of gable vent is stylish but vents poorly.

(b)

FIGURE 10-27(b) Installing soffit panels and eave vents simultaneously.

There are several types of ventilators and systems of construction to provide air access under the eaves. The simplest is the small screened vent unit which provides about 1/2 square foot of opening. There are vinyl and aluminum soffit materials that are perforated throughout to provide air access or exit. A site-built vent incorporates a channel lengthways of the soffit, which is screened (Fig. 10-27b). Any of these systems is better than none, although each has its individual merits.

The unit vent (Fig. 10-28) is an inexpensive aluminum frame with fins backed by screen wire. It is easy to install. One simply holds it upside down against the soffit in a desired location and traces around it. A hole is then jigsawed out about 3/4" inside the outline. The vent may be nailed in place with 4d galvanized nails or held with zinc-coated, continuous-thread panhead screws of 1/2" length.

A drawback with these little unit vents is their limited capacity. To be as effective as a continuous vent there would have to be one placed between each rafter-tail space. The climate characteristics will have an influence on the use of this vent. In northern states a unit vent might be found along the soffit every 8'. In a central zone, 4' spacing is reasonable. In the south and southwest, a continuous vent is a better choice.

Whatever the spacing, the first unit vent along the eave soffit should feed into the first rafter corridor alongside the gable. Figure out how many vents will be used on a side, then space them as equidistant apart as possible. Work it out in advance so that the rafter spaces from one end are no more than one rafter space different from the other end.

Aluminum and vinyl venting soffits are the rule with houses that are sided with this material. The soffit units are usually supplied in 10' lengths with a tongue on one edge and channel on the other. The material is custom cut at the site to lengths that will be assembled crosswise of the eave. This modular material can influence the design of the overhang. 10' is a split modulus that does not coordinate with the 16, 24, 48" modulus. A plancier width of 12, 15, 20, 30, and 40" depth will net economy from a soffit piece 120" (10') long. Conversely, there will be significant waste when the horizontal overhang is designed for plywood, such as 16, 24, or 32", and then covered with aluminum. Even though the primary objective in designing an overhang relates to the angle of the sun and the rafter length modulus, it is frequently possible to add this third consideration, the 10' divisible modulus. For example, it would make a significant cost difference to drop from a 32" overhang down to a 30" one to accommodate a vinyl module.

The vinyl or aluminum vented soffit is as nearly permanent as anything on the market. There is no screen to rust away, no surface to be repainted. It is impervious to rotting. For the very small difference in cost, it will be advantageous to use the vented sheets throughout the ventable area as compared to alternating a vent piece with a solid piece. Solid pieces will then be used only around the corners and up the rake overhang.

Site building a continuous soffit vent is simple and effective, especially where the soffit material is plywood or hard board. Two ribbons of soffit board are nailed to the overhang returns instead of one full coverage board. A parallel opening is left between the two boards (Fig. 10-29). Screen wire is stretched over the opening and stapled. A staple every 16" or so is plenty. Over each edge of the screen a narrow strip board is nailed. Where expense is of no concern, finished shapes of wood are applicable, such as screen mold, lattice boards, or half-round mold. A significant saving is realized by ripping strips from 1" or 2" lumber.

The staples holding the screen should be "popped" in between the rafter returns. The wood strips cannot be effectively nailed between the returns because the soffit board is too flexible. Therefore, they will be nailed on the return. Since the nail will go through the screen at this place, there is no need of a staple there. A power stapler, the small type used in cabinetry assembly, works well for attaching the strips even between the solid points.

The screen will not last forever. The homebuilder/owner may opt for screws to hold the strips. Screws will make the disassembly task simpler when the time comes to replace the screen. Rust-resistant zinc-plated screws or galvanized screws will resist rusting.

The width of the screen opening should be as wide as the vent formula requires, or wider. The greater the entry capacity, the greater will be the exhausting rate potential. There is no point, however, in having a much wider opening than that which exists in the area under the roof above the exterior wall plate or above the insulation container. Whatever distance is present over the insulation

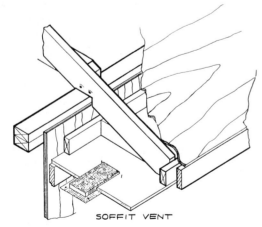

SOFFIT VENT

FIGURE 10-28 Unit vents in the eave soffit provide about 1/2 square foot per vent, are reasonable in cost and are simple to install.

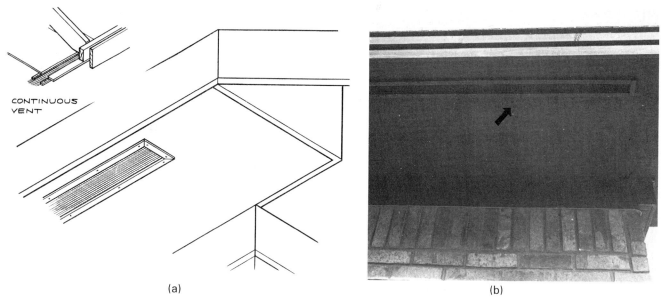

(a)   (b)

FIGURE 10-29 (a) Continuous soffit vent built on site is a very efficient means of taking in fresh air. (b) Most effective continuous soffit vent built on-site.

container will be an indicator for sizing the vent width. Screen wire itself has a blocking affect on air passage. Therefore, the screened area in the soffit may be a 1/2" to 1" wider than the passage over the wall.

WATER-SHEDDING EQUIPMENT

Uncontrolled water can cause inconvenience to people and damage to materials. Rainwater that cascades off a roof during a thunderstorm or just drizzles off for an extended period of time has to go somewhere. How it gets to a suitable destination is usually up to the designer of a house. If the way water is handled is not specified on the plan, it may end up in the lap of the house owner.

The author has been involved, as an expert witness, in several lawsuits where water was the culprit but where the contractor was held negligent and responsible because he did not provide adequately for its proper disposal. In one case the grading of a backyard was not in accordance with the plans. Inadequate runoff slant was provided. One night a thunderstorm caused a heavy rainfall. The rain from the roof and the flat yard ran into the basement window wells. It saturated the new fill dirt around the foundation. In a few hours the pressure was too great. Forty percent of the basement wall, the entire back side and partway along each end, collapsed. The concrete blocks were flung into the basement with such force that they crushed the new furnace, the water heater, and all the bathroom fixtures in their way. The court held for the plaintiff (the homeowner) in as much as the gravel bed below and above the footing

drain tile and the backyard grading did not meet the graphic and specified conditions stated on the plan. Gutters on the eaves alone might have directed enough water off the lot to have prevented the tragedy.

It does not take a lot of rain to damage a foundation under certain circumstances. One main theme emerges. Get the water away from the house as far as possible, as quickly as possible. There are traditional and basic ways to accomplish the objective. Sloping the yard away from the house is standard practice. A house on a natural slope or on a hillside will require recontoured valleys and drainage recessions on the high side to carry the water to the sides of the house where it can proceed downhill, around and away from the house. Additional ground tiles, "French drains," around a footing are added protection to keep water away from a foundation.

Gutters and Downspouts

The water that is shed from a roof where rain is frequent must be collected by gutters and diverted by downspouts. Gutters have generally been available in two basic shapes for over half a century, the half-round and the "ogee." Both shapes could be purchased in several widths. A large roof requires a wider and deeper gutter to accommodate the greater quantity of water that will be shed.

The half-round gutter is seldom seen on new construction anymore. It was fastened with twisted wire hangers or flat straps on the surface of the eave sheathing. Sometimes the straps were found nailed to the surface of the shingles. Rusting straps and the droopy nature of this

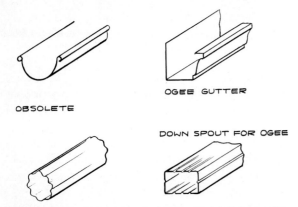

OBSOLETE

OGEE GUTTER

DOWN SPOUT FOR OGEE

FIGURE 10-30 The old half-round gutter has been phased out in favor of the more graceful ogee pattern (O.G.).

gutter style caused it to be replaced by the more stylish *ogee* shape (Fig. 10-30).

The ogee shape incorporates a laid-over U channel at the top outer edge to give stiffness. Below the channel a graceful elongated S-curved face flows to the flat bottom. The back side is straight, which makes it possible to fasten the gutter flat against the facia of the eave. Where metal drip edge is used, the back edge, which is taller than the front edge, can be snugged up under the vertical face of the drip edge. The little flare out on the eave drip edge bottom makes it a simple task to slip the back of the gutter up under.

The most common attachment system employs a spike and ferrule (Fig. 10-31). The spikes come in several lengths to accommodate different gutter widths. The nail must pass through the eave facia and into the end grain of a rafter tail when no backer board is present.

The *ferrule* is a tubular-rolled piece of galvanized sheet metal. Its length will be the same as the width of the gutter. To hang the gutter, the ferrule is wedged into the U and held at right angles to the gutter sides and horizontal. The point of the nail is aimed over the ferrule location, which in turn is aimed at the center of the rafter tail. One

must hold the nail and at the same time maintain pressure with the heel of the same hand against the face of the channel so that the ferrule does not dislodge. Strike the nail a sharp blow. This will cause the nail to puncture the channel. The nail is pushed through the ferrule to rest against the backside of the gutter. The ferrule, with the nail inside, is repositioned precisely over the rafter tail and driven home.

Facia boards that are not backed with 2 × 4 nail grounds make it imperative that the nail seats in the rafter tail. The nail should penetrate deeply. Three inches or more will not be excessive in the end grain of the rafter. Facia that is backed by 2 × 4s can be nailed anywhere along the line. Gutters of 4″ width may be successfully held in place with a nail every 4′ along the gutter. Larger gutters may benefit from nails spaced 32″ apart, especially where ice habitually freezes or builds up.

Slanting the gutter over its length will make the drainage more effective and prolong the life of the gutter. Where downspouts are installed at each end, the gutter will be placed high in the center and lower at the ends. Some builders and homeowners object to a gutter that is out of parallel with the eave. In such a situation the gutter may be installed perfectly parallel. It may require additional downspouts or wider gutters as the draining will take a little longer in a level gutter. Water will also stand in the level gutter, cause rust and thereby shorten the life of a galvanized gutter (a pretty good rationale in favor of vinyl).

Downspouts are the vertical pipes that conduct the water to the ground level (Fig. 10-32). A house with any amount of eave will require two elbows and a return pipe under the plancier. The return pipe is slanted downward a little toward the house. Where the water is ground spilled, a third elbow is needed at the bottom of the downspout to

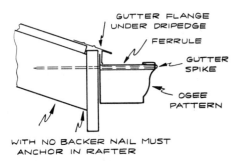

GUTTER FLANGE
UNDER DRIPEDGE

FERRULE

GUTTER
SPIKE

OGEE
PATTERN

WITH NO BACKER NAIL MUST
ANCHOR IN RAFTER

FIGURE 10-31 Spikes and ferrules or straps are used to hold the ogee gutter. The long spike must penetrate the rafter end where no facia backers of 1 1/2″ thickness exist.

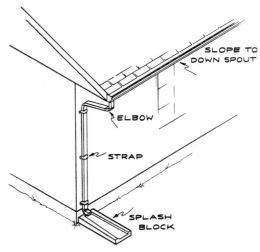

SLOPE TO
DOWN SPOUT

ELBOW

STRAP

SPLASH
BLOCK

10-32 Downspouts, elbows, and splash pads take the water on its way away from the foundation.

direct the water away. No elbow is needed when the spout is directed into an underground drain pipe with a vertical section.

A splash pad is a concrete spillway used under the bottom elbow. It prevents the water from eroding the earth away. A splash pad form or two will be handy to have when any concrete is being poured on the site. There is usually a little ready-mix left in the hopper after a job is completed. It can be used to make splash pads at no cost. A splash pad form is made purposely long. When the concrete runs out, a stop board is placed wherever the "mud" ends in the low end of the form. A ready-made form is handy, but a simple staked form in the ground will do. In haste a form can be assembled in a minute or two simply by standing some scraps of 2 × 6 on edge and backing them up with concrete blocks.

Slant the surface of the splash pad from rear to front. Indent the surface with a pointed trowel forming a water channel. Make the channel fan shaped. Leave a lip at the top. Before the concrete work is done around the house, there will be plenty of splash pads completed to supply each downspout.

Painting galvanized gutters is practical and possible. There is a long-standing myth that galvanized sheet metal will not hold paint. This will be the case if certain preparatory steps are not adhered to. The gutter components leave the factory with a light coating of an oily protectorate. When painting must be done soon after the house construction, it will be necessary to cleanse the metal with vinegar or an approved acid. Where time is not an element, the gutters and downspouts can simply be left exposed to the rain and sun for a couple of months. The weather will effectively wash away and bleach off the coating that interferes with paint adherence.

Painting the gutter and other parts has two objective elements. One is to prolong the life of the metal. The other is to sustain the aesthetic continuity of the house by blending the gutter with the same color as the siding.

Several years of life can be added to the gutter by keeping the insides covered with paint and keeping the gutter clean and empty of debris. A rust-retardant type of paint will be put on the insides of the gutter. Initially, two coats are warranted. After this, a single refresher coat is put on periodically or whenever the first sign of deterioration is observed, such as peeling, bubbling, or cracking. Any color will do, as the interior of the gutter is out of sight.

Coordinate the color scheme on the exterior of the rain-carrying system with the house. Blend the gutters with the facia and trim. Do not use contrasting colors. Such a contrast will make the downspouts and elbows stand out as unattractive add-ons. Above all, do not use Spanish tile red as a final coat. It is in the category of a primer. Such a color will detract from the beauty and continuity of most house colors.

Some gutter shapes, such as the ogee, will add to the beauty and line of an eave when blended with the same color theme. Where contrasting color is used, the effect will be to exaggerate narrow lines, unparallel slants and protrusions (downspouts, elbows, attachment clamps, etc.). The basic function of the gutter system is to provide a service, not to be an object of beauty. Blend it in with the same color as its background.

REVIEW TOPICS

1. Explain how to join metal drip edge at the ends so that there is no break in the stiffness.
2. Describe the relationship of the underlayment paper to the drip edge at the lower eave and at the rake eave.
3. Describe a method of joining metal drip edge at the peak of a roof so that there is no crack exposed and the two pieces stay together.
4. How should composition shingles be laid when there is a factory warranty?
5. Describe a simple mistake that can be made when measuring to cut an underlayment piece of paper for a roof valley. Explain how this error can be avoided.
6. Describe, as though instructing a beginner, all the cuts that should be made for the first starter shingle for the left-hand corner of a roof.
7. Explain precisely where to place the nails, how to hold the shingle, and how to drive each nail in a six-nail pattern.
8. Explain how to avoid a narrow exposure with the last course of common shingles at the ridge by anticipating and planning ahead.
9. Compute the number of cap tabs needed for a ridge 52' long.
10. Describe a saddle on a roof. Explain how to build one.
11. Explain how to construct a continuous ridge vent on site.
12. Comment on the advantages of a continuous soffit vent coupled with a continuous ridge vent.
13. Explain how one determines the direction that capping shingles should face.
14. Describe the rain carrying systems used to collect and dispose of rainwater from a roof.

Chapter 11

EXTERIOR COMPLETION————————

CLOSING IN THE HOUSE

In the sequence of building a structure where wood is the primary material, the weather will play an important role. Rain, snow, and ice can play havoc with building materials. Therefore, a primary objective is to close in the house as quickly as possible. The first goal of closing in is to roof the structure so that no rain will enter via the top. The second goal is to install windows and doors for further protection of the interior of the house. Most of the roof and floor deck sheathing materials in use today are laminates and wafer types held together with waterproof glue. The glue is of high quality and impervious to water, but the wood itself will soak up moisture, permitting its fibers to separate. Such separation takes place readily where knotholes are present on a surface layer of plywood sheathing. Edges where end grain is exposed are particularly vulnerable. These types of fabricated sheathing are not intended to resist or withstand repeated soakings over extended periods of exposure. Once the roofing is completed and the windows and doors (temporary or permanent) have been installed, the structure is said to be closed in.

Many builders prefer to hang a temporary door on the entrance through which materials will continue to be carried. There is much to be said in favor of this technique, as it will usually avoid damage to the permanent door jamb and casement. An old door from a salvage yard or a cut-down piece of plywood will serve. Where the door will be carried from job to job, surface hinges may be screwed to the door and nailed to the rough opening with duplex form nails.

WINDOW INSTALLATION

There are several window casement designs on the market which will require particular installation techniques. Regardless of any uniqueness, common objectives exist. The unit should be hung plumb, level, and square. If it is an opening-type sash, it should open and close flawlessly. It should be supported under the lower corners. It should not depend solely on nails through its flanges for support.

Windows with integral jambs and sills are placed in the opening from the outside, as are flange types. The frame is first centered in the opening at the bottom. A level is placed on the windowsill (not on the sash). This is one of the few places in a house where a 24 or 28″ level is used effectively. Place shims under a vertical jamb which checks low until the windowsill checks level. Place shims above the ends of the jambs under the header. The sill and the headboard should now check level. Place the level against the vertical jamb on one side. Move the frame to the right or left at the top until the jamb checks plumb. Check the other jamb. It should check plumb also. If it does not check plumb, measure the distance between the jambs at the bottom and the top. If the distances are not identical, the frame is not a perfect rectangle. In this case, compromise by moving the top of the frame in a direction that will cause

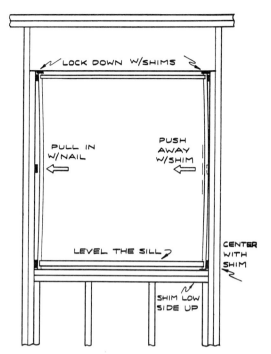

FIGURE 11-1 Place shims to hold jambs straight whether bowed in or bowed out.

the level to read the same amount in or out of plumb on each side. In other words, this imperfect window rectangle will be plumb on its vertical centerline.

Should the top and bottom widths be nearly perfect but the frame will not check plumb on both sides, it is likely that one or both sides are bowed. Hold a straight-edged board of a length close to the window height against the frame. Locate the bow. If the frame is bowed toward the rough-opening trimmer, you are in luck. Simply shim between the jamb and trimmer until it checks straight and plumb (Fig. 11-1). It will be necessary to place shims at the edge of the top and bottom of the frame on the opposite side to prevent the whole frame from moving over.

If the frame bows in toward the sash, a more difficult problem is faced. Ultimately, that frame will have to be held straight permanently with shims and a nail or two through the jamb. It is better to do the alignment with a clamp temporarily than with a nail. In any case the distance across the vertical jambs cannot be less than it is at the top or bottom because the sash will not operate properly.

Should it not be possible to plumb the vertical jambs because one of them ends up against the top face of the wall trimmer before it is plumb, the bottom of the frame will need to be moved away from that side of the opening. The best possible position of the frame will be attained when the opposite corners from top to bottom are equally spaced away from the trimmers (upper right and lower left, upper left and lower right).

A final check is made in two ways. Use a framing square in the lower corners of the jamb. Each corner should check square. Any variation will be cause to reset the shims until squareness is attained. Do not alter the levelness of the sill after its initial setting. When satisfied that all is square and plumb and the frame is solidly held by shims, operate the sash to see if it functions smoothly, without binding. Under a double-hung sash there should be no crack above the sill. Check a casement window from the outside. A casement window swings out on vertical hinges like a door. The clearance between the window frame and the jamb should be parallel on all sides. Any variation is cause to reset the casing. Perfect installation is the essence of trouble-free operation in the years to come.

Fastening the casing (the exterior trim) or the flange is next in order. Wooden casement trim is called brickmold. It is prudent to predrill this molding for the nails to prevent splitting. Only rust-resistant nails should be used. Hot-dipped galvanized are best. The length will be dependent on the type of backing behind the mold. Soft sheathing such as Styrofoam or blackboard does not provide adequate backing.

A 1 × 2 surround of wood should be nailed around the rough opening before the frame wall is sheathed (Fig. 11-2). Where a table saw is available, this surround material can be ripped from precut stud lumber or any scrap dimension lumber (1 1/2″ thick) most economically.

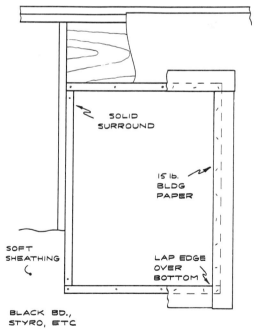

FIGURE 11-2 With soft sheathings a solid wood surround of the same thickness is nailed around the opening and then covered with a 4″ strip of building paper.

A seal (2 to 4″ strip of 15-lb building paper) is stapled over the surround and sheathing. Start at the bottom. Lap the side strips over the top edge of the bottom strips. Lap the top strip over the top ends of the side strips. These strips help protect against infiltration of unwanted air.

Where wooden surrounds are used, a 10d hot-dipped galvanized cup head or casing nail will be adequate to hold brick molding. Over blackboard (no surrounds) a 16d hot-dipped casing nail will probably be required to get adequate penetration into the wood behind the sheathing. Place a nail within 2 to 3″ from each corner. Space the other nails about 10 to 12″ apart. Each nail will be close to the outer edge of the brick mold and slanted toward the trimmer stud behind. Predrilled holes will prevent splitting. Cup heads and casing heads are not large. Keep the tap hole diameter smaller than the nail shank so that the heads will have adequate holding capacity.

The flanged window has a little less leeway for nailing. The rough-in size listed for this window style is often larger than necessary if a building is quite plumb. The flanges are of minimum width to cover such a wide gap between the window jamb. With excellent plumbness there is adequate flange to reach onto the surround. An opening that is not quite plumb may result in a flange whose edge just barely reaches onto the surrounding surface. To accommodate this minimum coverage at certain points on the flange, holes must be drilled close to the edges of the flange. Big-headed nails are best. A 1 1/2″ galvanized roofing nail slanted toward the solid wood will be a good choice. Unlike the brickmold, an aluminum or plastic flange should be drilled with holes larger than the nail shank so that there is no bind and the nail can be slanted adequately. When nailing the flange a guard should be held between the nail and the jamb. A piece of sheet metal or thin Masonite or plywood will serve to protect the edge of the jamb from a wayward hammer blow.

DOOR INSTALLATION

The technique of "hanging" a door has undergone several modifications since the coming of hollow-core prehung doors. As little as four decades ago the method was to install a wooden jamb as plumb and square as possible. Then the door was fitted to the jamb by planing off the edges and ends. This traditional installation method seldom netted a perfectly square door. The hinges were morticed (chiseled in flush) with hand tools. Some of the older installations had morticed jambs for the hinge butt with a surface-mounted hinge leaf on the door. This was called a face butt or half butt. These old hinges are valuable antiques now. They coordinate with porcelain door knobs.

Today's carpenter will usually hang the jamb and door as a unit. The door serves as a large squaring device, which facilitates a better job. Hinges are morticed into the jamb and door before the unit is installed. Hinge morticing jigs make it possible to rout a perfectly aligned door-to-jamb relationship. A power router does the cutting. Lacking this professional setup, a skilled amateur can still do an adequate job with hammer and chisel and the proper information.

Hinge Position

One of the primary visual indicators which exposes amateur or nonconformist construction technique is to see hinges on doors that are not positioned according to the industry standard. The Stanley Builders Kit probably did more to standardize hinge location on passage doors than any other factor in the history of construction. This placement jig has several options intended for different hinge quantities and sizes.

The Seven-Eleven Rule

When two hinges are used on a lightweight door or as an economy measure the "seven-eleven" rule is used. This means that the upper edge of the top hinge will be 7″ down from the door top. The lower edge of the bottom hinge is 11″ above the door bottom.

The "five and ten" rule is used for doors with three hinges. Three hinges are required on a heavy door such as a solid framed panel door or a solid slab door. Some good-quality homes where economy is not the objective will have three hinges on all passage doors. The five and ten formula places the top hinge down 5″, the lower hinge up 10″ from the bottom, and a third hinge centered between the two.

Whether the hinges are set with a jig or by measurement the seven-eleven and the five and ten rule should be adhered to routinely; otherwise, the builder's knowledge is suspect and may create cause to doubt other more significant features of the construction.

Positioning the hinge butt across the edge of the door relates to the casement thickness that will project beyond the jamb (beyond the door and wall surface). The pivot point of the hinge pin determines how far out the door surface will be swung. The door must clear the casement trim; otherwise, the hinges will be torn loose. The Stanley jig and other jig brands control this location of the hinge butt automatically. A distance of 1 1/8″ across the door edge will be adequate to clear casement moldings up to 5/8″. For thicker moldings keep in mind that the vertical centerline of the hinge pin must be beyond the surface of the door at least as much as the thickness of the casement trim; otherwise, the trim board will present a fulcrum to the door surface when the door is opened to its extremity and the hinge screws will be torn out.

Morticing the door and jamb requires craftsmanship and precision. Any misalignment, no matter how small, will cause stress on the screws. Eventually, the screws will pull loose, having stripped out their anchor holes. Perfect alignment exists when the pins of all the hinges are on a common axis, a centerline that runs vertically through the center of them all.

Perfect alignment is achieved by understanding and accepting certain principles and by adopting a perfectionist state of mind. These are the principles:

- Each hinge must be parallel with both the door edges and the jamb edges.
- The setback of each hinge butt must be identical to all others on both the door and the jamb.
- Corresponding distances between the hinges must be identical on the door and jamb.
- The mortices on the door edge must be a minimum of 1/8″ higher than on the jamb to provide clearance above the door when closed.

Principle 4 deserves comment. The Stanley jig has a little metal flipper on the end. Its purpose is to gauge this clearance. The flipper is turned down to hook over the door top. On the jamb its outer surface is aligned flush with the lower edge of the top jamb dado. The metal flipper gauge is about 1/16″ thick. This is not enough clearance between the door and the jamb. Two or three coats of varnish on each surface will close the clearance gap considerably. The slightest swelling of the wood from moisture in the house is apt to cause a sticking door. A 1/8″ minimum space will usually prove more trouble-free from the outset.

This is a good place to caution against omitting the finishing (sealing the wood) of the top and bottom of doors. A most important element in the prevention of door swelling is to make certain that all wood surfaces are well sealed. The most vulnerable part of wood is the open end grain. On a door this is found on the top and bottom at the corners where the vertical door frame ends are exposed. Any door, whether or not trimmed at the top or bottom, should be sealed. Because these surfaces are not seen, they are frequently left unfinished. These unseen surfaces do not necessarily require cosmetic stain; nonetheless, they should be sealed with varnish together with the rest of the door.

Setting a Door Lock

Door locksets are referred to as entrance, passage, or closet types. An entrance set is the locking type furnished with two keys. Locksets can usually be purchased in quantities with common keys. This is a convenience where several exterior entrances exist. One key will open all doors. It also provides additional keys at the outset so that duplicates do not have to be made for various members of the family.

Passage door sets are available with or without locks. The locking type is tripped from one side only and

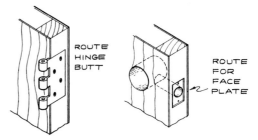

FIGURE 11-3 Standard door hinge and latch locations.

is referred to as a privacy lock. This type is customarily installed on bathroom doors and sometimes on adult bedroom doors. All other passage doors will have a simple latching function.

A closet door may be secure with a regular passage set that includes a knob on both sides, a bolt, and a strike plate. A simplified closet latch set is one that includes only a dummy knob. Spring catches or magnetic catches are used to hold the door shut in the same manner as a cabinet door.

Installation of a lockset (Fig. 11-3) is covered by an instruction sheet furnished by the manufacturer. Although a person may have installed many locksets before, it will be wise to glance over the instruction sheet when a different brand is encountered. The specifications may vary.

Placement of the lockset is important. There will be a template in the box which is to be folded around the edge of the door. There are prick points to establish the hole centers for the bolt and the shaft. The height of the set location is not usually specified. Like the hinges, there is a standard location for the lockset that should be followed. It is 36″ above the bottom of the door.

Beveling the door edge will usually be required where no more than 1/8″ of clearance exists. A tightly fitted door may have clearance in the closed position but will fail to clear while being shut. This is because the diagonal distance from the hinge pivot point to the back edge of the latch edge is greater than the face width of the door. To overcome this clearance problem, a bevel is planed on the lockset edge. The bevel need only be enough so that clearance exists for the edge to clear the jamb. Too much bevel will cause an alignment problem where the bolt plate seats in the door edge. Regardless of how much bevel exists, the bolt plate will still remain square with the door face. Therefore, a slight misalignment in parallelism will exist between the bolt plate and the door edge. The bolt runs into the door parallel to the door faces and on a centerline with the door thickness. Therefore, the bolt face will be square, at right angles, to the door faces. The bolt face cannot be angled to fit flush with a beveled edge. In order for no edge of the bolt face to protrude above the wood surface, the edge on the low side of the bevel will be morticed deep enough for the plate edge to be flush. On the high side of the bevel the plate will be slightly below the surface. The bolt face mortice should be made before beveling the door when using a power router. The router can then bear on the full surface of the square edge. The mortice will need to be deep enough to take into consideration the amount of wood that will be removed by beveling the edge.

In order not to alter the doorknob distance from the edge, one must adapt by moving the knob shaft hole farther from the door edge an amount equal to the bevel. Where the bevel is slight (1/16″ or less) the adaptation is made by placing the punch prick template on the back side of the door after it has been beveled.

Where one is willing to accept a wider crack between the door edge and the jamb (about 3/16 to 1/4″) no beveling is required. The marking template can be used on either face of the door, and the bolt face will be flush all around its four edges.

Hanging the Jamb

The door jamb is hung in basically the same manner as a window casement. It is centered, squared, plumbed, shimmed, and nailed through the jambs. Unlike the usual window, a door receives a horizontal shock each time it is shut forcibly (slammed). The vertical door jambs require adequate anchoring to the trimmers to withstand this direction of force. Nails of adequate length and diameter are driven through the jambs and directly under or through the shims. Plywood shims will split the least. Three-mil and 1/4″ panel scraps are good. Where two or more pieces of wood are used to build up an adequate thickness, a little glue between each will prevent them from falling away when split by a nail.

Nails to use may include cuphead finish nails or casing nails of a 6d to 8d size. Box nails with their larger heads are most effective but should only be used where the door stop will cover them. Since the shims are frequently placed directly behind the hinge mortices, this provides an index for locating three of the nails on the hinge jamb. No more nails are used between the hinges unless backed by shims because a nail in an unbacked location will pull the jamb out of line. Where holding power of the trimmer is inferior due to the softness of the wood, the builder will opt for a minimum of six nails placed one directly above and one below the hinge mortice locations and 4 nails equally spaced between.

Exterior doors require clearance at the bottom for a sealing sill. This type of threshold has a replaceable rubber or vinyl insert. The simplest type mounts on top of a wood threshold sill. Another style is wider and may incorporate a weather seal which is adjustable up and down under the door. A prehung steel door usually has this type. The prefabricated aluminum threshold is available in several heights. This is helpful where the framed opening is excessive in height. A taller threshold can provide a solution.

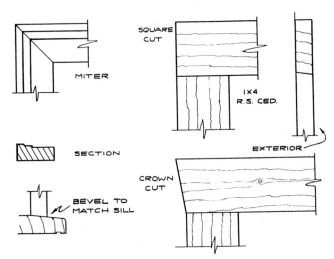

FIGURE 11-4   Contemporary door and window casing is mitered at the top corners and beveled at the bottom on the sill. Rough-sawn cedar trim is usually square cut or crown beveled at the head.

Trimming styles for exterior doors (Fig. 11-4) vary according to the architectural design of the house. Where patterned casing is used, such as brickmold, the top corners will be mitered. The bottoms will have a square cut receding bevel that matches the downward and outward slant of the threshold sill. The rain-shedding principle should be practiced with all exterior materials, including trimming boards. Any horizontal surfaces that are exposed to rain will deteriorate at an accelerated rate. Window and door sills are particularly vulnerable.

Board-and-batten rough-sawn houses will likely have a simple 1 × 4 casing surround of the same material as the siding. Frequently, the headboard will extend out over the sideboards at the top corners. The sideboards will butt under the headboard with a square-cut end. The top end of these sideboards should be beveled about 5 to 10° and installed in a drain posture. The top board is beveled to match on both upper and lower edges. This is accomplished expediently where a jointer is on hand. It is no great task with a hand plane and soft wood such as rough-sawn cedar. The bevel on the top ends of the sideboards is matched to mate under the edge bevel on the headboard. For this job of mating a T bevel is a handy tool to have for checking the bevels. The 2 to 4″ strips of black building paper are stapled around the door jamb the same as on the window openings, to seal against infiltration.

Nailing any kind of trim around a wood door jamb is a particular task at best. Some of the nails will be close to the inner edges of the casing. These must be slanted to enter the jamb. The surface contact area on the jamb is small. The casing is sometimes set back 1/2″ to form a rabbet, a door stop for a wood screen door. Metal combination storm and screen doors will not require so much dropback, as they are surface mounted through flanges.

Nails along the outer edges of the casing are slanted toward the trimmer stud. There should be two nails, one on each edge, within 2 to 3″ of each end of each casing board. Do not place them directly opposite each other. Space all other nails about 12 to 16″ apart on each side. Stagger them a little from side to side. For example, after the two top and bottom nails, the next nail will be placed on the outer edge at the midpoint of the height. The remaining space above and below will contain two more nails each on third points. On a brickmold style casing this will average out to a nail just under 12″ apart. The nails on the inner edge may be staggered down from the top miter cut so that each will be about 2″ lower than the outer nail position.

Lock the mitered corner joints at the top as soon as a couple of set nails have been placed in each of the three casing boards (Fig. 11-5). A small finishing nail (5, 6, or 7d) is driven down through the top of the headboard into the end of the side-board miter. Off-center this nail a little. Drive another nail through the edge of the side board into the top-board miter. Off center this nail in the opposite direction so that it does not contact the top nail. These nails will assist the corner joint to maintain its surface alignment while the remainder of the fastening takes place.

Plumbing, leveling, and squaring a door jamb are more critical than for a window. A window can tilt in or out at the top in conjunction with an unplumb wall with little affect on its functioning as long as its surface is on a straight plane. A door, by comparison, will swing one way or another (toward closed or open) if the hinged side is not vertical both in the direction of the wall and at right angles to the wall. It is irritating to a homeowner to have to use a door stop to keep a door open.

Adjusting for verticality in an unplumb rough opening is difficult (one where the top of the wall tilts in or out). One cannot set a jamb very far from parallel with the wall without causing major alignment problems with interior and exterior wall coverings. A wall frame that is more than

1/8″ out of plumb from interior to exterior should be rectified, at least at the door openings before proceeding to install a door jamb.

The side jambs must be parallel vertically as well as plumb. It would seem to be obvious that if both jambs were plumb, they would also be parallel. Here the element of human frailty enters the picture. A 4 or 6′ level is the standard tool for plumbing the edge of the jambs. The eye must center the bubble between the two lines precisely the same everytime the level is used. It is impossible to be that perfect and consistent given the nature of the instrument. A final check should be made everytime by standing a little way off and sighting across the edges of the jambs to ascertain their parallelism. This is often difficult or impossible where the door is in a confined area. Also, the distance between the jambs can be checked for uniformity at vertical intervals of about 12″.

Door sill installation method has undergone some transition over the years. The remodeler will find many old homes where an oak threshold was cut down into the floor header and joists. These members were chiseled out to accept the sill in a position that mated the top of the sill with the top of an oak or maple floor. Most modern door frame installations will have the sill resting on top of the subfloor. The underlayment floor layer butts the edge of the sill. A certain amount of the sill will protrude above the underlayment. This space is filled with carpet pad and carpet or ceramic tile. The threshold sealer provides enough more height to permit the door bottom to clear the carpeting.

The sequence of door jamb installation is the same as that of a window.

1. Center the sill and shim the lower corners of the jambs.
2. Plumb the side jambs.
3. Shim the side jambs at the top.
4. Shim between the header and the jamb tops.
5. Shim behind each hinge location. Make sure that the jamb is straight (not bowed toward or away from the opening).
6. Shim behind the striker plate.
7. Nail the jambs.
8. Nail the brickmold to the wall.

Bowed Jambs

Jambs that insist on bowing into or away from the door opening will have to be held in position with additional shims and a well-placed nail (Fig. 11-6). If the jamb needs to be bent toward the opening, a finish nail may be used to hold the jamb and the shims in place. Where the jamb has to be pulled toward the trimmer stud, a nail with a head is needed. Hot-dipped galvanized nails of 8d or 10d size or annular ringed flooring nails will be a good choice for the

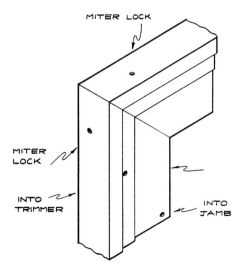

FIGURE 11-5 Brickmold casing is locked at mitered corner with a vertical and a horizontal staggered nail.

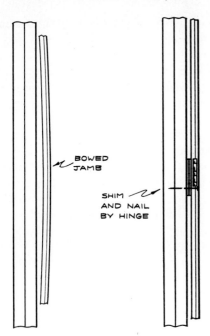

BOWED
JAMB

SHIM
AND NAIL
BY HINGE

FIGURE 11-6   A shim maintains the desired distance between the jamb and the door trimmer. A headed nail holds the bowed jamb in against the trimmer stud.

latter condition. Holding power is the basic requirement. Sink the nail head slightly below the surface with a 1/4″ metal drift punch. Putty over the head before painting. The objective at completion of the installation is to have a door with parallel clearance on the sides and top, a surface that is uniformly flush with the jambs all around, and a sill that seals tightly against infiltration. Obviously, the door should open and close flawlessly without great effort, and it should stand still in any position.

STORM DOOR INSTALLATION

There are three types of doors from which to choose that are hung on the outside of the exterior door jamb. The simple wood-framed screen door is in limited demand. Its days were numbered when the emphasis on fuel conservation became universal. The old style screen door is still obtainable, however, and comes in standard door sizes. The full-picture-window glass door takes care of cold season needs. It is also prevalent in areas where utility use cycles from heat to air conditioning with minimum calendar days between. The combination door is the most adaptable door in use. This design incorporates both a screen and storm sash so that it can readily be changed from a closed winter mode to a warm-weather ventilating position.

Installing a wood-framed screen door is quite simple. Where butt hinges are used, the hinge butts are morticed into the screen door edge first. The door is then held in place in the casing with temporary spacing shims. The

first attempt may reveal a need for planing. A minimum clearance of 1/8″ should be maintained on the top, bottom, and latch side after the door is permanently attached. When indexing the hinge butt mortices to the jamb, keep in mind that the hinge leaf thickness has not yet been inletted. It will add that much thickness to the clearance on the latch side after the hinge butts have been seated in their mortices.

Marking the hinge leaf locations on the jamb is most accurately done with a sharp thin-bladed knife. Press a slit into the jamb corner right at the edges of each hinge. A very sharp hard lead pencil will also suffice. The old-style wood drafting pencil in a lead grade from 5H to 9H makes an excellent marker for precision work.

Two other forms of hinges are available for wood screen doors. One is a half-surface-mount type. The surface-mount leaf is screwed on the face of the door, and the concealed leaf is morticed into the jamb. With this hinge type the order of installing is reversed. The hinges are morticed and screwed to the jamb first. The door is then blocked in place and the surface-mount hinge leaves are screwed to the surface.

Another hinge type is the full surface mount. These can be obtained with or without integral door closing springs. The full-surface-mount hinge is used only on flat casing. It is considered aesthetically offensive to inlet a surface leaf into the contoured surface of brick molding, thereby destroying the flow lines.

Full glass and combination storm doors on the modern market are made of aluminum or steel. They come complete with a flanged jamb. The entire unit is surface mounted with screws through predrilled holes. The flanges will mount on either brickmold or flat casing. Hang the unit with the door closed, being sure to maintain a parallel clearance at the top and latch side.

SIDING

The trim and siding phase comes next. Following the closing in of the openings, it becomes next in importance to cover the wall-sheathing materials against the deteriorating effects of sun and rain and against the potential of construction abuse. House frames sheathed with blackboard and particularly Styrofoam sheets are especially vulnerable to falling ladders, punctures from scaffold planks, and so on.

At this stage (closed in) some flexibility exists for priority setting and dealing with external influences. For example, on inclement days one can work on the interior provided that there are materials there awaiting installation. On good days work may go forward wherever one chooses. A little preplanning will make the working conditions more enjoyable. For example, when installing siding during hot weather it is often possible to work on the house side that is shaded and simply move around the house as the sun moves. In cold months one can reverse the technique and manage to stay in the warming rays of the sun except on the north side. There is a practical consideration to this technique also. Bricks or stone should not be laid in the direct rays of the sun on hot days if it can be avoided (it usually can). Such a practice will cause the moisture to be quickly baked out of the mortar and bricks. Adhesion is poor and the mortar will be weaker than if it had cured slowly.

Types of Siding

There are many types of siding of various shapes and materials. Wood and stone were the original natural materials. Man has fabricated many different types of materials since the days of laying one stone on another or one log on another.

Structural categories of most residences are *masonry* or *wood framed*. A masonry residence uses masonry products for both structural and veneer covering. In this classification, there are houses built of concrete blocks and those of double-walled brick (solid or cavity type). The wood-framed category includes houses that appear to be brick masonry but which are in reality brick veneered. Brick veneer or masonry veneer includes those structures which are framed and basically built of wood. The veneer is merely a covering that bears none of the weight of the structure. The brick or stone is then classified as a siding. Most homes being built today with brick and stone facing are of the veneer design because of the superior capacity for insulating the cavity and face of the frame wall. Conversely, most large apartment houses and commercial buildings are masonry and steel because of superiority in fire protection and permanency.

Wood sidings can be had in a variety of types, shapes, and sizes (Fig. 11-7). The intent of this text is not ency-clopedic; therefore, the concentration will be on installation techniques for common types, and on significant pitfalls.

Clapboard

Clapboard (bevel siding) has been around for a long time. In its original form the homebuilder simply lapped the lower edge of one board over the top edge of the board below, thereby creating a water-shedding effect. The design ultimately developed into a cross-section shape that tapered from a thick bottom to a thin top edge. Two rules are worthy of memorization and practice.

- Nail into solid backing (wood).
- Nail only through the outer layer of siding (just above the board below).

Few houses under construction today will be completely sheathed in wood. Some will have a sheet of plywood on each side of a corner to function as a wind brace. Most house frames will be covered with soft insulating materials such as fiberboard (blackboard) or Styrofoam. These types of sheathing do not anchor nails. Therefore, it is imperative that the nail location on horizontal siding types be directly over a stud and that the nail be long enough to penetrate the stud adequately to ensure holding the siding on. The amount of penetration needed is dependent on the stud hardness. Red fir and southern yellow pine, for example, will hold a nail with 1″ penetration, whereas spruce will need 1 1/2″ or more.

The nail position, distance up from the bottom edge, is determined by the amount of lap. Nails are placed only along the lower edge of each board. The nail must *not* go through the top edge of the board being lapped (Fig. 11-8). After installation the siding will shrink a little. If a board

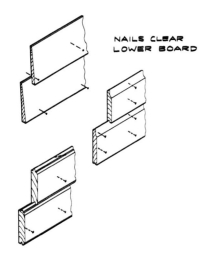

FIGURE 11-7 Three types of traditional siding.

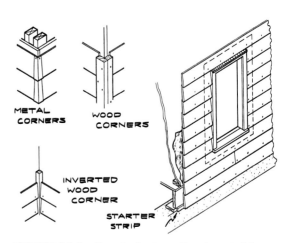

FIGURE 11-8 Details for installing bevel siding.

is pinned on both lower and upper edges, the shrinkage will cause it to crack horizontally down a grain line. A secondary reason for not double pinning horizontal siding is replacement ease. Should a board anywhere up the wall be damaged by a falling limb, a car bumper, or whatever, it can be slipped out and replaced without disturbing the remainder of the siding. The nails should be placed just far enough up from the edge to clear the top of the board underneath.

Hardboard siding comes in sheet form for vertical application and planks for horizontal application. The latter are 12″ wide by 16′ long. This Masonite-type material is usually primed on at least the edges and face, and some brands are primed on all surfaces. A bundle will usually contain a manufacturer's instruction sheet. These instructions should be followed for two reasons. The manufacturer has usually field tested the material to determine a satisfactory method. Second, when the instructions are not followed, there is little ground for complaint or adjustment should the system fail. Basically, hardboard manufacturers recommend the same nailing technique as that described previously for use with wood lap siding. Some recommend nailing through the upper lapped edge of the board below.

Starter strips for beveled or lapped horizontal siding are needed under the first course. Without this spacer the bottom boards would lie flat against the sheathing. The face would not be on the same angle as the boards above, which are lapped. The starter strip should be the same thickness as the part lapped above. Stock material can be purchased for starter strips, but it is costly. All forms available are sold by the linear foot at premium rates. The least costly alternative is to rip strips to the correct thickness from economy precut stud material. Hardboard siding planks are not beveled. They are of uniform thickness throughout. Once a job is under way or if this type siding has been used on a previous house, scraps will be available. Strips can be ripped from the scraps. Make the strips the same width as the amount of lap.

Frieze Board

A frieze is a decorative board banding the house horizontally under the eaves. On a house with a gabled roof the frieze may be continued all around to form a break between the end walls and the gables. The frieze adds class and style. It is usually found on all but the most economically austere designs. The frieze may be as little as a 1 × 2 or as wide as a 1 × 12. It is installed with its face vertical. Where the ends are joined, a scarf cut is used. A scarf cut is a 45° end miter cut (a bevel). The corners are mitered also so that no end grain is exposed and the joint can be locked from both sides with nails.

Some builders prefer to install the frieze before the siding, leaving the lower nails unset. The last course of siding is then tucked under and the frieze nails are set per-

manently. There are some advantages to knowing precisely where the lower edge of the frieze will be in relation to the top of the door and window casings and to the overall vertical span of the siding. Other builders will dope these things out by measurement and go ahead with the siding first.

Like all lumber the frieze is prone to shrinkage. There are two methods of combating the problem. Rub caulking into the end grain of each board as it is installed. This seals the most vulnerable part of the board, the open cells. Next, overlap each joint excessively, about 1/32 to 1/16″. Tap the nails again just before painting and the joint will tighten. Should too much lap have been allowed and the joint does not lie flush after tapping, a few passes with a plane will remove the high side.

Many illustrations show a rabbeted lower edge on a frieze board under which the siding is tucked. This is a rarity in actual practice. It is a feasible technique but has two objectionable factors. No stock material exists with a ready-made rabbet to suit the need. Second, the depth of shadow line is cut down when up to half the board thickness is cut away at the edge for a rabbet.

Installing the frieze is done expediently without loss of time or thickness exposure by spacing the frieze out over the top edge of the last course of siding. This is readily accomplished with a horizontal strip behind the top part of the frieze as was done under the bottom of the starter siding course. This strip is ripped to a thickness equal to the top

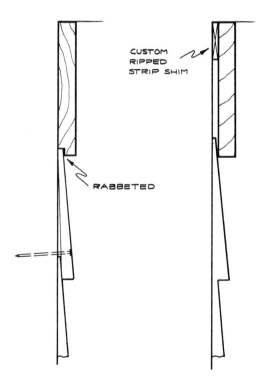

FIGURE 11-9 Frieze boards may be rabbeted to cover the top edge of horizontal siding or may be shimmed out in a vertical posture to lap over the siding.

siding board at the point of lap (Fig. 11-9). The lower edge of the frieze is lapped on top of the edge of the top siding course. A strip of the spacer material is tacked vertically behind each scarf joint and at all corners to provide a solid backup for nailing. The objective is to make the face of the frieze vertical.

Story Pole

The siding boards should have equal and uniform exposure from bottom to top wherever it can be arranged. Some designs will call for a frieze board to top off the siding, whereas others will omit it. Regardless of which design is used, the exposure of each siding board and the consequent lap must be determined before starting the second course. Left to chance, the last course at the top will surely be unequal and present an obvious nonuniform exposure, a sign of amateurism.

Installing the Courses. **The first course** should be installed to overhang the foundation uniformally, about 1/2 to 1″. This provides a rain drip edge so that water does not run back in under the wood sill. A soaked sill will lead to eventual decay, a condition called dryrot. It is prudent to seal the back side of the first course with paint at least a couple of inches up from the bottom.

After the first course is installed, take a vertical measurement from the bottom edge to the bottom edge of the frieze or soffit (if no frieze; Fig. 11-10). Divide the distance by a whole number that is one or two more than what

it would take to cover the area with boards laid edge to edge. Take 12″ hardboard as an example. You have just measured and found the height to be 97 1/2″. Eight boards would cover 96″. Nine boards laid edge to edge would net 108″. 97 1/2 from 108″ nets 10 1/2″ of excess for lapping. 10 1/2 divided by 9 nets a single lap of 1.17 or slightly under 13/16″.

Laying up each course by measuring the lap or the exposure each time will quickly compound any error, no matter how small. A good method of assuring parallelism and equal exposure of each board is to make and use a story pole for a guide, as masons do. Cut a pair of 1 × 2s or 2 × 2s to a length a few inches longer than the distance from the bottom of the first board to the point where the siding exposure ends at the top. Nail a small block at the point that is the same as the overall siding exposure height. Compute the exposure as per the example. On narrow bevel siding (4 to 6″), the lap should not be over 1″ or so for the sake of economy. On hardboard siding, any lap of more than 1″ or so will begin to create a crack under the edge due to the pivot angle, as a result of the absence of bevel on the face of the board. The corner of the top edge of each lower board becomes a fulcrum. When the lap is found to be too great or too small on the drawing board at the design stage, some adjustment can be worked out by varying the height of the frieze board. At construction time the only alternative to excessive lapping is to cut down the height of the top course. With wide siding, an inch or two taken off will not be objectionable. Any more than that will cause a mismatch of the bevel parallelism and will be quite noticeable.

Transfer the exposure heights to the story pole, starting from the block to the other end (Fig. 11-11). This

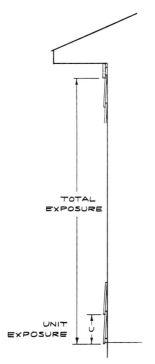

FIGURE 11-10 Graphic presentation of how to determine exposure and lap.

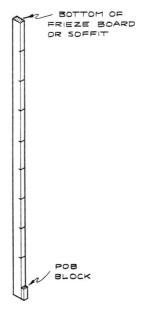

FIGURE 11-11 A story pole to match the problem cited in the text.

transfer must be super accurate, ending at one end with a division precisely equal to the first. In this way the pole can be used from either end. A sharp V notch cut with a knife or a straight slot cut shallowly with a hand saw will be seen better than a pencil mark.

Siding installation is basically a minimum two-person job. Even if one person does all the nailing, a helper is valuable to hold up the other end. The first course should be placed as perfectly straight as possible. Tack each board temporarily, leaving the nails exposed. Put a nail in each end and one in the center to prevent sagging. Put all the first course clear across a side of the house before starting any second-course parts. Use all the techniques of straightlining with string and sight. Place each nail so as to center through the starter strip and go on to anchor in the sill. Each nail will act as a guide for nails in boards above if it is placed directly below the centerline of a stud. *Do not* nail at the top of the board. When the straightness of the first course is proven, proceed to locate and nail the second course. Check for straightness and parallelism. Make any necessary adjustment. Sink all nails.

Indexing with the story pole from this point on will assure uniformity and parallelism around the entire house. Hold a story pole at each end of a siding board and transfer the mark from the pole to the siding that is being lapped. Hook the story pole block under the starter course. Mark another spot at the center point of medium-length board locations. Marks on approximate third points are advisable for long boards, which tend to sag considerably. A 16' board, for example, could use four index marks, one at the beginning, one at 5', one at 10', and one at the end.

Place a nail in each end first. Go to the intermediate locations. Raise the board to the mark and nail it there. Remember to nail into the studs. Sight the lower edge to confirm straightness. Complete the nailing. Remember that all the nails should miss the board below but be just above its edge.

One-person installation of siding is possible by placing a temporary, partially set nail in one of the index mark locations. This nail will support an end of the board resting on it while the carpenter nails the other end. After the board is nailed in several places the temporary nail is removed and a dab of caulk pressed into the hole. Many of the shorter boards between windows can be handled without a supporting nail, as they will wedge between the brickmolds enough to permit the first holding nail to be placed.

Joints. **Joint patterns on horizontal siding** should be made as unobtrusive as possible. The same rule applies to horizontal siding as to other rain-shedding materials. The end joints from one course to the next are staggered. Also, do not line the joints up on every other course. Start at the bottom with the longest pieces available. Start

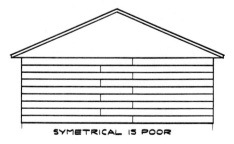

FIGURE 11-12 Symmetrically arranged joints in the siding give prefabricated appearance. Randomly arranged appearance is preferred.

the second course with a length that will end no closer than 4' to the joint on the bottom course. Do not repeat the bottom-course pattern in the third course, as this will begin to set up a jump-course joint pattern, which attracts notice. One of the visual characteristics of early manufactured houses that were transported in two halves was a joint seam up the middle of the ends. This giveaway was soon eliminated by installing the siding on site or by using vertical siding. The objective is consciously to create a *random* pattern of end joints so that the eye is not drawn to any specific area of the wall (Fig. 11-12).

As soon as breaks in the wall, windows, and doors are reached, it is often possible to span between them and to the house corners without joints. This should be done as much as possible. Save the cutoff ends for starters of a new course. Do not start a course with a piece under 32" long, however. Save these short lengths to complete a run that happens to call for a short piece.

End-joint techniques vary with the material. Beveled wood siding, usually cedar, is cut and planed to butt perfectly square. Rub some lead-base caulk into the end grain and butt the interim joints tightly together.

Joints at the brickmold will perform as expansion joints for both wood and hardboard siding (Fig. 11-13). A gap of 1/16 to 1/8" is left here. Rub caulk into the end of the wood siding before nailing it on. Caulk the gap completely full after installation. Caulking must be pushed into the gap with the nose of the applicator pointed slightly in the direction of advance. Dragging the nozzle will only lay on a surface bead, with little or no penetration. The air must be forced out of the crevise ahead of the caulk. Also, unless you can visually see the caulk rolling down into the gap, there is no assurance that it is penetrating.

Latex and vinyl types of caulking make a more resiliant expansion joint. Their life is also superior. When either of these two is used, it is better to rub the end grain with the same type of caulk that will be used to fill the gap. This will avoid the adhesion conflict of dissimilar materials.

Hardboard end joints should be accommodated in accordance with the manufacturer's instructions. A tight butt joint with this material will usually be the source of unending grief. The boards typically shrink and swell with the seasons. At times of high moisture, humidity, and many consecutive sunless days the boards may swell and bulge between the nails. The pressure is so great at times that it will force the nails out. In hot, dry, sunny times the boards shrink enough to open up cracks as wide as 1/4″ between the ends of full-length boards and 1/8″ at the laps. Plastic joint strips are recommended for joining the ends of hardboard. The strip is shaped like the letter H in its cross section. A strip is slipped over the end of the siding board. Slip the next board into the strip and bottom it solidly (no gap). Mark a light line down both sides of the H strip on each board. Pull the unnailed board away from the strip until a total of 1/4″ exists between the line(s) (it may all be on the new board side of the H strip). Nail the latest board. Tap the joint cover right or left until it is centered between the lines. The nails holding the ends of the two joined boards will require quite a bit of slant to reach the stud. It is important to locate where the stud is accurately, as the joint requires accurate centering. Even a slightly off-

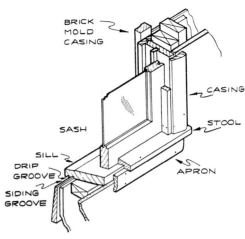

FIGURE 11-14 Window casements with an integral casing usually have a groove on the underside of the sill in which the top edge of the siding is pocketed.

centered joint cover will probably cause a defective nail anchor on the short bearing side. Omit nailing the ends of each board at the joint until the cover strip has been centered. Be careful to avoid hitting the strip when driving the nails. Only one nail is used near the lower edge, the same as in the field. This system provides for lateral movement of the boards without exposing an objectionable crack at the joint during shrinkage times.

Butt joints that are unavoidable on long uninterrupted surfaces must be arranged to end at the center of a stud unless wood sheathing exists for a nail base. With blackboard or Styroform sheathing it is imperative that all siding nails anchor in a stud.

Notching the siding will be required at window locations. Seldom will the lower edge of a siding course coincide exactly with the bottom of a window sill. Even if it happens by design or coincidence, the board passing under the window will still require notching away the portion that would have been overlapped had no window been there.

Wooden casements usually have a groove or a rabbet under the sill in which to pocket the upper edge of the notched siding (Fig. 11-14). The siding is notched to seat most of the way into the groove. Approximately 1/8″ clearance in the groove is left for sealing. A bead of caulk is run into the groove and the siding is pressed into the caulk to form an infiltration- and waterproof joint. Test the siding in the groove before spreading the caulk.

Manufactured Siding

Vinyl, aluminum, and steel horizontal siding are all dependent on the first course for the straightness of the siding that will be placed above. On these manufactured types of siding, no nails will be exposed (Fig. 11-15). On the upper edge there is a channel into which the lower edge of the next piece will hook. Above the channel there are perfo-

FIGURE 11-13 Siding-to-trim junctions should be treated as expansion joints.

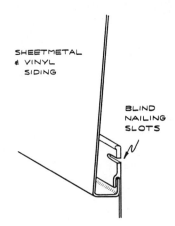

FIGURE 11-15 Aluminum and vinyl siding is blind nailed in slots made for the purpose.

rated horizontal nailing slots. A nail is placed in each slot that falls over a stud. Each nail is set lightly so that the slot will accommodate movement caused by expansion and contraction of the material.

Remodeling jobs where aluminum or vinyl is installed over old siding require some preliminary preparation. Surrounds and vertical furring strips are nailed on the walls. The furring strips do not necessarily have to be on uniform centers to mate with the nailing perforations, as these slots are continuous.

Nailing is unique. The manufacturer will recommend a nail size which usually specifies a larger head. The nail is *not* seated tight. The head should be in contact with the sides of the slot but only snug enough that the siding can stretch or shrink (Fig. 11-16). The nail is placed near the center of the slot or at least not touching the end of a

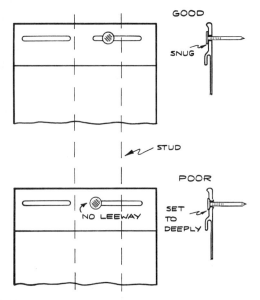

FIGURE 11-16 Nails should be snug but not tight enough to impede expansion and contraction of the siding.

slot. In this manner the siding can adapt to temperature changes and move laterally without buckling or placing undue stress on the nails.

End joints are generally lapped. A cutback area is provided at the bottom and top of certain designs so that no misalignment of the hook-in groove is created. Leave a small gap where the cutouts meet so that this end of the siding piece will *not* butt the adjoining piece and cause buckling. The manufacturer's installation instructions will indicate the recommended gap to be left. A new notch will have to be cut when using a cutoff piece in a new course.

The alignment of the base course is so important that it warrants emphasis. There is so little adjustment between the channel on the top edge and the hooking edge at the bottom that the first course must be laid nearly perfectly all around the house. The reward for this effort comes in the remainder of the job, which requires little attention to leveling and straightlining and therefore goes rapidly.

Cutting metal and synthetic siding is different from cutting wood or laminates. Sheet metal blades are used in circular power hand saws. Some installers use a regular blade put on the saw backwards to cut aluminum and vinyl (not steel). Surprisingly, the teeth, in the drag position, are not dulled by aluminum or vinyl any sooner than by wood.

Small circular saws are more effective and less dangerous than saws intended for woodwork. Intricate cuts not maneuverable with a circular saw can be made with a small saber saw (labeled by some companies a ''jigsaw''). Wherever possible all cuts are made from the back side, which avoids marring the face. When a cut must be made from the face side, the finish of the siding should be protected with masking tape. Another system is to tape the base plate of the saw. Aluminum, magnesium, and steel base plates on saws will leave a dark gray mark on the surface of the siding if not masked.

Channels and J strips are used around windows and doors to pocket the ends and custom-cut edges of metal and synthetic siding. Preformed corners are available to contain the siding at inside and outside corner junctions. Where all the exposed wood is to be covered, the installation will start at the corners, followed by the window surrounds and then the siding, frieze, soffit, and facia.

A word of encouragement is timely. Aluminum and vinyl siding are not difficult to install. The success of a good job lies more in the area of attitude than manipulative skill. Two elements are important: (1) get started right and (2) do not violate the principles of rain shedding. Leave no cracks open to weather or infiltration. Do not use butyl caulk as a substitute for good rain-shedding technique. Bend the first piece of trim (facia) to reach a corner around the corner. Lap the adjacent piece to the corner. Use no corrosive or dissimilar metal nails. They will rust and cause unsightly blemishes. Do not nail through the face of trim if it is possible to nail from an under edge or hidden place.

The do-it-yourselfer and the first-time builder can save a substantial amount of labor and franchise cost by installing manufactured sidings if the material is obtainable across the counter at reasonable unit prices. Kit and contract prices include a lot of costs other than labor.

Vertical Siding

Vertical siding requires more forethought than horizontal siding, as the material is running parallel to the structural frame of most of the wall and therefore requires backing. An exception is the frame that is completely sheathed with plywood or waferboard.

Vertical siding is available in board sizes or in sheet form. Board and batten was an early system of covering which is still popular. Many spin-off designs are available in metal and synthetic material, such as ribbed, grooved, and pressed contours.

Sheet siding is available in plywood, hardboard, and other composition materials. The standard width is 4'. Plywood comes in 8 and 9' lengths. The thickness of the sheet is often a determining factor in how the vertical edge joint is treated. Thin material usually has no joint and therefore requires a covering strip of some sort. Most plywood styles are 5/8" thick and have a leading rabbet and a trailing rabbeted edge.

Board-and-Batten Installation

Rough-sawn cedar is a popular wood for vertical application. Tragically, many board-and-batten installations are nailed incorrectly. The result is long vertical cracks and splits that develop as a result of shrinkage from exposure to sun and high temperature.

The most common nominal board width in the board-and-batten system is 12". Most boards will vary from 11 1/4 to 11 1/2". The "batts" are usually ripped from the same material. A generous and a less generous choice of batt width is possible. A 11 1/4" board ripped into four equal batts (three cuts) will net batts about 2 5/8" wide. The same board ripped into five pieces (four cuts) will net batts of about 2 1/8" width.

Successful nailing, of the board is achieved by nailing only in the center of the board (Fig. 11-17). This permits swelling and shrinking to occur without stress to the soft grain of the wood. The boards are centered in a 1' spacing modulus regardless of any variance in actual width. The gaps between them will vary a little, but the exposure will be equal after the battens are installed. Install the batts on the boards 12" apart, edge to edge. Mark the wall every 12" top and bottom. Center each board between the marks as you move down the wall.

Nailing the batten is the same as the boards, one nail only, midway between the edges. The batten nail does *not*

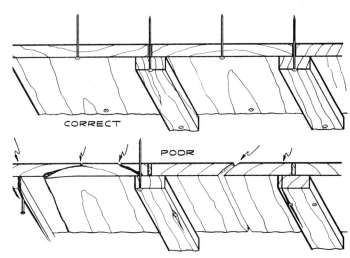

FIGURE 11-17 Board-and-batten siding must not be nailed next to the edges or through both boards. It should be nailed at the center so that it can shrink and swell without restriction from season to season.

go through the board underneath. It is a common *error* to suppose that a nail is needed on each edge to hold both the batten and the board firmly in place. This is a classic example of logic versus knowledge and experience. In this case logic is theoretical and loses out to the forces of nature, shrinkage, and weak wood grain. Note carefully the illustrations showing the correct and incorrect nail locations.

Nail backing is mandatory for board-and-batten siding. Horizontal wood backing must be provided at least every 24" or less up the height of the wall. Blocks or bands of wood are traditional. Blocks between the studs are no longer a feasible method, as they interfere radically with insulating methods. Bands of 1 × 4s are still in use. Several innovative systems are practiced, always with the objective of leaving the wall core open for freedom of insulating with full blankets.

One backing method is to diagonal brace the corners with steel braces of the T or flat perforated type on the inside of the frame, then surface band the exterior with 1 × 4s top, bottom, and every 16 or 24" between. Short blocking between the bands is required on those studs where the vertical sheathing joints will be. The sheathing is then applied over the banding. Blackboard is the least costly sheathing. Styrofoam of 1/2 or 5/8" thickness will improve the insulating quality considerably. Any greater thickness of Styrofoam will create a strain on the holding capacity of the batten nail that bridges the gap between the boards as well as the Styrofoam. These two depths plus the batten thickness will be in excess of 2" expanded before the nail reaches the anchoring wood. This system mandates 16d galvanized casing or headed nails, both of which may be considered excessive in size for the nature of the trim (battens, corners, casing, frieze, etc.).

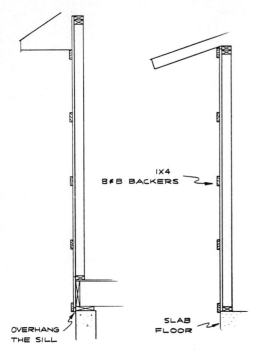

FIGURE 11-18 Horizontal backing boards are required for board-and-batten siding installation where soft sheathing is used.

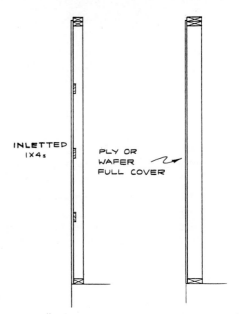

FIGURE 11-19 Continuous banding with 1 × 4 inletted ribbons will not interfere too much with the integrity of blanket insulation and will provide backup behind soft sheathing for board-and-batten siding. A full cover of plywood or waferboard is good backup on 2 × 4 or 2 × 6 frame wall. No other bracing required.

Another system is to sheath the frame first, then band it on the surface (Fig. 11-18). This provides a better nailing situation. Styrofoam sheathing must not be left exposed at the bottom, however, as it is vulnerable to insect and vermin infestation. A strip of wood surrounding the bottom nailed to the sill will solve this condition. For a wood-framed floor, rip strips the same thickness as the wall sheathing from precut stud stock (economy grade is minimum-cost material) and nail each strip to the sill before starting to sheath. The concrete slab floor has a combination sill/sole on which part of the sheathing should be attached to avoid an infiltration crack. The wood strip for this application is custom cut to fit the need. The sheathing butts to the top edge of the strip.

A third backup banding method is to inlet three 1 × 4 s into the framing system before sheathing the wall (Fig. 11-19). The location for these boards is on quarter points one-fourth up from the sill, one-fourth down from the top plate, and one board centered between these. It is a feasible system if the inletting can be done efficiently in a minimum of time with power tools. The sill plate and the top plate provide the top and bottom backing.

The best method may be solid wood sheathing. An analysis of labor time versus material cost may reveal that full wall sheathing with 1/2" CDX plywood or waferboard is as reasonable as any of the methods discussed above. No banding or corner bracing is needed with the full-wall wood coverage. All the labor time for banding is eliminated. The building is superior in strength to the systems involving soft sheathing. No diagonal corner bracing is required.

Reverse Batten and V-Grooved Siding

Sheet plywood wood siding is available in several patterns. A popular imitation of board and batten is called reverse batten. Instead of battens on the surface, this plyboard has relieved striations at intervals (12" is most common) which create shadow lines giving off the appearance of battens. Other designs have grooves on closer spacing. Eight-foot sheets fit standard wall heights with precut studs on concrete slab floors; 9' sheets adapt to standard walls on wood-framed floors.

Stud placement is critical if waste is to be avoided with sheet siding. The striated and grooved siding types are designed to be laid over studs placed on the 4' modulus system; therefore, the stud spacing must be either 16 or 24" OC. Once a sheet has been cut lengthwise (vertically), the unused side can only be used at the opposite end of the building or to start at another corner. The options for its use are very limited due to the rabbeted edges. The nominal width of the siding sheet is 4', but the actual width is 48 3/8". The rabbet accounts for the additional 3/8". The tongue of the leading edge is actually an extension of the striated batten groove (relief).

Placing the first sheet is accomplished by lining up the inner corner of the rabbet flush with the building line at a corner. Where the spacing of studs is correct in accordance with flush framing or setback framing, this will place the lead tongue edge on the centerline of the 4' modulus stud (Figs. 11-20 and 11-21). Reverse batten plywood siding may be nailed directly to the framework at a consid-

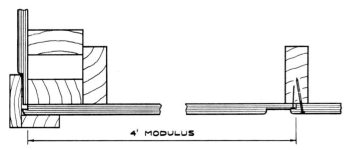

FIGURE 11-20 Reverse board-and-batten plywood siding applied directly to the wall frame.

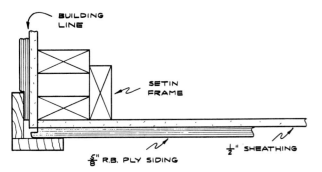

FIGURE 11-21 Reverse board-and-batten siding applied over 1/2″ sheathing with 1 × 4 corner trim.

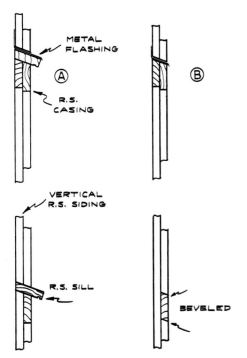

FIGURE 11-22 (a) A drip cap and sill are needed where there is no eave protection above a window or door opening as on the gable ends of a house. (b) Where such openings are adequately protected, a simple flat casing may suffice. In both styles the use of flashing at the top is a must.

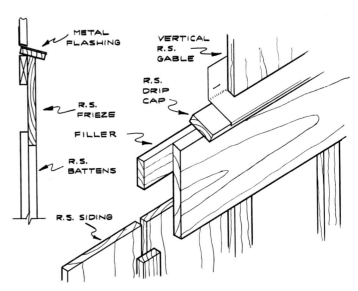

FIGURE 11-23 The same type of drip cap used on windows and doors may be used on top a frieze board on a gable end of the house.

erable saving. In this case the frame must be flush with the building line so that siding can hang below the top of the foundation.

Flanged-type windows adapt fairly well to vertical siding where the window is sheltered by an overhanging eave. A simple casing can be surface nailed around the window on top of the siding. Like other wood siding, a clearance gap of about 1/8″ is left between the siding and the window jamb for caulk sealing. The sill trim piece can be a two-piece design with a sill board at a slant of about 15 to 20° supported underneath by a surface board with a corresponding bevel on the top and bottom edges (Fig. 11-22). The side casings will butt on top of the sill board with a corresponding end bevel. The top board will be beveled on the lower edge. This board will meet the frieze board on its top edge. Where the frieze is at a higher level (soffit on the rake), a drip cap piece like the sill is an attractive capping piece (Fig. 11-23).

A simpler casing involves no more than a picture-frame-type surface-mounted set of four boards. The top corners may be mitered or butted (side board under top board). The bottom corners are usually butted, side boards on top of the bottom board. The bottom board should always have at least the top edge beveled to shed water away from the crack under the window jamb sill. Caulk this joint while installing the board.

Windows not sheltered by eaves present a special problem with sheet siding. Slovenly builders are inclined to ignore the water-shedding requirement at the top and simply caulk the upper edge of a surface-mounted casing board. Such a joint will ultimately fail. Water will get under the siding and begin the deterioration process. The striations in the siding form particularly vulnerable pockets for water retention. One of two systems of fabricating a

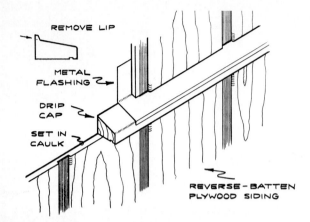

FIGURE 11-24 A stock drip cap molding may be used below vertical sheet siding as well as for horizontal lap siding, for which it was designed. The upper setout lip must be removed for smooth flashing.

drip cap is necessary. The first method uses ripped and beveled components of rough-sawn lumber. The second method employs a drip cap molding such as that used with brick molding. (Fig. 11-24). Both methods require flashing that extends up behind the siding to be foolproof.

Brick-Veneer Siding

Brick facing on a house is called *veneer* where it simply screens a surface and bears no substantial weight of the structure. The basic framing of a house is the same for a veneered house as it is for a house sided with other forms of siding. The differences arise from the dimensional decisions at the designing stage and from the manner in which the brick is blended with the trim of the house.

Design characteristics of siding a house with brick should be considered and determined on the drawing board. The question is whether the modularity of a structure should be based on the framing modulus or the masonry units. There are several considerations which will lead to the conclusion that a structurally wood-framed house should adhere to the modulus of wood (the plywood sheet), the basic 4' unit. Older traditional bricks were mainly standardized on a 4 × 8" modulus. Recent mass-produced units of 3 × 10" size and others have altered the modularity picture as far as brick is concerned. Actually, there is no longer a significant basis on which to consider brick modularity. There is, however, a basis to maintain modularity coinciding with the concrete block modulus (8 × 16"). A block building faced with brick is best designed with its exterior block line dimensions divisible by 8". It follows logically that any structure employing a block foundation with or without wood framing will best adapt to both masonry and wood when the dimensions fit the 8" and 4' moduli.

The basis for this reasoning lies in the nature and adaptability of the materials to alteration. One would think that wood is easier to reduce to custom size than a masonry unit. In a sense this is true. It is easier to cut and use a third sheet of plywood than to cut and use a third of a concrete block (especially if it is a two-hole block). On the other hand, it is not at all difficult to split bricks into thirds by trowel or by diamond masonry saw. There is great logic, then, to coordinating the blocks and plywood into dimensional units that will eliminate or minimize the cutting of either in a specific design. For example, a 28 × 44' house dimension is erected with all whole units of blocks in the foundation and full sheathing units on the frame walls. In addition to the ease of assembly, there is the reward of minimum waste. In reality, one can have greater square footage in the plan at little or no extra cost. Astute tract builders have practiced this concept of labor and material conservation since World War II with great economic success. The conclusion is that the brick-veneered house plan will benefit most by planning the framework around the moduli of 16 and 48".

The application of brick veneer to a frame shell will be cause for coordinated designing of the footing, a brick ledge, brick pockets (built-out frieze), and an overhanging gable wall to form a brick pocket. The brick pockets are all part of the carpenter's work. In the sequence of construction these woodwork features are constructed before the bricklaying. All casing around doors and windows is installed and brick pockets are formed and preferably painted or stained before the mason begins his task. This permits the mason to drop his lines and story poles from the exact corners where the brick will contact the frieze board. It permits him to grout all contact points with mortar so that there will be no openings between the masonry and the adjoining materials. Like most building materials, there will be a small amount of shrinkage, which creates a little crack at these junctions. A thorough caulking job after the structure has stabilized is the final sealing step.

Brick pocket depth is dependent on the brick size specified. Pocket depths can be made with stock materials that will fit most situations. For example, a pocket can be made with 2 × 4 blocks on edge with a 1 × 4 nailed flat to the lower end of these 2 × 4 drops. These drops are toenailed to the top plate and each stud. The frieze board is nailed to the drops and to the edge of the 1 × 4 (2 × 4s are excellent also for the lower backup, where cost permits). The frieze should hang below the pocket drop about 2" to give the mason some room to lift the last course of brick (soldier course) up into the pocket and lower each brick into the mortar. The 3 1/2" pocket made in this manner will accommodate the 3" brick that is so popular (Fig. 11-25). The actual depth of this brick is a full 3", so a "finger space" cavity of 1/2" will separate the brick from the sheathing. This is about the minimum that masons care to work with since any bulge or misalignment of the frame wall could reduce the gap so much that it would require the entire veneer wall to be set our farther. No mason will lay an unstraight wall by choice.

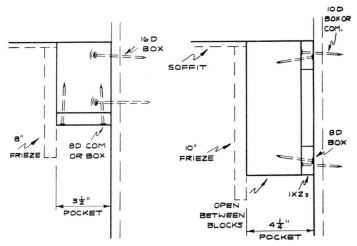

FIGURE 11-25 Typical brick pocket designs for actual-3″ brick and nominal-4″ brick.

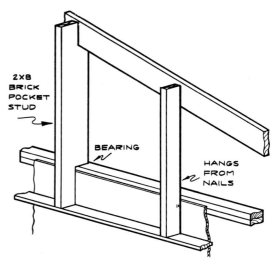

FIGURE 11-26 A traditional stick-built gable needs three or more notched setout studs that bear on the top plate to support the other studs, which are supported only by nails. The exterior face of the rafter and the sheathing are on the same vertical line.

Deeper pockets can be formed by varying the assembly methods. A 4 1/4″-deep pocket results from placing two 1 × 4s or 1 × 2s behind the 2 × 4 drops. This design is readily assembled at ground level in sections and raised. When done this way, offset the blocks so that they are right or left (uniformly) of the stud locations. When raised in place, the assembly is attached by nailing through the backingboards into the studs and plate. Deeper pockets can be shimmed out in other ways. To accommodate 6″ stone veneer, a pocket is made by using 2 × 6 blocks (5 1/2″ actual) backed with the 1 × 4s, for a total 6 1/4″. To up it to 6 3/4″, a shim of 1/2″ plywood can be used continuously or single pieces can be tacked to each drop.

A problem can arise around the windows. Whatever the pocket system chosen, the back side of the bricks must not be farther from the sheathing surface of the wall than the thickness of the window and door casing. Brick molding is made from "five quarter stock and measures 1 1/8″ deep from most mills. A 1/2″ space behind the bricks will leave about 5/8″ of brick touching this wood molding, which is adequate for grouting and caulking. Rough-sawn casing will range from 3/4 to 7/8″ thick, which reduces the brick-to-wood contact. Keep the casing depth in mind when designing the pocket. Incidentally, those builders aspiring to be professionals will benefit by knowing that the mason will judge the quality of the house by the straightness of the pockets and walls and the plumbness of the openings. The word gets around.

Gable setout is the other major adaptation required of the carpenter whose house will be brick sided up to the gable. This style will coordinate the brick pocket with a hung-over gable. The entire gable framework (all cripple studs) will extend beyond the sheathing below whatever

distance is required to form a pocket. The support of this overhang should not depend on toenails alone. A minimum of three studs of 2 × 8 size are needed to support the gable (Fig. 11-26). These are notched at the bottom to bear on the top plate. They are notched at the top on the same interior edge to receive the rafters when an overhang is planned. These 2 × 8 notched gable studs transfer the weight of the gable directly to the end wall.

On a trussed gable the brick pocket frieze backer studs can be supported adequately by nailing through the flat gable studs from the interior side into the pocket studs (Fig. 11-27). The nails through these supports should slant

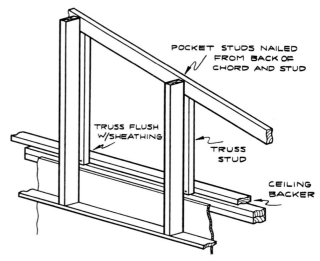

FIGURE 11-27 With trussed roof construction and/or flat stud placement the brick pocket frieze backer can be nailed from behind the stud for adequate support.

slightly upward to gain all the sheer support possible. The pocket studs will hang down below the plate line the same amount as the pocket blocks under the horizontal eaves around the corners so that a uniform transition level passes around the corner with both the brick and the frieze board.

A molded drip cap is needed above the frieze board on the gable ends. For rough-sawn and/or vertical siding, a drip cap can be fabricated by ripping a parallel bevel on each edge of a 1 × 4 or 1 × 3. This style requires a metal flashing strip running up behind the siding. Asphalt-impregnated building paper cut in 4″ strips is sometimes used but will not last as long as aluminum (Fig. 11-23).

A brick-faced gable will be treated with a pocket under the rake overhang of the eave. This pocket will be constructed something like the horizontal frieze pocket if it is a high pocket (6″ or more). Where a minimum pocket is adequate, it can be formed simply with a flat 2 × 4 and covered with a 1 × 4 rake frieze board. The soffit is installed first. Then a 2 × 4 is nailed to the soffit and into the soffit backer. The frieze is then nailed to the vertical edge of the 2 × 4. This nets a pocket height perpendicular to the rake of 2″, which is barely enough to contain a square brick end. Some larger bricks will require mitering of the corner of each brick. A 1 × 6 is a more attractive and more desirable rake frieze to the mason, as it will pocket any face brick without cutting.

A brick sill is another item that requires the attention of the builder and the consumer. Bricks laid on edge perpendicular to the wall under a windowsill, a door sill, or on top of a wainscot wall (a partial-height wall) are in a formation known as *rowlock*. In these three locations the rowlock course must be slanted to shed the rain away from the building. The greater the slant, the more successful will be its function. The bricks will need to be cut, as a full-length brick of the shortest type will hang over too far. The cantilever rule for corbeling applies to overhangs. The codes limit a masonry corbel or cantilever to 25% of the length of the unit. More than a one-fourth overhang exposes the brick to too much end leverage. It is more easily damaged or broken loose from its mortar bond. Sills with no slant or inadequate slant permit water to convect back under the window and door sill and cause deterioration of the materials. The house buyer should monitor the existence of a proper sill detail in the plans and during construction.

Wainscots require flashed junctions above the rowlock cap (Fig. 11-28). The flashing must go up behind the siding above the brick cap and extend onto the brick far enough to prevent water from penetrating behind the brick wall.

Weep holes are required in all exterior exposed brick veneer walls. A weep hole is a small hole or slot as large as the mortar joint at the intersection of a horizontal and vertical brick joint. Its purpose is to drain condensed water

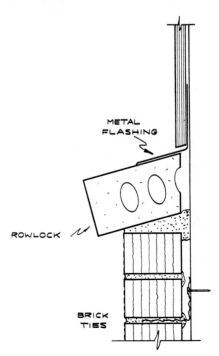

FIGURE 11-28 Flashing is a necessity behind siding that drains onto rowlock-laid brick veneer. Note the metal brick tie. One is required for every 2′ of brick coverage vertically and horizontally.

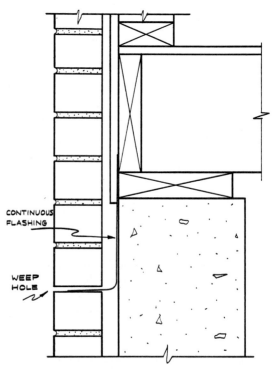

FIGURE 11-29 Weep holes in a masonry veneer wall are necessary to allow moisture from condensation to escape.

and moist air from between the brick and frame walls. The hole should be located in a course level below the first wood member of the house (the sill) but in a course that is above the level of the surrounding ground. Flashing is run up the face of the wood framing before sheathing is installed. It is bent out on top of the course of brick below where the "weeps" will be (Fig. 11-29). The sheathing is installed over the vertical part of the flashing. In designs where sheathing paper is used on the face of the sheathing, the flashing may be surface nailed to the sheathing. The first course of building paper is lapped over the flashing to form the watershed. The next course of brick will be laid on top of the flashing with mortar under and over the flashing. Bricks with holes must have the holes completely covered by the flashing. The flashing must not reach or protrude beyond the outer face. Some brick-to-brick contact is necessary to create a bond between the courses.

Masons have various ways of forming the weep. Some will simply leave out the vertical joint at intervals of 4' or less (the maximum between weeps). Others will place a steel dowel in the joint, grout around it, and ease it out later with a revolving motion. The latter method does not permit the placement of a screened vent as required in many locales. Regardless of the method, it is important to keep the passageway open to water flow. Punching a hole through after the bricks have been laid does not work, as the mortar is compressed behind the brick between the wall, where it forms an effective dam. The water will then stand between the weeps and ultimately break down the flashing. The most efficient weep is the manufactured one with shedding fins, which fills the butt joint cavity.

Sill sloping, correct overhang, and adequate weeps with flashing are three items of sufficient importance to write them into your masonry contract. Be very specific. The author has appeared as an expert witness in several lawsuits where these factors were in contention. Each case was won, appealed, and won again by the consumer on the basis of substandard construction practice. The result of the absence of weep holes, incorrectly flashed cap courses, and inadequately sloped sills and porches was evident in rotted floor sills, door sills, windowsills, and floor headers behind porches. The carpeting was moldy. There was even evidence of abnormally high respiratory affliction to the occupants due to the dampness in the house in all seasons. In this particular case the owner was awarded a sum equal to about one-third the cost of the total construction contract. The entire matter could have been avoided with adequate consumer knowledge, a specific contract (written specifications included), and some critical stage surveillance.

Brick ties, because they are hidden from view, are sometimes overlooked or ignored. A brick tie is a small strip of rippled and galvanized sheet metal about 3/4 × 6" with several nailing holes (Fig. 11-30). The tie is nailed to the wall through the sheathing into a stud. Most building

A TRACING OF AN ACTUAL BRICK TIE

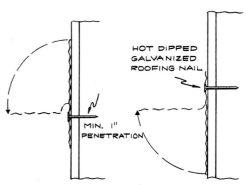

HOT DIPPED GALVANIZED ROOFING NAIL

MIN. 1" PENETRATION

FIGURE 11-30 Brick ties may be pulled down or up into the mortar joint.

codes call for ties throughout the wall on not greater than 24" spacing apart from each other both horizontally and vertically. Usually, the ties are placed from the bottom starters to as high as the installer can reach all around the building before brick laying commences. The remainder of the high ones are installed after scaffolding is in place. The ties are nailed flat to the wall and bent into the course joint on top of the wet mortar.

Brick ties are not intended to be structural devices; they will not hold brick to wood or wood to brick without adequate foundation under both. The ties *will* provide some lateral strength derived from the uniting of the two walls. The brick veneer will be considerably relieved of any tendency to teeter on its narrow base and fall away from the top of the frame wall. Foundation shifting from any cause will not have the calamitous effect on a tied wall that is characteristic of the collapse seen where no ties exist. Brick ties are beneficial and well worth the minimal cost. They should never be omitted.

Tying stone to a wall requires a different order of tie installation. Coursed stone permits ties to be prenailed in a horizontal line over a large portion of the wall initially. Irregular-shaped stone and nonuniformed height stone will not permit prenailing of the ties, as many of them will not coincide with the joint locations. To tie irregular stone veneer, each tie must be nailed individually at an appropriate bonding level. This calls for much more attention to monitoring of the locations of previously attached ties. These ties, now hidden from sight, must be recorded in some way to assure that the 24" minimum spacing rule is followed. Masons develop their own techniques. Some depend on memory (not often satisfactory). One simple method is to place a small piece of masking tape on the stone next to the tie location. Another method is to mark a future zone on the sheathing with a crayon where the next tie will be

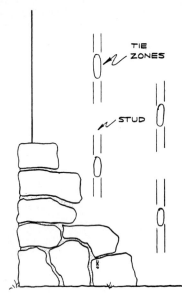

FIGURE 11-31 Masonry ties for a face-stoned veneer wall are indexed and nailed one at a time within 24″ of the last one.

needed. These zones can be indicated with a 6″ oblong mark vertically placed over a stud (Fig. 11-31). The top of the oblong is the extremity of the boundary. As soon as a tie is installed somewhere in the oblong mark, another oblong zone is marked above.

The basic responsibility for proper tying lies with the brick or stone mason. As with much of the hidden structure of a project, the assurance of quality details will be on the shoulders of an overseer. The overseer may be a consumer who has made himself knowledgeable or a professional who has been assigned the authority. Regardless of who carries the responsibility to see that this type of job is done according to specifications (or to code), it must be monitored at the actual time of construction. It is *never* good business to get there late and be forced to take someone's word that, "Oh yes, the steel is in the footing just like you want it," or "Actually, I always make a habit of putting more ties in than necessary just to be on the safe side." You will never really know unless you see for yourself at the time of construction or find out the hard way at a later date when something breaks down. The recent popularity of metal detectors has made it possible to confirm the existence of ties. If none are found *after* a wall is complete, the next decision will be a difficult one to face.

ADVICE ON PAINTING

In this text a lot of emphasis has been placed on the necessity to preserve wood at the construction site. Much attention has been focused on the nature of wood to swell, shrink, and deteriorate. It is always advisable to seal all forms of trim wood as soon as installed. The longer the delay, the more the wood is apt to warp.

Another reason to prime, paint (or stain), and finish is present when masonry veneer siding is used. The best sequence is to have all wooden trim finished before beginning the masonry. Painting with a brush will go much faster when one does not have to be careful about runovers or drips onto brick or stone. Paint may be sprayed on before masonry is installed without fear of overspray for those who prefer this method.

A final reason for trimming first is compelling. Mortar bonding in its fluid state is readily molded to the junctions between brick and wood. Reversing this sequence would cause much contour sawing where edges meet masonry. Visualize wood siding, a sheet of reverse board and batten, for example, being custom fitted to the vertical sides of a fieldstone fireplace.

Installing a frieze board after the brick is up would be unwise. Pounding on the frieze will break the bricks loose from their mortar bond more often than not. The mortar bond does not reach its ultimate strength until the twenty-eighth day. Even after that time it takes very little shock to crack a bond on the top course. It is clear for many reasons that all trim that contacts or is close to masonry should be installed before the mason is called in.

PHILOSOPHY OF EXTERIOR COMPLETION

Ethics and practicality walk hand in hand when building the basic structural parts of a house. The structure must be strong enough to be safe under normal stresses and strong enough to provide a reasonable margin of safety during abnormal stress times. A caring and thoughtful builder will demonstrate his responsibleness by including the little extras that protect against wind storms, tornadoes, and hurricanes. Those interested only in making money are always tempted (and frequently succumb) to shortcutting where elements are hidden from view.

The exterior finish of a structure does not provide much opportunity for economizing. Where the finishing touches are plain, austere, or lacking entirely, the appearance is so obvious that it will downgrade an asking price. Therefore, a quality job of finishing usually is worth the expense, as it will pay back at initial sale or resale time.

The consumer should be aware that a lot of flashy attractive finish on, and in, a house is not a reliable indicator of out-of-sight quality. An exposed aggregate driveway (washed granite stone), for example, is attractive—until it cracks. The underlying concrete requires special reinforcing techniques if cracks are to be reliably avoided. The best quality paint available on a house will be of little value if the material under it has not been protected by adequate condensation and moisture-proofing techniques.

High-quality cabinets will be wasted on walls that are warped and prone to cracks due to inadequate basic structure of the house frame. The list goes on and on. Truisms bear repeating. Good-quality builders work steadily throughout their lifetime. Shortcutters are prone to work stoppage and bankruptcy, not to mention lawsuits and forced vocational changes. The consumer is usually the best advertiser the builder can have. There is no substitute for quality construction and builder integrity.

REVIEW TOPICS

1. Explain in detail how to install a window with an integral casement.

2. How is an opening made ready for window installation where soft nonstructural sheathing is used?

3. Describe the key locations for shims and filler blocks around a door jamb.

4. Give the standard hinge spacing and placement for two- and three-hinge passage doors.

5. Explain how one "locks" a mitered corner of brick molding.

6. What usually happens to cedar siding of the traditional beveled type when it is mistakenly nailed at the bottom and top (through the lapped part)?

7. Describe a method of installing frieze boards that will not require a special edge to be cut.

8. The lap of bevel siding or hardboard plank siding should be in a range of 1 to 2". Explain fully how to cause it to be in this lap range and have all pieces equally exposed.

9. Describe how to make a story pole for a specific siding job.

10. Explain how to caulk between brickmold and the ends of siding around a window in order to have a long-lasting job.

11. Describe the correct way to nail board-and-batten siding. Include an explanation of the consequences of incorrect nailing.

12. Describe three optional methods of providing wood backup for nailing board-and-batten siding.

13. Explain how to place the first sheet of reverse board-and-batten plywood directly on a frame wall.

14. Describe how to prefabricate and assemble a brick pocket frieze backer section at ground level which will be hoisted and nailed as a unit to the wall.

15. Cite the regulation for brick ties and describe how to install brick ties for both brick- and face-stone-veneered walls.

Chapter 12
INTERIOR COMPLETION

PRINCIPLES OF UTILITY INSTALLATION

There are many hidden things behind the interior wall skin of a house. Common items found there in most modern structures are plumbing pipes for water supply, venting, and drainage, electrical wiring for telephones and electrical outlets of several types, and heating ducts to carry hot air into the rooms and others to return the air to the heating plant. Other popular conveniences, such as cable TV and central vacuum systems, require hidden components. Also, of course, there is the little door chime wire to remember.

To properly conceal these utilities behind the walls, the location of each must be carefully planned in advance. Leaving such locations to chance or to the habitual design of a subcontractor will probably result in shortages in places of need.

The jobs of plumbing, heating, cooling, and wiring involve skills that are within the realm of the amateur if adequate self-education is undertaken. Those ambitious and courageous enough to tackle these trades will do well not to try to get all the required information that is necessary by word of mouth. One should first search out and read reliable books on the subject to gain a basic knowledge and a grasp of the terminology. The next step is to contact the local building authority office and obtain information about codes and permits. Many municipalities will not permit an unlicensed person to install the three basic utilities unless under the auspices of a licensed contractor in the specific trade. When this second step is accomplished, it is time to get back into the research and plot your course in depth.

It is not the purpose of this text to teach the specifics of plumbing, heating, or wiring. This is left to the many good books that are to be found. A word of caution will be useful. Before purchasing a costly book, take the time to look it through carefully. Write down some pertinent questions concerning specific installation situations, then test the book to see if answers are there. Many books are attractive but only theoretical. When a problem arises on the job, you will need a manual with good clear answers and illustrations.

The intent of the following sections is to point out a few guidelines toward basic principles which are tried and true. Whether one tackles the job hands-on or subcontracts it, it will be advantageous to know what has been proven to be efficient.

The order of utility installation is important to some extent. Large items that would be hard to redirect or alter should be placed first. This would include such things as ductwork and ridged piping. Next will come the more flexible items, such as electrical wiring, telephone lines, and cable TV circuits. Finally, there is the soft insulation and a vapor barrier. Now the hidden core of the house is ready for a wall-covering skin.

PLUMBING

There are choices to be made in the plumbing materials to be used in the walls. There are two categories for pipe selection. One system involves hot and cold water supply.

The other system involves drain and vent piping. Supply pipes in the wall will usually all be of 1/2" size. Some 3/4" pipe will be used from the source to the water heater and to the first branch lines in the cold and hot circuits. This sizing helps to maintain pressure when more than one faucet is on at the same time. A trunk line or manifold setup is advisable where several outlets are anticipated to be in operation simultaneously on a frequent basis. Changes in direction are made by using 45 to 90° sweated-on elbows (soldered). Hard copper is usually used in crawl space houses and houses with basements where it can be run in straight lines and joined with couplings and elbows.

Soft copper comes in 50' or longer rolls. It is usually mandated in slab-floor installations that carry a "no-joint" regulation. Joints are made only above the floor. Soft copper can be bent quite easily to change direction. Care must be taken to avoid crimping the pipe. Once crimped, a high probability of leakage exists. Such flattening will also cause a reduced flow of water through the pipe. Benders are available that minimize crimping and make sharper bends possible.

Drain and vent pipe size is regulated by code. The size ranges from 1 1/4" in inside diameter to 4". There are two thicknesses of synthetic drain pipes. The heavier thickness (about 1/4") is used inside the house. The lighter weight (about 1/8") is used outdoors where permitted. Most codes permit 3" main drains made of synthetics. The size and quantity of dry vent pipes (those carrying no water) is also conditioned by the distance from the vented facility. For example, a tub, lavatory, and commode may all be vented from a common "stack" if the drains in each are within a certain minimum horizontal distance from the stack.

All vents should be "roughed in" to the wall cavities before any part of the wall is covered. Water supply pipes can be brought in through the walls or through the floor. A few more elbows are required for the wall-entrance location. Even so, this location is preferred, as it eliminates drilling through vanity and kitchen cabinetry shelves under the sinks. The floor-entry method is easier, however, for remodeling jobs where a sink is located in a new spot.

Slant vents and drains a little in the direction of flow (Fig. 12-1). All horizontal drain pipes should have a little drop toward the vertical stacks into which they flow in order to empty out completely. Long horizontal drains, particularly the main septic carrier, should be pitched to fall at a rate of 1/8" to the foot. More than this will sometimes run the water off too rapidly, leaving solid waste behind. Any less than 1/8" per foot will not provide adequate movement for all the contents. Be careful not to allow the pipe to sag anywhere lest the contents stand and create a blockage.

Dry vents carry gas and odors out the top. Any "horizontal" portion of a dry vent should slope up a little as it

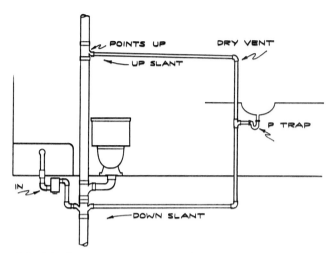

FIGURE 12-1 Typical one-wall drain system. Lavatory is revented because it is too far from the main stack (dry vent). Tub is shown "wet vented." Regulations differ.

travels toward its vertical vent pipe. This will permit the warm air to pass quickly up and away.

Water supply pipes require no pitch, as the water in them is under pressure and not affected by gravity. Hot and cold pipes should be kept apart from each other about 4 to 8" so that the hot and the cold water radiation are isolated from each other.

Wood butchering should be avoided. Major structural components such as floor and ceiling joists should never have their strength reduced by excessive notching or notching in the wrong place. There are rules in building code books pertaining to notching. Good sense mandates adhering to these rules faithfully. Drill a hold instead of notching wherever possible. Where notching is the only possible way to place a pipe, be sure to bring the notched board back to its original strength by reinforcing it (Fig. 12-2). Nail a splice alongside. A splice on a joist that does not reach the bearing points will be significantly more effective where glued as well as nailed. Should a joist require near or complete severing, it will be best to install headers, following the same rules as those for openings in a floor.

A nifty bathroom wall design that eliminates notching completely is one framed with a 2 × 6 sole and top plate. Wherever a horizontal vent is located, pairs of 2 × 4 studs are placed flat leaving a 2" clear passage between. A 2" spacer board (actual width) is positioned horizontally above the pipe between the studs. One nail through each stud into this board will produce a stiff, straight, and flat wall surface. No holes or notches are required for the vent pipe, which passes between the flat pairs of studs on its way to the main stack (Fig. 7-88).

Another method of re-venting, as this is called, is to run the sink vent vertically through the top double plate into the attic and there cross over to connect to the main stack vent. There is a structural disadvantage in this de-

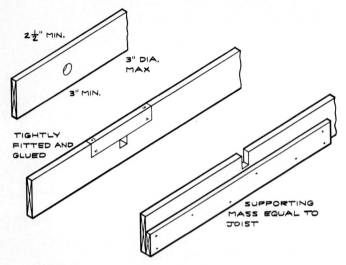

FIGURE 12-2 Holes for plumbing drilled through structural lumber detract the least from strength. Notched joists should be reinforced in one or both ways shown above.

sign. The top double plate must be cut or drilled. Where the plate runs at right angles (crosses) the ceiling joist, the weakening is not significant, as a joist on each side of the hole will be firmly toenailed to the plate. Where the partition runs parallel and between two joists, some special attention should be given to firming up the weakened plate. This can be accomplished by positioning a 2 × 4 ceiling block on each side of the hole. Lay these blocks flat on the plate and nail through the ceiling joists into the ends of the blocks. Surface nail the blocks to the ceiling backer and plate in the same manner as the backer blocks were installed. The same method can be used with a single 2 × 8 or larger drilled block. Center the width of the block over the pipe hole in the partition. Nail it in place, avoiding the hole location with the nails. From the underside, place the hole saw in the hole in the plate and proceed to drill through the block for a perfectly aligned hole. Attention must be directed to drilling in as nearly perfect a vertical direction as possible. The hole in the latter method will be passing through 4 1/2" of wood. Even a slight cant may cause a problem in placing the vent pipe.

Metal protector plates will provide peace of mind from concern about puncturing the pipe with drywall nails. Any type of sheet iron that will not be punctured by a nail may be used. The length of the metal plate should be about 2" longer than the diameter of the pipe it protects. For the sole, it needs to be as wide (high) as whatever amount of sole is exposed above the underlayment flooring. For the top plate, a single piece, 2 1/2" wide (high) or two of the bottom-sized pieces are needed. The 2 1/2" plate is aligned with the lower edge of the double-top plate. The ceiling board takes up the upper 1/2". Mortice the wood with a chisel, half hatchet, or a router a little deeper than

the metal plate thickness. The added depth will accommodate the nailheads that will protrude above the metal. Illustrations relating to the foregoing three paragraphs may be found in Chapter 7 (Figs. 7-86 through 7-91).

Indexing PVC

There is a unique feature of PVC pipe that can cause great consternation and waste for the novice plumber. The pipe joints are fastened with a solvent that sets almost instantaneously. There is no way to disassemble a PVC joint once the solvent has been applied and the two pieces pushed together. A misaligned joint can only be sawed off and thrown away.

The best assembly routine is to index the exact position of each elbow, T, Y, or bend (Fig. 12-3). Start the process by fitting each piece dry. When a pipe is cut, chamfer the inside edge with a half-round file or rough sandpaper so that water will flow freely. Chamfer the outer edge a little, removing all scraggly chips so that the pipe will press into the joint opening smoothly. Start the assembly at the main drain source and work up and out like the trunk and limbs of a tree. Work toward the end of the vents above the roof. After large segments of the system are fitted and assembled, each joint is indexed with a line passing at a right angle across the junction of two pieces to be joined. Where there are several joints of the same kind and size, place a matching number on each piece at the point of indexing. Remember the flow direction. All Ys that drain downward will position to slope downward. All Ys in the dry venting posture will slant up. This Y is upside down. In a one-story house, this will include all the dry-vent Ys above the sinks. This is an important detail, as a reversed Y will not carry the odors out as it should.

Permanent assembly may begin as soon as progressive fitting and indexing are complete. Disassemble from the top down. Lay out the parts in a clear space. Start with the bottom part. Spread the solvent on both surfaces. Press the

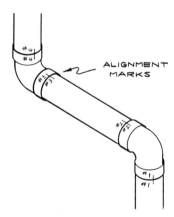

FIGURE 12-3 Indexing PVC pipe is accomplished with match-up alignment lines and reference numbers.

parts together quickly. Align the index marks accurately. A little ooze-out should be seen around the joint, which will assure an air and water tight joint.

Pressure testing is required in most municipalities. This involves plugging the lines, filling them with water, and applying air pressure through a valve. The amateur home plumber may have to call in his master plumber overseer for this service, as the equipment involved is not readily available any other way.

Water Supply Pipe Assembly

Assembly of water pipes requires a different element of attention. Since these pipes are run in pairs to the sinks, tubs, and showers, it must be kept in mind that the ultimate destination calls for the cold water to come out on the right side and the hot on the left. Some manufacturers of PVC pipe make the cold pipes white in color and the hot pipes orange. This makes installation simple. In the case of copper pipe or cream-colored PVC used for both hot and cold, a system is needed to avoid crossing over and reversing lines at the destination. Several techniques can be devised. A simple foolproof method is to run all cold-water lines first. Then go back over the course and run the hot lines. Another technique is to identify the hot-water lines with a ring of black electrician's tape at the end of each pipe. A can of orange aerosol paint can be used to code a hot pipe near its end. Avoid getting paint on the end where the solvent will be used. Whatever the system used, it will be worth the effort. Retrofitting a bungled job is costly and often aggravating.

Working with copper in terms of assembly and sequence is similar to working with PVC, but the tools are different. Some of the tools and supplies required are a pipe cutter, a soldering torch, steel wool, and flux. Watching a pro sweat copper pipe together makes it look easy. If one has never done it, there should be an adequate program of practice before attempting a full house job. Set up pipes and joints in various angles and positions and solder them until proficiency is gained. Put together, take apart, clean, and reassemble until confidence exists.

Hazards of plumbing with copper are present whenever an open flame is used. The dry wood of the exposed framing is particularly vulnerable. Whenever a joint is made with wood close by, a tin shield or asbestos cloth should be used to guard the wood. An adequate fire extinguisher at hand is a basic requirement.

DUCTWORK

Forced-air heating plants move hot air through round or rectangular sheet metal corridors called ducts. Cold-air return ducts are not necessarily made of metal. A com-

monly utilized method of ducting cold air back to the furnace is to "pan" a couple of side-by-side joists cavities. Sheet metal is nailed to the underside of the joists. A register opening is cut in the floor above.

A main trunk line duct for warm-air distribution is frequently run the length of a basement or crawl space. The most efficient location is next to the girder. In this position the register "takeoff" runs will be of comparable length (Fig. 12-4). This large rectangular duct is sometimes called a plenum trunk. Smaller ducts, most often round, elbow out of the top of the trunk and proceed down a joist cavity toward a register. The connection between this pipe and the register is called a boot (Fig. 12-5). The boot may exit through the floor or through the sole plate of the wall. The system of ducting between joists is concealable; therefore, it is favored for finished basements.

Registers may be located in the walls or the floor. A register in an exterior wall will suffer several disadvantages. The boot, and the elbow above it, will be adjacent to the sheathing on the cold side of the wall of a conventional single 2 × 4 studded wall. A significant heat loss results, as there is little or no space behind the ductwork for adequate insulation. It is much more time consuming to cut out the sole and floor and chisel away part of the

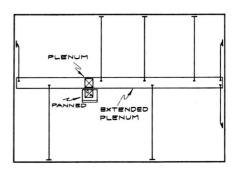

FIGURE 12-4 An extended plenum (trunk) with top-takeoff round pipes suits the basement setup best.

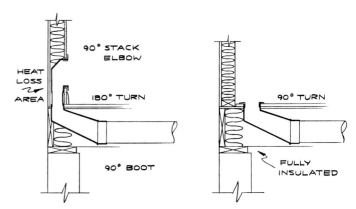

FIGURE 12-5 Floor outlets have advantages over wall registers during construction and after.

floor box header to form a rectangular opening between two studs than it is to saw a rectangle out of the floor a few inches away from the wall. Another fault of the wall register is that the heating air must do a near U turn to get into the room. Each turn reduces output velocity to a certain extent.

Register Location Principles

Evolution in the building industry takes a long time. Belief in, followed by acceptance and adoption of a principle take even longer. The old cliché, "It was good enough for my father and his father so it's good enough for me," is frequently the stumbling block to technical progress. A case in point is the carpenter who still frames a house with a half hatchet when there is no chopping to be done. Such a transition in the heating industry took place in the decade surrounding World War II. Central heating had been in vogue for some time. A typical installation had a large coal-burning furnace in the center of the basement. From the top rose several large, round ducts angled and spread like major limbs of a huge old tree. In a small or moderate-sized house these asbestos-paper-covered ducts were seldom over a few feet long. Each reached into the nearest room, where a register was mounted on an interior partition. A large cold-air floor or wall register was found by the front door and sometimes another by the back door. It was a gravity-feed system where the heat rose of its own volition. The house doors, which had no weather stripping, were the greatest source of infiltration. The theory was to gather the cold air into the return register at the drafty door as well as to pull some of the heated air from the central area across the floor. With continuously burning coal (the fire was never allowed to go out completely), the system worked fairly well. At best it was a great improvement over the European-style fireplace in each end of a house or the pot bellied stove, where you burned on the front and froze on the rear. With the advent of natural gas and fuel oil, the era of the coal-fired furnace was doomed, much to the delight of all the young lads whose duty it was to fire and maintain the furnace. Conversion units popped up all over the country. The old cast-iron grates were taken out of the firebox and an oil or gas conversion burner was shoved in through the ash dump door. The problem with the new innovation was that it did not work. The newfangled thermostat would call for heat and the flame would ignite. It had to burn a long time before the rooms warmed up. The house would heat up momentarily, but the cast-iron or firebrick firebox did not absorb or sustain the intermittent heat. As soon as the thermostat shut down the burner, the rooms would cool rapidly. Few houses had insulation of any type. Some people went back to coal. Others hung on and complained until the industry came through with electric blowers to move the hot air at a faster rate. This helped with new units but did little for the conversions, as the blowers simply removed more quickly what little warmth the firebox walls gained. Conversions were soon known universally for their inefficiency and high cost of operation.

Meanwhile, consumers with new gas or oil furnaces complained about the great temperature variation between on and off cycles and about cold spots and drafty areas. Tests showed that there could be as much as 7 to 10° difference from an interior-wall side of a room to an exterior-wall side and even more from floor to ceiling. When smoke tests were run, it was found that cold air spilled down the windows and doors and slid into the room. In the meantime, the hot air from the traditional centrally located registers was going directly to the ceiling.

Perimeter heating was not born in the twentieth century. When U.S. troops went into Korea in the early 1950s, they witnessed perimeter heating as it has been practiced in parts of the Orient for centuries. Clay pipes laid around a one-room dwelling had several exit holes into the room at various places around the perimeter. A small fire was built adjacent to a larger hole. A person would be stationed there operating a hand bellows to push warm air from the fire into and around the pipe.

In an effort to overcome the many problems encountered during the evolution from hard fuel to liquid and gas, heating engineers reversed the register location, putting hot registers under windows and cold return(s) in a central interior location. The success was remarkable.

It is now the standard of the industry for hot-air registers to be placed under windows and adjacent to doors. The hot air warms the entering cold air. As it moves toward centrally located cold-air returns, it is tempered. Very little temperature variation exists throughout the room.

Low Registers versus High Registers

The controversy continues about the location of registers in slab-floor houses. It seems to be all too common for some builders to rationalize a system as adequate when it is easier or less costly to install. Some technicians and engineers will concoct elaborate quasi-documentation to (seemingly) prove a system. Such has been the case for furnaces and ductwork placed in the attic with registers in the ceiling or high on a wall. The real reason for using this inefficient location is more apt to be a reluctance to get involved in underslab duct planning, preparation, and placement. Another reason is the loss of space taken up by a furnace on the slab. There is only one real test that will prove the superiority of the floor register compared to attic installations. That is to have two identical houses to field test, each with the different system. To date there appears to be no documentation of such a practical test to validate a ceiling installation. Where comfort and minimum operational cost are the criteria, the homebuilder will be wise to place the heat entrances at floor level and by the perimeter walls. Heat rises naturally. It is difficult or at least more costly to force it down from high registers. The ducts under a slab or crawl space may fan out wagonwheel fashion (Fig. 12-6) directly from the hub (the heat plenum exchanger). Disproportionately long runs can be accommodated with larger-diameter pipes.

The furnace on a slab will be a reverse-flow type called a counterflow. The hot air is discharged out the bottom, the used air returns through the top. A lowered ceiling in a centrally located corridor serves well as a return-air duct conveyer. Registers face into rooms that are adjacent.

Duct-size proportioning in a crawl space or basement needs to be determined quite carefully lest the plenum trunk be turned into a pressurized manifold or the rooms be pressurized. A trunk that is too large for the quantity of air taken off by the duct runs will cause the blower to overwork. The number of square inches of air taken off the trunk determines the trunk cross-section size. It should match closely. For example, if there are to be eight registers in a house and the furnace is centrally located, there might be four feeder ducts from a trunk on each side of the furnace. If the feeder ducts are 6″ in diameter, there is a total of 170 square inches to be supplied, 85 square inches

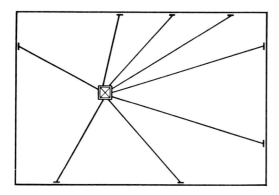

FIGURE 12-6 A box plenum on the bottom of this counterflow furnace with individual round pipes adapts well to crawl spaces and slab floors. Cold air is drawn through wall registers into the top.

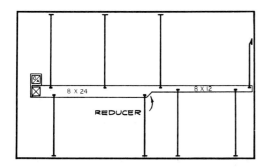

FIGURE 12-7 A plenum trunk may be reduced in size proportionately according to what percentage of the load remains.

toward each half. A trunk line with a cross-section dimension of 8″ × 12″ (96 square inches) would supply adequate air down each side. If the furnace is placed at the end of this house and uses a single trunk, it would have to start out being 8″ × 24″ (Fig. 12-7). The size could be funneled down after it passed a takeoff, or two, or more. Let us say that it is reduced once at a point after four runs have been taken off. The trunk plenum would start out with a size of 8″ × 24″ and reduce to 8″ × 12″.

A limiting and controlling gauge at the time of planning will be the size of the hot-air opening on the furnace. The total cross section of the trunk lines should not exceed the square-inch size of the opening through which the air must pass coming out of the furnace. The opening is designed to accommodate the capacity of the fan to move air.

CENTRAL VACUUM

A central vacuum cleaning system is relatively simple to install. There is a semipermanent location to be established for the collector tank. A spot in the basement or in an attached garage is preferred over one in the house. From the tank a permanently installed rigid tube will extend through the house. These pipes are generally made of lightweight PVC. They are assembled to elbows and Ts with the same technique as that used for water drains and vents. The room outlet covers have plunger switches so that when the cover is lifted the vacuum motor on the remote tank turns on.

Locating vacuum outlets follows the philosophy that all corners and the interior of the house should be reachable by the flexible hose that plugs into an outlet. Therefore, if a 20′ hose is supplied for a rectangular house that is 28′ wide and 56′ long, two outlets on a centrally located bearing wall could serve a minimum requirement. Careful assessment of the floor plan may reveal that three or more well-spaced outlets would be a wiser choice. From an operational standpoint, the system will work better with fewer outlets, as there is less leakage from covers as the gaskets deteriorate.

Because the system works on an airtight suction principle, each cemented joint must be airtight. Unlike a poor water connection, which leaks out, the vacuum leak will suck air into the pipe. After the piping has been assembled and cemented, it should be tested. With all outlet covers closed, jump the switch wire at any outlet, which will turn on the motor. Use a smoke tester or water around the outside of every joint that has been made. If there is a leak, the smoke or water will be drawn into the pipe through the hole. Such a pinhole leak can usually be sealed by applying solvent directly over a leak while the motor is running. The suction draws the solvent in and simultaneously dries it. *Caution:* Do not allow the vacuum motor to run longer than enough to check a joint or two at one location. Because there is no vacuum outlet open, the suction fan is drawing against a "dead head," which may cause it to burn out the motor.

WIRING

Wiring is the most adaptable of the three utility conveyers. It can easily be routed around rigid pipes, ducts, and structural materials. Therefore, it comes next to last in the sequence of concealed installations.

To assure safety, electric components that are a permanent part of a structure are highly regulated by local and national codes. Inadequate wiring can lead to overloading a line (more demand is put on a circuit than the wires can carry). In such a case the excess heat generated will "blow" (melt) a fuse or trip a breaker. Fuses and breakers are matched to wire size. Putting a penny under a fuse should never be done, nor should a larger fuse be installed than the wire size indicates. Such practices serve only to nullify the safety reasons for having a fuse or breaker. These safety devices are there to warn of a problem and to prevent a sustained overload which may result in fire.

Wire Size and Load

Understanding the relationship of wire size to demand on it is important for a house builder whether he does the work himself or contracts the wiring job out. There is a layman's formula with which to compute the size of wire needed for a particular circuit. A *circuit* is a leg of the system composed of so many feet of wire and so many outlets and fixtures that will be safeguarded by one safety breaker in the main panel box. Wire is code numbered according to the amperage it will carry. In theory, 1 "amp" will carry 100 watts of load. To find how many watts of load a wire size will carry, apply the formula amps times volts equal watts (A × V = W).

Houses built in the period between World War I and World War II made use of electricity primarily for lighting. An average-size house of one or two stories commonly had a 60-amp fuse box containing four circuits of 15-amp capacity each. The wire size was number 14. At 110 volts this netted a theoretical circuit capacity of 1650 watts or at 115 volts, 1725 watts.

As more and more electrical gadgets and appliances became popular and available, it became mandatory to include greater capacity in the electrical system. By the end of World War II the average new house was sporting a 100-amp system. Today it is common to find entrance panels with a capacity for 20 to 30 circuit breakers with amperage capacities of 150 or 200. The National Electrical Code® is constantly being updated with new and more demanding requirements. The certified electrician must keep informed and be abreast of the latest demands.

The wire size in standard use today is number 12 with ground. The cable will contain two insulated wires (white and black) and a bare ground wire. The number 12 wire is rated at 20 amps. In theory this size should carry 2200 watts at 110 volts up to 2400 watts at 120 volts. In practice, a load is planned for not more than 75% of capacity. This yields a 25% margin of safety, which guards against an unknowledgeable person who plugs in several chords to a particular duplex outlet and unwittingly chances an overload.

Unique loads may require a separate circuit alone. Examples are a furnace, a water heater, a dishwasher, the kitchen range, a garbage disposal, and a trash compactor. Amperage, wire, and breaker size must be sized correctly for each appliance.

Self-wiring is permitted in most regions of the United States by the homeowner house builder provided that all codes are met or exceeded and the job passes inspection. Some municipalities require that the installer do the job under the license umbrella of a certified (licensed) electrician. In any case the job is within the scope of the budget-minded builder of his own home. It requires study and comprehension of a good text with understandable diagrams and adherence to the code.

Installation Techniques

Some helpful hints may save some sour notes later in the job. Two difficult and frustrating troubleshooting experiences stand out in the author's experience. The house was near completion. Interior plastered walls were being painted. It was difficult to get enough light to see the depth of color in the bathroom for a second coat, so the painter rigged a floodlight. Then he switched on the mirror lights. They grew dim and went out. A check of the breaker revealed that it had tripped. Since the light had been tested before covering the walls and turned on many times since, a real mystery existed. A new breaker did not change anything. The wiring plan was consulted, which revealed that an adjacent bedroom was on the same circuit. The painting was taking place in the evening. The lights were also on in the bedroom. A 6'-long baseboard hot-water heat convector had been nailed to the wall between a pair of duplex outlets. Touching one of the bare nailheads that held the convector to the wall brought a tiny tingle to the fingers. A check of the metal surface with a voltage tester indicated some "juice" in the metal. One by one the nails that held the convector were pulled. The third nail pulled was an 8d common. The voltmeter went dead. There was the culprit. A small hole was cut in the plaster to reveal the cause of the short. The nail had penetrated the hole in the stud through which the electric wire went from one duplex to the next and then on to the bathroom. The nail had passed between the two wires in the cable, touching neither directly. It skinned enough of the insulation from each individual wire to cause a minute leakage across. When all the lights were on and the extra flood added, it was enough to overload the bleeding circuit and cause the voltage drop farther down the line, in the bathroom.

This story points up the logic for drilling wire passage holes in the studs as nearly centered as possible, so that nails through the exterior sheathing will not be hit by the auger bit nor will plasterboard nails on the interior of the wall enter the cable holes. Obviously, nails that are long enough to enter a hole that is centered in the 3 1/2″ width of a stud should not be used in the known vicinity of wiring.

Another case of bleeding current was found at a knockout hole in the entrance box. An overzealous electrician's trainee had tightened down much too hard on a wire clamp. The clamp squashed the cable insulation just enough to cause a bleeding short across the wire but not enough to trip the breaker until an additional load was placed on the circuit. Clamps that squeeze vinyl insulation should never be cinched more than snugly.

The same is true of staples. Very slight contact of the staple with the wire is all that is required. Do not drive a staple over a wire to an extent that the wire covering is pressed. Pulling a staple should never be done by prying out with a screwdriver or hammer claws. Use nothing between the staple and the cable, as the insulation will surely be squashed. Pull staples only from the outer side with pliers. Grasp the staple squarely across the top and pull straight up.

Stringing Wire

Some professionals will take pride in the appearance of the wire after it is strung. An effort will be made to avoid spiraling the wire as it is pulled through holes in the structural wood members. The wire is drawn from the center of a coil through a cutout hole in the cardboard packing box. To avoid spiraling, the wire box will have to be revolved many times to counteract the spiraling. Not much concern is given this problem in walls. It becomes more noticeable in basements, where wiring is frequently left exposed.

Parallel or diagonal stringing is another option open to the person stringing wires. Again the location may be the element of determination. Exposed wiring in a basement is usually run parallel or at a 90° angle to the joists. Coming out of the entrance box the several cables are run in neat parallel formation up the wall to a joist cavity. Passing along the joist channels the wires are stapled to the face of the joist. When a turning point is reached, a gentle curve is made with the cable. From that point on it is necessary to drill a hole through each joist through which to pass the cable. Several cables may be run through the same hole. A 1/2″ hole is the minimum size for a single cable; however, a 5/8″ hole will make the pulling easier. Larger holes are needed as more cables are run together.

Hole location should be in the upper third of the joist whenever possible to get a drill into position. Go no closer than 2″ to the deck sheathing lest the auger hit a hidden nail from the floor sheathing. Keep the hole or holes close to the outer or inner bearing ends of the joists so that any potential weakening will be held to a minimum.

Diagonal stringing of wires is sometimes practiced under two conditions. Where the wire is under the floor in a crawl space, the appearance is not a consideration. A wire may be taken in a straight line from its origin to its destination. If one wishes to make the route quite straight, a chalk line is snapped on the underside of the joists. The marks left by the chalk will indicate the angle that the hole is drilled. Since the shortest distance between two points is a straight line, it follows that a considerable amount of wire footage can be saved by this method.

Hanging wires from bare staples on the underedge of joists is a *poor practice*. In time the floor vibration and the weight of the wire can cause insulation to fail. In turn, a voltage leak across the staple may develop. In damp crawl spaces the staples may rust enough to disintegrate completely over a period of years.

Wiring in the attic may involve both parallel and diagonal systems. There will be situations where a long circuit supply wire will go straight down the attic, perhaps snuggled up to a strong back or cradled in the V of W truss webs to a junction box. From the covered steel junction box the legs of the circuit will fan out, heading directly toward their outlets (ceiling lights, for example).

Wiring through insulation is an element to consider in the attic. Before the energy crunch of the early 1980s, many houses contained no more than 6″ of insulation between the ceiling joists. The wires could be strung and stapled over the top of the joists. This posed no great problem to the insulation installer who hung the insulation from below. With present-day depths of 10 to 12″ of blanket or blown insulation, it is advisable to put as much of the wire as possible above the insulation level. It can be effectively attached to truss webs, purlins, or rafters around the perimeter.

Fixture boxes are positioned slightly above the finished ceiling level. In this position the light-fixture cover will pull up tightly to the ceiling when the screws are installed into the box.

A simple gauge to check box position (distance below the ceiling joists) can be made from a scrap of 1/2″ plywood about 8 to 10″ wide and about 30″ long (Fig. 12-8). Cut out two or three holes just large enough to encompass an octagon metal fixture box or a round plastic box. Ceiling joists will be spaced on centers 16 or 24″ apart. Box location frequently falls between them. The gauge board is held tightly on the underside spanning two joists with one of the test holes over the box. No part of the box should protrude below the board for a ceiling made of 1/2″ gypsum board.

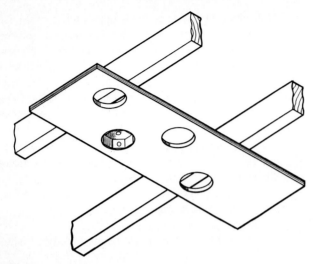

FIGURE 12-8 This gauge board may be used to check the correct electric box depth below the ceiling joists.

Locating a fixture in the center of a rectangular room is a simple task. Set a temporary nail in the junction of each corner at the ceiling level. String a diagonal line between the two nails in opposite corners. Without cutting the line, take it across the wall, either right or left, wind it around the third nail, and string it diagonally across the room to the remaining unoccupied nail. The intersection of the string indicates the center of the room. Center the box directly over the string intersection.

Two or more fixtures should be located in the approximate center of each half of a long rectangular room (Fig. 12-9). Dividing the length of a room into thirds for the placement of two lights might seem logical from an appearance point of view; however, the distribution of light will be unequal. Dividing a room in thirds, especially one with dark-paneled walls, will cause the center of the room to be brighter where the light beams overlap. The ends of the room will be dimmer. A room whose walls are painted

white or a very light color will reflect the light back into the room better. Even so, there will be a concentrated area between the two lights where too much overlap occurs. Fixture placement with light walls is less critical. For a room that is less than twice as long as wide, the placement of two lights will be an educated estimate based on the factor of lighting overlap between the fixtures and the reflective potential of the wall coloring. The distribution of light will usually be better where there is more space between the lights than between a light and an adjacent wall.

Doorbells, Chimes, and Thermostats

Wiring to signal devices such as doorbells and chimes and wires to thermostats are usually of the low-voltage type. A transformer is placed at a conveniently exposed location so that it can be replaced readily should it wear out and fail. Power for a single bell can be taken from the closest power source to the bell or to its button. The transformer is positioned between the 110-volt source and the bell or button. A chime with a button at the front and rear doors will require more forethought in choosing the best power source and the placement of the transformer and the wires. Sometimes where multiple annunciators exist, the transformer will be mounted in the entrance breaker box. Keep in mind that low-voltage bell wire is much less costly than number 14 or 12 wire.

Bells and chimes should be located in accordance with their intended function. A chime with a single tone for the service entrance and a double tone to indicate that

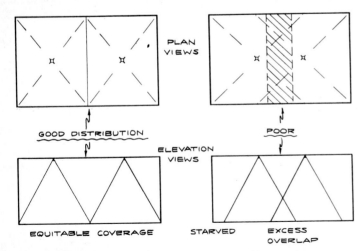

FIGURE 12-9 A ceiling fixture placed in equal room segments disperses the light more equitably.

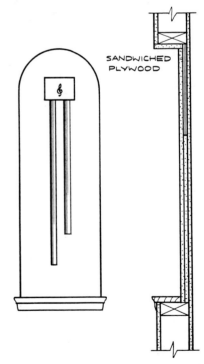

FIGURE 12-10 A recess, such as one for a door chime, should be backed with wood.

someone is at the main entrance must be located in a position that can be heard from all rooms in the house.

Chimes may be recessed in the wall for two reasons. A crèche-type recess (arched top) has been popular for many years. Aside from the enhanced beauty of long brass tubes hanging in a recess, there is a practical reason. Frequently, the chime will be located in a corridor, a traffic area. Protruding from the wall surface, the chime would be a hazard. A recess permits the entire mechanism to be out of harm's way.

All or a portion of the back of the recess must have a wooden backup plate to anchor the screws from which the chime box will hang (Fig. 12-10). This wood backer is handily made from 1/2 or 5/8″ sheathing plywood sandwiched between the wallboard on the other side of the wall and the piece that forms the back of the recess.

The thermostat that controls the heating and cooling temperature of the entire house must be located with great care. The thermostat must be in a spot where the sun will never shine on it, summer or winter. It should be centrally located on an interior partition. It must not be in the direct line of a hot-air register, nor should it be above a cold-air return. Avoid a location that would expose the thermostat to the heat of an electric lamp or a fireplace. To produce the best blend of temperature between the floor and ceiling, locate the thermostat midway up the wall.

Thermostat wire may be run through the stud wall to the furnace, or it may be routed up into the attic or down into the crawl space or basement. Whichever route is most conserving of wire may be the basis of choice. On the other hand, a route that provides the least amount of drilling may be compelling.

Telephone and Cable TV

These wiring jobs are usually carried out by company personnel, at consumer expense. This being the case, it only becomes necessary to place your orders for a convenient time. That time is before any wall covering has been put on the interior of the framework. It is best to have the electrical wiring service completed before the telephone or TV wiring is started. It will prevent conflicts of outlet location. The TV installer, particularly, can coordinate the antenna outlets better with the electrical duplex outlets into which a television set will most likely be plugged.

CABINET SOFFITS

Upper built-in cabinets in the kitchen and sometimes those in a bathroom will have boxed-out areas above the cabinets called soffits. Sometimes this closed dummy boxing is called a bulkhead because its construction is similar to that of compartmented areas in large ships. The purpose of the

cabinet soffit is simply to close in a more or less inaccessible area so that it does not become a dust catcher. Most homemakers who are principal occupants of the kitchen cannot reach the area of the soffit, so it is considered a nonfunctional place by the majority of builders.

The standard height of the soffit is 12″. There is a potential of several cubic feet of storage in the soffit location for those brave souls who do not fear mounting a step stool. The author has utilized this area in several houses to add a cubic foot of storage for each linear foot of counter and appliance frontage simply by installing 1′-high cabinets above the rectangular cabinets.

Soffit Construction

The framework of a soffit is attached directly to the wall studs and the ceiling joists; therefore, it is constructed before the walls are covered. There are many different ways to "hang" a soffit successfully. Only a few examples are shown and described on these pages. Should one deviate from these plans, it will be prudent to keep one principle in mind. All members that support the weight of the soffit by hanging from the rafters should be attached with nails at angles to take advantage of the principle of shear stress (not tension), lest the weight pull the soffit down from the ceiling.

Parallel soffits are those that run in the same direction as the ceiling joists. Perpendicular soffits are those that cross the ceiling joist usually at right angles. Hanging the crossing soffit is less complicated, as there is a ceiling joist every 16 or 24″ from which a hanger board may be attached.

Two basic methods of construction stand out for the builder's choice. One uses the structural framework principle. The other uses the box beam principle. The structural framework technique may be less costly if it can be done by using scraps of 2 × 4s that might otherwise be discarded. The box beam technique is quicker to build but may cost more for materials. Where there is a high labor cost factor, the box beam method could cost less.

A structural framework soffit (Fig. 12-11) is started by building a facia frame. The work is done on the floor. A 2 × 4 forms the top of this ladderlike structure, and another 2 × 4 of identical length forms the bottom leading edge of the soffit fascia. When in position, both pieces will have their flat surfaces on a horizontal plane.

Hold or temporarily tack the top 2 × 4 to the ceiling joists. Mark lines across the top of the board along both sides of each joist. The vertical cripple studs forming the facia ladder will all be placed to the right or to the left of these marks with their edges on the line. Lower the board to the floor. Remove the nails. Lay the board alongside the other 2 × 4 and transfer the stud locations to the second board.

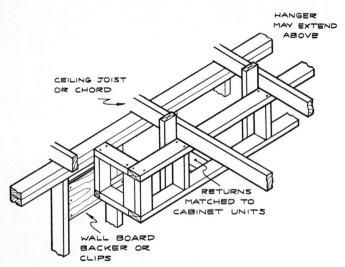

FIGURE 12-11 A soffit may be preassembled on the floor, hoisted into place, and attached to the ceiling joists and wall studs.

The soffit height is 12″ in a room that has been framed with precut studs. The underside of the soffit should be at or near a height of 7′ above the floor. In taller rooms the soffit will be higher, to make up the difference. In the standard-height room the cripple studs in the facia frame will be duplicate cut to a length of 9″. The 2 × 4s on top and bottom add 3″, to net a 12″ high frame. Nail the frame together the same as on a stud wall, using the angled-nail pincher technique. Note in Fig. 12-11 that the end stud is faced differently where a soffit ends in the open (not against a wall). This covering system permits the corner to be secured together with top and bottom nails instead of toe-nails.

Hanger boards are installed next. This board is a 2 × 4 which will extend from the bottom edge of the soffit to the top of the ceiling joist or a few inches above. Its minimum length will be 12″ plus the joist height (3 1/2, 5 1/2, or 7 1/4″). Where blown insulation is specified, it will be advantageous to allow a few inches to protrude above the joist. This will help eliminate the possibility of the upper end of the hanger splitting when it is nailed to the joist. Where a double layer of insulation blanket is to be used, the second layer will run across the joists. In this case the protruding hangers are objectionable, as they protrude into the second layer of insulation. The hangers should be cut to fit flush with the top of the joists.

Nail a hanger to the back side of the facia over each cripple stud where ceiling joists or chords are on 2′ centers. A hanger to every other joist may be adequate where joists are on 16″ centers. Place two 16d sinkers or box nails into the top board, one nail in the center of the cripple, and two nails into the bottom board. Tap holes must be bored for the two bottom holes. Even if it were possible to nail this

location without splitting, the board will probably split later from the heat and shrinkage. The top of the cabinets are anchored to the lower 2 × 4 which is hanging from these nailed straps. Splits from the nails at the bottom of a hanger strap will render it less than adequately supportive.

The bottom ladder may be assembled to the facia ladder on the floor or it may be stick built to the facia and wall after the facia is hung. Retro assembly will virtually make the cripple installation a 100% toenailing job. If this is to be avoided, the back board against the wall can be nailed to the cripples before hoisting into place. End nailing of these cripples is superior to toenailing. However, the other end of the cripples will be toenailed to the bottom facia 2 × 4 since it is impractical to nail through the 3 1/2″ width of the board.

Placement of cripple studs is sometimes coordinated with the cabinet modules so that screws can be placed into them at the end of each cabinet top frame. It is difficult to accomplish this objective precisely, so it is more often ignored than practiced. Cripples in the soffit bottom should be omitted from the area where an electrical box is specified. Cripple location will not be critical where an external fluorescent fixture is used. A wire pigtail is left hanging through a hole in the wall covering. It is attached inside the fluorescent box later. Spacing of the cripples is not crucial. There should be one at the ends of all soffits and others to serve as spanners about every 16″ or less.

The depth of the soffit is not a standardized figure. It depends somewhat on whether there will be a molding around the top of the cabinet, and how big it is. In the United States, the cabinet itself is quite standardized, at 12″. On the soffit the added thickness of wall covering (wallboard, paneling, or whatever) can be ignored if the same thickness of material is put on the wall below the soffit. Therefore, if a 3/4″ cove molding is to be used, the soffit should extend a minimum of 1″ beyond the cabinet. This will permit a 1/4″ overhang of the soffit beyond the molding provided that all components are perfectly straight. Since this is seldom the case with wood, most builders will opt for a greater overhang in order to get the parallel comparison of the molding at a greater distance from the edge of the soffit. A 13″ depth is an absolute minimum; 14″ would not be considered excessive. Wider moldings will call for even more horizontal depth.

The lower back board can be made of a half of a 2 × 4 (2 × 2). It will be positioned with its greatest width vertically so that a uniform 1 1/2″ faces into the room. Half a 2 × 4 measures approximately 1 11/16″ × 1 1/2″. The sawed edge is faced up. A 14″-deep soffit design will take horizontal cripples 9″ in length, the same as the verticals, so they can be duplicate cut together with the vertical cripples. Their summation is: lower front board, 3 1/2″ plus cripple, 9″ plus back board, 1 1/2″ equals 14″.

Raising the soffit is at least a two-person job. Assuming that the entire soffit has been assembled on the floor, there still remain some details of alignment to be done first. Measure out from the top plate the exact distance of the horizontal depth of the soffit frame where the soffit starts and where it ends. Snap a chalk line along the underside of the ceiling joists. Measure down the studs at each end of the soffit location from the joists the exact height of the soffit frame. Strike a chalk line between these points. Hoist the soffit frame into position. Wedge it up at the ends with a couple of braces to the floor. Nail through the hanger boards that are closest to the ends. Use only one nail at this point. Slant each nail downward to give sheer support. Push the facia in or pull it out until it lines up with the chalk line. Nail a hanger adjacent to the center of the soffit. While pushing in or out, nail all the other hangers. Put only one nail in at the top of each hanger, as the lower part of the soffit may need to be pulled in or pushed out, in which case the hangers will need to pivot slightly. Attach a string line across the front edge of the bottom board of the soffit. Pull it very tight and position it about a nail diameter below the front edge. Start a few nails into the back board. Line up the ends first about 1/16" higher than the chalk line on the studs. Having the back board slightly high will cause the front edge of the cabinet to snug up tightly to the soffit. Set the nails at the ends. Set one at the center after aligning the board above the line. Now check the front lower string line. If the front edge is behind the line, the back board will need shimming out. If the front board cannot be pushed back to the line, locate the stud or studs that are protruding and notch them until the board in front lines up perfectly. Permanently set all the nails in the back board.

Check the horizontal straightness of the front lower edge next. Even though a single nail is set in each hanger, it will move a little if need be. It is important that this edge at the front be as straight as possible, as it is the most visible. Tap the hangers up or down to make the edge perfectly straight in accordance with the string. Remember, the string must be very taut to give a true no-sag reference.

Bar clamps are very useful to the soffit installer. As few as two 24" clamps will make it possible for one person to adjust and complete the nailing of the soffit. Bar clamps have a nasty habit of falling off once pounding begins. If a pair of clamps is all that is supporting the soffit before nailing begins, it will be prudent to block the clamp in position with a 16d nail or a loop of wire around the bar and a joist.

Backup plates are needed at or behind the ends of the soffit. These two areas present a vulnerable spot for a crack to develop in plaster or gypsum board. The backerboard is made and installed the same as curtain and fixture backers. The backer is easier to install before the soffit goes up; however, it is possible to retrofit them in most situations.

Insulating the soffit makes sense, as there is no reason to heat or cool a nonfunctional dead space. The wall behind the soffit should be insulated before the soffit is installed. As the ceiling will have fill insulation or blown-in cellulose, it is an easy matter to fill the soffits simultaneously. It is more time consuming to cut and fit blanket or batt insulation into the soffit, but it will be worth it over a period of years. The latter will be done from the room side after all electrical wiring, hood vents, and any other hidden installations have been placed.

Parallel Soffits

L-shaped and U-shaped kitchens will have one of the two or three soffit legs running parallel to the ceiling joists. This necessitates a different support arrangement, as there is rarely a joist in a perfectly aligned position for hangers to be attached. However, it is usually possible to use the ceiling backer board blocks which secure the partition as an anchoring board for the soffit hanger (Fig. 12-12). A U-shaped kitchen has partitions around the U. Whichever wall(s) runs parallel to the soffit will have ceiling nail backers and blocks above. The soffit hangers and cripples must be calculated carefully to coincide with the location of the overhead backer blocks.

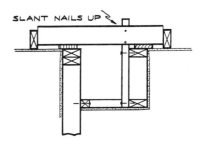

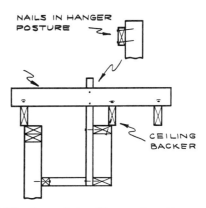

FIGURE 12-12 A parallel soffit may be effectively hung from the cross blocks above the ceiling backup board or from purlins crossing the two joists between which the soffit is located.

Boxed Soffits

A boxed soffit uses surface plywood as a part of its structural integrity. The frame on which the plywood is nailed may be simplified—built with fewer hangers and spanners (cripples)—because the plywood forms a continuous backing for its finish covering (Fig. 12-13). The stiffness and no-sag characteristic of plywood on edge makes it possible to have fewer hangers to support its length. A hanger every 4' or less will usually be adequate. A soffit that is 8' long can then be hung from a hanger in the center and one from each end that is freestanding. The wall-butting end of a soffit requires no hanger, as it will be nailed through its frame into a backer board on the wall.

A soffit over 8' long will take more than one piece of plywood. Wherever the butt joint of the plywood is made, a hanger should be placed. Therefore, a cripple and hanger must be correlated with the ceiling joist above, and the plywood joint made over the center of the cripple.

Another feature to remember with the plywood-boxed soffit is to reduce the size of the cross-section frame girth by the thickness of the plywood sheathing since the thickness of the wall covering is yet to be included (Fig. 12-14). For example, the frame without boxing is to be 12" high. Therefore, a frame to be boxed with 1/2" plywood should be 11 1/2" high.

Also remember to form solid corners at the freestanding end of a soffit. In makes no difference which piece of sheathing runs past the corner, the end piece or the facia piece. One is cut flush with the framework corner. The other fully laps the end of the first piece to form a solid corner.

A soffit usually continues uninterrupted over windows, range hoods, refrigerators, and built-in ovens. It is good to know in advance where vents from these appliances will of necessity pass through into the attic. By hav-

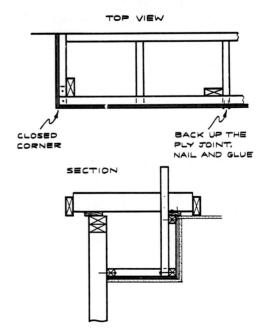

FIGURE 12-14   Details of a boxed soffit.

ing this information it will be possible to avoid cutting out ("butchering") structural members. Also, one can provide structural backup from which to mount a hood or light fixture.

INSULATING THE WALLS AND CEILING

After all the framework is completed and all the hidden wires, pipes, and recesses have been installed in the exterior walls, it will be time to install the insulation. Two philosophical considerations are important at the outset. One deals with the quantity of insulation to be used. The other relates to the quality of the installation process. Both of these considerations need to be examined due to the long-range implications on operational economy.

Quantity concepts changed drastically in the early 1980s. "Thermal" construction became the magical word with which to clinch a new house sale. Unfortunately, many houses masquerading as "thermal" were only moderately well insulated. Many window brands with two glass panes set in butyl are characterized as thermal, although the advantage is scarcely different from that of single panes with storm windows. The term "thermal" is so broad that it can be used to describe any form or quantity of added material that resists the passage of heat. A consumer can easily be a victim of the residual of the barest minimum of insulation described as thermal or the benefactor of a truly well conceived and insulated house. Only when he or she knows the precise quantity and type of insulation material used and the quality of the application will it be possible to predict the comfort and the cost of living in a particular house.

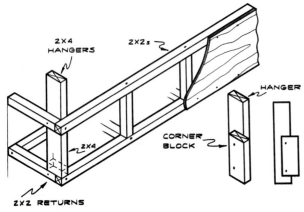

FIGURE 12-13   A plywood-sheathed soffit gains strength and rigidity from the boxing principle. Structural members can therefore be smaller and hangers fewer in number.

The quality of installations, one might think, would be fairly uniform in the construction industry. It is not. There is a great potential for losing the optimum insulation capability of insulation by poor installation. A 3 1/2″ batt of insulation placed between studs, for example, in theory will provide a resistance factor of 11 (R-11). In actual practice this will occur only when the blanket is perfectly installed. Faulty installation is characterized by several things. A gap at the top or around an electrical outlet box will be detrimental. Any place where the fibers are unduly compressed, kinked, lapped, or not permitted to expand fully into the opening will subtract from the full potential. For maximum efficiency all surfaces and edges of blanket-type insulation must be in contact with the surrounding woodwork and sheathing.

Quantity of Insulation

Countrywide zoning maps are available from various sources which will indicate the recommended quantity of insulation and/or the minimum R value for any area of the United States. Utility companies, municipal building inspection offices, and insulation manufacturers are ready sources of this information. Generally, R-19 is being specified for walls in all but the extreme southern belt. R-11 used to be an accepted standard until fuel cost began to skyrocket in the late 1970s and early 1980s.

The R-11 batt or blanket is customized to coincide with the 3 1/2″ depth of a stud. Therefore, a 2 × 4 stud wall cavity is limited to R-11 in the core. It is possible and practical to raise the resistance factor by sheathing the outer walls with a high-intensity insulation board in order to approach the R-19 goal. Dense styrofoam and beadboard sheet materials will be advantageous for this purpose. A close scrutiny and some adaptation will be required to make up for the lost holding power of siding nails, as the foam boards have no holding power whatever. Similarly, other methods and materials will be required to achieve adequate wind-bracing objectives.

The 6″ stud wall was conceived in the northern United States specifically for its superior depth to accommodate 6″ of blanket insulation (R-19). In conjunction with sheet-type insulboards of high R rating, a superior thermal wall can be achieved. To gain an alternative cost-comparable design, one has but to consider the double-wall design described in Chapter 11. It will prove more than 25% superior to a 6″ wall with comparable sheathing.

Ceiling insulation is equally or more critical in terms of quantity and installation. Because heat rises it will collect under the ceiling and ultimately escape through the materials. A general rule of thumb is that the insulation in a ceiling should rate about twice as high as the wall, up to R-40. From there on, the diminishing cost-effectiveness warrants consideration.

There are three generally accepted forms of insulation for ceilings: blanket, blown, and fill. Blanket is the expanded glass-fiber type, which comes in rolls and in two widths, to fit 16 or 24″ spaced ceiling joists. It can be purchased with a paper-backing vapor barrier or "unfaced." Blown insulation is a form of fire-retardant-treated cellulose. It gets its name from the technique of blowing it into an attic with air pressure. Fill insulation is a loose bead or granular-type insulation which is simply emptied from bags into the attic and spread to a uniform depth. Some of the materials commonly available are perlite, vermiculite, and Zonalite. Although the fill insulations are relatively easy to install, they suffer from a serious fault unless used in a confined space. In a typical attic that is adequately ventilated, the wind currents will shift the lightweight fill from one area to another, thus destroying the uniformity of depth that is desirable.

Attic Insulation

Blanket insulation may be laid in a single layer to the same depth as the ceiling joists. By present standards this is seldom enough, since residential trusses usually have 2 × 4 lower chords, and conventional roofed houses seldom have ceiling joists over 2 × 6 or 2 × 8 size.

A recommended technique to attain a higher R factor is to layer the blanket insulation (Fig. 12-15). For example, should the specs call for 10″ of blanket insulation, the first layer would be a 3 1/2″ blanket laid between 2 × 4 ceiling joists topped by a nominal 6″ layer laid at right angles over the joists. For a 2 × 6 ceiling joist the order would be reversed. For an R-38 requirement, two layers of

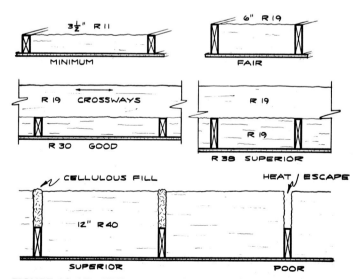

FIGURE 12-15 "R" means resistance to heat loss. Layering helps eliminate exfiltration places. Top layers are laid perpendicular to joists, bottom layers between joists.

6″ insulation are installed. One layer of 12″ blanket laid in the joist cavities does not meet R-38, as the joists will be exposed between the blankets, permitting as much as a 20 to 50% loss of efficiency. This loss can be overcome by filling the channels with granulated cellulose.

Another area of great heat loss is the area directly above the exterior wall plate. Unless preplanning has wrought a raised thermal truss, this area will be shallow in depth. Remember that fibrous insulations do not work well when compressed. Only when expanded are the cells large enough to encapsulate (trap) dead air and form an adequate thermal barrier. A conventional 2 × 6 rafter with a birds-mouth seat cut or a truss with 2 × 4 chords will have only about 4″ of depth from the top plate to the underside of the roof sheathing, not enough room for adequate insulation needs. This area in the ceiling is most vulnerable to heat loss by exfiltration.

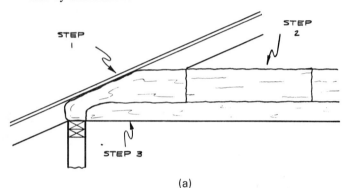

(a)

(b)

FIGURE 12-16 (a) A nonthermal truss or conventional rafter setup requires special attention to avoid great heat loss over the top plates. Where there are eave vents, corridors must be arranged over the insulation. Insulation stops are needed when blown-in insulation is used or a raised truss exists.

Blanket insulation is best put in before any ceiling covering, such as gypsum board, is installed. It can be installed effectively from below the ceiling joists only if the blankets are paper backed. The double-layering system can be all accomplished from below. This is advantageous with low-pitched roofs of 4 in 12 or less. The top layer is installed first, perpendicular to the joists (Fig. 12-16). Short pieces are cut to go over the top plates between the rafters. These pieces are made long enough so that the inner end will touch the edge of the first continuous blanket that is rolled out across the joists close to the top plate. Roll out the blanket to its full length, then slide it up against the short pieces all along the wall. Each adjacent piece to come is fluffed out and snuggled up tight to the preceding piece so that there are no air gaps. Work from each side of the roof toward the center of the ceiling. The last opening will seldom, if ever, be the exact width of the insulation, so a cut-down strip will be required. Custom fit it. Cut it a little wide so that it will compress against each side. Do not fold an overly wide piece in an attempt to make it fit. Sometimes a couple of inches of needed space can be gained by compressing the previous layers toward the eaves.

The lower layers can be put in place from below. It is a difficult job to do alone. Two workers make it easier. Also, the use of T braces will simplify the hoisting (T braces are described in the gypsum board part of this unit).

Put on safety glasses of the goggle type that hug the face. Wear a long-sleeved shirt and lightweight leather or rubber gloves if it is not too uncomfortable. The second that you pick up the insulation, tiny particles of fiberglass begin to float about. The person who insulates for a living should wear a respirator mask of some type as well as goggles for overhead work. Persons who choose not to wear protective clothing or gloves can avoid minute slivers in the fingers to some extent by blowing across the hands after each contact with the raw fiberglass. If some irritation is experienced, it is not long lived, as simple washing will usually carry away the slivers. One should be very wary of rubbing the eyes at all times. In any case the itching that may attend insulating is seldom significant enough that it should discourage the do-it-yourself.

Lay the insulation roll on the floor with the fiber side facing up and the open end toward the exterior wall. In this position it is parallel to the ceiling joists. The roll will probably unwind itself and end up at the other side of the room. Cut it off about 4″ longer than the distance across the room. Wedge the remaining roll between a couple of studs on the interior partition so that it does not unroll any further. Pick up the insulation from underneath the paper backing. Step up on your low scaffold plank or step ladder and proceed to tuck the blanket up between the joists. Staple the 1″ paper flange to the vertical surfaces of the sides of the joists. Make the outer edge of the flange flush with the lower edge of the joists. With two people working, one will lead out, stretch, and hold while the second person staples. A T brace or two placed across the joists under the insulation will help immeasurably. It will require a staple about every 6 to 8″ to support the blanket, as friction fitting is not applicable in this position. Be certain that the beginning end is tightly compressed against the starter piece that was installed first above the plate. This is the most critical exfiltration place in the ceiling. Be very careful not to tear the paper with the nose of the stapler.

It is possible, though more involved, to put an uncut blanket across the full span of the ceiling. Such a practice is preferred where it can be accomplished. Lay the blanket roll on the other side of the interior bearing partitions, those parallel to the opposite exterior wall. Feed the starter end of the roll up into the attic while folding it lengthwise with paper out and down. With the aid of one or more helpers, carefully snake the blanket over any and all perpendicular partitions until the exterior-wall starting point is reached. Staple and work back toward the roll. Complete the job in the remaining area, making sure not to cut the piece short. The concluding end must compress and fit as well as the starting end. During the snaking, be careful not to tear the paper, as the main purpose is to sustain a continuous leak-proof seal throughout.

The first and last joist cavities, the one on each end of the house, will be narrower than those in the field. Cut the blanket about 1″ wider than the cavity width. The fiberglass will thereby compress snugly against the sides of the joists. Any small inconsistency in width will seldom result in a void.

Leave no secluded area without insulation. Be especially conscientious about small voids around chimneys, backer blocks, vents, and wiring. The smallest leak can allow exfiltration—like air out of a punctured tire. It takes only a few voids to seriously damage the integrity of the whole system.

An attic access or a fold-down stair will account for significant loss unless insulated and weather sealed (Fig.

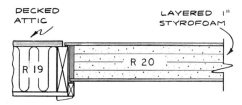

FIGURE 12-18   Using Styrofoam layers for the core of an access box will reduce the height of the box. The economical bead board type will net a value of about R-5 per inch of depth.

12-17). An access with only a single piece of paneling or plywood on the opening is like a single-pane window. Build a box door as deep as the insulation depth surrounding it. Build a frame around the opening to hold the surrounding insulation away from the box. Fill the trapdoor box with insulation. Fasten a top board of light plywood on it. Let this top board hang over the box on all sides so that it rests on the opening sides. Place a weather-seal gasket between the box top and the top of the opening casement. Use a material such as felt. Foam rubber deteriorates rapidly in hot weather. Place another weather seal between the bottom of the box and the casement stop at the lower edge (Fig. 12-18). The opening is now insulated and sealed against exfiltration.

Folding stairs are more difficult to insulate, though not impossible. A dense Styrofoam sandwich on the bottom face of the door will add some R value but will not be equal to the ceiling rating. A box above the stair comprised of several layers of dense Styrofoam will complete the requirement. It can be a push-up type or hinged to fold out of the way if there is adequate height under the rafters.

Wall Insulation

Fiberglass batt insulation is by far the most prevalent type used in exterior wall cavities. By any standard the payback will always be worth the installation cost for as much as can be put into an exterior wall where heating and cooling days of the year are substantial. There are two general blanket types available, vapor-barrier backed and friction fit. They also go by the terms "faced" and "unfaced."

The faced type is available with a reflective foil backing or with an asphalt-impregnated vapor-seal paper backing. The foil is said to turn back heat rays. Both types will provide an effective moisture barrier when properly installed.

Good installation mandates completely filling the stud cavity. This will not be accomplished simply by stuffing the blanket into the opening, as the edges will catch here and there and compact, leaving unseen voids behind the edges. A putty knife or a paint stick sharpened like a chisel makes a good tool to push the edges of the fibers to the back of the cavity.

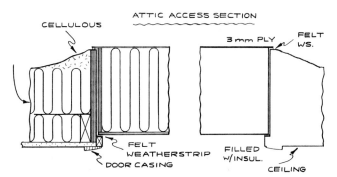

FIGURE 12-17   The attic access is insulated on a par with the ceiling by constructing a lightweight box filled with insulation and weather stripping around both upper and lower points of bearing.

Carefully separate the blanket at the bottom where there is wiring to be enclosed (Fig. 12-19). Feed the back half of the insulation up, over, and down behind the wire and tuck it behind the duplex outlet box (Fig. 12-20). Cut a neat rectangle a little smaller than the box in the front half of the blanket and fit the insulation around the box. Do not shove the full-depth blanket in on top of a wire that crosses between studs or pull the full thickness down behind the wire. This is a sure way to reduce its effectiveness. Those cold-air drafts that come out of duplex outlets are certain signs of faulty insulating techniques.

Unlike the ceiling, which requires the paper flange to be stapled to the joists' vertical surfaces to provide sheer grip, the wall installation will not need this type of support. The paper flange is stapled to the facing edge of the stud. Line the 1″ flange edge up 1/2″ from the other side of the

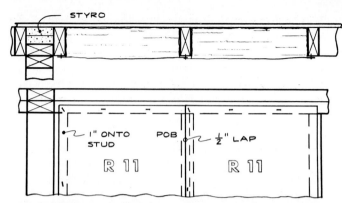

FIGURE 12-21   Lapping the vapor barrier paper correctly can save almost 50% of the staples. After the first stud (POB), staple through both paper edges simultaneously. Note the layered Styrofoam insulation in the intersection post behind the blocks.

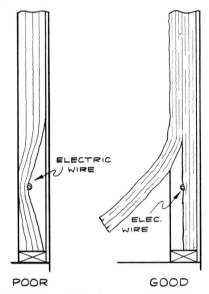

FIGURE 12-19   Carefully separate the insulation blanket. Pull the back half down behind the electric wire.

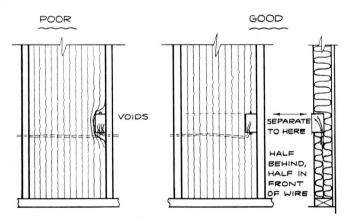

FIGURE 12-20   Great heat loss will occur around electric boxes that are not insulated correctly. Split the insulation and tuck half behind the box and wires that cross. Cut away a rectangle from the front layer where the box is.

stud (Fig. 12-21). A total of five staples is adequate to keep the paper flat and taut. The leading edge can be held with less since it will be lapped 1/2″ by the succeeding blanket flange, and the staples from that flange will secure both pieces when placed in the center of the stud. This lineup provides a 1/2″ overlap of the flanges.

Precut stud-length batts are made a little longer than the opening so that the top of the blanket can be compressed up against the top plate. The paper will then lap onto the plate so that a couple of staples can be put in to support the blanket while stretching it taut and smooth.

Friction-fit batts come in stud lengths for nominal-4″ deep walls on 16″ centers. For 6″ stud walls on 24″ centering, the batts are most obtainable bagged in half-lengths. Start at the top and press the batt in with some compression against the underside of the top plate. Fluff the side out and in so that the cavity is completely filled. When using two-piece batts, be certain that the ends in the center touch snugly and that contact is made with the plate at both top and bottom.

Insulate all other cavities that do not contain full batts or blankets. Custom fit the larger openings with cut pieces. Stuff all the small cracks that remain around window and door frames. Check corner posts and intersection posts. Leave no cavity without insulation, no matter how small or insignificant it may appear. Each void constitutes a future leak, a drain on the homeowner's purse.

Plastic Vapor Barrier

A vapor barrier for unfaced batts is made by draping sheet plastic over the entire wall. Start on the face of a partition stud with a full 100′ roll of 8′ plastic. Use as few staples as possible, but be certain that the plastic is held firmly to the top plate. It should cover the horizontal joint of the double plate to reduce the potential of infiltration. Make no cuts whatever in the entire roll. Run it over all windows, doors, electrical outlets, and any other openings. Do not cut these openings, except necessary entrances, until after the wallboard is installed. This system will produce a tight, well-held vapor barrier with little potential for leakage. After the drywall is on, it is a simple matter to cut around the inside of the window jambs with a knife. When the end of the roll is reached, lap a new roll over it. Cover a full stud cavity width (16 or 24″) with the lap. Remember, do not cut or stop the plastic in each room. Run it over each partition intersection so that an airtight seal exists. The plastic will pucker a little going over the sole and a little more under the top plate. Slit the corner of the plastic on each side of the plate so that it can lie flat. Staple the corners down to the plates.

On a super-insulation design where the objective is a totally leak-free house, sheet plastic will also be used to cover the ceiling. It will take some ingenuity and conscientiousness to make it completely tight, as the plastic cannot be fed over partitions where trusses are used (the webs interfere). Each contact at the upper plates is made by permitting a fold of a couple of inches of plastic to run down onto the vertical face of the top plates. At the room corners a fold is made like a paper package. Any damage to the plastic, such as a hole poked in, should be sealed with nylon tape or plumber's tape. After the ceiling and wall skin are installed, each room will be a tightly sealed compartment, free of drafts and exfiltration.

There was a period in the history of building when it was thought that a house should breathe in order to dissuade condensation. Now it is known and accepted that a house need not be built to leak to achieve an absence of condensation. It can and should be built airtight for the sake of heating and cooling economy. The necessary periodical exchange of air that prevents condensation can then be controlled at will by the occupants rather than left to chance by leaky construction.

DRYWALLING

For many years prior to World War II the most common wall covering was wallpaper on top of plaster, or textured and painted plaster. Wet plaster was spread over fuzzy rough wooden lath. These lath boards were about 3/8″ × 1 1/4″ × 40″. Lathing in the cities was a vocation all to itself. Watching a lather swing his hatchet hammer was like seeing a symphony in rhythm. He could set a nail and with a single whack drive it home through the lath into a stud. The hatchet hammer on the back stroke would revolve in his hand almost imperceptibly to the eye, coming forward with the hatchet side to sever the excess of the lath at a point dead center over the stud. It was done that way for centuries until gypsum lath was invented.

Wet plaster was applied in three separate coats. The first coat was called the *brown coat*. It was hairy and clung well to the lath. The second coat was the *scratch coat*. It was a finer-grade composition. While still wet and soft it was striated in random swirls to create a uniformly roughened surface. The final topping coat was made of fine-grained lime. It was troweled to a smooth surface for wallpaper application or given some configuration for painting.

Wet plastering, as the system was called, was slowly phased out throughout the country. Except for specialty work, the craft has been replaced by the drywall system. The demise of wet plaster came primarily because of one poor construction feature that was eliminated by "drywall" (gypsum wallboard). The wet-plaster process took up about three weeks of the building schedule in lost time while waiting for the moisture to dry slowly. It was so humid in the house that new wood window casements would run water on the surface, soaking all the wooden parts. They would swell shut and delay the painting job interminably. All cabinet and trim work had to be delayed until the humidity reached a low-enough level not to cause swelling. Some aesthetic features of the wet-plaster era have been lost. Many homes of even modest budget had coved ceilings and arched passageways, which are impractical to make with dry products. There is a nostalgia to some of these grand old homes which should give the remodeler cause to pause and reflect before tearing them out and doing them over. The wet-plaster trade is not extinct. It can be located on demand, although it is now a specialty in the residential field.

Plaster Board

Plaster board is a general term for gypsum board. Both are sheet forms of wall-covering board. The gypsum plaster is sandwiched between paper. As a building product for wall covering, it is universal. The most common type is faced with a manila vinyl-sealed paper. On the back side is a less costly gray paper. Other designs of gypsum wallboard are available with prefinished surfaces of woodgrain decals, fabric patterns, and wallpaper-like designs.

The Drywall System

The system of drywalling and the term *drywall* have become synonymous with gypsum board. In fact, few if any builders refer to the product as anything but drywall. As a system, drywalling means the installation of gypsum wallboard, followed by taping and leveling of joints with compound. The great advantage to the construction industry of drywalling over the wet-wall process is time. No time is lost. The drying time for the joint compound is usually overnight, or at most, a day or two in damp weather.

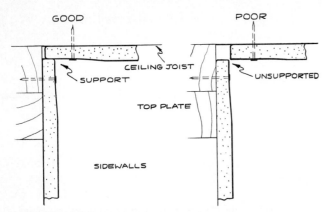

FIGURE 12-22 Ceiling sheets are installed first so that wall sheets will support them. Leave about 1/8″ clearance.

Installing Drywall

For the most part, drywalling is an independent trade, although carpenters and handymen can and do install drywall sheets satisfactorily. The art of joint finishing, however, is a highly skilled operation and not often within the capability of the casual dabbler. It is a manipulative skill similar to the troweling of flatwork masonry.

The sequence of drywall installation is from the top down. There is a definite logic in this order. The ceiling boards are placed and secured first. The wallboards are put on horizontally. The top course is placed and secured first so that its upper edge will support the edge of the ceiling board (Fig. 12-22). This also provides a cup joint on both edges (ceiling and wall) so that the joint tape and compound can have some depth and the corner will remain square. The lower wallboard is installed last. It is pressed tightly against the board above by the use of foot raisers or levers. The house constructed conventionally with precut studs will have a little extra height so that with two horizontal sheets and a 1/2″-thick ceiling sheet, all boards will go in without trimming the bottom sheet. A precut stud (92 5/8″) plus a 2 × 4 sole (1 1/2″) plus a double top plate (3″) adds up to 97 1/8″. Theoretically, the ceiling and wall board takes up 96 1/2″ of height (less on the cupped side of the ceiling board). In practice, all components—the floor and the top plate—would have to be perfectly straight and parallel to have 5/8″ of space left over. Such perfection is not the rule; therefore, the 5/8″ becomes a buffer zone to accommodate imperfections in alignment (levelness, plumbness, and parallelism).

Drywaller's Objectives

Drywalling is one of the those seemingly simple jobs that can really be goofed up, or it can be accomplished reasonably well with knowledge and desire to do a good job. Some

stated objectives will hopefully set the stage for the latter. By careful adherence to the instructions and illustrations that follow, the learner will:

1. Know the preferred direction to place drywall sheets on the ceiling and walls.
2. Be able to make a bill of materials for a room or a full house.
3. Evaluate and establish the best cup joint and square-edged butt joint locations.
4. Know how to plot and arrange the most feasible sized boards to cause the least number of end joints (there are no cups on the ends).
5. Know specific nailing and gluing patterns for different places.
6. Make cuts for length, width, electrical outlets, and openings to a tolerance of 1/8″ without tears or fractures.
7. Raise and secure boards with or without assistance using supporting aides.
8. Know the proper nails to use and how to seat and dimple them.
9. Know several methods of securing butt joints where no cupped edge exists.

Wallboard Direction

Wallboards are placed perpendicular to joists and studs wherever the area is greater than 4′ × 8′. A surface that is no longer than a sheet may be covered with a single piece installed parallel to joists or studs provided that it can be put in place. A 2′ × 4′ closet, for example, could have a single 4 × 8′ sheet for the back wall and a 23 1/2″ piece for each end cut lengthways from a full sheet. In this case there is no reason to cut a 4 × 8 in half, making two 4 × 4 pieces, just to form a horizontal joint at the center. Where a full sheet can be maneuvered into place, the necessity of taping and compounding a midheight joint is eliminated.

Ceiling placement of full and sublength boards follows some rules designed to minimize stress cracks. One of the most frequent callbacks on new construction is due to cracked end joints in ceiling drywall. There are two reasons for this, one of which has to do with proximity of joints (the other reason for joint failure is covered later under a discussion of how to make a strong end joint). Plan the whole ceiling arrangement before starting. Sketch a layout on paper to clarify the situation graphically.

Rooms under 16′ in length can and should be covered with full-length boards. This eliminates any end butt joints, a serious objective. Drywall is obtainable in 8, 10, 12, 14, and 16′ lengths. There is a trend away from 14 and 16′ lengths, as the weight and awkwardness of handling are objectionable. Nonetheless, if manpower is available, these

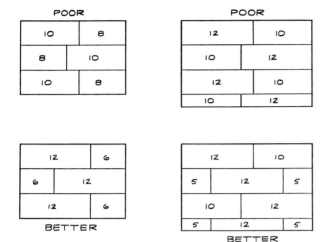

FIGURE 12-23 Joints should not be allowed to just happen. Place them to fall far apart and not in the central area of a large room. These rooms are 12 × 18 and 14 × 22.

lengths will provide the best job. Some yards stock only 8 and 12′ lengths. Assume for an example that 12′ is the longest available board and that the room to be covered is a rectangular shape 12 × 18′ with ceiling joists spanning the 12′ direction. The first rule to keep in mind is to stagger the joints as far apart as possible *and* avoid any in the central area of the room. The center is the area of greatest flexibility of ceiling joists or truss chords. Any flexing from an imposed load will set in motion the possibility of a failed joint in this locality. See the diagrams shown in Fig. 12-23 denoting poor joint location and those indicating better joint location. A proper arrangement of sheets does not occur by chance but must be planned. Determine where the first full sheet or nearly full sheet will be placed. Then mark all future end locations on the joists with a carpenter's red crayon or felt-tipped pen.

Plotting the Materials

There are two ways of going about the business of mapping board location, estimating needs, and creating a bill of materials from which to order. One method is to do it piecemeal. One might reconnoiter the total square footage of all the wall and ceiling area in the house (the ceiling can be taken from the square footage on the floor plan). Do not discount doors and windows. Then order some common modules. For example, where 12′ was practical for the longest length, an initial order may be placed for as many sheets as would cover 75 or 80% of the total. Then begin the job. All ceilings are covered first. Cutoffs are carefully stacked. Each cutoff is used wherever possible. When the supply of boards is exhausted and none of the scraps left over will fit anywhere, an assessment of the remaining areas to be covered is made. This method is favored by those who shun the analytical planning exercise for its tedium or

difficulty. A few dollars more for waste is considered well worth the cost to avoid the mathematics.

The analytical approach to estimating and making a bill of materials requires more planning. The main result is less waste of materials. Contractors often opt for the first method, except that an attempt will be made to order 100% of the estimated need, thereby producing a single invoice. The contract price is usually based on a square-foot cost of purchased material; therefore, waste becomes profit. By comparison, the lump-sum contract will be hurt by waste or overordering.

Individual room assessment is the first step in producing the detailed materials bill. A floor plan can be used on which to outline placements of sheets for each room. Bear in mind that each sheet will be placed at right angles to the ceiling joists. The cup joints usually run lengthways of a rectangular house. L-, T-, and U-shaped houses may have joists in the wings running at 90° to those in the main body of the structure. The actual direction must be known in order to plot the proper direction in which the ceiling sheets will be positioned.

The ceiling is actually plotted better from inside the house rather than from the plan. The best placement is more obvious when looking at the actual construction. Any question of lengths is readily answerable by counting joist spaces or by measuring the real distance.

Modular placement is the name of the game in the analytical method of computing drywall need. The project is a jigsaw puzzle where full modular pieces are inserted first followed by segments. Start by working out the ceiling puzzle on paper for each room.

Next, lay the walls of the room out into a straight line as you would cut one corner of a box and fold it out flat. Draw it to scale or use 1/4″ graph paper (make a 1/4″ square equal to 2′ × 2′). Draw the vertical lines where the corners of the walls are. Draw in the doorways. The bottom of the doorway may net a small saving in wallboard. Most windows may be ignored, as they usually cut into both the upper and lower sheets, for a total module loss. Only where a series of windows go down to the baseboard or floor can a saving be realized.

Place end joints above and below windows whenever possible, never at the corners of openings. The header area above a window is usually an area of solid backing which makes for a good drywall joint. Most windowsills are lower than the midpoint of the wall, so any end joint in the area below the sill will be shorter than if it were made elsewhere where it would be a full 48″ high.

Code the foldout wall diagram with numbers indicating the sheet length that is required to cover an area. Remember that this is a modular number game of units, not a square-foot analysis. Several small segments that take less than a full sheet can be coordinated into a single sheet. A double number stated like a fraction is one way to code

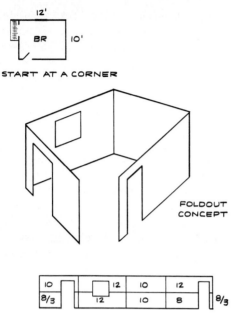

FIGURE 12-24 Make a foldout pattern layout for the walls of each room. Start the foldout at any corner. Label and code the laid-out pattern.

it. The top number is the sheet length from which the piece will be cut. The bottom number is the quantity of pieces coming out of that piece (Fig. 12-24). All that remains is to label the schematic with a room description.

Accumulating a total ordering list is a simple matter of addition. Make a foldout schematic for each room. Add the sheets of each size required. Then total all room orders by sheet size. Do the same with the ceilings.

Why bother to order different lengths? Why not just order all long sheets? Several reasons are worth considering. One is the difficulty of handling the bigger sheets and the extra cutting that will be necessary. There will be a larger accumulation of subsized cutoffs to attempt to use. Added cost may also be a compelling consideration, as the larger sheets usually cost more per square foot.

Cutting Gypsum Board

There are a number of tools for cutting drywall, any of which will work adequately. There are some preferred places for some tools.

Cutting a straight piece off the end of a board or the edge is probably done best with a knife-edged tool (linoleum knife, drywall hatchet, pocket knife, etc.). Use a straightedge guide. A drywall square is effective up to 4′. Always cut away from the T of the square as cutting toward it usually dulls your knife as it passes over the metal T. A leftover strip of plywood with one factory edge (the uncut original edge) makes a good 8′ straightedge. For the cleanest break, cut the board on both sides, especially when getting close to an edge or end (Fig. 12-25). The backside cut

should be a little undercut so that the leading edge will be the face side. The little gypsum knobs that remain after breaking can be rasped off with a drywall rasp board or a course sandboard. Do not attempt to rasp away paper to shorten a board, as it will only fray and make a poor joint. If the paper needs shortening, use the straightedge and knife again.

It is not always necessary to cut the back side. On crisp, dry days the board will be brittle. A cut line on the face side is usually adequate. The board is snapped gingerly in the same manner that glass is scarred and broken on a line. The scrap or smaller segment is folded back and a knife run down the valley.

To cut away the corner of an L-shaped piece, the cut must be made on both sides of the board (Fig. 12-26). The gypsum is snapped and broken on one line first. Then it is snapped on the other line. A little flexing and the scrap corner piece can be eased away. A little insurance against tearing the paper beyond the corner intersection may be had

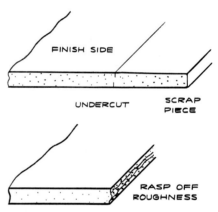

FIGURE 12-25 Cutting away a strip close to an edge is best accomplished by cutting both sides. Little knobs remaining may be rasped off.

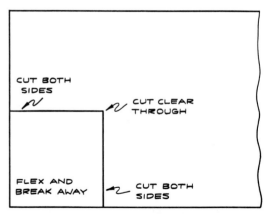

FIGURE 12-26 To remove a corner, cut both finish and back side of the pattern, sever completely through at the corner, and flex the cutout until it falls free.

by making sure that your knife penetrates completely through the gypsum at the intersection of the cut lines. Do not allow the cut lines to go beyond the corner, as this will encourage the break to do the same. Another technique to avoid inside corner-breaking problems is to press a drywall bayonet saw through at each leg of the corner and saw away from the corner about 1″. A woodworker's compass saw (often incorrectly called a keyhole saw) works well for this purpose.

Measuring and Custom Fitting

In earlier chapters relating to woodwork it was advised that wood to be fitted to an opening should be cut a little long, then trimmed back to a precise fit. Such is not the case with drywall cutting. The difference is because the drywall system employs a fluid joint compound intended to fill voids, whereas gaping joints in wood patched with a filler is a sure sign of poor craftsmanship. There are other reasons for not fitting a long sheet of gypsum board tightly into an opening. Gypsum absorbs a lot of moisture, which causes swelling. A board on the ceiling or wall that touches at each end of the room cannot expand lengthwise, so its only alternative is to bow outward from one joist or stud to the adjacent one and sometimes cause "nail popping."

Labor saving will be realized by planned short cutting wherever the end of a sheet butts a corner. Plan to allow a 1/8″ minimum clearance at the ends. For example, where a surface can be covered from one end to the other (an inside fitting), 1/8″ should be allowed at each end (Fig. 12-27). Therefore, the sheet will be cut 1/4″ shorter than the actual measurement of the area length being covered.

Unsquare corners cause problems if the condition is ignored before cutting the wallboard. The squareness of corners can be monitored by measuring. A framing square can also be used, but its smallness can produce a faulty assessment. Check out the corner squareness by measuring the full length of a ceiling across the ceiling joists from corner to corner parallel and adjacent to the wall. Next move out from the wall 4′ and measure again, parallel to the first measurement. Where a room is perfectly rectangular or a parallelogram, the measurements will be iden-

tical. If it is trapezoidal, one measurement will be larger or smaller than the other.

Check each corner with the square when there is suspicion or evidence of out-of-squareness. The large door hanging square, made from a plywood cutoff scrap, is an excellent tool for checking the squareness. Where one corner of the ceiling is square and the other is not, start the installation against the square abutment end and custom angle cut the wallboard to the other end.

Bear an important element in mind about pattern cutting. If you are cutting the ceiling board on a table, it must be remembered that the lengths will be reversed from side to side when the face side of the board is up because on the ceiling the face side is down. Many a sheet has been miscut because the person doing the cutting forgot that the sheet will be revolved 180°, which reverses the sides.

Cutouts

Light-fixture cutouts can be located in a number of ways. Measuring is one of the poorest methods. It usually results in an oversized hole and a difficult patch job. One method is to put the panel up in place. Hold it with T bars. Press or pound with your hand around the electric box. Let the panel down. There should be some faint indentation marks which allow tracing a box or pattern. A similar method is to use a fine bead of dark caulking. Cut the nozzle of a new tube so that a very thin bead comes out. Apply a bead all around on the box edges. Press the panel into it. Colored chalk can also be used. Squeeze the plastic chalk bottle sharply so that a mist of chalk dust is blown onto the box edges. Enough of an outline will be transferred to the wallboard so that a real box can be traced onto the position. These impression methods have one good feature in common. It is impossible to cut the box hole in completely the wrong location, as is often done when measurements are used.

Remove the box hole plug by first cutting the tracing with a knife. Since the pattern is on the back side, make the cut a little larger (about 1/16″) than the pattern. Push the point of a knife until it just breaks through the face side at four places around the circle (or octagon). Turn the sheet up on edge or over. Retrace the outline by centering a box or a template between the four punched slots. Use the bayonet saw or keyhole saw to cut out the plug. Be very careful not to tear the paper. Some fixtures (porcelain, for example) just barely go beyond the box, so there is very little room for error. One-eighth inch is about maximum.

Wall-outlet cutouts may be removed in the same manner. One must be careful to secure the upper edge of the sheet tightly against the ceiling for boxes that are in the upper half of the wall. This can be done effectively by using two half-length T boards of 49″ height (Fig. 12-28). The top T bar is made 12 to 14″ long with a 5/8″ groove about

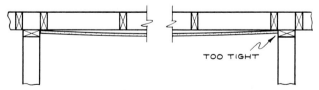

FIGURE 12-27 Cutting a board to the full dimension of an opening usually results in too tight a fit or crushed joints and broken corners. An 1/8″ clearance per mating edge is the rule. In this view the board should have been cut 1/4″ shorter than the distance between the partition frame.

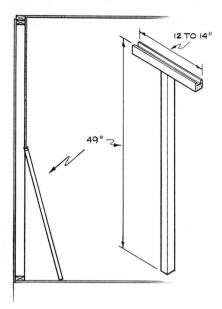

FIGURE 12-28 Use a pair of half-height T braces between studs to hold the top course sheet of wallboard tightly against the ceiling board while nailing. Be sure to mark the stud locations on the ceiling before raising the upper wall sheets.

1/2″ deep. This length will permit it to slip between the common stud spaces (14 1/2 or 22 1/2″ wide). The gypsum board is hoisted into place and held there until the little T boards are wedged under the edge in two balanced locations (approximate quarter points).

Should the upper plate line at the ceiling dip down at any point, a decision will be necessary. A small dip near the center can be compensated for by positioning the board so that a crack of equal width appears at each end between the board edge and the ceiling. The center area should be touching tightly.

A crack in excess of 1/8″ above each end of a top-course wallboard may be cause to cut the edge of the sheet to the actual contour of the ceiling. This contour can be drawn on the immobilized board by scribing a parallel line starting at the edge of the board opposite the widest gap (Fig. 12-29). Hold something under the pencil to space it out to this point (your finger, a nail, a pencil compass). With the other end of the pencil against the ceiling, draw it clear across the length of the board, making a mark parallel to the ceiling. Kick out the T boards at the bottom while holding onto the sheet. Lower it carefully. Cut precisely on the line. It will be necessary to cut both sides, bearing down with considerable pressure to reach the center of the gypsum. It is not possible to break off a slim piece like this with a cut on the face side only because there is a double layer of paper on the back side where the gray paper laps over the manila paper.

Small gaps between the top wallboard and the ceiling board can be filled with compound and allowed to dry

before taping. Larger ones will take multiple fillings, as each application will shrink. This delays the job for 24 hours. It is simpler to custom fit the edge than to do an extensive filling job. Any gap over 1/16″ should be filled a day before taping begins. Failure to do so will set up a condition for breakdown by leaving a void (an air pocket) behind the tape.

Marking boxes in the lower half of the wall is done in a similar manner. Instead of T boards, a metal foot lever called a drywall raiser is used (Fig. 12-30). Makeshift raisers can be made by planing a long bevel on the end of a 1 × 6 or a 1 × 8 board. A 1 × 1 or a strip of molding can be nailed across the board about 2″ back from the bevel to form a fulcrum. The wallboard is brought into position with the upper edge under the edge of the top wallboard, which has already been installed above. The raiser(s) are jammed against the sole plate with the wallboard on top of them. The installer then steps on the raiser with heel pressure and snugs the board up tightly to the board above. The board

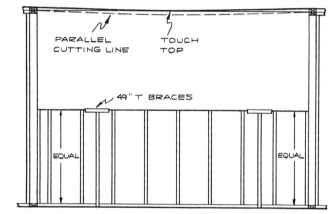

FIGURE 12-29 Mark a cutting line parallel to a plate line that is bowed down or up or crooked. Custom cut the edge to fit the irregularity. The lower edge should be parallel to the floor when making the contoured mark. The illustration is exaggerated for graphic clarity.

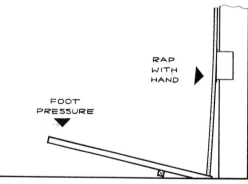

FIGURE 12-30 Hold the lower panel up snug against the edge of the top panel with a foot lifter. Rap the board sharply over the box to form an impression on the back side.

is not immobilized as the one above was. It must be held there until someone can establish the electrical outlet box impressions on the backside.

After all cutouts have been removed, the board is again put in place and nailed. The upper board, with its pair of supporting T board braces, will stay in place while nailing proceeds. The lower board must be held up or blocked up until a sufficient quantity of nails is installed to support the weight. This quantity is dependent on the size of the board. Place the first nails anywhere along the bottom or at marked locations in the field. Do not place the first nails along the top edge, as the board will tear away from them under the weight should the support be relaxed too soon.

The height of switch and duplex boxes is somewhat standardized but not mandatorily so. Some electricians stand the duplex box on top of their hammer; some measure. Duplexes are usually between 12 and 16″ above the floor level. The rule is *consistency*. Place them all at a uniform height.

Switch boxes are most conveniently set with the top at 48 9/16″ below the ceiling joists. A 1/2″ gypsum ceiling will then position the box a small fraction of an inch below the bottom edge of the top wallboard. This makes it possible to saw or cut out just three sides of the box opening from the top edge of the bottom board. It also simplifies marking the location, as the box is clearly visible and traceable at the top of each side of the box. Hold a spare box up to these marks and trace around the three sides. For any other thickness of ceiling the box will be set 48″ plus the ceiling thickness down from the top of the plate.

Duplex outlet boxes for countertop appliances in the kitchen and bathroom are usually installed at a height of 40″ (Fig. 12-31). The standard countertop height is 36″. The backsplash may extend as much as 3 to 4″ above the counter. The duplex faceplate should clear the backsplash.

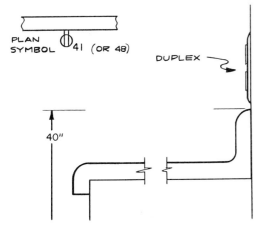

FIGURE 12-31 Duplex outlets other than those 12 to 16″ above the floor are marked with an inch designation, indicating the distance from the floor to the bottom of the box.

They can also be placed at the same height as switch boxes, for the sake of standardization.

Specialty outlets may be designated on a plan at any specific height to meet a need. Regular duplexes along the walls of living rooms and bedrooms will not be labeled with height figures. Any other outlet that is not installed at this lower uniform height will have a definitive height dimension next to the duplex symbol. Without this height callout (given in inches) the electrician will assume that the box is to be installed at the low standard level of 12″.

Strengthening the midpoint horizontal joint of the wallboard can be achieved in a number of ways. There was a time when 2 × 4 blocks were nailed between the studs to back up the joint area; however, the block is an objectionable obstruction to a good insulation job. It is an unnecessary cost item and is time consuming to install. It came about partly as a vestige of the old firestop block used in balloon framing and later as a centering spacer. Some things are not questioned and just keep on happening long after the need has disappeared.

A simple and economical way to stiffen the horizontal edge joint, which will later be taped and compounded, is to run a bead of panel adhesive along the top of the lower sheet just before it is pressed up against the other sheet. Go down the junction as soon as the nailing is supportive and flex the boards in or out at any location between studs where the edges do not line up perfectly. The edges can be flexed into perfect alignment. In a few seconds the adhesive will immobilize the joint. Use a thin bead of adhesive, as squeeze-out is undesirable. Squeezed-out adhesive will interfere with the taping operation. Some installers prefer carpenter's glue to panel adhesive, as it can be mopped smooth with a wet finger, thereby eliminating hard beads that protrude later.

Kitchen and bathroom wallboard positioning presents a unique potential. The centerline joint can often be eliminated completely where there are long lengths of wall covered by upper and lower cabinets. The exposed area between the upper and lower cabinetry encompasses the normal location of the horizontal wallboard joint. A half-sheet of board, cut lengthways, is installed on the upper quarter of the wall, followed by a full-width sheet through the middle half sector of the wall. The bottom quarter of the wall is covered with the remaining half-cut sheet. All the joints are now underneath (behind) the cabinets (Fig. 12-32). These joints should be taped and compounded to bring the surface to a straight line and to assure an infiltration-proof joint on the exterior walls. Backing or immobilizing with adhesive is unnecessary, as no pressure will ever be exerted against the joint. The resulting joint-free area between the cabinets presents a smooth uniform surface, free of compound, for papering, tiling, or whatever covering is desired. The same technique can be used in a bathroom or laundry room where long cabinets are planned.

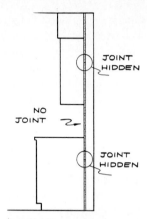

FIGURE 12-32 Behind cabinets that run full length of a wall, a joint at midpoint can be eliminated by splitting a wall board and placing half at the top, a full sheet through the middle, and a half at the bottom.

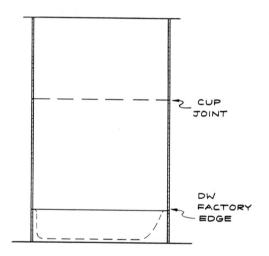

FIGURE 12-33 Lay the first sheet of water-resistant wallboard with its closed factory edge along the tub rim. Custom cut and fit the pieces above.

Tub and shower enclosures should be fitted with water-resistant wallboard with the closed cupped edge adjacent to the top flanges of a tub or shower. This vulnerable area should never have a raw, exposed gypsum edge on the wallboard. Even the papered edge should not be resting tightly against a tub surface. A 1/8″ gap is provided so that a channel will exist to fill with a waterproofing seal. Due to this exactness, this sheet is put on first (Fig. 12-33). The remaining area above must be carefully custom fitted. Measurements are taken at each end. The board is cut close enough to slip in snugly at top and bottom. The cut edge will be at the top. Remember the reverse orientation problem when laying out the cut. Even though a straightedge is to be used, it will be prudent to pencil mark the cut line full length of the board. This will help eliminate a false cut should the straightedge slip during the cutting process.

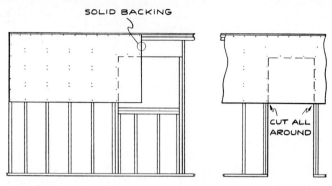

FIGURE 12-34 Saw out a window opening. Cut both sides and top of an interior door opening with a knife, flex, and pop it out.

Do not custom cut wallboards to fit around openings in a wall. Most cutouts for these locations will leave a board in an L or U shape. Such a piece is vulnerable to breakage from the inside corners out when it is being moved into position. A better method in most cases is to nail an uncut piece over the opening and then cut out the opening (Fig. 12-34). A drywall saw is held against the rough frame and worked toward the corner of the frame until the scrap falls away into your free hand. A doorway presents ready access to both sides of the overhanging board. A neat way to cut this piece out is with a knife and a straightedge on the face side. The upper corner can be accurately located on the face by punching a nail through the back side at the intersection of the header and trimmer. The back side is cut quickly simply by drawing the knife along the edge of the trimmer stud and the header. After both sides are cut, the board is wobbled to and fro until it falls away. An advantage of this method is the reduction of plaster dust (a characteristic of sawing).

Framework Surface Preparation

Now that the reader has some background on installation sequence and placement of sheets, it becomes important to learn the techniques that make the difference between a neat job and a shoddy project. The wet-plaster system has one advantage over the drywall system. Wet plaster can be molded to cover up most of the minor obstructions and depressions that are found on framework. For the finished surface of drywall to appear flat and straight, it is required that the framework below be flat and straight. Corners, junctions, and parallel pieces of wood must meet as intended without obtrusions, depressions, or misalignment. This factor places a much higher requirement on the accuracy and quality of the so-called rough framework.

Each surface to be covered must be carefully inspected for any type of imperfection that will affect the ultimate surface and alignment of the drywall (Fig. 12-35). A stringline should be used to check the ceiling flatness across the joists and diagonally. There may be a joist with

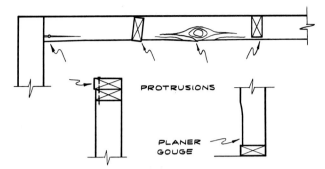

FIGURE 12-35 All protrusions and subsurface areas of significance should be leveled by removing or filling.

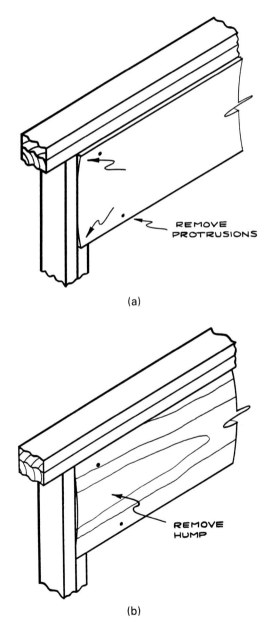

(a)

(b)

FIGURE 12-36 To make a flat surface for wallboard, cupped edges of a header that protrude (a) and a humped center (b) must be removed.

its crown reversed (down) which must be flexed up and held with a strong back. Occasionally, a truss web is misaligned, which malforms the lower chord relation. It has to be detached, reset, and regusseted. Knots close to the edge of joists and studs are common causes of trouble. The protrusion is discovered by holding a long straightedge such as a 4 or 6' level against each board. The hump must be sawed to a straight line. *Protruding nail heads* should be driven flush to the surface. *Cupped headers* over windows and doors frequently protrude at the corners or center. Each protrusion must be eliminated (Fig. 12-36).

Earlier in the text, the importance of not splitting the ends of plates was stressed. *A split plate* must expand to the interior and/or exterior. The widened board will hang over. Such an overhang on the interior must be cut off (a difficult job in the inside corner).

A thorough inspection, room by room, and marking with a red crayon is the layout forerunner to success. Mark a whole room as a unit. Then proceed methodically to make all the necessary corrections.

Phasing the surface preparation can be multistage. Where there is a large quantity to be done on the interior surfaces of the exterior walls, it will be accomplished easier before the insulation is installed. The same is true for the ceiling. By contrast, the interior partitions may be left until just before the application of the drywall.

Ceiling End Joints

There are three successful methods of butt joining the uncupped ends of gypsum board on a ceiling. There is one notoriously poor method which accounts for many contract callbacks (defective work that fails within the warranty period).

The poor butt joint is one that meets end to end on the underedge of a single ceiling joist or lower truss chord (Fig. 12-37). This board presents a nailing surface of

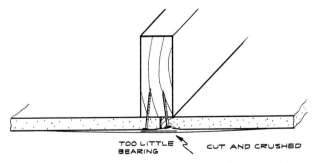

FIGURE 12-37 This type of poorly conceived end joint is the cause of many warrantee callbacks. Crushed gypsum, nail-cut paper, and uncentered nailing surface make it the poorest choice available. The protrusion of the tape and compound are usually visible under artificial light. Hairline cracks and complete separations are common to this joint design.

1 1/2". *If all conditions were perfect*, squareness of the room, straight coursing of the drywall sheets, perpendicularism, and straightness of the joists, the end of each gypsum board sheet would bear on a scant 3/4" surface for nailing. Since perfect conditions rarely, if ever, exist, one or the other of the sheet ends will be short-changed as to nailing base. It is common to find failed joints with 1/2" or less backing. The plaster is usually fractured around the nails from attempted dimpling (setting of the head below the surface too close to the edge).

Another fault of this method is the basic nonfeasibility of the square edge butt, which does not provide a cup (recession) for the finish joint taping. Such a taped joint must be taped and compounded above or beyond the common surface (actually below the ceiling line). Attempts are made to taper this downward humping joint cover so that it will not show. The compound is said to be "feathered out." The result is a wide compounded area with a depth of material held to a minimum. There are two problems. Any flexing or slight vibration of the ceiling causes the tape to rupture or peel and a hairline crack appears. The alternating dryness and moisture in the air then begins the process of loosening the tape. From there on it is all downhill until reparation time. This constitutes one of the most difficult reparation jobs in a warranty. It can be done with complete satisfaction only by using two new joints on both sides of the joist, as in method 1 described below.

The second fault with the square butt surface joint is that it is readily discernible at certain times of the day and night. It sticks out like a localized sag when lights create a shadow area on the far side of the bulge. Under artificial light one can easily locate the joints and identify the sheets of the ceiling. Attempts are often made to mask this undesirable condition by spraying a heavy coat of spatter finish on the ceiling. Spatter coating is attractive but will not solve the problem of a basically flawed joint. For those who will not be dissuaded from using the poorest joint, the only saving grace is to use an adequate adhesive under the butt joint.

Objectives of butt joining the ends of gypsum board sheets should include three items. First, locate the joint in a place or manner that creates the least vulnerability to stress that may result in failure. Second, support the joint permanently. Third, form a recess for tape and compound that is comparable to the cup edge system on the long sides of the sheets.

Contrary to popular belief, a joint positioned or suspended between two structural framework members will meet the objectives more successfully than will a joint placed over solid wood. Such a joint is illustrated in the United States Gypsum manual. Method 1 described below and shown in Fig. 12-38 places the joint in the middle quadrant between the ceiling joists. In this position the flexing of the joists under load or vibration is absorbed by

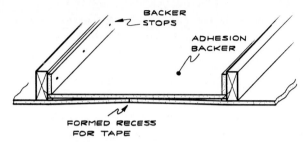

FIGURE 12-38   This is the best method of joining board ends between joists.

the joists but not transferred to the drywall joint. Many drywall installers reject this technique, due to the time and nuisance factor. The sad truth is that a poor job often results in a warranty callback and the nasty job of doing over what could have been done right initially.

Method 1.   Plan to make the sheet ends butt somewhere near the center of the space between the ceiling joists (Fig. 12-38). The board ends that extend beyond the joists must have a little flexibility in order to form a recess for tape and compound (a substitute for the missing cup). The closer the joint is to the center of the space, the more flexible the end of each board will be. Obviously, this system will work better with joists or chords on 24" spacing than with those on 16" spacing since about 4 more inches of wallboard can be hung over.

Assemble the parts in the following order. Assume 1/2" drywall for a ceiling.

1. Nail cleats to the sides of the joists 5/8" above the lower surface of the joists.
2. Toenail a horizontal drywall backer board against the lower edge of the cleats.
3. Spread a continuous bead of adhesive in a serpentine pattern or spread parallel lines perpendicular to the joint about 1" apart, back and forth across the joint area.
4. Install both sheets of drywall rapidly. Space the nails closer together on the joists adjacent to the butt joint.
5. Position a T brace to press evenly and equally against each side of the joint. Press (prestress) the joint a little more than 1/8" above the ceiling line. Leave the T brace in place overnight if possible, or at least until the adhesive has become rigid enough to support the bent-up ends of the two wallboards.

All the backup materials may be scrap if scrap is available. The cleats serve only to keep the backup board from being pushed up. Any small piece of wood strip will suffice. Even 1/2" × 3/4" strips will do where enough canted nails are used. Drywall strips about 3″ wide will suffice if one edge is straight and square (the cup-edged scrap is preferred).

On a single house job, where there is no scrap pile at the outset, the first few back boards will be cut from a full sheet. Frequently, a sheet is dropped on a corner and damaged at unloading time. That is the sheet to use. Cut off from the end a backer that is 14 1/2 or 22 1/2″ wide, to fit the joist spacing that exists.

Drywall adhesive dries on its surface very quickly. Enough T braces should be readied so that both sheets of ceiling board can be raised and secured without delay. Five T braces are usually adequate, two for each sheet and one under the joint. Concentrate most attention on getting the joint prestressed and pressed as quickly as possible, then go back and complete the field nailing. Of course, the boards must be accurately positioned and secured with a few nails to be certain that no overlaps or gaps are created before securing the end joint.

At first glance it may appear in Fig. 12-38 that bending up the stiff ends of the drywall would create a leverage that would tend to pull down the backer board. This is true until the adhesive solidifies. Once it has hardened, it partially fills the gap next to the joist so that the pressure no longer exists. Also, gypsum has no memory or grain stresses. After it has been in the curved profile for a few hours, it will stay that way permanently with no stress.

If the T brace supporting the joint is needed elsewhere, it may be possible to remove it after a few hours. One can test the adhesion of the joint by gently starting to remove the brace. Flex the middle of the brace pole while pushing out the bottom with your foot (Fig. 12-39). Keep an eye on the joint area. If the joint ends do not appear to move downward more than the amount they were prestressed, the brace may be removed.

After the brace is removed, an inverted valley will exist. Taping and compounding may proceed as for a cupped joint. It will take more compound, however, as the depression extends farther than the width of two mated cups. If one desires to see or know in advance how far the feathering should go, a straightedge is laid across the depression and drawn across the ceiling boards. The outer edges of the depression may be marked for future reference to show the minimum boundaries for filling and feathering.

After the first and second steps of taping and compounding, a final coat of compound is screeded across the joint. The longest possible trowel is desirable for this final leveling, as the objective is to produce a flat surface from one joist to the other on the ceiling line. High spots can be sanded off using a long sandboard (16″ or more). Once perfected, this joint will be sturdy and virtually undetectable.

Method 2. The next best joint is made by creating a recess and adding a backer board on a joist. Each joint in a room should be established, marked, and prepared before starting to hang the ceiling board. Mark each 4′-wide junction with a red carpenter's crayon. Mark a line across the joist at each end of the joint location, then add a squiggly line along the joist from crossmark to crossmark.

Cut a 3/32 to 1/8″ deep recess from the underside of the joist or chord on all marked localities. This can be accomplished in one pass effectively with a hand power plane. Making this cut with a skill saw is also effective but should be attempted only by a very experienced operator, as working overhead is a dangerous operation with a skill saw. Every precaution is advised, including safety goggles (not glasses) and a solid floor scaffold of ample width and length.

If the cut is rough and not too straight, the high spots can be smoothed off with the hand plane. Do not permit the recess to become deeper than 1/8″. Remember that the depth of the recess is what determines the quantity of compound to make the tape joint.

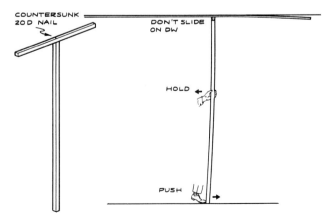

FIGURE 12-39 Place the T where desired. Hold in place with your hand. Push the bottom away with your foot until the T bar is wedged tightly under the sheet.

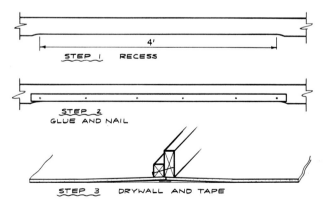

FIGURE 12-40 Planing and scabbing the joist provides a recess for the taping and compounding of an end butt joint. For graphic clarity the depth of the cut (3/32 to 1/8″) is exaggerated in this illustration.

Next rip a 2 × 2 to a length a few inches over 4′ (Fig. 12-40). *Glue and nail* it flush with the recessed surface on the face of the joist. Use at least six 10d common nails spaced equally apart. Stay 2 or 3″ away from the ends of the 2 × 2 to avoid splitting. Lay the wider side of the 2 × 2 against the joist. The glue is most important.

The objective of the backer is to provide a more adequate nailing base for the end of each sheet of gypsum board. With the added 1 1/2″ of wood, the bearing surface is now 3″. Glue each ceiling board to the joists with two or three beads of adhesive and space the nails no farther than 4″ apart. Drywall screws may be 6 to 8″ apart on this joint.

In a long room or any room where two or more joints will be made in the same course, the cleats are placed on the same relative sides of joists. This placement will maintain the modular spacing continuity so that full-length sheets can be installed without cutting or without running short. With the addition of the cleats, all ceiling board ends will have up to 1 1/2″ of surface on which to be nailed.

Use a T brace a couple of inches back from each joint before attempting to nail the drywall ends. Pressure must be exerted all along the end of each board while the nailing proceeds. Without this constant overall pressure, the ceiling board may break away downward from each nail as it is singly installed. After all nails are seated, a single T brace may be positioned to straddle the joint, thereby sustaining the pressure on the adhesive (Fig. 12-41). This will free one T brace for use elsewhere. The waiting period before removing all pressure will be shorter than in method 1, where no fasteners were used.

Method 3. The last adequate method involves a recess with only minimum bearing (Fig. 12-42). Where joist or chord spacing is nearly perfect and perpendicular

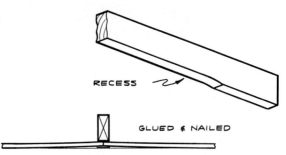

FIGURE 12-42 This technique ranks third from the good-to-poor illustrations shown thus far. With perfect centering of the joint, good gluing technique, and nailing that does not cut the paper or crush the gypsum, a possibility exists for long, trouble-free existence.

to the walls and partitions, it will be possible to come close to a full 3/4″ contact of the end of each drywall sheet with the joist.

The procedure is carried out in three simple steps.

1. Locate and mark all joint locations.
2. Cut the recess gain at each location.
3. Glue, butt, and nail both ceiling board ends on the 1 1/2″ bearing to complete the joint.

Omit the dimpling of nailheads. The nails will be so close to the end of each ceiling board that it is nearly impossible to dimple the nailhead without fracturing the gypsum. The recess made in the joist will usually be deep enough to allow space for compounding and taping over the surface-aligned nail heads. T braces are required as in method 2.

Adhesive is of paramount importance in all three joining methods because the boards are sprung up. In

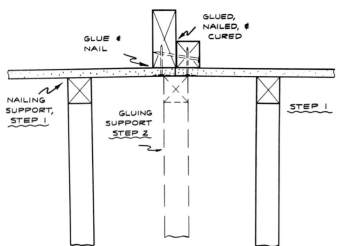

FIGURE 12-41 Use a brace on each side for solid contact while gluing and nailing the boards. Place a semipermanent T support over the joint *before* removing the outer two. Leave in place until the adhesive is firmly set.

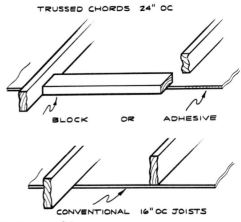

FIGURE 12-43 The joints running across the ceiling joists may be nailed to backer blocks or bonded together with adhesive. The bonding technique is usually adequate for the narrower 16″ conventional spacing. The wider 24″ spacing typical of trussing will benefit substantially from blocking to which the cup is glued and edge nailed.

method 1, a large quantity of adhesive is involved. In method 2, there is adequate surface to run two or three beads for each ceiling board. Method 3 offers the least surface area (3/4″ or less for each board end); therefore, attention must be given to meticulous and effective coverage with adhesive. The success of this minimum method will depend largely on the effective holding power of the adhesive.

Supporting the cupped joint edges between ceiling joists may be accomplished by installing blocks *before* drywalling begins, or if joints are tight enough, by using panel adhesive on the edge (Fig. 12-43). All fitting must be done before spreading the adhesive bead.

Butt-Joined Wall Joints

Where drywall is positioned horizontally on walls and partitions, there will be several end joints to deal with. An objective is to minimize full 4′ end junctions by preplanning the arrangement of full sheets so that joints come above doors and windows and below windows. By so doing, an upper-course joint, in particular, can be held to about 14″ in vertical height (the approximate distance from the ceiling line to the top of the window). Any window that is tall enough to have its sill below the top sheet of drywall will also produce a butt joint area of less than full 4′.

In larger rooms or where long expanses of unbroken partition exist, a full 4′-high joint may be unavoidable. There are three alternatives open to the drywaller.

Alternative 1. Install 8′-long drywall sheets vertically. There will be no butt joints without cupped edges on the surface. There is nothing objectionable about this method, but be prepared to defend your logic and rationale, as there are too few old-timers around who will understand it. Also remember to *stagger the vertical joint location of sheets* on the opposite side of the partition. Joints should not be present on both sides of the same stud, as this permits a flexibility weakness in the system (Fig. 12-44).

Alternative 2. Install long sheets horizontally. End the sheet at the center of a stud. Butt the next sheet tightly to the first. Surface bond the tape. Cover it and feather the compound out broadly in the hope that it will not be noticeable and that the thin layer of compound will not crack. Stagger the sheets in the adjacent course. A joint weakness is created if one joint is above another on the same stud.

Alternative 3. Follow the design of method 1 used on the ceiling. End the sheets midway between the two studs. Fabricate with cleats and backer board and adhesive. Place a 1/8″ × 3/4″ strip straddled over the joint (Fig. 12-45). Staple it in three or four places so that it stays put.

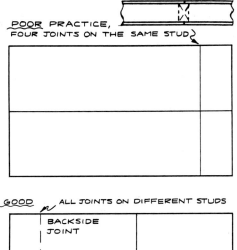

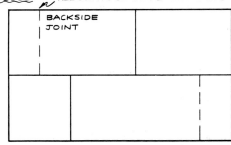

FIGURE 12-44 End joints on a partition should not be made on the same stud on the same surface or on the opposite side of the wall. Of the possible four joints no more than one per stud is the rule as shown here.

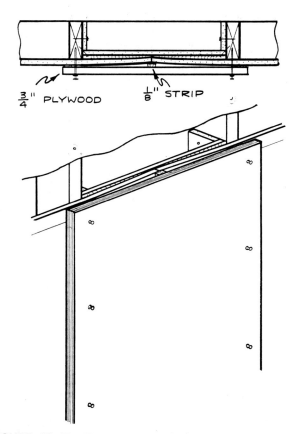

FIGURE 12-45 This recommended wall joint between studs is completely concealable after the temporary pressure board is removed. The pressure board technique works equally well on the ceiling in place of the T brace.

Place a 3/4″ piece of plywood that is 20 to 24″ wide and 4′ high over the strip. Two to four inches of this board will lap beyond the studs on either side of the joint. Nail the plywood board over the wallboard to the studs with eight form nails (double-headed) of 12d size. Use four nails per side. Set all eight nails so that the points are protruding slightly through the underside before placing the board on the wall. Each nail will be positioned in a row of four on the long side of the plywood, parallel and 16″ apart from the other row. Their formation is such that each nail will anchor in a stud. Start the nails closest to one end about 5″ away from the end. This will help prevent them from splitting the ends of the studs adjacent to the plates. The other nails are placed equidistant apart.

Install the board over the stapled strip. Nail all of one vertical side first. Drive the nails only until the board touches the wallboard. Do not overpound. Apply pressure to the other vertical edge with your subdominant hand and sink the remaining nails. It may take a second person to do the pressuring on dry days when the board is very stiff. When the plywood is flush with the surface, the little spacer strip underneath will have depressed the wallboard enough to provide a recess for tape and compound netting a completely masked joint. For permanence and best looks, alternative 3 is the best joint to use. Future convenience is also attained because baseboard trim will not have to be relieved (planed on the back side) in order to pass straight over a built-up hump of compound. Nor will the compound have to be cut away from behind the baseboard (the alternative to baseboard relieving). Leave the board in place overnight. Remove carefully with a wrecking bar by pulling the form nails. A set of boards, removed with care, may be used repeatedly. The eight nailholes remaining in the drywall are simply filled with compound.

Successful Nailing of Gypsum Board

Nailing would seem to be elementary, but the sad fact is that some drywall installations are unsuccessful due to poor nails or poor installing technique (Fig. 12-46). There are several elements that affect the holding power of nails used with drywall. They are the species of wood into which the nails anchor, the type of nail, the positioning and frequency of nails, and the expertise with which the nail is installed.

Wood species use has changed in the past half century. Until World War II there was little concern for conservation of timber. Structural members of a house were generally high grade and of harder wood than found today. Lath nails were smooth and gun-metal blued. In the heavy, dense wood studs and joists, the nails held well. After the war, the lumber supply and the timber forests began to be depleted rapidly. Softer woods of less adequate strength and nail-holding ability were put on the market. The drywall system was becoming popular at about this same time.

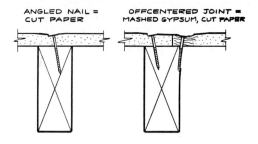

FIGURE 12-46   Poor nailing technique is often the cause of future drywall failure, particularly with ceilings that depend solely on nails.

The problem of popouts soon reared its ugly head. The steel industry responded with an annular ringed nail which has superior holding power in soft wood. Carpenters quickly dubbed it a "ring shank." Annular nails are currently available in sizes from the mighty barn pole nail down to the diminutive panel nail.

A true drywall nail in its purest form is ringed along all the portion that will be anchored in the wood (Fig. 12-47). Maximum holding potential is thus guaranteed. There are other forms on the market labeled drywall nails. One is a nail with a head large enough to qualify but no rings. For holding power this nail is hot dipped in galvanizing tanks. The resulting rough encrustation on the shank of the nail gives it some superiority over a smooth nail.

Some recent imports masquerading under the box label of drywall nails are nothing more than 4d nails with slightly larger heads and resin coating. The resin is of doubtful benefit because it is partly stripped away and its adhesiveness nullified as it passes through the gypsum.

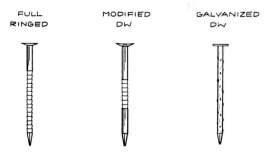

FIGURE 12-47   Three recognized drywall nails with good holding characteristics.

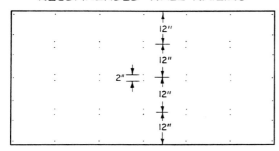

RECOMMENDED WALL NAILING

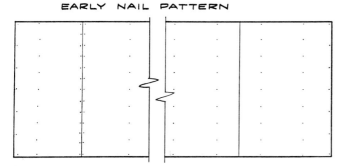

EARLY NAIL PATTERN

FIGURE 12-48 Nailing patterns for walls and ceiling that will prove adequate for most conditions provided that nails of correct type and length are used and good nailing technique is practiced.

A good test of the efficiency of these three types of nails is to nail a scrap of drywall to a 2 × 4 with two or three nails of each design. Pull them out successively. It will be quite obvious which is superior.

Positioning the nails has also undergone transition. In the beginning, the drywall sheets were installed vertically. All nails were installed an equal distance apart, those on the cup edge and those in the field. After gypsum board hanging evolved to the horizontal position on the walls, it was found that holding power was improved by grouping the nails in pairs 2″ apart (Fig. 12-48). Should a nail fail for any reason, the companion one would do. This formation also has the advantage of reducing the time for compounding over the dimples.

Spacing in the field is generally on 12″-centered pairs. For example, vertically up the 4′-wide board a nail will be placed at 1″; 11 and 13″; 23 and 25″; 35 and 37″; and 47″. There is just one nail at each edge, which is within the cupped area.

Fastening the board to the ceiling, unlike the walls, will benefit from evenly spaced nails because the board is hanging by the nailheads (tension rather than sheer stress). Without adhesive, more nails are needed. A nail every 6″ will not be excessive. The factor involved is the quantity of nailhead surface required to support the weight imposed, assuming that the nails will not pull loose from the wood. Too few nails can set up a predisposed failure condition where first the surface paper gives away around the nailhead followed by fracture of the gypsum. This is why it is so important to avoid overdimpling (fractured gypsum) or paper cutting from a nonparallel nailhead (slanted nail).

Dimpling a nailhead (Fig. 12-49) is a skill born of dexterity and practice. The process is characteristic of drywalling, for the specific purpose of providing a depression for the compounding, the covering up of untaped nails. Dimpling is not a unique experience on drywall, as it occurs repeatedly on structural woodwork. Construction nails are usually given a final blow to sink the head at least flush with the surface and preferably slightly below. There are two significant dissimilarities between frame nailing and drywall nailing. The drywall nail must not cut the paper or crush the gypsum plaster between. To do so is to lose most of the effective holding power on ceiling applications. Wall application is not quite as critical since the wallboard is hanging with sheer stress on the nail shanks. The nails on the wall can be compared to so many little hooks.

The second dissimilarity is that drywall nails must be driven as perpendicular to the surface as possible so that the head is parallel to the surface. Again this is most important on the ceiling because the board depends on the nailheads only for support unless adhesive is used throughout. All nails in the field are nailed straight, at right angles to the surface.

It takes only three or four whacks to put in each nail: one to start it, one to put it flush with the surface, and a final pop shot to dimple it. The first two blows are of the follow-through type. The dimple blow is made like cracking a whip. The downward motion of the hammer is abruptly restricted at the critical moment of impact. It is the same psychomotor response as that called "pulling a punch" in boxing. It takes practice and feeling to develop the skill of dimpling.

Unfortunately, the most difficult and exacting part of the house drywall job comes first, the ceiling. The novice builder usually finds the backhand hammer swing to be the most difficult. The ceiling calls for a lot of backhanding. About the only relief for this problem is to adjust for the height of individuals so that each is at the best possible height relation to the ceiling surface. Short-legged horses upon which scaffold planks are placed will aid. Whatever

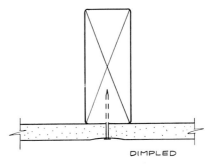

DIMPLED

FIGURE 12-49 "Dimpling the nail" means sinking the head below the surface with the rounded head of a hammer or drywall hatchet without breaking the paper or crushing the gypsum.

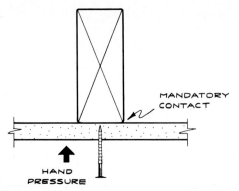

FIGURE 12-50 Hold the wallboard tightly against the stud or ceiling joists while driving a nail. Contact must be sustained throughout the nail driving to avoid breaking out the back side of the board and crushing the gypsum around the nail.

the setup, room space is needed for a couple of T bars or a Gyp-C-Jack.

Pressure on the wallboard is required during nailing, whether it is ceiling or wall application (Fig. 12-50). Start the nail, then press the board firmly against the nailing surface with the subdominant hand. Sustain this contact pressure until the nail is dimpled. Failure to follow this practice consistently will result in unseen damage on the back side of the board. A nail that is permitted to pull the board toward the stud or joist breaks the plaster under the paper and frequently goes unnoticed until a future problem erupts.

Rectifying a faulty nail is not difficult. Usually, a new nail can be placed a couple of inches away in undamaged territory. The old spot is simply grouted over with compound. This procedure is advisable wherever a known or suspected weakness in nailing appears.

Checking for high nails needs to be done systematically before starting the tape job. There are two touch methods that work effectively. One can perform the first check subconsciously after it becomes a habit. After the dimpling blow, gently slide the head of your hammer across the nailhead. If the head protrudes, a metallic sound will be heard, a clear indicator that the nail needs to be driven a little deeper.

A final overall check can be made with a framing square. Grasp the body at the end. Place the tongue against the wall or ceiling and quickly run it over all the nails in a line. To inspect a ceiling, simply walk along pressing the tongue against a row of nails. The square will make a little snapping sound as it passes over a protruding nail. Stop and sink that nail.

Corner Bead

In a typical house, there will be a number of places where drywall goes around a right-angled corner. There are vertical corners on partition ends, jogs in walls, room divid-

ers, recessed bookcases, and openings. Horizontal corners are present in most homes on kitchen soffits. Gypsum board that passes around a corner must be protected from physical damage and given a finished appearance. To achieve these objectives, a sheet metal V-shaped protector is used. It is called a drywall corner bead. After application, compounding and painting, nothing will show to indicate the presence of the metal-protected corner.

Curiously, this corner bead is manufactured in 10' lengths. All vertical corners extending from floor to ceiling in a conventional-height house will require custom cutting of the bead to an appropriate length. The bead should butt the ceiling. On the lower end, some builders will extend the bead almost to the floor. This method will necessitate planing off a portion of the back side of the baseboard. If this is not done, a machine-cut miter joint on the baseboard will stand open. The corner with its buildup of compound and corner bead is not perfectly square. Another builder technique is to permit the baseboard to make the small outward bend over the feathered compound and make the miter cut a little less than 45° to close it. Another technique is to end the metal bead at the top of the baseboard. No compound is permitted below this level.

The problem only presents itself where drywall is full thickness under the corner bead (no cup). The bead metal and nails will all be above the surface line. This cannot be avoided completely. The problem can be modified a little by using cutoffs from cupped edges of sheets on narrow corners. This works nicely on soffits, archways, and ends of dividers. It keeps at least one side of a corner bead flange below the surface line.

Fitting drywall to an external partition corner (Fig. 12-51) is the easiest form of fitting in the house. Simply choose a sheet long enough to go beyond the corner and nail it in place. Then cut the back side adjacent to the framing by drawing a knife along the corner. Fold it back to a point less than 90°. Run the knife up this crease on the face side. Install the adjacent piece and repeat the process. The resulting corner will be lapped (Fig. 12-52). It

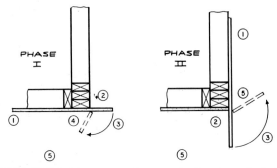

FIGURE 12-51 An external corner is fitted precisely in a few seconds by following these steps: (1) install a board, (2) cut the back side with a knife, (3) snap the scrap and fold it around, (4) cut the crease, and (5) rasp off the knobs.

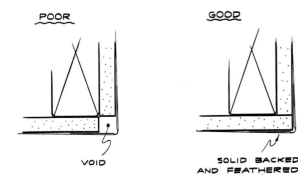

FIGURE 12-52 A lapped corner provides sturdier backing for a corner bead and makes it easier to install the bead.

presents a desirable solid backing for the corner bead. The method is foolproof in terms of fit and calculation error. A sandboard is used to eliminate any gypsum knobs that protrude above or beyond the surface of the corner, as these will interfere with the seating of the metal corner bead.

Corner bead installing involves the principles of straightness, centering (bisecting the corner angle), and parallelism. One method is to nail the ends first. Press the bead toward the point of the corner. To assure that the corner of the bead bisects the wall corner precisely, each flange must be an identical distance away from the corner. If "eyeballing" does not produce accurate results, a pencil mark can be placed on each side. The flanges are brought to the mark or to points equidistant from the marks. Nail the top and bottom first.

The handiest tool to assist in positioning the remainder of the bead straight and true is a 6′ level. Hold the level against the rounded corner of the bead. Apply pressure with both hands held about 3 to 4′ apart. One hand pressing in the middle may bend the level. Ignore the bubbles. This is an exercise in straightness, not plumbness. Plumbness was dealt with at framing time. Note how much movement, if any, is required on each flange side. Set the level aside. Press the bead to the points of reference and place a nail on each side above and below the center of the height. There are two hole sizes on the flanges. One is just large enough for the diameter of a drywall nail. The other is about three times that diameter. Put the two gauge nails into the larger holes. Stagger them apart from each other about 4 to 6″. Sink the nails until the flange is snug to the drywall surface. Recheck the straightness again with the level. If a slight outward bow exists, hold a small wood block over the bead to protect it from denting. Tap the block with your hammer. The bead will move inward. The bead will hold its position if there is enough pressure from the nail heads. Check the straightness again. When the strip is straight, complete the nailing by dividing the distances in half until there is a nail about every 8 to 12″. Press in or tap out as you go. Finally, check it by holding the straightedge (the level) on the corner of the bead and on each side.

The stud corner post may not be perfectly straight. The manner in which the bead is installed presents the last opportunity to create a straight corner by installing the bead straight. The feathered-out compound will complete the impression of a straight situation. Where two beads complete the end of a divider partition or arch, remember that the two should be perfectly parallel before compounding begins.

A three-surface corner junction (Fig. 12-53) requires some miter cutting of bead ends. Where more than one piece of metal bead is required, a corner or butt joint is necessary. The lower corner of a free-hanging kitchen soffit fits this categroy. Ends of flanges must not overlap and create too much thickness. On the three-surface corner the meeting flange ends are mitered back away from the point of intersection about 43°. On straight-run junctions, the flanges on one or the other butting piece is mitered a few degrees so that there is no contact between the flange ends.

The beads should touch at junctions so that a continuous hard corner is presented. Lineup of the beads is difficult but possible with no backup. A simple way of providing continuity (a smooth flowthrough) is to use a nail for a dowel pin. Cut the head from a nail of the same diameter as the bead groove. Cut it in half to make two dowels. Slip this little steel dowel half its length down the groove of the first bead that has been installed. Crimp it with pliers if it is loose. Install the next piece over the protruding dowel. Nail the bead in position and then crimp it over the dowel. When nailing at the corner, be mindful of where the wood is that backs up the drywall. Nail only into sound backing.

Bead corners longer than 10′ will benefit from the use of a string line or a chalk line. A chalk line is snapped from

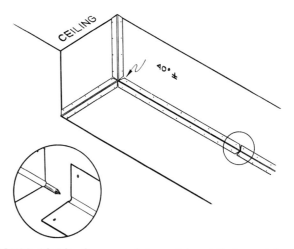

FIGURE 12-53 Corners of drywall bead that meet from three surfaces are mitered a little less than 45° to prevent overlapping metal. Straight junctions that lack solid backing may be pinned with small dowels made from half a nail pinched in the groove.

the beginning and ending points of the flange edges on both adjacent surfaces of the corner. On a soffit, these are the vertical face and the underside. Set a few nails alternately while pressing the flanges to the chalk lines. Hold a string-line along the bead to check the straightness before completing the nailing. It is important that a soffit be as straight as possible along the lower leading edge. It is here that the junction of cabinets and soffit will be most critical.

Compounding the Drywall Joints

Not everyone will handle the taping and compounding of joints well. It is a highly developed skill. A competent crew of journeymen with adequate tools and machines will put all the tape bedding, tape, and cover coat on a moderate-sized house in a working day. A novice working alone will take weeks to finish a house completely. The cost is a factor to consider. A contract crew may bed tape one day, finish coat another day, and return for a few hours of touch-up sanding on a third day. These are not always consecutive days, as it frequently requires more curing time than overnight. The contract cost for finishing alone is about equal to the cost of the wallboard material. With this knowledge, one has a basis on which to make a decision as to whether one wants to tackle the job or if some alternative wall covering will be considered, such as paneling or wet plaster.

Should one decide to forge ahead, a good first step is to get one steadfast rule firmly embedded. It is: Any compound that goes on and remains on above the wall or ceiling line surface must later be removed the hard way, by sanding. The opposite of this rule, the true fact, is that properly applied, the compound requires very little sanding to render a flat, paintable surface.

How can one avoid the entrapment of compound buildup? It is simple. Screed. Screed means to scrape off all that which is above the surface. The cupped joint, for example, presents about a 5″-wide trench into which the compound bed, the tape, and the covering coat is initially troweled. Any operator using the hand method of bedding would likely spread and bed with a 3 or 4″ knife (a wedge-shaped spreader with a handle). To assure that no compound remains above the surface line of the wallboard, however, it will require a 6″ knife, which will span across the cupped valley. A 10″ T-shaped knife or a trowel will actually perform the function better.

Perforated tape called Perf-A-Tape is the most economical type in use for covering the cupped joints and inside corners (Fig. 12-54). Tiny holes are burned in this 2″ tape, which permits the bedding compound to penetrate the paper. The bedding side of the tape is fuzzy next to the edges. The design improves the tenacity of the tape. Self-adhesive grid tapes are available but are quite costly by comparison.

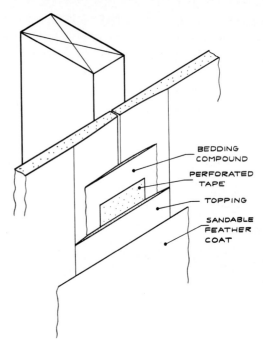

FIGURE 12-54 Drywall joint finishing is a three-stage operation: (1) bed the tape in compound and cover it with a screeded coat, (2) apply a finish coat and feather out the edges, and (3) remove high spots and small trowel-formed ridges with a sandboard.

Spreading the bedding for tape is tricky. The compound loses its adhesiveness very quickly when exposed to air. The tape must be pressed into the compound within a matter of seconds; otherwise, it will not stick. If embedding is delayed a moment too long, the embedded tape will develop bubbles underneath and peel away from the bed. Only a few feet of tape can be bedded at a time by one person. Usually, about 4′ is the limit. Corner tape should be folded first before pressing it into the compound.

There are two types of machines on the market for tape bedding. One is nicknamed a "banjo," the other a "bazooka," both due to their musical instrument shape. The banjo taper is basically a box dispenser which permits rolling the tape through wet compound before it is placed. The bazooka is a long tube and roller that facilitates taping the ceiling joints from floor level. Both machines incorporate the same principle, to put the tape and compound on simultaneously. In many areas these machines can be rented. It is a good investment in time and callback insurance. Without an automatic taper, the next best system is to involve a partner or two. The lead-off person spreads the bed, the second person presses in the tape, and the third person covers it immediately and screeds it flush. From there on it can be a one-person completion job.

Shadow testing is a method of identifying high and low spots of compound. The creamy manila color of compound makes it difficult by sight alone to see rolls and depressions. Such slight malformations can frequently be identified better with the sense of feel in the hands than by sight. A true gauge of the contours is a straightedge backed by a light source. The straightedge must be long enough to bridge the compounded area. A 10″ trowel will serve well for most of the cupped joints. A framing square body (the 24″ leg) is adequate for larger feathered spans.

Hold the straightedge nearly perpendicular to the surface. Draw it slowly along the compounded joint or area. Hold a trouble light or flashlight behind the straightedge as it is moved along. Depressions will show up as cracks of light between the straightedge and the surface. Actually, unless both ends of the straightedge are touching the surface of the drywall, what is revealed is a high spot. Wherever the straightedge can be rocked from end to end, no filling should take place until the high spot(s) has been sanded off and another shadow test performed. There is a great possibility of complicating the problem by adding more compound to "smooth out" a rolling or roughness situation. Keep the important rule of thumb in mind at all times. *No excess compound should be left above the surface of the wallboard line.* Adding compound when subtracting is called for will only complicate a solution or lead to an uneven finished surface.

Material Characteristics

All building materials have characteristics that affect such considerations as when to purchase, storage life, how to store, where to use, and how to protect for long life. Gypsum products, properly chosen and applied, are popular and satisfactory products for residential construction use. Some of the manufacturers' listed products and uses are the following: Board thicknesses include 5/8, 1/2, 3/8, and 1/4″. A single layer of 5/8″ drywall provides a strong wall surface with increased resistance to fire. It is used extensively in commercial applications. Single-layer 1/2″-thick drywall is currently a universal residential system for wall covering. 3/8″ is used in the double system of layering and for overlaying on a remodeling job. 1/4″-thick sheets are used as an underlayment for 1/4″ paneling and for overlay remodeling.

W/R (water-resistant) drywall is characterized by its green paper covering. It is the only type of gypsum-based wallboard recommended for interior locations exposed to dampness. Regular drywall (cream-colored paper) should never be used as a base under bathroom tile or adhesive-bonded plastic-coated hardboard. The gypsum core of W/R is protected with an asphalt emulsion. Even so, cut edges or exposed edges should be further sealed with a specially formulated W/R sealant.

Store drywall sheets flat and out of the weather. When stored in the house, one should keep in mind the great weight involved. A stack of drywall 2 or 3′ high will put a tremendous strain on floor joists, especially when the

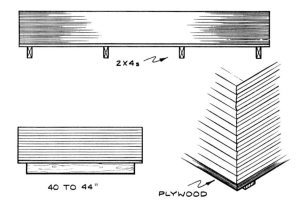

FIGURE 12-55 Twelve packs (24 sheets) of drywall stacked neatly on an unassembled pallet of plywood and scrap 2 × 4s. This gypsum board should be in good condition when ready to use.

stack is in the middle of the span. An attached garage with a concrete floor is a good place for drywall awaiting installation. Plywood sheets laid under the stack will help prevent the first few sheets from absorbing moisture from the slab (Fig. 12-55). Due to the vulnerability of drywall to damage, it should be brought to the job site only when it is time for it to be installed.

Drywall comes packaged two sheets to a pack. Each end of the pack is held together with a heavy paper tape strip. To transport one sheet at a time, first grasp the end of the tape and sharply pull away. It will tear off neatly all the way across. Repeat on the other end. The finish face sides of the two sheets lie in the pack touching each other. Do not grasp the end of the top sheet of the fresh pack and slide it across the lower sheet in the pack. Any small grain of sand or plaster that is trapped between the sheets will roll or drag, leaving an indented track which later requires compounding. Occasionally, a little curl of torn surface paper will develop. The resulting damage is difficult to repair with compound. The damage may require discarding or downgrading the sheet.

Compound is available in powder form and in ready-mixed all-purpose form. The key to which form one should choose lies mainly in the quantity and expertise of the appliers. One person working with hand tools will not apply compound fast enough to warrant a large container of ready mix. The frequent opening and closing of the container will render the last portion useless. Compound deteriorates over a period of time. It glazes over and dries out rapidly when exposed. It loses its adhesion quality for tape bedding. Purchase only in quantities that can be used up within a few days. Storage over longer periods may prove fruitless.

In powder form there are different types of compound for different purposes. A type for tape bedding has superior adhesion qualities. A top-coating type is designed to sand easier. All-purpose compounds simplify inventory and prevent possible use of the wrong kind. Some loss of superior adhesion and surface quality is sacrificed in the trade-off. Both types should be brought to room temperature before application or mixing begins.

For those with an interest in obtaining more information on the detail and scope of drywall, an excellent reference is the *Gypsum Construction Handbook*, published by the United States Gypsum Company, 101 South Wacker Drive, Chicago, IL 60606. The price is nominal and will be quoted by the company upon request. It is an authoritative handbook and well worth the small investment.

PANELING

The patterning and cutting of wall paneling is similar to that of drywall. A notable difference, however, is found in the finishing media. The basic finishing medium for drywall is compound. It is fluid in nature. This fluid characteristic couples neatly with the nature of drywall edges to be easily damaged. This provides an application method which allows the installer to intentionally cut a drywall sheet short to assure that it will fit on the first try without breaking corners and edges. The fluid filler takes care of the gaps.

Fluid fillers for paneling are seldom used, with the exception of small repairs. The system for covering corners is either to mate the two adjoining edges perfectly or to cover an internal or external corner with a piece of molding (Fig. 12-56).

Edge joining of sheets on a common surface may also be done by tight fitting or by covering with a coordinated strip. The thickness of the paneling and the material will dictate the finishing system to some extent. For example, three-ply 1/4"-thick hardwood paneling that is basically stiff can be butt joined at the edges effectively. Three-mil-thick imported panels of soft wood, such as Luan mahogany, usually must be glued to any underlayment and frequently covered at the joints to eliminate rippling. Although Luan and some other forms of mahogany are classed as hardwood, they are soft and pliable by nature.

Other forms of paneling use various cores and backings that have characteristics with which the builder must be familiar. Compressed and glued sawdust is a common backing material for less costly paneling. A photographic vinyl overlay gives an impression of real wood. Indeed, the panel for the most part *is* wood, but it is totally devoid of grain. Much like drywall, it is prone to corner damage. Grasped in the wrong place and flexed a little too much, this particle board panel frequently breaks in half. Nonetheless, with proper handling, adequate adhesive installation, and quality trimming, a good-looking job can be had.

Hardboard is another common backing material for synthetic paneling. It is strong and durable in a surface structural sense. Wood-grained photographic decal surfaces as well as wallpaper and fabrics are available on hardboard backing. The trade name Masonite is frequently associated with hardboard.

Cost consideration will require an analysis of all the materials required to install a particular type of paneling. Consider these principles. The thinner panels may require costly cover and joint trim. Corner coves and surrounds are sold by the piece or by the linear foot. When quoted as 12, 17, or 23 cents a foot, it does not sound like much. It could end up costing as much for the extra time and adhesive as for the thin paneling itself. At first glance, a good-looking piece of paneling at a third the cost of another seems like a good deal. Have a closer look and then make a decision based on all the facts at hand.

Panel Layout

Paneling is usually left until after the installation of a hardwood floor or of underlayment. It is explained here due to its similarities to gypsum board.

Layout of the paneling is done in accordance with the finish carpenter's philosophy. It is usually better to make the piece a little large and be able to trim it than to make it what seems to be correct dimensionally only to find it is too small. It is a mistake to assume that because the panel is square, the area for which it is being customized will also be square.

Whether a pattern is laid out on the face or the back of a panel may depend on the type of saw being used and/or the size of the teeth. A circular saw and saber saw (portable jigsaw) should be operated on the back side of panel-

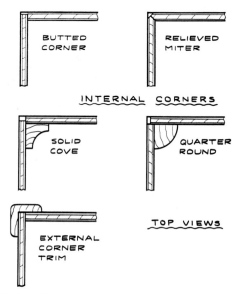

FIGURE 12-56 Internal paneled corners that are fitted without trim, internal corners with trim, and external paneled corner with wood trim.

ing or plywood, as less surface splintering will thus occur. The teeth on these saws tear the most on the side of the material where they exit the cut. The chipping takes place on the top side with a saber saw or a hand-operated skill saw. Chipping can be minimized somewhat with finer-toothed blades, but a sacrifice in cutting time will result. A hand saw, table saw, or bandsaw chips on the underside where the teeth exit the material. Fine teeth are recommended for panel cutting. A hand saw should have no fewer than 10 points per inch (a number 10 crosscut).

Getting started squarely on each wall will not necessarily occur simply by pressing the first sheet into the corner of the room. A room condition that is not perfectly square, straight, plumb, and level will require careful assessment before placing the lead-off panel. In this situation, parallelism may be more important than plumbness. Striated paneling (vertical grooves) can produce some weird effects if the grooves are not parallel with doors, windows, and room corners. Where these three "vertical" reference lines are not parallel, a compromise will be necessary. Line up the paneling parallel with the reference lines in the room that most dominate the sight impression. For example, the door casings will be very noticeable alongside a dark groove in the paneling unless the groove and casing are parallel. A nonparallel situation will give the impression of an unsquare door opening or a room that is actually tilted. A badly out of square room may be adequate justification to avoid paneling with vertical grooves and choose paneling that does not contain a lot of vertical lines.

Checking for squareness and parallelism can be done by measurement and by testing with a long level. Hold the level vertically against the key places: corner, door jamb, and other openings. Compare plumbness. Next, measure between suspected unparallel edges, where several reference points check plumb and one does not. Probably the logical compromise is to align the paneling with the majority. Remember that every upright reference in the room can be parallel and still not be plumb (they may all tilt in the same direction). This happens where a frame is inadequately braced before sheathing. Another consideration is the length of the upright reference. For example, a corner is the longest reference taken vertically. A door is likely to be next, and windows that do not extend to the floor would come last. Consider also that the vertical jambs on a window are frequently obscured by curtains and a priority rationale emerges. Doors and corners will be more important to align panel grooves with than windows. In the case of too many misaligned reference points, a panel with highly figured woodgrain with little or no vertical lines will do the best job of disguising the unsquareness of the room. The remodeler who is faced with a house that has settled or was built before modular materials were used will benefit from learning well how to assess the conditions in a room before choosing or beginning to install paneling.

Pattern reversal is such a common and repeated problem that it warrants continual reminders. Remember that laying out a pattern on the back side of a panel will always reverse the direction of L and U shapes and the location of openings such as electric boxes. This assumes that the top and bottom references are not mixed up.

There are situations such as grain configuration where a panel mates better to the last one installed by placing a certain edge adjacent. In this case, the panel will have a specific top and bottom relationship. Hold the panel in place to make the determination. Then revolve the panel 180° horizontally while still in an upright position. Mark the back side "UP," "TOP," or with an arrow before laying it down to draw the pattern upon it.

Index wherever possible. It is always more foolproof to put the panel in place and index openings and cuts than to transfer measurements. Reach behind the panel with your trusty red crayon and X mark or circle the general area where a duplex outlet is to be patterned.

Marking electric box cutouts can be a frustration. Paneling cannot be patched as readily as drywall, especially if cut in completely the wrong place. Some helpful hints may help avoid that tragic experience. Follow these simple steps:

1. Hold the panel in position.
2. Reach behind and index the box location.
3. Measure from the closest vertical reference (the room corner if it is the first panel, the adjoining sheet edge from then on) to the edge of the electric box.
4. Measure from the ceiling down to the top of the box, not from the floor.
5. Transfer these measurements to the panel back.
6. Trace an electric box of the same size below the tall measurement and on the proper side of the edge distance mark. Remember, if you turned the panel around, all is reversed except the height.
7. Cut out a plug that is 1/4″ smaller than the outline all around.
8. Hold the panel in place off the floor against the ceiling and against the room corner or adjoining panel.
9. Check the hole against the box. Re-mark it if it needs adjustment.
10. Finish cut it.

Index window and door locations onto a panel with the panel propped up in position. More often than not, the edge of a panel will terminate somewhere within the window or door location. This provides the opportunity of reaching behind and tracing the cutout. This is the most foolproof method available. Pattern layout should resort to a transfer of measurements only when no other indexing method is present.

Cutting the Panel

Most panel cutting will take place on sawhorses with supporting 2 × 4s underneath. The following three rules apply:

1. Support the panel adequately so that no pieces break away causing damage.

2. Arrange supporting 2 × 4s so that cuts go between them, not over them.

3. Protect the surface of a panel that is facing down from damage from its supports. Protect the surface of a panel that is faced up by putting protective tape on the saw base or the panel.

Do not saw beyond an inside corner with a circular saw. Stop at the corner or short of the corner and complete the cut with a hand saw or saber saw. A practical team of power tools for panel cutting is a small circular saw with a 4 or 4 1/2″ blade diameter for medium to long straight cuts and a saber saw for pocket cutting, such as duplex and switch box openings. The circular saw blade with the front of its baseplate against the surface is pressed down into the wood at each side of the box opening and retracted. The saber is inserted in the kerf to complete the cutout.

Attaching Panels

Generally, panels of 1/4″ thickness or more are nailed to the studs through the backing. Thin panels are glued to the gypsum backboard. This is not intended as a rule. The rule is to do what is required to assure that the panels will stay in place as intended. This may involve a combination of nails and adhesives throughout. With overall adhesive, a few nails may be used in strategic places only.

Adhesives. **Panel stiffness** is a key element that influences the method of installation. Stiff panels can usually be installed with either nails or adhesive. Adhesive is the material to use where no exposed nail heads are desired. Nails are more certain where conditions of dampness or extreme heat may cause an adhesive to fail.

Thin panels will usually require adhesive throughout and possibly some nails to hold down rebellious curves and bubbles. Some thin panels seem stiff enough to install fairly well without overall adhesive contact but later succumb to blistering and edge rippling due to swelling. Swelled areas between studs are nearly impossible to rectify after installation—another argument for doing it right in the beginning.

Adhesive may be spread in a variety of patterns. Follow the manufacturer's recommendation if it comes with

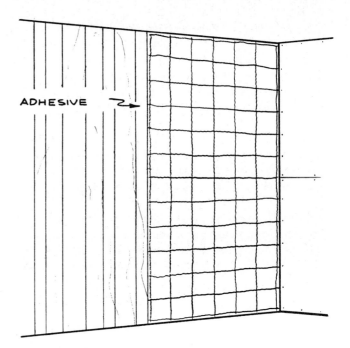

FIGURE 12-57 Adhesive beads in a grid pattern will hold many kinds of paneling to a wall surface successfully.

the panels or with the adhesive. In the absence of such information, a grid system may be followed (Fig. 12-57). A bead of adhesive is spread on the wall surface both vertically and horizontally on 6 to 8″ spacing intervals. When the panel is pressed into the adhesive, a little pad of adhesive spreads out at the grid intersections. A bead of adhesive should always be spread around the perimeter. Experience will tell how far in from the edge to place the bead so that it will not press out beyond the edge when pressure is applied. Pressure must be applied all over the sheet until adhesion takes place. Where a nailed-on baseboard is to be applied later, the panel can be nailed below the top of the baseboard line with 4d nails. These nails, which have larger heads than panel nails, can also be used along the top of the sheet if a corner mold will later be installed to cover them up.

Nails. **Panel nails** come in two standard lengths. The short ones are about 1″ long, the longer ones about 1 1/2″. The annular rings give the little panel nail great holding power. The heads are small but flat on both sides to give adequate pull-through protection. The length of nail needed depends on the panel thickness, how much backer thickness exists, and the holding quality of the wood behind the backing wallboard. In some localities, special-purpose gypsum backer board is available with gray paper on both sides and square edges (no cups) at less cost than regular drywall. Drywall backer, regardless of type, does not provide adequate holding power for any kind of nail. Nails should always be placed to reach into wood, a stud or plate.

Coordinating grooves in panels to fall over studs takes planning and forethought. Studs must be located accurately so that every vertical butt joint of the edges of panels will fall precisely centered over a stud. When the edges are accurately aligned, the grooves will automatically be over studs, as they have been designed that way. The blacklash from this design is that if the edge of a panel is misplaced (not over a stud), all the grooves will be off. This alignment is important because the proper and least noticeable location to put an exposed nail in the field of the sheet is in a groove. The exception is the thin sheet, where grooves reduce the thickness to a point of uselessness for nailing. In such a case, nails should be staggered from side to side along the groove, and/or this paneling should be glued.

Placing the first sheet into an exterior wall corner usually requires cutting off 4″ or more of the panel width. Such will be the case with a modularly designed house with 2 × 4 frame walls. Say, for example, that the framework is on the building line. The corner post built up of 2 × 4 studs will subtract 3 1/2″ of the 48″ distance to the center of the stud that is on the 4′ major module. Another 1/2″ is subtracted for the drywall backup board on the adjacent wall. Any variation will affect this formula, such as an exterior wall frame that is inset on the box floor to provide flush-mounted sheathing.

Indexing the actual stud location is a more positive way of dealing with the placement of the first sheet of paneling. The nails holding on the backing board will show the approximate location of the stud. Although every nail in the gypsum board may have hit the stud, few, if any, will be dead centered. Hold the edge of a long level through the center of the greatest quantity of nailheads that can be bisected. Draw this centerline vertically starting about 4″ above the floor over the stud where the edge of the first panel edge will be positioned. A couple of inches above the floor drive a 4d nail through the drywall 3/4″ right or left of the centerline. If it touches wood, move away from the centerline 1/8″ and drive it through again. Do the same on the other side of the centerline until a clear 1 1/2″-wide x-ray profile of the stud location is established. Repeat this probing procedure 3″ down from the ceiling. Nailing above that level will risk hitting the top plate. This probing should take place on the stud that will receive the edge of the panel, usually the third stud (not counting the corner).

Patterning the first sheet is now possible by measuring horizontally to the corner from the center of each probed area. Should these two measurements vary substantially, it will indicate the presence of an out-of-plumb corner or field stud. Assessment and adaptation must follow. Find out first how plumb the corner is. Adapt the panel's vertical orientation in accordance with the principles of parallelism to other dominant features of the room, as described a few paragraphs earlier. It may develop that the

lead edge of the panel will of necessity be diagonal across the stud from top to bottom. If such is the case, see to it that the panel edge passes through the center of the stud at a point halfway up the height of the wall. This will assure the best nailing base that can be achieved without canting (tilting) the panel unduly.

Press the top of the sheet up to the ceiling with the edge in the corner and nail it. If the wall exceeds the panel height, it will be better to have the gap at the bottom behind a wide baseboard than at the top behind a narrower cove molding. In the unsquare situation, let only the high corner of the panel touch the ceiling. Occasionally, the unsquareness is such that a panel cannot be placed without trimming. Trim it at the top. Trim it so that the top edge more closely fits or partially parallels the ceiling. The top and bottom are usually covered. Precise fit here is not necessary. Precise junctions of the edges *are* required.

Start nailing at the center of a panel and work out. This is a good rule but sometimes it is necessary to place a few nails along the edge to prevent the panel from shifting while field nailing progresses. Nail spacing is optional depending on panel stiffness and how well the nails are holding. Six to eight, sometimes 10 to 12, inches will prove adequate in the field. The vertical edges will require more. Put enough 4d regular nails (coated are best) along top and bottom to assure that there will be no ripples under the cove and baseboard. A considerable savings can be realized by using these nails in hidden places (under molding). Their cost is only a fraction of panel nail cost. No closer spacing is required around windows and doors than in the field, as these areas are effectively held down by the casing or corner mold that will cover them later.

Dealing with nail color is something to be considered. Standard colors that are available in panel nails are black, white, tan, and brown. Others are made for specific panels. For surface nailing, obtain and use the color that most closely blends with the color of the panel. Many panels have grooves that are a darker color than the panel. Match the nail color to the groove as much as possible. Where a close match is not possible, use lighter nails on light panels and darker nails on dark panels. The contrast will not appear as great.

The vertical edges of a grooved panel have a half-groove. Frequently, this half-groove is not wide enough or thick enough to be nailed. Nails will have to be placed on the panel surface close to the half-groove. Stay within 1/4″ of the groove so that each nail can be driven straight and will hit the stud. Choose a nail color that blends well with the surface of the paneling.

Set each nail head flush with the surface wherever possible. It will punch its own countersink. Avoid using a nailset. A nailset has a tendency to chip off the color coating on the head of the nail. It is also very easy to slip off the hardened nailhead and punch an unsightly hole alongside. A pop action on the final blow, as described for dimpling a drywall nail, will produce a flush-set head. Avoid slanting any nails, as the head will then fracture a half-moon cut in the veneer of the panel and leave an unsightly depression. All exposed nailheads should be left flush with the surface and smooth to the touch for dusting and waxing efficiency.

Drywall Panel Backing. **A unique problem** exists with dark-grooved panels placed over drywall backing which is seldom thought of until too late. The light-colored gypsum board backing will show through any joint that is not compressed very tightly. The slightest amount of panel shrinkage or shifting will expose this sliver of light. The tiniest slippage during nailing will cause it. A preventive solution is to darken the area behind the edge junction of the panels (Fig. 12-58). Many materials for darkening will do. An aerosol can of black paint can be used to spray a strip up or down behind the junction areas. A panel can be nailed onto three studs first, leaving the lead edge unnailed. A black felt-tipped marker is then run down the area while holding up the edge of the panel. If one forgets and nails the edge of the panel, the marker can be pressed into the corner of the edge and firmly run down the backing board. The fluid in the marker will spread under the edge a little. Dark oil stain applied with a small brush will produce the same result. Dark brown or black crayons will make a lasting mark. Black crepe paper or plastic film can be cut in 2″ strips and stapled at top and bottom to mask the area. Whatever the method, it will be worth remembering, to eliminate a pesky problem before it occurs.

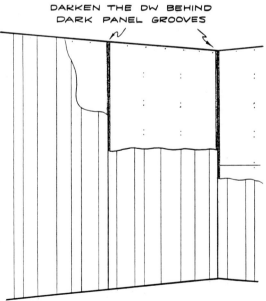

FIGURE 12-58 The area behind a panel joint should be darkened when medium-to-dark paneling is installed so that there is no chance of the light-colored backer board showing through.

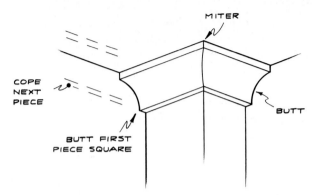

FIGURE 12-59 The internal corners at the ceiling line are trimmed with cove or crown molding. Internal corner pieces are butted and coped. External corners are mitered.

Moldings. **Applying molding** to "trim out" the paneling may be a labor of love or a nasty frustration. Any tool or machine that will cut a 45° miter will simplify and speed the job. For external corners, the casing or molding is mitered. No end grain will show when the mating cuts are made correctly. Molding that meets at an internal corner may be mitered or coped (Fig. 12-59). To cope means to cut a mating contoured profile on the end of molding. Molding around the top of the wall at the ceiling junction is called *crown mold*, as it resembles the crown mold on the exterior of some period homes. Smaller molds are called *bed mold*.

Crown mold is obtainable in many shapes and sizes. It is usually installed first. An objective is to cause the grain of the molding and the contours to flow uninterrupted around internal and external corners without exposing any end grain or losing the profile of the pattern. To achieve this objective, the external corners are surrounded by molding ends that are mitered (cut at a 45° angle to go around a 90° corner).

Internal corners may be trimmed in the same manner by mitering the molding. A problem frequently develops with a mitered internal corner joint. Shrinkage occurs and the two intersecting molds move apart, causing a gap. Unless the ends of the miters are stained or painted before installation, the gap will expose bare wood, which often contrasts with the color of the stained surface. The condition can largely be avoided by cutting the end of one piece of the mold to match the contour of the other. This is called coping because it was done with coping saws before the existence of so many power tools. Also, it produces a coping pattern in reverse. *Coping* is a general term for fancy trim around the top of a building. Most wall-to-ceiling junctions will be crowned with a concave-shaped molding called *cove*.

Installing the first piece of cove is simplest because both ends are cut square when a single piece will span the full length or width of a room. The back corner of each square-cut piece usually requires a little chamfering with a

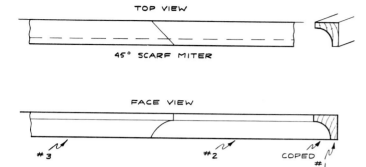

TOP VIEW

45° SCARF MITER

FACE VIEW

#3   #2   COPED #1

FIGURE 12-60 Joints between corners of this small cove are scarf cut at 45°. Install in order of numbering.

pocket knife to mate with the compounded drywall corner. From there on, one end of the molding will be coped to mate with the face of the square-ended preceding piece at the corner of the room. It will be cut square on the lead end where it butts the next corner of the room. The last pieces require coping on both ends.

Where a cove molding piece is not long enough to reach the full length of the room, the leading end is mitered at a 45° angle to form half of a scarf joint (Fig. 12-60). This is the same lap-type joint used on the cove facia board outside. There is a remarkable difference when setting up to cut a cove scarf joint. A cove that is symetrical (the pattern is identical from side to side) can easily be revolved in the miter box and end up not fitting its partner. Square-cut butt joints should never be used, as the slightest shrinkage will open up the joint to the same problems as those described for the internal miter joint. Ceiling cove must be situated in the miter saw or radial saw with the back side against the fence and its lower edge on the table, the same position as found on the wall.

External corners are always mitered to prevent the exposure of end grain. It is advisable to cut the piece a minute amount long. When installing the first piece that will go around an external corner, have a short piece with a mitered complementary end at hand to hold in place as a gauge. The gauge miter is held against the miter of the piece to be nailed. It will show precisely how far the first mold should extend beyond the corner. Do not try to eyeball the hangover of the first piece by sighting the inside of the miter with the corner. It will almost always cause the miter to fall short of its required position.

Spread glue on the mitered surfaces as each piece is fitted. Do not wipe off any excess that squeezes out the corner. It will seal the surface grain and prevent stain from penetrating. Come back later and peel off the slightly hardened glue. The glue may be wiped off immediately from the trim that will be painted.

Lock the joint with two small finish nails, one from each side. The little barbed panel nails are also excellent joint holders if they can be driven parallel enough with the

grain and still present a head fairly square with the curved surface of the cove.

Nailing the cove is a particular job. Small coves are solid throughout. Larger sizes are usually hollow on the back side. A triangular void will exist behind the larger cove mold. One might subconsciously think that a nail driven at a 45° angle centered in the face of the cove would draw it snuggly into the corner. On exterior walls and partitions perpendicular to ceiling joists, such will be the case only where a nail hits a joist. If the joists cannot be located, reliably and routinely, it is necessary to change the angle of the nail so that it anchors in the upper plate. On the end walls of a gable-roofed house and partitions that are parallel to ceiling joists, a ceiling backer board will provide anchoring for the cove nails. Consciously attempt to x-ray visualize the locality of solid wood into which each nail can anchor. A sense of ''feel'' is important when mounting anything over gypsum board. One must sense by feel and sound whether or not a nail penetrates an adequate anchoring zone. Gypsum alone is not an adequate anchor with any kind of nail.

Door Casing. **Casing the doors** will phase into the trimming sequence in relation to the junction made between the casing and paneling. There are three alternatives resulting from the manner of panel fitting.

1. Install the paneling before the door jambs are installed (Fig. 12-61). With 1/2″ drywall backing and 1/4″ paneling the jamb depth of an interior passage will be the same as for the wet-plaster system (3/8″ lath and 3/8″ wet plaster on each side plus 3 1/2″ of stud equals 5″). One-half inch drywall plus 1/4″ panel on each side plus the 3 1/2″ stud also equals 5″. With this combination the same-depth jamb will be ordered. Another possible combination (economy alternative) is 3-mil paneling with 3/8″ drywall backing, which combines nicely with the stan-

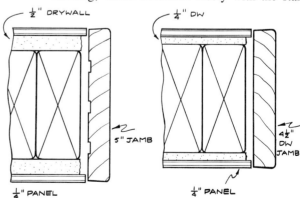

1/2″ DRYWALL   1/4″ DW

5″ JAMB   4 1/2″ DW JAMB

1/4″ PANEL   1/4″ PANEL

FIGURE 12-61 Various combinations of backer board and panel thickness can be used to match stock jamb widths.

dard drywall jamb (4 1/2" depth). Three-mil panel is ever so slighly over 1/8" thick. Another alternative is 1/4" panel over 1/4" drywall to match the drywall module jamb. In all these combinations the paneling is traced in place to the rough openings in the same way that the drywall was, and cut. It can usually be nailed in place and cut out in similar fashion if desired.

2. Install the door jambs before the paneling. Omit the casing. Temporarily tack the panel or have someone hold it in place over the door opening. Trace the required cutout. Cut parallel to but far enough away from the lines to accommodate the thickness of the jamb. About 1/8" more than the thickness away will make fitting easier. A precise fit is unnecessary, as the casing will cover the area completely. Installation of jambs and casing is explained a little later in this chapter.

3. Install drywall jambs less the casing. Hold or temporarily tack casing in place. Trace around the casing onto the drywall with a sharp pencil. Remove the casing. Cut a rabbet in the back outer edge of the casing that is as deep as the thickness of the panel and out 1/4 to 3/8" across the casing. The rabbet can be machined on a jointer, a table saw, or a shaper or can be cut with a router. The panel is then cut to pattern so that it will be under the rabbeted edge of the casing. (Fig. 12-62). This is a good method of holding down the edges of thin panels that tend to bulge between nails. It is also a good method for retrofit jobs where replacement of jambs is not warranted.

A poor alternative of joining a panel to a casement is to butt the junction. It is possible but so meticulous and time consuming as to be unreasonable for the one-time builder and unfeasible for the professional trimmer.

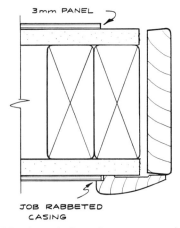

FIGURE 12-62 A technique for accommodating 3 mm paneling with stock jambs is to rabbet the casing. This method also works well for remodeling jobs.

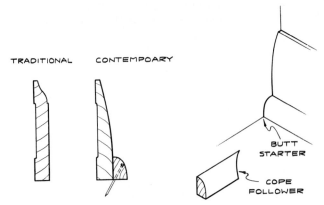

FIGURE 12-63 Baseboard and base shoe are butted and coped in the same manner as crown coping.

Baseboard and Base Shoe. **Baseboard and base shoe** are next in the trimming sequence after door casing is completed and floor underlayment or hardwood floor is laid, whether it be a wetwall, drywall, or paneled wall skin. Two common baseboard designs are popular and available at most suppliers (Fig. 12-63). One is the streamlined type, which gently curves from a 1/8" flat top outward and down to a bottom about 1/2" thick. The other is the pattern casing. The back side is hollowed out on both styles throughout the central section to make it easier to pull the edges tight to the wall surface. For this reason finish nails should only be placed along the top and bottom, not over the hollow-backed area. Use nails long enough to bridge the drywall (and paneling) which will penetrate the soleplate or stud at least 3/4". Since the top of the baseboard is thinner, the nail used there will be a size smaller than the one used at the bottom.

Butting the baseboard to a door casing is a simple matter of cutting the baseboard square where the door mold style is a little thicker than the baseboard. Where the two molds are the same thickness, the end of the baseboard will require a little rounding over on the face to make it appear finished.

Internal and external baseboard and base shoe corner junctions are handled the same as crown molding junctions. A machine method of indicating the pattern to follow can be effectively established by vertically mitering the end of the board first (Fig. 12-64). A coping saw is then used to cut along the contour where the miter cut severed the face. Undercut the pattern slightly less than 90° to the face. This will permit the face edge of the coped end to fit tightly against the face of the adjoining baseboard in the corner.

Base shoe is a smaller piece of rounded molding placed against the floor and baseboard. The upper edge is

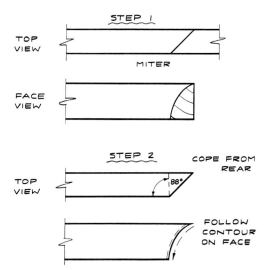

FIGURE 12-64 Patterning a coping cut can be done by first making a vertical 45° miter. Next cut the cope from the back vertical side following the contour line made by the miter on the face. Undercut a few degrees so that the face contour touches tightly on adjacent piece.

rounded to shed dust. The purpose of the base shoe is to form a seal between the flooring and the baseboard. It is common for the wood materials in the floor and wall to shrink a little. A crack often develops at the bottom of the baseboard. The base shoe is nailed in a bedding compression mode so that the bottom and back press equally against the floor and the wall. To accomplish this objective, each nail is driven diagonally through the surface at approximately a 45° angle. The nail is not intended to go through the baseboard; however, it is difficult to miss it and still pull the shoe tight to the surface. The 1/2"-thick base shoe is not sturdy enough to permit the use of large long finish nails that will reach the sole or floor sheathing. Solid wood backing like the wet-plaster grounding board of wet-wall days is no longer used. With drywall there is no need for the screed guide (plaster ground board). The popularity of wall-to-wall carpeting has reduced the need to use base shoe. There is no reason for expensive hardwood flooring to be laid under wall-to-wall carpeting. Many consumers prefer to put their money into long-lasting quality carpeting instead of hardwood flooring which would be completely covered. As a result of this evolution, the function and use of base shoe have substantially disappeared although it is still used where hardwood floors are prescribed.

Corner Trimming. **Vertical corner trimming** comes next in the paneling sequence. Internal corners may be trimmed with a molding or the panels may be carefully fitted (mated) so that no molding is required. A cove-shaped molding has a small advantage over a convex quarter-round pattern. The cove with its concave pattern will butt the ceiling cove and the baseboard edges with less overhanging

surface. A small corner cove may therefore be cut square on each end. It will blend fairly well even though the junction is not in perfect unity. For coverup purposes, use the smallest cove or quarter-round obtainable for the internal corner.

External wood corner mold for paneling is shaped in its cross section like an angle iron. Several sizes are available. Wooden corner mold of this shape is delicate and easily breakable in transit or storage. If stepped on, it will most certainly crack lengthwise. It is also vulnerable when being installed. A hammer blow too close to the corner may crack the grain. This L-shaped molding may be used around rectangular archways, windows with paneled casements (paneled rough opening), and the end of open partitions (divider walls). Aesthetics or necessity may dictate the choice. Wide pieces are needed to cover poorer panel junctions. Wide corner mold is easier to nail. Nails placed close to the outer edges can be driven straight and will hit solid wood backing. Narrow corner mold will require some angling to hit solid wood, as the first 1/2" of the corner behind is gypsum. Why not put nails diagonally throughout the joint of the corner mold? It is possible, but a large quantity of breakage may result. Just one too many blows or too hard a final blow will break the mold. Careful side nailing is preferred. Remember that retrofit paneling over old drywall will usually mean nailing through hidden metal corner bead. The resistance will be felt when the nail first contacts the flange. A pop-type blow is needed to puncture the metal without bending the nail. Once punctured, normal delicate hammering may proceed. It is all but impossible to nail directly into the corner of a hidden drywall corner bead in the retrofit situation. The nail will simply veer off to left or right and enter the cavity between the panel and drywall. No holding power results. Corner nailing of wood corner trim *is* possible and can be done successfully where no metal bead is hidden below. Follow these precautions.

1. Be certain that the corner board is not twisted. Start a nail at the top and the bottom to assure its straightness and stress-free contact throughout.
2. Use a nailset as soon as the nailhead is close to the wood surface. Do not hit the wood with the hammer head.
3. Use long ring shank panel nails. Sink each head with the nailset just enough to hold putty filler. The wood is too thin for successful use of cuphead finish nails. Their heads are too far through the board after setting to have adequate holding quality.
4. Do not nail closer than 16" apart. Once attached, the board is quite stiff, due to its angle-iron shape. It does not take a lot of nails to hold it in place.

Paneled corners without corner mold will be mitered. Whether or not this mode of finishing is feasible is partly dependent on the thickness and material characteristics of the paneling. The mitered corner will be comparatively sharp and vulnerable to damage. Fuzzy-grained wood will continually present the threat of slivers and splintering. The mitering option on an external corner seldom warrants the time loss. An internal corner, however, can be fitted rapidly with a butt joint.

An alternative to woodtrimmed corners is to use one of many synthetic moldings that are available. Some are shaped like wood cove and have molded grain. Others are shaped with flanges and pockets so that no exposed nails are required. Internal corners of this type may be installed with adhesive with no danger of failure. Whatever the trimming method or material decided on, it is important to look on the paneling and trimming project as a total integrated process and consider all facets at the outset, especially where cost is important.

UNDERLAYMENT FLOORING

Particle board is a modularly shaped sheet of fabricated material. It is comprised of pressure-glued small chips of wood and sawdust. It is dense and fairly stable when kept dry. In $4' \times 8'$ sheets, it is readily obtainable and 100% usable. Its moderate cost and ease of installation have made particle board the standard of the industry for a carpet underlayment surface.

The sequence of underlayment installation is optional but somewhat influenced by wall and ceiling coverings. For example, one builder may wish to lay the particle board before any wall-surface materials such as gypsum board or paneling are installed. The rationale may be that there will be less chance of damage to wall surfaces and ceilings from the handling of the large heavy boards. Another builder may opt for this risk to avoid the mess to the top surface of the particle board, such as gobs of dropped drywall compound, spilled stain, gouges from dropped tools, and other residuals of the finishing process. A third builder may compromise by putting down the particle board in all places except those where linoleum or tile will be laid with adhesive binders, places like an entryway, bathroom, utility room, and kitchen. Adhesives require a clean surface for adequate binding to take place.

Special area underlayment is determined by the uses that are served. All or most of the areas mentioned in the foregoing paragraph are to some extent subjected to moisture. Particle board is not recommended for underlayment where it may be subjected to liquid saturation at anytime. If there is any doubt of this, one can perform a simple test. Place a small strip of particle board half immersed in a container of water overnight. Take it out the next day, measure the thickness of the wet end, and compare it to the thickness of the dry end. The swelling that results will not go back to the original thickness after it dries. In time, repeated soakings will usually cause the particles of wood to disintegrate away from their glue bond. The board reverts back to a crumbled mass of loose chips. In fairness to the manufacturing industry, it should be noted that more durable products are constantly being developed. Waferboard, for example, is made of larger chips of wood bonded with waterproof glue. It does not disintegrate with repeated soakings.

Waterproof underlayment is needed in the bathroom, the kitchen, and laundry. It is so easy to ignore this and simply floor the entire house with a common nonwaterproof board that it happens repeatedly. The unfortunate result is experienced at a later date when a water closet (toilet) has to be reset and the floor around it replaced. Sometimes the condition has progressed to an advanced stage of rotting, so the floor joists and other structural parts are affected. Dry rot (a fungus condition) is often accelerated by the presence of dampness, humidity, and occasional wetting from plumbing leaks and dripping condensation.

Before purchasing the underlayment for damp areas give some thought to the *transition junction*, where one type of flooring meets another. An objective is to keep the finished levels as nearly the same as possible. This can frequently be arranged by using a different-thickness board in the specialty area. The common board thickness for most of the house will probably be $5/8''$ (particle board). A bathroom with inlaid linoleum adjacent to a wall-to-wall carpeted corridor will benefit from a $3/4''$ waterproof-grade plywood. The added thickness plus linoleum will more nearly equalize the levels of the junction. Another feasible combination is to use a second layer of exterior-grade $1/4''$ plywood over a common-height layer of exterior-glued plywood. Remember that the best system of tub installation is to have the underlayment and linoleum both run under the tub, so it must be installed before the frame walls are covered. The flooring must be zealously protected from that moment on.

Use adhesive in addition to ringed nails or screws to secure $1/4''$ ply underlayment to other underlayment. Cut and dry fit all the required pieces first. Then take up and remove the pieces and set them aside. Run parallel beads of adhesive $4''$ apart across a workable area to form a grid pattern. Work rapidly. Replace the fitted boards in position. Quarter-inch plywood is fairly flexible and demands the best possible nailing routine to prevent crowning (rising up between nails). Use ring shank nails every $8''$ along the joists and every $4''$ along the edges of the plywood. Place a nail every $8''$ between the joists. Stagger these to center between the nails that are in the joists. The result will be a flat solid base that will last for decades.

Junction strips to cover the transition line between two different floor coverings are obtainable in a variety of materials, such as chromed steel, aluminum, wood or vinyl. The strip bridges any difference in levels. It holds down the edges of materials and prevents scuffing. The strip provides a lowprofile ramp to help prevent tripping.

Countertops are another vulnerable area to moisture deterioration. Although many factories use particle board for the core material for preformed countertops, it is not recommended for home-built cabinets. Edges and corners chip off easily. Screws strip out easily. Most important, it is not waterproof. A leaky faucet may seem like a minor irritation. When it leads to a major repair job due to a disintegrated countertop, the significance of waterproof wood will be fully understood.

Vapor Barrier Underlayment

A vapor barrier of 15-lb building paper is customarily installed between floor sheathing and particle board underlay or strip wood flooring. This asphalt-saturated paper is sometimes called felt. A roll contains 450 square feet. With a minimum lap, the roll will cover about 400 square feet.

The floor must be very clean and free of all bumps or *obtrusions* above the sheathing. Check for nail heads and gobs of drywall compound. Protruding nails are easy to spot, as they are worn shiny from traffic. Occasionally, a sheet of plywood has had an extra scrap of ply pressed into its surface at the factory. If it protrudes, it should be removed. Pull it off with the claws of your hammer or plane and power sand it down to the surface level. Sweep away all debris. Vacuum to remove any particles overlooked.

Lay the building paper adjacent to the longest exterior wall first. The joint along the exterior sole plate and the subfloor should be caulked before fastening this sheet, to ensure against infiltration. Allow 1/2″ of the paper to fold up over the caulked joint (Fig. 12-65). The combination of caulk and paper will prevent any potential infiltration of air under the sole. The surface of the paper prevents infiltration of air or moisture from beneath the floor.

Lap the next piece of paper over the first white line on the black felt, approximately 2″. Put only a few staples in to hold the paper. One every 4′ is plenty. Remove any staples later that cause rippling of the paper as the underlayment or flooring boards are laid.

The building paper vapor barrier is omitted only when underlayment flooring, plywood or particle board, is glued to the subfloor (the U.S. Plywood–recommended system). The paper serves several purposes in addition to forming a vapor or infiltration barrier. It aids in sound control between stories. It forms a cushion over uneven surfaces. It deadens squeaks. Its greasy surface aids in driving strip tongue-and-groove boards tightly together.

WOOD FLOORS

Although wall-to-wall carpet currently accounts for the greatest square footage of flooring, there will continue to be calls for tongue-and-groove strip flooring and parquet flooring. *Parquet* (pronounced par-kay) means "small square." A finished wood floor is laid before the installation of baseboard and base shoe.

Wood Parquet Flooring

Wood parquet (Fig. 12-66) is usually fabricated from thin narrow T&G (tongue-and-groove) strips of hardwood. The strips are glued together to form a square. Then the edges are tongued on two adjacent sides and grooved on the oth-

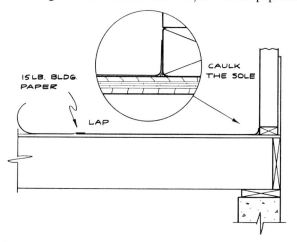

FIGURE 12-65 Caulking around the exterior soleplate plus turned up building paper provide a good infiltration seal at the edges and throughout the floor.

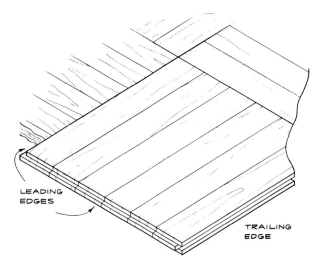

FIGURE 12-66 Parquet flooring is prefabricated in squares which are laid progressively with the tongued edges leading. The bonding agent is adhesive.

ers. When assembled on the underlayment (required in addition to sheathing), a checkerboard pattern results from the alternating strip grain. Although expensive, the parquet floor is popular for entryways and other special nooks. Wood parquet is installed with adhesive much like square tile. If a piece is warped and offers resistance to lying flat, a small brad may be driven at an angle through the leading tongue. It is always advisable to predrill a hole to prevent the thin hardwood from splitting.

The pattern of layment is either to have a seam or a full tile at the centerlines of the room. This most frequently results in cut pieces around the perimeter (partial tiles). The cut-off pieces will frequently be usable as starters and finishers in every other course. This will be the case where the dimensions of the room accommodate so many tile units plus a little less than half of one more unit on each side.

Most parquet flooring comes prefinished. The floor is complete after it is laid. It should be rolled or walked on immediately to assure contact and spreading of the adhesive. When comparing costs of finished floor types, remember to add the cost of proper underlayment panels for those types that are glued.

Strip Flooring

T&G strip flooring is available in both hard and soft wood. The traditional hardwoods most commonly used are oak and maple. The softwoods used are fir and pine. In cities where a half-dozen or more lumberyards exist, there is usually one that specializes in vintage materials. If you have use for a newel post, some five-quarter pine, or a wooden closet rung, the company that has these items will likely carry tongue-and-groove flooring.

Characteristics of T&G hardwood are somewhat unique. For example, it comes in bundles of varying length ranges. "Shorts" are bundles of 12 to 18″ in length or 12 to 24″, or whatever the mill designates. The longer the bundle range, the higher the price. Long lengths bring a premium price, but these prices are laid faster and make a stiffer floor.

The T&G flooring board is said to be *end matched*. This means that one end has a tongue while the other has a groove. These tongues and grooves dictate the direction taken while laying the floor. The first board is laid with the edge groove toward the wall that is perpendicular to the floor joists. This is a hard-and-fast rule that must never be violated when 1/2″ sheathing is used. Running parallel to the joists will cause ripples, sags, and a squeaky floor. The tongued end is positioned next to the adjacent wall (Fig. 12-67). From there on, the tongued edge and tongued end will be in the leading exposed position. The piece that reaches the other wall is cut a little short (up to about 1/4″). This amount of space is left all around the room

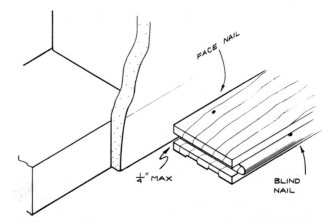

FIGURE 12-67   The first piece of flooring leads with the tongue and is surface nailed under the baseboard and shoe.

between the flooring and the walls for expansion. The first piece will have to be blocked out to keep it from driving against the wall. The spacer blocks may be removed after several boards are nailed. The cut-off end of the last board in each course is taken to the opposite side of the room to start the next course since it does not require the grooved end adjacent to the wall.

Nailing is a particular job. The first strip requires surface nailing on the edge adjacent to the wall. *Drill tap holes* slightly smaller than the nail shank diameter. Each tap hole must be centered over a joist. The hole should be as close to the edge of the board as possible without entering the groove (about 1/2″ from the edge). The baseboard and base shoe will then cover the nailhead.

Nails on the lead edge are started in the corner formed by the top of the tongue. The angle is about 50 to 60°. Some flooring can be nailed without pretapping a hole. If it is noted that a crack develops on each side of the nail, tap holes should be drilled routinely.

Nails have evolved from the rectangular cut nail familiar to retrofitters through the cup-head finish nail to the screw-shanked tempered wedgehead. The latter will rarely bend and is stiff enough to pass through hardwood with little deflection.

Sinking the head calls for a unique technique. Cup-head finishing nails are sunk flush with the tapered cupped point of a nailset. The tempered flooring nail causes the nailset to bounce off the head and damage the tongue. The Stanley nailset and any other square-headed set is adaptable for setting the wedge-head tempered nail. The nail is driven to a point where it can no longer be hit without damaging the wood (Fig. 12-68). The nailset is then laid with the square head flat in the trough on top of the tongue.

Place the round shank of the nail set over the nail. Position it with the nail under the full diameter of the shank just above the tapered end. Rap the set smartly over this

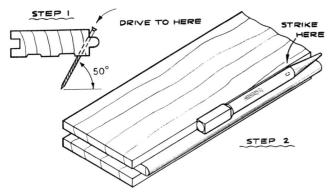

FIGURE 12-68 Sink the nail with the side of a nailset to avoid damage to the wood from hammer marks or from splitting of the tongue of the board with the point of the nailset as it slips off the hardened flooring nail.

point while holding it in place. The nailhead will be sunk flush enough to clear the groove of the next board.

Driving the boards tightly together is accomplished by using a short length of the same T&G board. Match the groove over the tongue of the board being driven. With your hammer head lying flat on its side on the floor, rap the tongue side of the block. Also use this block on the end of the new board to drive it onto the end tongue of the preceding board, then work the long edge into place. Drive and set the nails. Sometimes the nails will not pull the board up tightly. Use the block again and reset the nails. It is easy to get T&G boards out of parallel by forcing them tighter together at the ends or in the middle. After four or five courses are laid, check the parallelism by measuring from three or four places along the lead edge back to the starting wall.

The last board usually has to be ripped, as the distance remaining is less than the board width. Also, the space may not be parallel with the wall. Custom rip the board to the same dimension that exists from the wall to the *edge* of the tongue on the previous board laid. This will permit the final piece to be dropped in and wedged onto the tongue with a wonder bar or ripping bar (Fig. 12-69). It is drilled for surface nails the same as the first board.

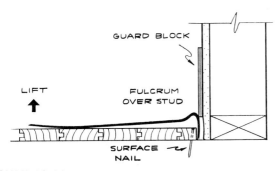

FIGURE 12-69 Either end of a wonder bar provides leverage to squeeze on the last board and hold it tightly while each nail is driven.

Keep pressure on the bar to hold the joint closed while sinking each nail. Again, it is very important to anchor each nail in a joist.

Unfinished Flooring

Sanding is required of unfinished strip flooring. Floor finishers prefer not to have door jambs and casing installed at the time of sanding, as it is so easy to damage them.

Closed grain wood such as maple, pine, and fir require no grain filler, as they are of the closed-grain classification. They will, however, benefit from a deep penetrating sealer. Oak is open grained, which means that there are long cavities running with the grain figure. To obtain a smooth surface that is easier to clean, a paste filler is rubbed into the open grain. The excess is rubbed off flush with the surface. Burlap works well to remove the excess. Coarse shavings will also work, but the polluted shavings must be constantly brushed away from the working area to assure that the grain is adequately filled and the excess filler is all removed. Liquid fillers are available and are moderately successful. The problem with any liquid of heavy viscosity is that it tends to bridge a grain opening, thereby forming an air pocket underneath. As the liquid dries, it shrinks. The bridge breaks and the gap is exposed again much as it was before. Regardless of which filler type is used, a thorough close range inspection should be made before proceeding with the finishing coats. Unfilled spots or areas will show up as a slightly different color when the finish is put on.

Door jambs and casings will be fitted snugly on top of the finished floor surface.

PARTICLE BOARD UNDERLAYMENT

There are three systems of installing the second layer of floor for carpet underlayment. Strangely, the variance in method is dictated partially by the type of roof framing that exists. For example, a house with a trussed roof which does not depend on interior bearing partitions for support may be wisely erected as a shell initially for any of three reasons. First, it will be closed in against the weather sooner. Second, the entire interior can be floored as a single unit (Fig. 12-70a), thus avoiding much labor time. Third, the floor will be considerably stiffer under and around partitions.

A modification of the unified technique is to raise only the center or centrally located bearing partitions upon which the ceiling joists of a stick-built roof depend for support (Fig. 12-70b). With this variance, large near halves of the house may be floored without the interruption of many little partitions. The time taken to floor half the house will be little, if any, more than it will take to floor a single bedroom with his and her closets and a bathroom attached.

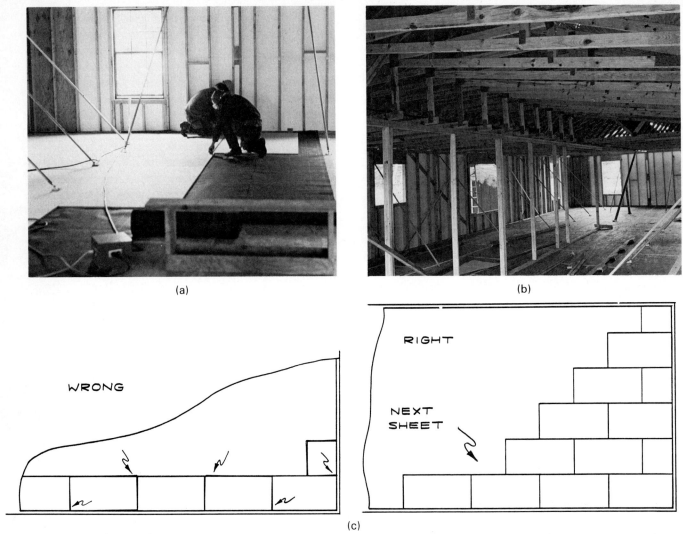

(a)

(b)

(c)

FIGURE 12-70 (a) Floor underlayment installation is greatly simplified by the open building system. (b) A single centrally located bearing wall (partially studded) permits a major part of the underlayment to be installed with few obstructions. (c) Each board helps align those alongside when laid as seen in the "right" pattern shown in the lower view. Laid as shown in the upper view, even to a chalk line, small discrepancies at the end joints will compound into sizable cracks along the edges.

The third method is the traditional way of erecting all partitions on the subfloor initially. The particle board then requires much measuring, cutting, and seemingly endless fitting throughout the maze of partitions.

Full Floor Layment

Full floor layment in conjunction with the open interior building concept has so many good things going for it that it is highly recommended by the author. Remember the special techniques for bracing throughout the sequence, as therein lies the safety of the technique.

All particle board *ends* should terminate at and over the center of a joist. Begin by rolling out two courses of building paper perpendicular to the floor joists and parallel

to the long exterior walls. In this manner the joists can be located at the wall junction directly under a stud, provided that the direct in-line modular system of framing has been followed. Two courses of paper will cover a width of a little less than 6′. Therefore, the floor sheathing will be exposed from there on, which exposes the end joints and field nails in the sheathing. If these are properly placed, the joists will be locatable by reference. A line between the field reference and stud reference *should* locate the joist accurately. Where there is doubt, a final technique is to drive a nail through the sheathing 3/4″ right or left of the expected joist center, then go under the house and locate it. If the nail hits solid wood, move farther away from the assumed centerline 1/4″ at a time. There will be an entirely different feeling when the nail misses the joist. It is extremely important to place the first sheet properly, as all those to follow will depend on it. Remember that the joists are accurately centered on 16″ but that some of the sheathing sheets have been shortened to provide one expansion gap.

Starting the first sheet requires custom cutting to length. The length will be a half- or full-sheet module minus the exterior wall depth and a small clearance gap between the sole and the underlayment. The author has for many years practiced a technique related to this gap which eliminates a future problem. With precut studs, a 1/2″ drywall ceiling, and a 5/8″-thick particle board underlayment, the remaining height in the room is exactly 96″. Since rough framing is never perfect, it becomes impossible to sandwich two 4′ horizontal courses of drywall or an 8′-high sheet of paneling into this theoretical space. Therefore, much cutting is involved to fit the lower course. To avoid this problem completely, the particle board underlay is spaced out away from the wall sole about 1/2 to 5/8″. This allows a 5/8″ clearance adapter, which is identical to that existing with slab floors. It also provides room for a floor raiser to be slipped under the edge of the board or panel.

The lead edge of the underlayment should be the uncut factory end. It is likely to be perfectly square and straight. Place the on-site cut end adjacent to the sole. Strike a chalk line full length of the back paper. This line will be 4′-5/8″ away from each corner at the ends of the run. Do not align the particle board sheets with the wall. Align them with the chalk line.

Lay two sheets along the first course. No more! Put only four temporary nails in each of these. Leave the nails exposed so that they can be pulled. Unlike intentionally separated sheathing, the underlayment should be as tightly joined as possible. Start a third roll of paper. Unroll it far enough to assure a proper lap. Staple part of it with as few staples as possible. Start a second course of underlayment. The lead piece of the second course will be of such a length as will set up a 50% staggering pattern (Fig. 12-70c). Align this sheet and tack temporarily. Now lay the second sheet of the second course. At this point the potential exists for tightly joining all edges and ends of the four pieces, in perfect alignment with the stringline. Loosen the nails and gently tap them into alignment as required until all joints are tight and headed straight down the chalk line.

Laying the rest of the particle board throughout the open space continues in the same manner. Never let a course run more than one sheet ahead of another. Keep all courses progressing at once in a staggered pattern. Never nail down a sheet permanently that is running out ahead with no sheets alongside to guarantee the integrity of the whole. By following this technique, an entire floor of a house can be laid so well that the edge of a piece of paper cannot be slipped into any joint between the underlay

sheets. The pride in such workmanship is a far more permanent reward than any that money can buy.

Major modular floor widths such as 24′ (six sheets across) and 28′ (seven sheets across) will net an edge lap over the sheathing joint equal to the wall depth and inset amount of the particle board. This is about 4″ with a 2 × 4 wall. The mid mod house depth of 26′ width or wings of 14, 18, or 22′ will have half-width sheets of sheathing on one side or the other. A larger lapover is achieved by starting the underlayment on the side of the house where the half-sheets of sheathing are. By so doing the lap will be much closer to the center of the sheathing panels and consequently offer the potential for a stiffer floor. The same theory and practice holds true when considering where to start in terms of end lapping. End joints of the underlayment should *never* be allowed to match those of the sheathing. Such an arrangement would create a significant absence of stiffness in a localized area. The best setup is to have all joints in the two layers staggered apart from each other as far as possible. If the subfloor sheathing starts with a full sheet, start the first particle board with a sub-half piece, or vice versa. From there on all joints will automatically be lapped correctly.

Half-Floor Layment

The next best alternative is to lay the floor in halves completely. This potential presents itself where only a center bearing partition is in place at this point of development. This is a very feasible technique. It approaches the full open concept in benefits and falls short only in two areas. It eliminates the good affects of a full tie over the centerline of the house. This is not a serious loss, however, as particle board does not contain a lot of tensile strength as does plywood. Where plywood sheathing has been arranged to run over the center junction of the floor joist, the need for the particle board to do the same is minimal. The only other objectionable feature from the intrusion of the partition is the extra labor time needed to cut and fit two more joints, one on each side of the long wall.

Traditional Layment

Laying particle board in the traditionally framed house is at best a time-consuming nuisance once a person has experienced the rapidity and "clean" joinery of the open-layment method. Where *all* the partitions are in place at the outset of the underlayment task, the job will still employ all the placement rules described earlier. The difference is that every room is a separate entity, an island unto itself, with which to deal. No master plan evolves. All the turns and door jamb jutouts must be measured, laid out on the board, and cut. Many butt joints will be saw cut on the job. Little continuity of factory edges will exist except in the central areas of large rooms. This involves much more linear area for error and careful fitting. It is not a difficult job for a competent craftsman with high-quality goals, but it does present a challenge that is avoidable by accepting the validity and many benefits of either of the open-concept techniques.

Bracing

Bracing, as explained in Chapter 7, is so important as to warrant some review. Since there are no braced partitions to strengthen the exterior walls in the open concept, a diagonal brace to the floor every 8 to 10′ is called for down the wall while construction is under way. As soon as the laying of particle board is begun, these braces are removed *one at a time* and reset immediately from the bottom of a stud up to a ceiling joist. By so doing the floor area is cleared so that the papering and boarding can proceed uninhibited.

Nailing

Nailing particle board is unique to other forms of wood. Particle board has some characteristics that require consideration. The board is comprised of such small particles of wood that it has no grain direction in the cellular sense. This might be considered an asset when compared to true wood, but it is not. The particle board simply crumbles and whole chunks break away as compared to wood, which cracks and splinters but does not disintegrate. Because there are no large cells but only small chips surrounded by adhesive, there is no place for a nail to expand its surrounding. How does this affect nailing? Unfortunately, it affects it in several negative ways. Nails in the field will break out a crater on the back side, unless firm contact with the anchoring surface is maintained. This makes it extremely important to nail only over and into floor joists. A nail driven in unbacked sheathing will bounce the sheathing away from the particle board with each blow. A crater usually breaks ahead of the nail point before the nail penetrates the flexible wood intended to anchor it. The chips that push out comprise a lump between the surfaces, which in turn causes a slight hump. When hit again, the head of the nail fractures its way through above the crater and all holding power is lost.

Edges are equally vulnerable in different ways. The wood close to an edge usually breaks away when a nail is pounded excessively in an attempt to sink the head below the surface. Corners are especially vulnerable to breakage. A major cause of edge breaking is the use of nails of too large a diameter. The hardened flooring nail is an excellent choice for particle board. Its sectional shape displaces a path easier and its holding power is superior. Coated nails are also a good choice. Their diameter is smaller than that of a common nail. The heads are thinner and gently countersunk for easier entry. Common nails are a poor choice for all the opposite reasons. In some instances, drilling tap holes will be the only way to avoid damage from nails. The practice is recommended for difficult end-nailing situations.

Nail spacing on particle board follows the same objectives as any type of sheet decking. About one and one-half times as many are placed on the ends as are placed across the field. With shorter nails and joists of poorer holding characteristics (softer), more nails or longer nails for greater penetration will be needed. Generally, the range for distribution will be 8″ in the field with 6″ on the ends to 6″ in the field with 4″ on the ends. Do not nail the particle board between the joists into 1/2″ sheathing. It is too thin and springy to hold adequately. Should the building paper show a tendency to bulge up in front or under the particle board, pull the staples ahead and let the board press the paper down as you go.

Permanent nailing may progress on any sheet that is surrounded by lead sheets. Only after there remains no doubt that a sheet will not be moved should all the nails be installed permanently. It is almost impossible to take up a sheet of particle board without destroying it after nails have been driven home in several places.

An advantage of grain-free particle board is found where working on small, confined floor spaces. Unlike plywood, which must cross the joists at right angles with the major number of plies, particle board may be laid in any direction. Its strength is equal both crosswise and lengthwise of a sheet.

Remember that where the particle board has been applied to a half or whole floor without interfering partitions, all those partitions to be built will require studs reduced in length by an amount equal to the thickness of the underlayment material.

PREHUNG DOOR JAMB MATERIAL

An integrated system for interior door framing and casing is ready made for the carpenter who recognizes the simplicity and benefits. It begins by framing the rough opening with a single 2 × 10 header centered in the depth of the wall with a flat 2 × 4 under the header which bears on the vertical trimmers to complete the common vertical plane of the rough opening (Chapter 7).

The door jambs are butted up under this style of header (Fig. 12-71). The bottoms of the side jambs will *not* rest on the floor but will be up about 3/8 to 1/2″ above the carpet-underlayment particle board. Wall-to-wall carpet installers appreciate this gap, as it permits pad and carpeting to run under the jamb. It avoids the down-slanted surface (tacked through the doorway), which holds dust and

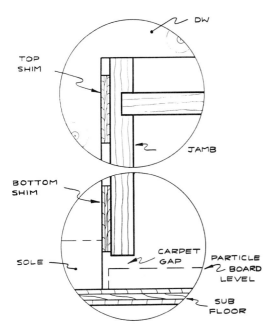

FIGURE 12-71 The single 2 × 10 with 2 × 4 uniform header makes it possible to hang a precut door jamb without alteration where wall-to-wall carpet is specified.

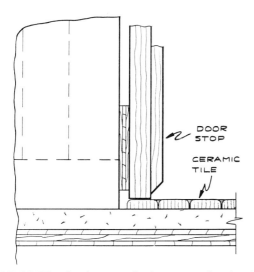

FIGURE 12-72 Jambs over linoleum or other hard floor coverings should be custom fitted to rest on top of the surface. If the jamb is hung first, leave the proper space so that the tile can be run under the jamb.

dirt. Of course, jambs adjacent to tile flooring should be set exactly to clear the thickness of linoleum, vinyl, or ceramic tile (Fig. 12-72). Some contractors prefer to lay these floor coverings before the jambs are set, which eliminates precision cutting around the jambs and stops and permits the jambs to be set directly on the finished surface. Where jambs rest on the floor, the stop should be mitered upward at a 45° angle to eliminate interference with carpet and linoleum.

A door hung in the uniform-headed opening will swing about 1″ above the finished floor. This is ideal to accommodate both the rug-clearance and cold-air-return objectives.

Many books still quote the old 82″ rough-in height as a standard. It is no longer high enough. Those who choose to use a built-up 4 × 4 or 4 × 6 header with cripple studs (in spite of the advantages of the single unit header) should make the rough opening height 83 to 83 1/2″ high for all locations where carpeting will be used. Failure to do so will result in the necessity of sawing off a portion of the door (a poor and unnecessary practice).

Jamb Kit

Jambs can be made from stock lumber. It is seldom cost effective to fabricate a jamb set this way, however, unless an economical source of clear lumber is available and one has a table saw and a jointer and lots of unpaid time.

An interior jamb kit consists of two side jambs and a head jamb. All these pieces are slightly beveled on the edges (3 to 5°). The wide side of each beveled board faces the opening. It is not possible to assemble the sides incorrectly because there is a dado (a crossgrain groove) at the top of each side jamb into which the head board fits. It *is* possible to assemble the headboard upside down. The wide side of the bevel-edged head board faces down.

Cutting the headboard to length takes some thought and care if one is to avoid the necessity of door planing later. The total length of the headboard will be actual door width plus the sum of the depths of the two dados plus the sum of the two clearance gaps at hinge and latch side of the door. The latter figure is the only variable in the summation.

Two schools of thought abound about door clearance. One school says to make the clearance wide and ample enough so that there is no possibility of binding, chafing, or sticking should the door swell in humid times of the year. The other school champions a perfect 1/8″ uniform crack all around the top and sides.

Flush-morticed hinges will dictate the clearance to be that of the gap between the hinge leaves when held parallel in the closed position. It will be 1/8″. There is no rationale for varying this clearance on the hinge side, as door swelling will show up only on the latch side.

To successfully open and close a door with 1/8″ clearance on the latch-side position, it is advisable to bevel the latch edge. A square edge will not have adequate clearance. The installer must bear in mind that two or three coats of varnish or paint will add enough thickness to close the intended gap.

Advocates of a larger latch-side clearance, such as 3/16 to 1/4″, will cite the advantages of nonbeveling, plus the fact that the latch bolt faceplate is morticed flush

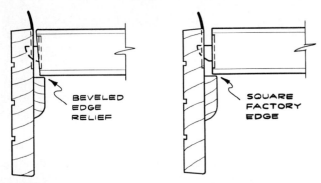

FIGURE 12-73 Two alternative techniques of fitting a door relate to the length that the head board jamb must be cut.

to the square edge and looks neater than one seemingly canted across a beveled edge (Fig. 12-73). Geographical areas of great seasonal variance in temperature and/or humidity will find the wide clearance to be less troublesome.

Prehung doors are sometimes fitted too tightly and will require planing. The prehung door that has been bored for a lockset and fits too tightly will require square planing *on the hinge edge only* since the hole for the door knob cannot be altered. The hinges will require remorticing. The amount required to be planed off may be as much or more than the depth of the original mortices. Maintain the indexing (the exact location) of each hinge by deepening the perimeter of the mortice with a chisel before planing. Then plane off the necessary relief and remortice the hinge butt. The chisel marks will indicate the exact location of the new mortices.

Jamb Depth

There are two standardized jamb depth sizes available from the lumberyard. The smaller of the two accommodates the drywall system. It is 4 1/2″ deep to span a 3 1/2″ stud with a 1/2″ layer of a gypsum wallboard on each side. This jamb size will also fit a 1/4″ paneled partition with an underlayment backing of 1/4″ gypsum board (1/4″-thick gypsum is not stocked universally).

Jambs for wet-plaster jobs may be difficult to find because their primary use is in retrofit remodeling. In the larger cities there is usually at least one lumberyard that specializes in vintage items. With some tools or power equipment any jamb that is large enough to begin with can be machined to a custom fit.

Installing a Prehung Door

A prehung door usually includes the surrounding jambs assembled and sometimes cased and a door with hinges morticed and attached to the jamb. The jambs have door stops attached to all three sides. No lockset is furnished, al-

though the door may be bored to receive one. The assembled kit is available in right- or left-hand-swinging formation.

Installing the prehung door kit is simple and quick. Leave the door in the jamb. Set the whole assembly in the opening. Block it up off the floor to the desired height. Occasionally, the header is not perfectly level. In such a case, block the jamb tightly up under the *low* side of the header. Block up the other side only high enough to maintain a parallel clearance between the door top and the head jamb after the hinged jamb has been plumbed.

Most kits have two temporary nails driven through the jamb into the door at the bottom and top of the latch side to keep the jamb from breaking away while being handled. These nails must be removed before inserting the kit all the way into the opening. Wait until the last moment to remove these nails. Block the jambs immediately after pulling the nails. This is important because once pulled, the weight of the door can drop the hinge side only and crack open all the corner joints in the casing or jamb dadoes. Some kits do not include casing.

Most kits have cardboard or plastic spacer shims stapled or taped between the door and jamb on the latch side and top. These spacers maintain the proper clearance during installation. Take them off and discard them after the door set is firmly nailed in place.

Shim the jambs at the critical locations as described for exterior doors in Chapter 11. The prehung jamb and door should not be suspended only from the casing which is nailed to the wall. The kit may have one side of the jambs pretrimmed, and packaged trim is furnished for the other side. In this case, shim the jambs from the open side, being careful not to drive the casing off the other side. Kits without prefitted casing are simply custom cased after installation. Some builders prefer to do this after wall painting is completed.

At one time jamb thickness was as much as 7/8″. In a rough opening 2″ wider than the door, there was very little space left for shimming if the door was left full width (few were). Now the prefabricated jambs of some brands are milled to a scant 5/8″ thickness. Some economy types are fabricated from short lengths of wood that are *finger joined* and glued. This jamb will have more than ample shimming space in a rough opening 2″ more than the door width. In fact, one may wish to precut and make use of plywood shims of 3 mm, 1/4″, 3/8″, and 1/2″ scrap to take up the excess space. These 2″ × 3″ blocks may be nailed to the trimmer studs at the correct locations before plumbing and leveling of the jambs. Tapered shim shingles are positioned on a block spacer or used alone for infinite adjustment (Fig. 12-74). There should always be a wide block about 3″ × 4″ behind each hinge where a gap exists so that long replacement screws will not have to jump across to reach the trimmer stud. Unless the door is to be

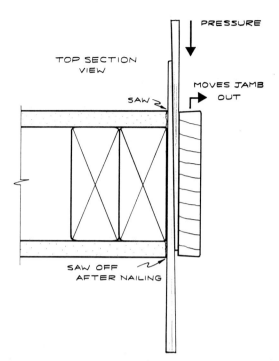

FIGURE 12-74 Typical shingle shimming of a fairly wide gap to produce a straight and plumb door jamb. Excessively wide gaps may be shimmed with a block of the exact size needed or a combination of shingles on a block.

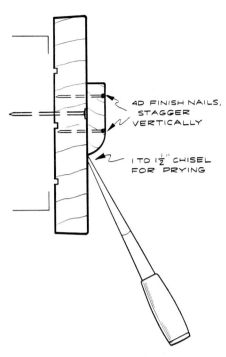

FIGURE 12-75 Door stop may have to be removed during installation to readjust its position. Use a wide chisel. Slip the wide sharp point under an edge of the stop and gently pry it off.

centered in an opening or corridor, it is best to place the jamb against the trimmer on the hinge side and space it out only enough to make it plumb and straight.

Nailing the jamb may proceed as soon as the assembly is firmed in place with temporary floor blocks and permanent shims. Where there is an objective to hide the mounting nails, the door stop is removed from the jambs. Do this very carefully using a stiff putty knife or a wide wood chisel to ease under an edge and gently pry away the stop (Fig. 12-75). Place each nail in the jamb only where the stop, when replaced, will cover the nail. Use nails with heads (finish nails with little cup heads have inferior drawdown ability). Number 6d at 7d box nails will hold well. Sink all heads flush with the surface. Nail only through the shims (a plywood shim is superior because it will not split).

Test the door swing. Remove the factory spacers and work the door through its intended arc. There should be no strain on the hinges in any position, no bind, and no reluctance to close fully. Make adjustments in the jamb where the door clearance is considered excessive, undersize, or unparallel so that the clearance will be adequate after finishing materials have been added.

A typical binding area is the door stop contact on the hinge side. About a 1/16″ clearance is needed there between the door face and the edge of the stop. A factory "prehung" may come through with no clearance there. At the assembly plant, the door is put in the jamb, and the stops are butted to the door and stapled or power nailed to

the jamb. After varnishing or painting the junction is too tight. Set the stop back from the door when reinstalling it. This will necessitate using new nails first in different locations so that the originals do not fall into the old holes and pull the stop back to its original position.

Nail the casing onto the wall and to the jamb to complete the job. There is an alternative to the poor holding characteristic of the traditional cup-head finishing nail. The 1 1/2″ panel nail on the outer thicker side of the casing will do a superb job of drawing the casing down tightly to the wall surface. It seldom splits the casing, as the sharp annular rings tear and sever the grain instead of wedging it apart as a smooth nail does. The shorter panel nails are excellent for nailing the inner thinner side of the casing to the jamb. Care must be taken not to angle the nail to the surface. The head must be flat to the surface if a puttying job is to be avoided. Panel nails are stiff and brittle. They cannot be bent to square up a head with the surface as a regular nail can.

The head of a panel nail is about the same diameter as that of a cup-head finishing nail. Panel nails come in enough colors to meet most needs. Where possible to set the head square and flush to the surface, no putty will be needed, thereby eliminating a time-consuming detail.

Some factory-installed casings have the top corner miters locked in alignment with metal splines. Corners that are not splined can be effectively held in alignment by driving a 1 1/2″ panel nail down through the top casing into

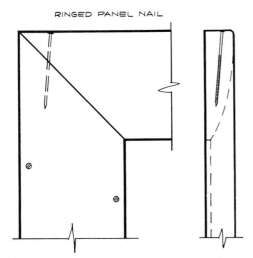

RINGED PANEL NAIL

FIGURE 12-76 Long ringed panel nails are excellent corner miter fasteners.

the end grain of the side casing (Fig. 12-76) while holding the face of the casing in perfect alignment. A little carpenter glue on the surface of each miter before assembling will aid the joint's permanency. Place the nail in the thicker part of the molding about 1/2" in from the corner. The first surface nail on each side of the corner should be kept away from the corner about 4" so as not to pressure or crack the miter joint open. Apply these two nails simultaneously with alternating hammer blows. The final seating is done with a nailset and very gentle taps of a finish-weight hammer (13 oz, or less).

The latch hardware ("doorknob") of a nonlocking type is called a *passage set*. A set that locks from one side only is called a *privacy set* (used on bathroom doors). The type used on exterior entrances are referred to as *keyed entrance sets*. *Common keyed* means that security-type locks can be purchased in groups of two or more locks that use the same key. All types include an instruction sheet for proper installation.

CABINET INSTALLATION

It is a rarity for cabinets to be built on site nowadays as they frequently were during the painted-cabinet period from the 1930s through the 1950s. Ready-made finished cabinets in many styles are available from most cashway lumber dealers as well as other building supply centers. Some savings may be realized by constructing all parts of kitchen and bath cabinetry on site except the face frames, doors, and drawer fronts. These parts may be ordered from a custom cabinet shop to face site-built frames and shelves.

Constructing finished cabinetry is not a job for the novice. It is a skilled trade requiring an extensive investment in machines and equipment and much experience.

Hanging preassembled top cabinets requires minimum tools and a little help. Purchased cabinets usually have

lightweight plywood backs, often as thin as 3 mm (about 1/8"). No attempt should be made to use this type of back for attaching the cabinet to the wall. Screws should pass through only solid wood frame members into the wall studs. These horizontal frames are found at the top and bottom of the cabinet and sometimes under shelves. They are usually about 1 1/2" high by 3/4" deep.

Locating the Studs

Locating the studs is done first by sound. Most cabinets will be located on a wall with at least one duplex electric outlet. The outlet is usually nailed to the side of a stud. Tap on each side of the box with your knuckle or hammer. The side that sounds and feels solid is where the stud is. Mark a point 3/4" from the edge of the duplex box (not from a cover; Fig. 12-77). Hold a level vertically by the mark. Make another vertical mark at a point that will be just below the upper cabinet. Determine the area that will be covered by the cabinet. Make marks to right and left of the first pilot mark at each stud into which screws will be placed.

Probing through the wall board is the last-resort method of confirming the location of the structural anchors. Choose a spot that will be covered by the cabinet. Use the tapping and sound method to get close. Drive a small nail, number 4d or so, in the most likely spot. If it hits wood, pull it out and move right or left 3/4" and puncture the wallboard again. Continue the practice until both edges of the stud are established. No more exploring should be required if all the other studs are spaced properly and are plumb. Measure from your pilot stud in multiples of 16" to right and left. Do not settle for a single exploratory nail that hits wood on the first try as an index. It could be very close to the edge of a stud. The center location is the

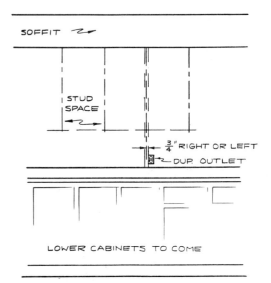

SOFFIT

STUD SPACE

3/4" RIGHT OR LEFT

DUP. OUTLET

LOWER CABINETS TO COME

FIGURE 12-77 Locate studs behind a wall by referencing right or left of an electric box.

goal for sure and sound anchorage. Magnetic "stud finders" do not find studs. They try to find drywall nailheads. Should a nail be off center (most are), the centering objective will be faulted as well.

Installing the Upper Cabinets

Prepare some temporary braces to extend from the floor to the bottom of the cabinet. Each brace should be about 1/4 to 1/2" longer than the distance so that it can be wedged tightly in place, thus putting pressure on the underside of the cabinet ends. This will in turn press the top of the cabinet firmly up against the soffit. With a helper, hoist the cabinet into place and brace it to the floor. Locate and mark all places where supporting screws can be used, where screws will anchor in solid wood.

Use flat- or oval-head screws. Round heads make future cleaning difficult. Drill screw holes at the center of the frame boards at each of the marked locations. The drill bit should be the same size as the screw shank or very slightly smaller. The shank of a screw is the smooth part between the head and the threads. Countersink each hole so that the screw heads will be flush with the surface (Fig. 12-78).

Good-quality shop-built cabinets have tops, bottoms, and shelves dadoed into solid ends. These are self-supporting on the face if supported adequately at the back. Screws in the top-mounting stringer will be tensile stressed in their effort to prevent the top of the cabinet from falling forward away from the wall. These top screws must be long in order to reach and hold in the studs (Fig. 12-79). These top screws may be placed horizontally, as the sheer stress is placed primarily on the screws farther down below

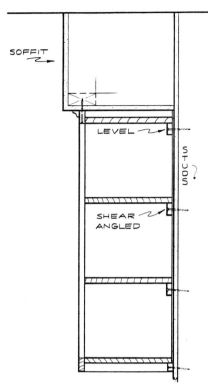

FIGURE 12-79 Factory- and shop-made cabinet units usually have dado-held shelves, thin panel backs, and rails. Long screws are needed to hold them to the stud wall.

the lower shelves. Where front anchoring to the soffit is desired with this type of prefabricated cabinet, it may be achieved by carefully drilling pilot holes vertically through the front cabinet facing.

Module cabinets may be assembled with bolts or screws before raising, or raised as individual units and then fastened together. Where the individual units to be gang assembled are small in width, it will be better to fasten several of them together before hoisting them. Fasten as many units together as can handily be put up. Some factory-made units came predrilled. Others are made with face wood on both ends so that they can be used independently or clustered. This type is usually undrilled. To gang assemble undrilled units, clamp them together first. Alignment should be perfect. Start with a pair. Clamp them with C clamps or handscrews, being careful not to damage any finished surfaces or put unnecessary strain on any joints. Bar clamps are better for small assemblies, but long bar clamps are seldom available outside the cabinet shop.

Installing the Floor Cabinets

Installing floor cabinets is much simpler. They do not require temporary bracing or holding up. Base cabinets are simply put in place, adjusted, leveled with shims, and attached to the wall studs in a few solid places. Some preliminary work is usually required where wall fixtures exist.

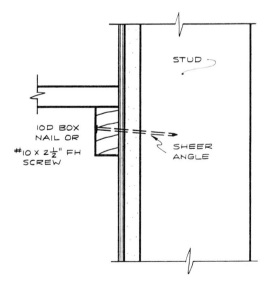

FIGURE 12-78 Shelf support rails provide a means of mounting top cabinets to the walls. Long thin nails or screws with flat or oval heads may be used to fasten the cabinets to the studs.

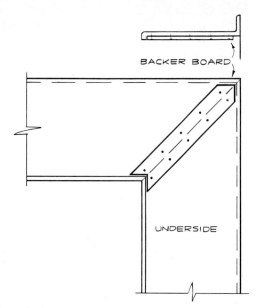

BACKER BOARD

UNDERSIDE

FIGURE 12-80 A preformed cabinet top that passes around a corner should be carefully mitered and backed underneath by a board that is secured with glue and screws. Failure to do this will almost always result in a ridge (a slight shoulder) where the Formica topping meets.

Plumbing openings for supply pipes and drains must be located and drilled through cabinets that have backs or through bottoms where S traps are used instead of wall-routed P traps. Accuracy in locating and cutting these openings is important because the pipe flanges used to cover the gaps are only so big. Measurement is the least reliable way to transfer the pipe location to the cabinet back. Place the cabinet against the roughed-in plumbing stubs. Reach down behind the cabinet and outline the hole areas. Remember the dishwasher wiring and the garbage disposal hookup.

Finishing

Joiner strips and corner adapters are stock items supplied to make the transition between cabinet units where they join and/or pass around corners. Cabinets do not always fit squarely into corners. Facing filler strips are obtainable to solve this problem. Your cabinet dealer will furnish spec-ification sheets listing all these items, as well as the stock sizes of all the cabinets available.

Contoured countertops that meet at a perpendicular corner require mitering at a 45° angle in order for the rolled front lip and the splashback to match perfectly (Fig. 12-80). After dry fitting this joint to perfection, a backup board of 1/2" to 3/4" plywood should be glued and screwed to the underside to guarantee that the joint cannot separate. The board should be no less than 4" wide so that a minimum of 2" contacts each side of the joint. A larger piece will be beneficial in stiffening and leveling the corner joint. Be extremely careful not to permit any screw from seating so deeply that the point pushes up and/or cracks the laminate surface covering. Most preformed tops have the thinnest grade of laminate. Dry fit the entire assembly first, then disassemble it, apply the glue, and reassemble it in place.

The body of the preformed top is usually made of a dense particle board. Overpowered screws have a tendency to strip out. Just before applying the final turn, it may be prudent to back out the screw and rub a paraffin cube across the hole. The paraffin deposit will be pushed ahead of the screw into the seat. Draw the threads of the screw across the paraffin. Roll the screw threads between thumb and index finger. Replace the screw in the hole and seat it fully. Experience will teach how much pressure can be applied without resulting in stripping the hole. Clearance holes are needed in the backing board so that the board can be drawn snugly to the countertop. A tight clearance hole will cause a misinterpretation of the pulldown pressure required. In this case it is possible to strip the screw anchor hole and not know it. The holding power is then nil.

Basic tools for installation include drills, screwdrivers, and a level. A ratchet brace with a screwdriver bit is handy to turn in the screws in the inside of a cabinet, where it is difficult to make a full revolution with any other type of driver. Power drivers are quick and handy in places where a straight shot at a screw is possible. Because of the angled approach required to set many of the cabinet hanging screws, the Phillips-head screw is preferred to the slot-head screw. Screwdriver bits do not slip out of the Phillips head as readily. Keep in mind that attachment screws should be as unobtrusive as possible. Never put a screw into a finished surface in full view.

R E V I E W   T O P I C S

Plumbing, Heating, Electric Installing, and Insulating

1. Describe clearly the difference between a dry vent and a wet vent. Explain in your description the way Ys should face and pipes should slant.

2. Explain the options when a drain pipe needs to be run through a floor joist. Cite the regulations involved.

3. Explain the difference between a plenum trunk system and a box plenum and pipe system of air distribution. Also mention where each is adapted to fit best.

4. State two faults with a wall-placed heat register which will be the cause of higher heat bills.
5. Explain the effects of placing electric ceiling fixtures at third points of a long room as compared to placing them on quarter points. Recommend the better system.
6. Describe the differences and similarities of a structural cabinet soffit and a boxed-type soffit.
7. Describe the term ''layering'' of insulation and explain how it is done above a ceiling.
8. Describe a good way to insulate above an attic access opening in a ceiling.

Drywalling

9. List as many objectives for wall board installing as you can remember.
10. Explain the reason for the sequence of installing the ceiling sheets first, followed by the top wall course, and last, the bottom wall course.
11. Give two reasons for cutting wallboard a little shorter than the opening it will cover.
12. Describe the difference between cutting wood to fit a particular place compared to cutting gypsum board to fit an area that will be taped and finished.
13. Describe a half-height T brace, including dimensions and quantity needed to secure a wallboard in place.
14. Describe the methods of locating and providing openings in drywall panels for electric boxes.
15. Explain how to hang drywall behind cabinets where no joint is wanted between the upper and lower cabinet units.
16. Describe precisely how to position the drywall sheets in a bathroom around a tub or shower enclosure. State the type of drywall to use.
17. Explain the preferred way to install drywall over a window area and over an interior doorway area.
18. Describe the problems and usual results of attempting to fasten the ends of drywall sheets to a single ceiling joist.
19. Explain the process of attaching the ends of two sheets of drywall to a scabbed, recessed joist from start to finish.
20. Describe the correct location of gypsum board end joints to be made on a partition, including both sides of the wall.
21. Describe the technique of joining two wallboard ends between two studs and providing a cup for the tape and compound.

22. Drywall gypsum board is cut a little smaller than the area to be covered. Paneling is cut the same or slightly larger. Explain the rationale for this difference in techniques.

Molding

23. Explain the reason for butting the first molding strip to an internal corner and coping the piece that adjoins it.

Underlayment and Finish Flooring

24. Describe how to put down underlayment felt to counteract infiltration.
25. Explain all the factors involved in choosing the location of the first piece of underlayment board that will be installed.
26. Describe the two major elements in the technique of positioning the sheets of particle board so that all edges and ends touch tightly against each other.
27. Explain the technique of installing (a) the first piece of hardwood strip flooring, (b) the rest of the pieces throughout the field, and (c) the last course against the far wall. Cover all subjects, such as positioning, nailing, cutting, and so on.
28. Describe parquet flooring and describe how to position and install it.

Installing Door Jambs

29. Explain fully how to plumb and level a door casing.
30. Write a short discourse about the two philosophies in regard to the latch edge of a wood door.
31. Explain how the bottom of a jamb may be installed to provide more efficient carpet installation and maintenance.
32. Describe how to install a door stop so that there is no bind after finish is applied. Include a method of removing and adjusting the door stop for more clearance without damage to either the jamb or the stop.

Hanging Wall Cabinets

33. Describe more than one method of locating all unseen studs in a wall on which a cabinet is to be hung.
34. Describe how to support an upper cabinet during installation with minimum workers available.
35. Explain how to make a perfect miter joint at the corner of a preformed countertop.

Chapter 13
STAIR CONSTRUCTION_____

IMPORTANCE OF KNOWLEDGE

The design and costruction of a stairway is one of the more challenging enterprises in the construction of a house. It is one of the significant parts of the house that will affect the comfort and safety of the occupants for as many years as the structure is used. A stairway is seldom constructed satisfactorily without some comprehensive education or training in advance. The inadequate, uncomfortable, or substandard stairway constitutes one of the most common structural errors frequently found in houses of every age. For this reason alone, it is important that novice and professional aspirant alike prepare to understand all the elements that affect the final positioning and profile of the stairs. Because this is an area of frequent faulty design, it is important that learning by copying be avoided. Running next door to see how it was done in another house is apt to result in the perpetuation of faulty design over and over again. Of the hundreds of stairways designed and built by the author, no two have been identical because the stairwell cavity or area is never identical. Designing and cutting the stringers is a customizing job for each project. It matters not that the same floor plan is used for a duplicate house. Small dimensional variations will exist from one structure to another. The concrete floor in a basement, for example, will vary in height a fraction of an inch. Any variance in stairwell height or length will affect such things as the bearing proportion of the stringer head, the unit rise of each step, the tread run depth, and the head clearance. All of these dimensional features ultimately are reflected in the slope of the incline, the depth of foot space on the steps, and whether persons of all normal heights can traverse up and down in an erect and comfortable manner. The formulas, tables, and information to follow will provide the necessary knowledge in order to lay out and construct well-conceived and functional stairways.

Stair construction has undergone considerable change since the turn of the century. Hardwood, custom dadoed stringers with their accompanying treads and wedges are no longer common. Modern construction is typically accomplished with construction-grade hidden parts and covered with finished materials that can be assembled on the site. The descriptions and illustrations that follow deal with current practices only.

TYPES OF STAIRS

There are many types of stairs. The variations are found mostly in the stairwell or absence of a well. There are *open stair flights* which have only the supportive side stringers (carriages) and treads (steps). This type is frequently found connecting the first floor to a basement. A *closed stairway* is one where a set of stairs is sandwiched between partition walls. This type is considered to be the safest design. There are other innovative designs for specialized situations. In this category are *spiral stairs* (to conserve space), *pull-down stairs* (for infrequent access to attics), and others of aesthetically conceived origin. More flexibility in design is possible with welded steel than with wood. Nevertheless, the vast majority of residential houses have wood stairways, due to the lower cost of materials and the facility of being able to custom build them on the site.

The *winder stair* is one that has steps shaped like thin slices of pie. Steps of this shape may be used to turn a

330

corner with less space being used than a platform or landing would involve. A spiral stairway usually has all winder steps. Winders are less comfortable to walk on. The area of the step that is deep enough to accommodate your whole foot is usually limited. It is dangerous to attempt to walk on any part of the winder step except that which is deep enough from the nosing (the forward edge) to the back edge. A recognized advantage of the spiral winder stairway is its vertical compactness. It can be installed in a square-floor area of minimum size. For intermittent or emergency use, the spiral stairway serves a viable function. For regular traffic from one living area to another, the conventional stairway is a better choice.

STAIRWAY SHAPES

There are some basic stairway shapes as looked on in a floor plan. The *straight-line stairway* (Fig. 13-1a) is obviously the most direct route between two floor levels. It is also the simplest and quickest to build.

The L-shaped stairway (Fig. 13-1b) is one that makes a right-angle turn somewhere along its rise or descent. The turn is accomplished by making one of the step

levels into a platform (an intermediate landing) or by using two, three, or four winder steps to transverse the turn. The landing design is preferred due to its greater safety. An accident victim has a better chance of surviving a fall down a half flight of stairs to a landing than a fall down a full flight. The elderly and the infirm find an intermediate landing a welcome oasis in the journey from one level to another.

The switchback (Fig. 13-2) is a design that reverses its direction 180° at a midpoint in the flight. Again, the intermediate landing presents the safest design. In this stair shape, however, a significant amount of floor space can be conserved by the use of winders (Fig. 13-3a). Whatever amount that could be conserved in the corner by using winders with the L shape can be doubled with the switchback design.

The U shape (Fig. 13-3b) is a combination of Ls. It is practical when some reasonable use can be made of the area between and under the stairway. To conserve the greatest amount of floor footage, steps may be designed in each of the three segments of the U. For example, the steps progress upward, then turn 90° at a landing, progress upward again to the second landing, turn 90° again, and progress upward in the last of three flights to the ultimate floor level.

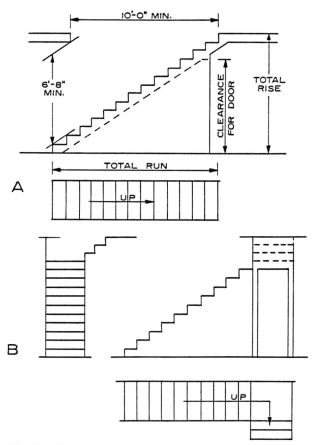

FIGURE 13-1 (a) The simplest stairway is straight from one level to another. (b) An L-shaped stair will turn a corner by using a landing. The space underneath may be used for storage.

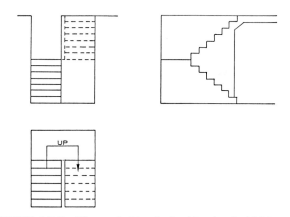

FIGURE 13-2 The switchback doubles back 180° on a landing platform.

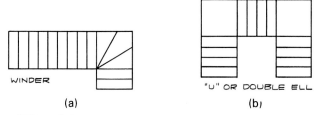

FIGURE 13-3 (a) A winder is a flight that contains triangular or trapazoidal steps to round a corner. (b) The U shape, sometimes called a double L, makes two 90° turns on landings to reverse its direction.

PLATFORM LANDINGS

A landing is constructed much like a second-floor level. It is a miniature floor. To provide adequate head bearing for the stringers, the landing joists and headers are usually 2 × 6s or larger.

One method of supporting the ends of the joists is to lap and nail them to the face of the surrounding partition studs (Fig. 13-4a). Support, in addition to the nails, is provided by trimmers under the joists extending to the partition sole.

Another joist support technique is to inlet a ribbon (Fig. 13-4b), like the one used in the balloon wall frame system. The ribbon is less costly in material expense. Another advantage of the ribbon is that it forms a solid backing for any type of wall skin that is applied under the landing (wallboard, paneling, etc.).

A third method is to build a box of headers like the main floor. The joists may be put into the assembly to complete it (Fig. 13-5). The whole component is then raised into place. It is surface nailed to the partition studs that surround the well. These nails should be slanted down a few degrees to provide good sheer stress.

The height of the landing must be assessed carefully. The finished surface of a landing must coincide at precisely the same level as if it were one of the steps. An objective in the construction of a flight of stairs is to create identical heights for each step. It will be seen later, when laying out the stringer cuts, how the top and bottom steps are affected by the thickness of floor-covering materials. The same consideration must be applied to the landing surface height.

STAIRS TO A BASEMENT

There are three common construction designs of stairs from a first floor to the basement level. They are the open stair carriage, the housed stair carriage, and the closed stairway with notched carriages.

Open Stairway

The open stairway contains a minimum of materials (Fig. 13-6). The basic stair flight could contain as little as two stringers and a quantity of treads. To pass a typical building code, it must have a handrail for safety. This, in turn, would require a post at the bottom of the flight to which the rail is secured. Partway up the flight the rail is secured to the floor opening joist. At the top it is secured to a wall stud.

The stringers are of 2 × 10 or 2 × 12 girth. Steps are usually 2 × 12s which net a depth of 11 1/4″. Attaching and supporting the steps to the stringer is accomplished with cleats or dadoes (Fig. 13-7a). The dadoed type is called a *housed stringer* (Fig. 13-7b).

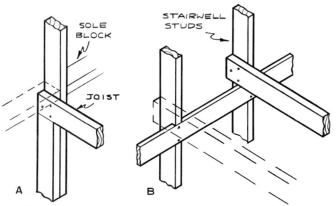

FIGURE 13-4   (a) Face-nailed platform joists supported on stud trimmers; (b) joists supported on an inletted ribbon.

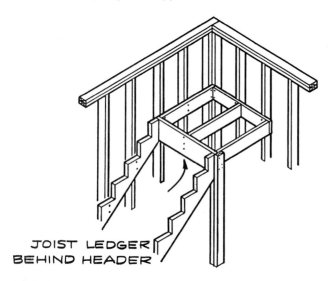

FIGURE 13-5   A boxed platform floor may be preassembled or nailed in place to the stairwell studs.

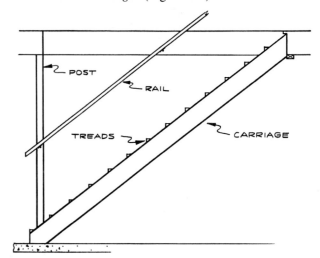

FIGURE 13-6   The basic minimum open stair flight is composed of two carriages, treads, a handrail, and a rail post.

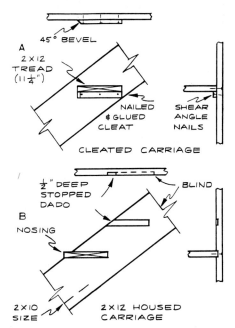

FIGURE 13-7 (a) Cleated carriages benefit from having the step toward the rear. (b) Dadoed carriages will sustain their compression load best with the step ahead of the uncut portion of the carriage.

The cleated stringer, in spite of its limitations, will often be the choice of the novice, due to a lack of appropriate tooling or expertise. There are some options as to where the treads and cleats may be positioned horizontally across the stringer. Placing them close to the back of the stringer has an advantage in that the front top sides of the stringer protrude beyond the treads, thereby providing a little curbing. Small as it is, this curbing is helpful to toddlers or persons who may need to feel the identity of the boundaries of the steps with their feet.

There is also a structural consideration. Steps on cleats that are toward the back side of the stringer provide the stringer with a better top bearing posture. Steps that align with the front edge of the stringer will leave a portion of the stringer head bearing unsupported. This is an undesirable condition. It is severe with 2 × 12s and moderate with 2 × 10s except in cases of maximum unit rise and minimum tread depth (also an undersirable situation).

The dado method (pronounced "day-doe") is superior to the cleat method since the weight on each cleated step is born on the nails that hold cleats to the carriage. A better system is to dado the carriage to accept the steps. This method requires more time and skill. A dado is a groove cut crosswise of the grain of a board. In the stringer, the dado is at an angle to the edge of the planks. It qualifies as a dado instead of a groove because the annual grain rings in the board are severed. The groove, by comparison, is ploughed out in a direction more or less parallel with the grain.

In cabinet making, dadoes are usually cut halfway through the thickness of the board. Cutting halfway through a 1 1/2"-thick stringer would reduce its strength to that of a 3/4" board. A 1/3-depth cut (1/2") is enough depth for the step bearing and leaves a stringer that is adequately strong. Builders who do not maintain woodworking shops are not likely to have dado heads (blades) of sufficient capacity to cut a 1 1/2" dado in a single pass on the radial saw. It is possible to do the operation with smaller dado heads by making two or more passes to plough out the 1 1/2" dado. In the case of the open stairway it is assumed that the step to be pocketed in the dado will be dimension stock rather than the more elite milled treads of oak.

A housed freestanding stringer poses different structural considerations when placing the steps across the breadth of the stringer. The stringer is reduced theoretically in strength throughout the portion affected by the cut-out dadoes. The term "theoretical" is used because once the steps are glued and nailed into a snugly fitted joint, the strength is somewhat restored. Nonetheless, a stringer that is dadoed on the front top side will be stronger than one where the blind dadoes are run in from the back underside. Therefore, where steps are installed to the front of the stringers and some auxiliary bearing can be designed to accommodate the head bearing shortcomings, the best of both conditions may be met.

Fastening the steps to the dadoed carriage is accomplished by gluing and end nailing. The success of the holding power is dependent on two elements: the accuracy and tightness of the dadoed joist and the effectiveness of the nails. Ordinary nails have a tendency to work loose. They are smooth. The vibration from walking on the stairs frequently causes them to work out of the end grain of the step. Resin-coated nails are slightly better. Ring shank nails (annular nails) have the most effective holding power for this purpose. They can be purchased under the name of pole barn nails. A tightly joined step-to-stringer dado joint that is glued and nailed with three 12 or 16d pole barn nails will form a rigid stairway. It will survive many years of use.

A stop plate of some sort is needed with a free-flight stair. This stop, sometimes called a kickboard, is needed at the bottom of open stairs to keep the carriages firmly in place. Without a stop plate, the carriages hang from the top end and can be loosened by vibration. There are two simple stop plate designs. A traditional stop is made with a 2 × 4 as long as the width of the stairway. It is fastened to the floor with power nails or concrete anchor bolts. Holes are drilled in the concrete. Vinyl or lead liners are inserted. Lag screws (bolts) are used to hold the 2 × 4 in place. The bottom of the carriages are notched to fit over the 2 × 4 (Fig. 13-8).

Another method of anchoring is to use a short length of angle iron on the inside of each carriage. A piece of

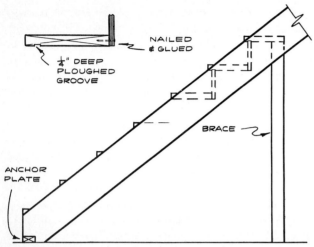

FIGURE 13-8 An anchor plate keeps the staircase from sliding out. A knee brace near the center of the carriage cuts the stress in half and provides a solid feeling to the open stair. Risers nailed to the back of the steps eliminate sidesway.

1 1/2″ angle iron, as long as the stringer bearing end, is lag bolted to the concrete floor and cross bolted to the stringer with two carriage bolts in each direction.

A stairway of the design described above is limited in width to 3′ by most codes since it employs only two stringers. Intermediate support may be provided simply by placing a 2 × 4 post under each stringer at a point midway up the stringer. With the dadoed design, these posts may be placed against the inside face of the stringers. The upper end bears tightly under a step. Such intermediate support cuts the free span of the stringer in half. It makes it stiffer and capable of carrying heavier loads. It does not, however, improve on the step capacity since that is related only to the span of the step (length across from support to support) and the girth of the step. The intermediate supporting posts will remove any springiness from the stringers. Consequently, a greater sense of strength will be felt. For wider free flights, a third-cut type of stringer can be used at the midpoint between the outer stringers.

Cut Stringer Stairway

The cut stair stringer usually requires the largest plank available, a 2 × 12, when it is in a free-flight design (no surrounding walls). Triangular pieces are cut out of the carriage stringer at each step location. Each step is made up of two pieces, a tread and a riser. The *tread* is the horizontal step board. The *riser* is a board placed vertically at the back of the step.

The cut stringer loses a lot of its strength from the removal of the cutouts. Most codes mandate that there be no less than 3 1/2″ of solid wood remaining from the point of the cutout to the under edge of the stringer (Fig. 13-9).

In a closed stairwell, this loss of strength is of little concern, as the stringer can be face nailed to each stud along its span. With the free-flight stairway, however, much care must be exercised not to overweaken the stringer with poorly executed cutouts. When the maximum cutout is executed, the 3 1/2″ remaining, in reality, is equivalent to a 2 × 4.

Some freeflight stairs with cutout stringers have no risers, as an economy measure. Such a stairway should have intermediate supporting posts *without exception*. The top of the post will have a pitch cut which matches the slope of the stringer. The post end is carefully pilot drilled and toenailed to the under edge of the stringer. Another suitable technique is to bolt a post to the inside face of each stringer with two carriage bolts.

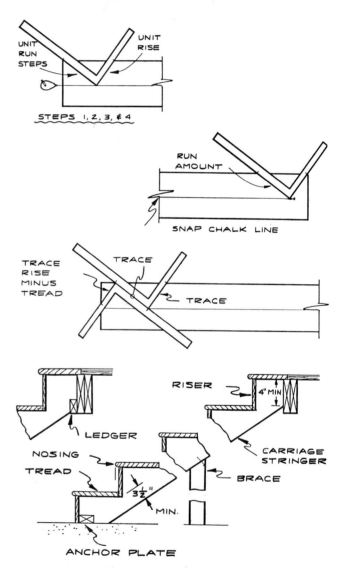

FIGURE 13-9 A notched stringer for use as an open stairway will benefit greatly from risers and intermediate support posts because its effective portion is seldom equivalent to more than a 2 × 4.

Risers perform a supporting role to the stringer of a free-flight stairway. The riser should extend downward behind the step. It is then glued and nailed to the back edge of the tread. This formation removes all the potential flexibility of the tread when it is subjected to a concentrated weight (a 200-lb body on one foot). The weight is actually supported by two risers, the one under the front edge of the tread and the one nailed to the back edge. Visualize standing on top of the edge of two boards, totaling a height of about 15″ (two risers) and a little over 3′ long. It is rigid. Where 13 or 14 of these tread and riser sets are placed into a stringer carriage formation, the resulting stiffness is impressive. Each set is like a large angle iron. The builder who will rout out a shallow groove (1/4 to 3/8″) under the front edge of the tread and glue in the top of the riser will have produced a stairway unsurpassed in construction quality.

Plywood is the best choice of wood for the riser, though solid wood of 3/4″ thickness is satisfactory. The multidirectional grain structure of plywood will not split when toe-kicked. A regular board used as a riser will sometimes split when the weight on the back of the step pulls downward on the crosswise running grain.

Closed Stairway

The closed stairway is one constructed between partitions. It is most commonly found between aboveground floors, although partitioned-off basements may also have a closed stairway. The most used carriage stringer design in a stairwell is the cutout type. There are two practical ways of mounting the carriage stringers. They can be nailed directly on the surface of the wall skin (plaster, drywall, or paneling) or they can be nailed on top of an unnotched finish stringer and a 1 × 4 filler.

The surface-mounting technique calls for the carriage stringers to be nailed on the surface of the wall with nails that anchor in the studs. Because the stringer is usually of a self-supporting design, a single well-placed 16d common nail into each stud is adequate. The nail is placed in the lower 3 1/2″ area of the stringer. Do not nail through the triangular part that holds the tread and riser. This triangular part is vulnerable to splitting off.

A third stringer may be required. If so, it will be centered between the outside stringers. The code maximum width of the stairway with two stringers is 30″ when 5/4 (1 1/16″) treads are used. The maximum is 36″ when 2″ (1 1/2″) treads are used. Therefore, all stairways 3′ wide and over will require three stringers. It is rare to find a stairway with only two stringers since the minimum code stair width is 32″.

During rough construction, the stringers may be temporarily installed as soon as access to the second story is desired. Temporary rough treads are tacked on them so that workers have easy access to the second floor. After the house is closed in and rough plumbed and wired, the stringers may be removed to drywall the partitions in the wall. The stringers are then installed permanently. It should be noted that many framing illustrations show the stringers as though they were mounted directly against the studs. This technique diminishes the bearing space for the treads from 1 1/2″ to an inadequate 1/4″ after the wall skin and notched finish stringer is added. Installing carriage stringers directly to studs was abandoned when the drywall system took over. Placing the stringers permanently onto bare studs will cause much unnecessary inefficiency. Drywall, or whatever material, will have to be cut around all the notches (a total of 28 notches). Each cut will require some kind of backup between studs to eliminate the flexibility of the wall skin. Beware of the illustration that does not make it clear that carriages and baseboard stringers are both applied on top of the wall skin and not directly to the studs as they were in the days of wet plaster.

After the stringers have been permanently installed on the face of the drywalled stairwell, a nominal-1″ finish stringer is made for each side of the stairs. This 3/4″-thick board is a wide piece that serves as a baseboard. It is notched on the lower side in the opposite pattern to the structural stringer. The pattern may be traced directly from the carriage before it is installed. The risers and treads are going to butt snugly against the face of this stringer (Fig. 13-10). The cutouts on this trim stringer do not have to be precise. The riser is usually 3/4″ thick and the tread is either 1 1/16″ or 1 1/2″. This allows for some leeway in cutting the trim stringer since the ends of the treads and risers will cover up to the amount of their thickness. The trim stringer is nailed through the wall covering into the studs with finish nails of 8 or 10d size.

A simpler way to fashion a baseboard is to nail a 1 × 12 board to the wall first (Fig. 13-11). Nailed directly below this 1 × 12 is a 1 × 4 filler. The carriage stringers are then nailed on the surface of these boards. The exposed width of the baseboard needs to be only wide enough to be below the tread contact point and as high above the nosing

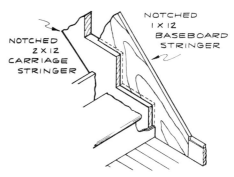

FIGURE 13-10 A notched baseboard stringer is fitted to position above the carriage stringer.

FIGURE 13-11 A full-finish baseboard stringer lies partially behind the notched carriage. A filler board is placed below to sustain solid nailing throughout.

as desired. This will generally be the same stock width as the stringer or one size smaller. The 1 × 4 filler is nailed to the wall below this trim board. Its lower edge should not protrude below the lower edge of the carriage stringer. To locate this position the stringer is placed with its head and base bearings in alignment. The underside is then traced on the wall. The carriage is then removed and the 1 × 4 filler is nailed just above the line. The notches of the stringer may also be traced to assure that the trim stringer above is placed correctly to accommodate the risers and treads (parallel to the tread nosings).

WHEN TO BUILD THE LANDING

It is not practical to construct temporary landings (platforms) as is done with temporary stairs during rough construction. The platforms are constructed at the time of rough framing as described in an earlier paragraph. After the platforms are in place, each flight of stairs from one level to the next is handled like an independent little stairway. Reminder: One must be constantly aware that variable thickness in the surface materials placed on top of the subfloor affects the height of steps and platform landings. It must be taken into account when establishing the position and height of the platform frame and the first and last step cutouts. To maintain equality of step height, it is necessary to add or subtract height for any variable.

The box-framed platform can be constructed against walls that have been covered, but it suffers a basic weakness. Its support will be derived mostly from nails. Where surface mounted, these nails usually bridge across (through) some gypsum to reach the studs. This is a vulnerable weakness unless additional support is provided. Where the cavity underneath the landing is unfinished or closed, this poses

no problem. A short 2 × 4 post is placed under each corner of the box frame. The top of the post is placed in the direction that will cause both adjacent side boards of the box to bear on the top of the vertical 2 × 4 post.

INSTALLING RISERS AND TREADS

After stringers and trim boards are in place, the length of the risers and the ends are custom fitted to each opening. Birch plywood is a favorite material for risers that will be exposed. It is suitable for painting because of its closed-grain surface. It also stains well and blends with oak or maple treads. The high cost of hardwoods makes wall-to-wall carpeting a comparable and attractive alternative to the hardwood staircase. Risers for the carpeted staircase may then be made from an A-C grade of plywood at a considerable savings.

Risers are nailed to the vertical edges of the stringer notches. The stringers ideally will be identical in profile. This is seldom the case. With a three-stringer frame, some adjustment of the tread or riser surfaces is usually necessary (Fig. 13-12). Use the straight edge of a riser board across the tread supporting surfaces of the stringers to test. If one tread base of the three is high, trim it down. If one is low, shim it with a strip ripped from the edge of a 2″ board. The step tread should end up resting on all three

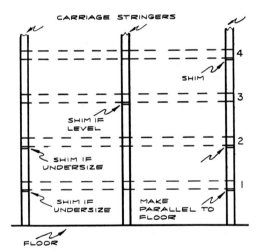

FIGURE 13-12 Here are shown four typical misalignment situations. First step: Make the tread parallel to the floor or level by shimming the outside stringer steps or cutting down the center step. Second step: Check step heights from floor. Determine whether center step is high or side steps are low. Shim up or cut down according to correct height and levelness. Third step: If the tread is level, shim the center step. If it is unlevel, cut down the step on the high side. Compare with height from the floor. Fourth step: If the tread checks level, shim the low step. If the tread checks high over the step that it does not touch, cut down the center step.

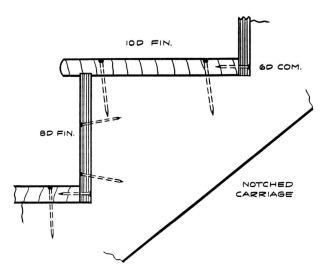

FIGURE 13-13 Grooved treads and risers that bear on the carriage step will provide a sturdy staircase.

bearing surfaces and be level. The riser should touch all three vertical edges of the stringers and be square to the walls. These criteria will determine whether to shim or reduce the riser surface.

The top edge of the riser is placed flush with the cutout surfaces of the stringer unless the treads are grooved (Fig. 13-13). For the grooved tread the riser will extend above the stringer the exact amount of the groove depth. The bottom edge should rest on the stringers. In this way the weight on the tread is transferred through the riser to the stringer instead of to the nails that hold on the riser.

Treads are custom fitted in length to each step level. They are surface nailed with finish or casing nails. A hardwood tread will require drill tapping to avoid splitting. The nails at the ends of the tread should be placed no farther than 3/4″ away from the end of the tread. The notched

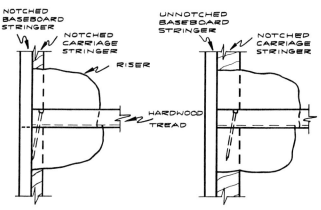

FIGURE 13-14 The step tread will bear on only 3/4″ where a notched baseboard stringer is used. The full stringer lapped by a notched carriage provides 1 1/2″ of bearing for the tread. In both cases a pilot hole should be drilled for each hole and should be slanted toward the thickest body of the carriage step.

trim stringer above the carriage stringer covers up half the thickness of the bearing surface. The tread is supported by the remaining 3/4″ of surface (Fig. 13-14). The tap holes must be slanted toward the stringer; otherwise, the nails will miss the stringer and slide down the surface. All nail heads should be set below the surface so that the filler rubbed into the open-grain surface of the oak tread will cover and disguise them. Dimension lumber treads may be nailed with either finishing or full-headed nails. Screw-shank flooring nails are good for pulling down warped treads. Concentrate them toward the high points of the tread.

Mounting the stringers on the vertical surface of an unnotched trim board and a filler leaves the full thickness (1 1/2″) of the stringer exposed upon which to mount the treads and risers. This changes the nailing technique. The nails are placed farther back from the ends of the tread. Somewhere between 1 and 1 1/2″ is adequate. A little slant is still needed to make sure that the nail enters the stringer. A note of caution: When driving the nail in this area it is exceptionally easy to damage the finish stringer surface with hammer dents. A sheet metal shield is an excellent preventive tool to have on hand. Hold it in position to cover the face of the trim board while hammering in the nails.

DESIGN AND CONSTRUCTION RULES

Many a stairway has been made by trial and error. There is no need to subject oneself to such a task, a potential ordeal, when the use of a few rules and formulas will make a product of near perfection possible. It makes sense to know the rules and principles before attempting a layout on either a working drawing or a carriage plank. The rules from FHA, MPS, SBCCI, and others are:

- **The minimum effective depth** of a cut stringer is 3 1/2″ (the lower side of the stringer) perpendicular to the rake.
- **The top bearing end** of the stringer (the vertical edge) shall not be less than 4″ unless otherwise adequately anchored.
- **A center stringer** is required when the distance between the outside stringers is greater than 30″ for 1 1/16″ treads or 36″ for 1 1/2″ treads.
- **Headroom** should not be less than 6′-8″ measured vertically from an imaginary line intersecting all nosing extremities to the lowest obstruction above.
- **Open stairs** shall have an anchoring system at the bottom.
- **Winders** shall meet the common tread depth not farther than 18″ from the hub of their acute angle. (Fig. 13-15a).

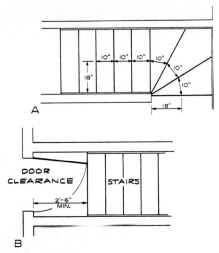

FIGURE 13-15 (a) Winders must have at least a full-depth tread at a point within 18″ of the small end of the tread. (b) The minimum depth of a landing is 30″ or whatever the door width is if it is wider than 30″.

- **A landing** at the foot of a stair run shall not be less than 30″ deep ahead of the tread nosing (Fig. 13-15b). The step rise should not be less than 7″ or greater than 8″ (The lower limit is not regulated).
- **The tread run** (the horizontal cutout on the carriage) should not be less than 9″.
- **The tread** should not be less than 10 1/8″.
- **The nosing** should not be less than 1 1/8″ or greater than the tread thickness.

The following principles also apply:

1. The sum of the unit rise and run should equal 17″, or the sum of two rises and one run should equal 25″.
2. The overall run of a stringer does *not* include the head bearing end of the stringer.

Ignoring this last bit of knowledge has probably been the greatest cause of ill-designed and constructed stairways where detail plans were not available or not correctly interpreted. With these basic rules and principles the reader is now ready to attempt the computation required to draw a dimensioned profile and to lay out the stringer on a plank.

PREDESIGNED OR CUSTOM-DESIGNED STAIRS

There are two ways to go about designing stairs. One way is to design the carriage first. The length of the rough opening in the floor is then established from the section view.

It is transposed to the floor plan. On the floor plan enough length must be provided to accommodate the total run of the stringer. The *total run* of the stringer is the sum of the units of run. The *overall* run of the stringer includes the horizontal top of the head bearing part of the carriage, which is covered with flooring. Another variable exists with an open stairflight leading to a basement. A portion of *one* step at the bottom can fall under the ceiling (the first floor). There will still be adequate headroom. These two design conditions make it possible to have a rough opening in the floor which is approximately one-half unit run shorter than the overall run. When the stairway is designed before the floor plan is completed, a section drawing is made to scale (the larger, the better). The factor that will control the minimum possible rough-opening length will be the headroom. *Headroom* may be defined as the vertical distance from a line connecting the nosings of the treads to the lowest obstruction above. *Head clearance* is another term for this distance. It will be noted that this minimum height of 6′-8″ conforms with the standard door height most commonly found in a residence.

The second and more common method of designing a stairway is to allow a recognized minimum space or more for the stairway on a floor plan. A stair detail plan may not always be furnished. It then becomes the builder's job to figure out the layout (Fig. 13-16). A rule of thumb for the length of a rough opening in the first floor leading to a basement is a minimum of 9′-6″. A second floor opening should not be less than 10′ according to this rule of thumb. These lengths are true in essence, but they do not include the distance required for the bearing head of the carriage. Six to eight inches must be added to the floor plan opening to establish the rough opening.

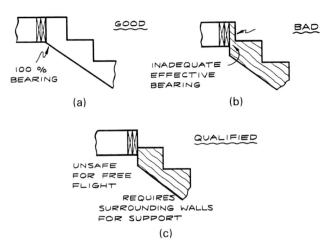

FIGURE 13-16 (a) Ideal head bearing posture where all the end of the carriage stringer is leaning on the headers; (b) poor design for any circumstance; (c) poor design for a free-flight stair but would be tolerable for a stairwell, where the carriages can be nailed to the studs of the well partitions.

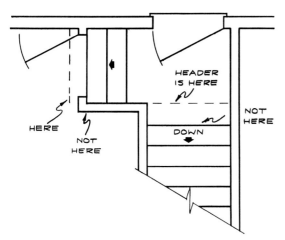

FIGURE 13-17   The line on a floor plan indicates where a step changes levels (the edge of the nosing on the landing or floor). The header should be at least 8″ farther back as the floor runs out on top the head of the carriage.

A significant error is frequently caused by misinterpretation of the floor plan. On the plan a line is seen which represents a change of levels. This line is the edge of the nosing on the floor level. It does *not* represent the location of the joist header in the rough floor (Fig. 13-17). The header will be about 6 to 8″ back from this plan line. On those occasions when a header is incorrectly placed at this nosing line, the intended total run of the stringer will be shortened by as much as one unit of run. This will cause a stringer to be made with higher rises and a steeper, less desirable pitch. This also affects the headroom by shortening it. This problem may cause an inspection failure. The builder may be required to tear out and redo—a costly remedial situation. Few of the parts can be reused. Only the risers can be cut down to size. The treads will be too narrow. The stringers are a total loss.

Another error frequently occurs at this point. Assume that the builder followed a good detail plan and placed

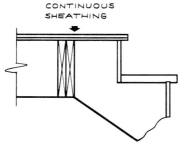

FIGURE 13-18   Permit sheathing and underlayment to extend beyond the header 10″ or more. Cut it off to form a standard nosing after the stair carriages are permanently installed. Do not cut it off at the header, which would destroy its tying function.

the floor header in the correct location. The intended stairway leads to a basement. As is the logical custom, the concrete basement floor will not be poured until the roof is completed. Therefore, the stair stringers will be one of the last framing details. In the meantime, the first floor will probably be sheathed with plywood. The sheather forgets to allow the sheathing to extend beyond the headers into the opening. It should extend to the point where the first riser will be. By ignoring or forgetting this, a valuable tie is lost. The uninterrupted sheathing at this location should form an effective tie from the floor frame onto the top head of the stringer (Fig. 13-18). An effective method of assuring this sheathing tie is to let it hang beyond the header 10 to 12″. At this stage it is not known where the precise dropoff point will be. By leaving this excess sheathing, it is possible to cut it precisely after the stringer is installed. Usually, the whole plywood sheet can be left intact and the cut made later.

Let us assume that the architect or designer follows the latter technique; floor plan first, stair detail second. Some limitations are now imposed on the design. The stairway incline is confined to a cubical well of certain dimensions which cannot be altered without changing the floor plan. The total run is confined to the horizontal length of the opening. The total rise is a fixed amount of distance. The project is now one of customizing the stairway profile to these dimensional limits.

Total Rise

Total rise is the distance vertically from one floor surface to another for which the stairway is to be designed. It does not matter whether the stairway is curved, straight, or one of the turning designs. The sum of the unit levels in the stairway is the total rise. The dimension to use for the total rise number is the *actual* height that exists. A designer or carpenter should never scale a drawing to get this number. It must be derived by mathematics and by actual measurement. The individual components are assessed for their actual size. Take two examples, a typical basement height and a first floor-to-second floor height.

A typical block wall basement will contain 12 blocks of height. The unit block height (laid measure) is 8″. Twelve blocks net a total height of 96″. A 4″ concrete floor is poured on top of the footing where the blocks sit, so 4″ is subtracted from the 96″, leaving 92″ of block wall exposed above the floor. A wood sill rests on top of the wall, which adds 1 1/2″ of height. Fiberglass sill sealer is completely compressible, so it adds no height. The box floor has 2 × 10 joists and headers, so 9 1/4″ of height is added. The subfloor is 1/2″ plywood and the underlayment flooring is 5/8″ particle board. The problem is:

$$92 + 1\ 1/2 + 9\ 1/4 + 1/2 + 5/8 = 103\ 7/8''$$

For practical purposes this figure could be rounded to 104″. This is a theoretical addition of materials to be used for drawing purposes. On the site, *the height should be measured and taken exactly as it exists for the purpose of laying out the stringer.*

From first to second floor, a typical total rise will accumulate the following addition. The 5/8″ particle board underlayment is conventionally laid on top of the subfloor, as are the partition soles (the open-building technique is an exception). Where the stringer rests on the subfloor, the particle board reduces the room height by 5/8″. For our sample problem this can be subtracted immediately from the sole height (1 1/2 − 5/8 = 7/8″ of sole height above the finish floor level). There remains the following quantities to add: 7/8″ of exposed sole, a precut stud of 92 5/8″, a double plate (1 1/2″ + 1 1/2″) of 3″ and a ceiling/floor joist of 9 1/4″, a 1/2″ subfloor, and a 5/8″ underlayment on the second floor. The problem is:

$$7/8 + 92 \ 5/8 + 3'' + 9 \ 1/4$$
$$+ \ 1/2 + 5/8 = 106 \ 7/8''$$

On a calculator the problem looks like this:

$$.875 + 92.625 + 3 + 9.25 + .5 + .625 = 106.875$$

The sum will vary according to the material sizes. For example, 2 × 8 joists will reduce the figure by 2″, to 104.875″. On the site the actual height should be found, but be careful to add materials that are not yet installed, such as flooring.

Number of Risers

Most basement stairways will have 13 or 14 steps (units of rise). The construction of the foundation wall affects the height, which in turn affects the quantity of steps that will qualify under the minimum-maximum rule. The first floor-to-second floor stairway, where precut studs are used, will usually have 14 units of rise.

Apply these unit-rise modules to the basement example. Try the number 13 first.

$$104'' \div 13 = 8'' \text{ actual rise}$$

This is an acceptable unit rise, although it is at the top of the maximum range. It is the steepest incline considered practical. The next full quantity of rise units to produce a shorter unit of rise is 14. Divided by 14, the 104″ nets a unit rise of 7.4285714″ (by calculator). Reduced to a fraction of an inch, it comes out just under 7 7/16″. This is a more comfortable step when climbing. It requires a little more total run to maintain the headroom desired. In most cases this will cause a small loss in floor space. Such a loss

is well worth it in terms of the added relief, climbing comfort, over a period of years.

The total rise in the first-to-second floor example was 106 7/8″. Fourteen units of rise creates the following problem:

$$106 \ 7/8 \div 14 = 7.6339285$$

The fractional inch, .6339285, transposes to 20.29 thirty-seconds or slightly over 5/8. Therefore, the unit rise dimension that can be used in the layout process is 7 5/8″. When using a calculator, the fractional-inch remainder can be multiplied by 32 first to see if one can find the rise to the closest 1/32″. This can be rounded to the closest 1/16 when it falls within the upper or lower quadrant of the whole decimal (upper or lower 25%). When it falls in the middle two quadrants (.25 to .75) it should be left in thirty-seconds of an inch. Decimal fractions, in this midrange, are closer to the nearest thirty-second than to the nearest sixteenth. When dividing a stringer into equal units of rise, working to a 1/32″ tolerance is quite possible and practical for the good carpenter who keeps his pencil sharp for the layout.

Run Unit Depth

The quantity of treads (run units) is always one less than the quantity of risers. This is because the stringer starts with and ends with a riser. The last step, so to speak, is the floor, both at the bottom and the top (see Fig. 13-9).

The unit run, according to the rules, may be as much as 1 1/2″ less than the tread depth since 1 1/2″ is the maximum overhang of the nosing dimension lumber treads (Fig. 13-19). A stringer notch can be designed to accommodate a dimension lumber tread precisely so that the tread

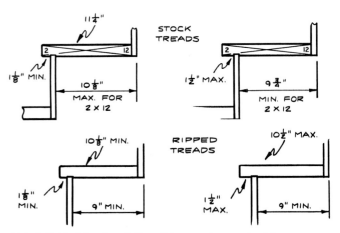

FIGURE 13-19 Stock 2 × 12s may be used without customizing where the unit run range falls within 9 3/4 to 10 1/8″. From the minimum unit run of 9 to 9 3/4″, the 2 × 12s will have to be ripped to a size 1 1/2″ wider than the run figure.

can be used without ripping. For example, any run variation between 9 3/4″ and 10 1/8″ will accept a 2 × 12 tread (11 1/4″). On the 9 3/4″ run the tread will hang over the maximum 1 1/2″. On the 10 1/8″ run the 11 1/4″ tread will hang over the minimum amount, 1 1/8″. Therefore, all units of run that fall between 9 3/4″ and 10 1/8″ may be fitted with stock 2 × 12s without machining. Units that fall between 9″ (the minimum) and 9 3/4″ (the minimum for stock 2 × 12) must be custom ripped. For maximum nosing (1 1/2″ with dimension stock) the tread will be 1 1/2″ plus the unit run dimension.

Typical Unit Run Problem. **A typical run** situation is as follows. The designer has provided 10′ of length on the floor plan in accordance with the minimum rule of thumb. The 120″ is divided by 13 to net a 9.23″ unit run. The .23 fraction may be rounded to .25 (1/4″). This unit of run is smaller than is acceptable for the stock 2 × 12 range. Therefore, the treads will need to be custom ripped to 10 3/4″. By adding the maximum nosing (1 1/2″) to the unit run (9 1/4″), the deepest tread possible is 10 3/4″ for this stairway.

This example makes the assumption that the face of the bottom riser will be directly below the floor opening above. In this position the head clearance will be the room height minus one unit of rise. In the 12-block basement example the room height is 93 1/2″, 12 blocks (96″) minus a 4″ concrete floor plus a 1 1/2″ sill. Subtracting the 7 7/16″ bottom step from the 14-riser example, the headroom is 86 1/16″ (Fig. 13-20). This is a case where the step could be extended out under the opening above a few inches without compromising the headroom. It could extend to a point where the nosing pitch line measured 6′-8″ to the opening above. It is also an example of the nontechnical approach to stairwell design. Had the stairway been

laid out to scale on a drawing first, it would have been found that an opening a few inches longer would make it possible to use treads of full 2 × 12 stock. The run units would need to be designed at a minimum of 9 3/4″. Thirteen of these units would make a floor opening of 126 3/4″ (10′-6 3/4″). This design will produce the maximum nosing. It then comes down to a question of expending a little more floor space above to maintain better headroom or lengthening out the stringer to attain deeper treads at the cost of minimum headroom.

From this exercise it can be seen that a little mathematics can make it possible to know the floor opening length that will be needed when you want to use full 2 × 12 treads. It also makes it clear that the two rule-of-thumb figures (9′-6″ and 10′) for rough openings are not only deceptive but limiting. All treads will be less than 11 1/4″ deep with these openings. The origin of the 10′ rule may have sprung from the FHA rule that a double header perpendicular to the floor joists which forms a side of the stairwell may not exceed 10′ in length. This points out the fact that a partition wall under those joist tails is a superior method of supporting them. The header in excess of 10′, on the other hand, can simply be supported by a third post at the center, making a total of three (Fig. 13-21). The center post will also double as a support for the carriage.

LAYING OUT THE CARRIAGE STRINGER

For years, the conventional method of laying out a stringer has been to step off the notches with a framing square. The method is *not* as accurate as it could be. It is plagued with the short-measuring-instrument characteristic. It has more potential for inaccuracy than exists when a room length is measured with a ruler instead of a tape measure. Appendix 9 contains a table of hypotenuse moduli which will make it possible to lay out a stringer more accurately.

Step-Off Method

To practice the traditional step-off technique, the framing square is placed on the stringer. The rise is traced along the tongue (the 16″ side) and the run is traced along the edge of the body (the 24″ side). The tracing must be done on both outside or both inside edges of the square throughout the task (Fig. 13-22). The rise and run figures are located on the square and held flush with the top edge of the stringer. The square is then moved ahead to the next cutout and traced again. This is repeated as many times as there are cutouts. The accuracy of the step-off technique suffers from the multiple movement and the short-measuring-tool syndrome. The edges of dimension stock are rounded. It is difficult to set the square down precisely over the last mark looking down on a rounded edge. Second, it is difficult to line up two sets of locations and figures and trace along two edges without permitting any movement in the square.

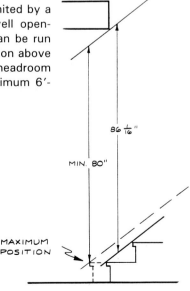

FIGURE 13-20 Where the unit run of a stringer is limited by a minimum-sized stairwell opening, the lower step can be run ahead of the obstruction above to a point where the headroom line indicates the minimum 6′-8″ point.

86 1/16″

MIN. 80″

MAXIMUM POSITION

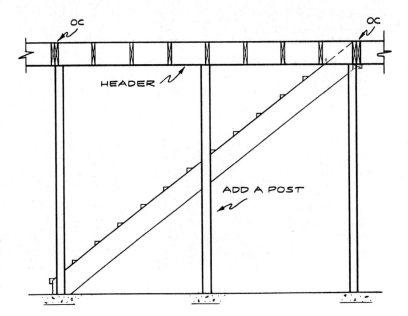

FIGURE 13-21 A stairwell header on the long side which is over 10′ long may be supported adequately by adding another post at the center of the span.

These inaccuracies can be partially eliminated by using a pair of clamp-on gauges. These gauges are useful for rafter layout, stair stringers, and any other place where uniform angles are desired. With one placed on the rise mark and one on the run mark, the square will return to the identical angles each time it is moved along the plank. This leaves only the task of lining up the lower gauge mark over the previous rise line. With practice the position of one's head and the angle of the vision will become more consistent. A fairly accurate set of tracings will result.

Proof testing the layouts is done easily by measuring between the points of the cutout tracings. The hypotenuse of each triangle must be identical to the others to pro-

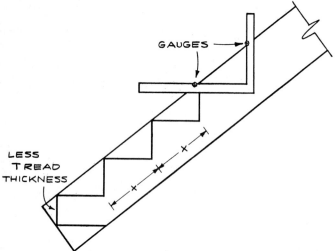

FIGURE 13-22 "Stepping off" the carriage pattern is more accurate when gauges are used on the framing sqaure and the hypotenuse of each step is constantly monitored for equality.

duce uniform steps. To check the accuracy of run and rise depth (distance from the point to the underedge of the stringer) a measurement is taken at right angles from the underedge of the stringer to the point. It will be found that without gauges on the square the accuracy and uniformity will not be good. With gauges it is improved. The accuracy can be made as perfect as the thickness of a pencil line when gauges are used in conjunction with the hypotenuse table.

Crooked Board Problem

To understand why it is difficult to plot perfect cutouts, it is necessary to comprehend the nature of lumber. The perfectly straight 2 × 12 plank in the length needed is a rarity. Some accommodating lumberyards will allow you to pick through a pile until you find two or three that appear to be suitable. Even so, by the time they are transported to the site under the rays of the hot sun or perhaps get soaked in a rain shower, the shape begins to change. One of the quickest and most certain ways to alter the shape of a board is to lay it flat on the ground for a few hours.

Visualize an extremely crooked plank with cutouts traced on it. It is readily seen that the hypotenuse line parallels the curve of the edge of the board. In this configuration none of the run lines are parallel to each other and none of the rise lines are parallel to each other. When the stringer is plotted with the crown up, the hypotenuse units are longer than natural. If the cutouts are plotted on the concave edge, each hypotenuse will be shorter. In neither position, crown up or crown down, is a crooked board a good choice for a stringer. To produce level steps and plumb risers it is necessary to have a straightedge as a guide by which to lay out the step.

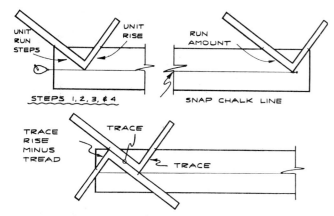

FIGURE 13-23 The first four steps toward laying out a carriage stringer involve accurately locating and marking the hypotenuse line which will pass through all the junctions between each step and rise.

Stringer Layout on a Straight Board

Let us assume that three straight boards have been acquired. If not, let us conclude that three can be machined to a point where the crowned edge is now straight. To have uniformly wide boards, each of the two or three will have to be ripped parallel using the narrowest dimension as the standard. Let us use the hypotenuse table for a uniform 10″ run unit (Appendix 9).

1. Place one gauge on the outside edge of the body of the framing square at the 10″ mark. Place the other gauge on the outside of the tongue at the place that will net your exact unit of rise. Place the square on the surface of the plank with the gauges touching. Adjust the gauges if necessary until the rise and run lengths measure correct from the edge of the carriage to the point of the square.

2. Place the square on the surface of the board with the gauges touching the top edge (Fig. 13-23). Place it close to the bottom end of the stringer. Make a sharp pencil dot at the corner of the square.

3. Move the square to the other end of the board and make a dot at the point of the square.

4. Draw a chalk line tightly the full length of the board and passing over the two dots. Snap it. When working alone, place a small nail in one dot to hold the end of your chalk line. This line is the hypotenuse behind (below) all the step triangles.

5. Locate the first rise mark at the bottom. Only the first rise will be reduced by an amount equal to the tread thickness. Place the square with gauges in the approximate location. Place a second square under it with the bodies back to back. The tongue of the lower square will be in a position to trace the first rise (pointing down). The gauge square is in position to trace the first run and the second rise (tongue pointing up). Slide the assembly down the board until the rise figure, minus the tread thickness, is at the lower end of the board, the corner on the underedge. Trace along the vertical edge of the tongue of the lower square. This is the first rise mark.

6. Take away the lower square without moving the upper square. Trace along the lower edge of the body on the gauge square. This is the first run step. Trace along the outer edge of the tongue. This is the second rise line.

7. Make a baseline parallel to the first step, starting at the bottom point of the first rise at the end of the board (Fig. 13-24). Lay out the profile of the kickboard.

8. Find the hypotenuse figure on the table in Appendix 9 which corresponds to your rise and run combi-

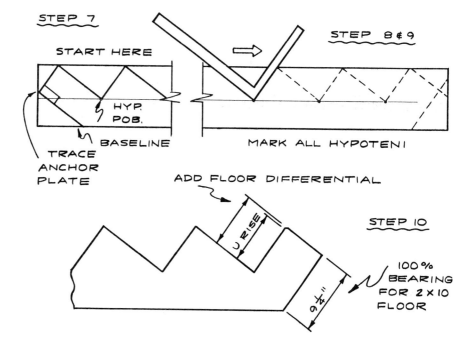

FIGURE 13-24 The bottom bearing of the stringer is laid out parallel to the bottom step. Trace the kickplate cutout. Mark and indent all the hypotenuse points on the chalk line. Place the point of the square on each indentation and trace all the remaining profiles. Plot the top rise line and the bearing head line.

nation. Starting at the point of the first cutout, mark off the figures along the chalk line as many times as there are cutouts. Indent the position with a nail point and circle it with a pencil.

9. Move the square gauge up the stringer to the second point. Place the corner of the square precisely on the hypotenuse point. Trace the rise and run lines along the edges of the square. Move along to each succeeding mark and trace.

10. The last level mark will be the one where the top of the stringer meets the underside of the flooring. The stringer board may not be long enough for the tongue gauge to rest on the edge out beyond this point. Remove the gauges from the square. Place the tongue of the square alongside the last rise line pointing down. The blade is pointing to the underedge of the stringer. The height figure on the tongue is aligned with the last tread line. This height may be different from that of the other rises. When the tread thickness is thicker than the combination of floor materials, the last rise will be greater by the amount of difference. The height is the unit rise from the upper floor level minus the total floor thickness. Trace all the way across the stringer on the top of the blade (Fig. 13-23). *Example:* When 1 1/2″ treads are being used on steps below but the sheathing and underlayment floor comprise the topping of the stringer, a discrepancy will exist. Assuming that the floor sheathing is 1/2″ thick and the particle board is 5/8″, the sum will be 1 1/8″. The 3/8″ difference will be made up with the top rise unit of the stringer in order to reach the underside of the flooring. The point of the square will

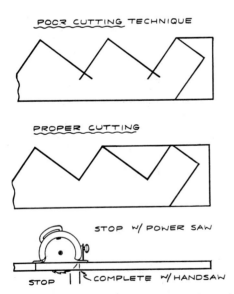

FIGURE 13-25 Do not weaken a stair stringer by over running the saw cuts. Complete the power cuts with a handsaw, holding the blade perpendicular.

protrude a little beyond the front edge of the stringer. The resulting absence of this little point of wood on the last step is of no consequence, as the riser supports the front edge of the tread.

11. Locate the head bearing. Place the square with the outer edge of the body along the top level line. The tongue will be pointing down and on the underside of the stringer. Move the square right or left until the figure on the tongue that is the same as the actual size of your floor joist header is in line with the underedge of the stringer. Trace a plumb line along the tongue. This will produce a head on the stringer which bears 100% on the header, an ideal bearing.

Cutting the Stringer

Cut out the stringer very carefully (Fig. 13-25). Cut only in the scrap wood, leaving the pencil lines intact. *Do not cut beyond the point of the cutout.* The circular saw may be used for most of each cut, but the cut will have to be completed with a straight saw, either hand or power.

After completing one stringer it may be used as a template. Whether one chooses to use it or not will depend on how accurate it appears to be. The accuracy can be proofed to a certain extent by placing the framing square into each completed cutout and checking the squareness and the rise and run figures. The variance between cutouts can be checked across the outer points. This distance should be the same as used on the hypotenuse chalk line under the cutouts.

Should the proofing show inaccuracies to any degree, it will be best to lay out the remaining stringers independently. After they are laid out, the first stringer can be placed on top of the layout. This will produce an overall picture of the problem and suggest where it can be improved.

After all three stringers have been cut, clamp them side by side with the bottoms and tops perfectly flush. Inaccurate lineup of run levels and rise surfaces may be rectified to a certain extent by trimming. Caution and judgment are needed. Like shortening table legs, too much trimming may defeat the project.

Choosing a Unit Run

Each hypotenuse table has been made for a specific unit run. The unit run is controllable by design. Any figure from 9 to 10 1/8″ may serve. The 2 × 12 dimension tread is the largest stock tread available. It is practical on unit runs from 9 3/4 to 10 1/8″. This depth of run nets nosing overhang variables from the 1 1/2″ maximum to the 1 1/8″ minimum depth nosing.

These variables provide the floor plan designer with some latitude in choosing the total run. He can pick a unit run size and tread combination and multiply the run units by the quantity of steps to find a total run. The total run is then worked into the floor plan. Remember that there is one less step than rise. For example, if the choice is for 14 risers, multiply the desired unit run by 13. Let us say that a full 11 1/4″ unripped tread and a maximum 1 1/2″ nosing are desired. The run unit will be 9 3/4″. 13 × 9.75 = 126.75 or 10′-6 3/4″. Since the bottom step can run out under the ceiling a few inches before contacting the minimum height line which touches the nosings, it will be safe to allow a space on the floor plan of about 10′-6″ plus or minus an inch or two. This rule-of-thumb designing technique assumes a basement wall height comprised of 12 block units (96″) minus a 4″ concrete floor. Should the designer be cramped for total run space the sacrifice can be made by shortening the run units and ripping the treads to a depth that does not exceed 1 1/2″ more than the unit run.

Choosing the unit rise does not present as many options. The total rise is a fixed design dimension. The height is derived from the size of the materials that are combined. There are usually no more than two choices when divided by a number that will result in a suitable rise (7 to 8″). It is then only a choice of a higher unit rise combined with a shorter run or a lower unit rise combined with a longer total run and deeper treads.

Reading the Hypotenuse Table

There are tables presented in Appendix 9 which cover the range of run units in 1/8″ modules for uncut 2 × 12s and 2 × 10s. For any run figure between these modules the builder/designer can easily work out his own hypotenuse by substituting the actual figure into the Pythagorean theorem, $a^2 + b^2 = c^2$.

The first step is to **establish the exact unit rise and run** dimensions that apply. This is accomplished by measuring the actual length of the opening in the floor and the actual height from one floor level to the next. Remember to add thickness for materials that are not yet on the top floor or subtract for materials that are not yet on the bottom floor. Also remember to allow several horizontal inches (approximately 6″) for the head bearing that projects out from the floor joist header.

Find the table of uniform run units that matches your unit of run or is slightly less. Taking a higher run will decrease headroom. Where your plan permits the bottom step to extend beyond the headroom point, a slightly larger unit-of-run table can be used. Find the horizontal line in which your rise number appears in the left vertical column.

Choose the one that is the closest in whole sixteenths of an inch. Move across this line to the right vertical column. Here you will find the hypotenuse of each step triangle. If your rise number is an uneven fraction, it should be interpreted to the closest 1/32″. This number is then matched to the closest thirty-second on the table, or a hypotenuse figure can be chosen which is between the two that are above and below your rise number. For example, if your rise turns out to be 7 13/32″, the 13/32 is between 3/8 (12/32) and 7/16 (14/32), so the hypotenuse will be between these two lines on the table. This would seem to be splitting hairs when it comes to cutting out notches with a saw that may remove a 1/8″ kerf. It is significant, however, when laying out with the step-off method. Fourteen risers with a 1/16″ error in height can result in 7/8″ of error in the total rise. The result will be a carriage with steps that slope toward the nosing or slope toward the riser, depending on whether the error was oversize or undersize.

The tables that appear in Appendix 9 span a unit rise range of 7 to 8″ and a unit run range from 9 to 10″. The rise numbers are computed to the nearest 1/16″. If a small error occurs in total rise, the unit hypotenuse may be lengthened out or shortened a small part of a thirty-second inch to compensate. For this type of accuracy a very sharp round lead, hard lead pencil, or a prick punch will do a better job than a flat carpenter pencil. A 5H to 8H drawing pencil of the drafting type will work well.

For those who enjoy and feel competent with the calculator or computer the problems may be worked with decimals and related to the inches on the framing square that are divided in tenths.

FHA MINIMUM STANDARDS

The Federal Housing Administration Minimum Property Standards (Table 13-1) are constantly being revised. These requirements constitute reasonable minimums to adhere to, whether or not the house comes under FHA jurisdiction. There is only one minimum with which the author would take issue. That is the 6′-4″ headroom for a basement stairway. Many people in the United States find this height to be oppressive. A common disability that goes along with the over-six-footer is back trouble. The builder who builds to sell will limit his prospects with this low-clearance stairwell. The owner who builds to live in the house may suffer years of aggravation. If he attempts to solve the problem by selling, he may have to wait for a customer whose height does not pose a problem in the short stairwell. It seems logical to stick with the door height standard of 6′-8″ as a minimum head clearance for any stairway that will have frequent use.

TABLE 13-1

Stairway design

	Private Exterior Stairs (Attached to Dwelling)		Private and Common[a] Interior Stairs	
	Entrance	Basement	Main	Basement
Minimum clear headroom	—	—	6'-8"	6'-4"
Minimum width[b]	2'-8"	2'-8"	2'-8"	2'-8"
Minimum tread[c]	11"	11"	9"	9"
Minimum nosing	—	—	[d]	[d]
Maximum riser[c, e]	7 1/2"	7 1/2"	8 1/4"	8 1/4"
Winders[e, f]	Run at point 18" from converging end should not be less than straight portion.			

[a]Stairway serving two living units.

[b]Clear of handrail.

[c]All treads shall be the same width and all risers the same height in a flight of stairs.

[d]Closed riser, 1 1/8" nosing; open riser, 1/2" nosing.

[e]In a building required to be accessible to the physically handicapped, the maximum riser is 7 1/2". Winders or open risers should not be used in such buildings. The width of a landing should not be less than the width of the stairs and its depth should not be less than 2'-6". The swing of a door opening on a stairway should not overlap the top step.

[f]Winders are not permitted in common stairs.

REVIEW TOPICS

1. Sketch and label a single-line plan view of each of the following stair types: (a) straight run, (b) L shape with one landing platform, (c) switchback, (d) U (double L) with two landing platforms, (e) L with winders.

2. Explain what a "freestanding" or "open" stairway is.

3. Compare and discuss the comparative merits and faults of a cleated and a dadoed stair stringer design.

4. Of the three carriage stringer designs for a free-flight stairway to a basement, which requires knee braces the most? Explain why.

5. Describe fully the penalties that will be paid if stair carriages are permanently nailed to bare studding and the staircase is then completed.

6. Where three notched carriage stringers are required, the slightest difference in step height will cause the tread to bear only on two steps. Analyze the various situations and describe how to go about correcting each so that each tread will bear equally on all three steps.

7. Describe the technique of fastening the ends of hardwood treads to a carriage under a notched baseboard stringer and to a carriage on the surface of an unnotched baseboard stringer.

8. Explain why so many stairways are altered in a detrimental way due to incorrect floor plan interpretation. Tell how this can be avoided.

9. Explain the faults incurred with the step-off method of laying out stringer steps.

10. Describe each step in order using the hypotenuse table (Appendix 9) that will lead to a successful layout of a stair carriage stringers. Remember to clarify the differences between the bottom and top steps and the common steps between.

11. Describe the technique and care that should be taken when cutting the notches in a stair stringer.

Chapter 14
THERMAL-CONSERVING CONSTRUCTION_____

PRACTICAL PRINCIPLES

Many features that produce fuel savings in a home have been known for a long time. Early settlers to the great plains areas of the midwest built sod homes because of the shortage of trees and lumber. Although the sod home was not prestigious, it was quite efficient in a thermal sense. The temperature below the frost line is approximately 52°F. This reservoir of constant warmth needed only a small supplement of added heat from a fire to provide a livable temperature in the cold winter months. In the heat of summer the cooler earth temperature provided a tempered comfort zone.

When cheap fuels were abundant, homes were most often built with little or no thought of insulation. Indeed, insulation in most of its present forms was unheard of as recently as 50 years ago, although some recognition of insulating principles could be seen on a seasonal basis. Farmers would stack bales of hay or straw around the high foundations of the farmhouse to ward off the penetrating cold. Detachable wooden-framed screens were taken down and replaced by storm windows when winter approached.

Some insulating products came on the scene quite accidentally. At Iowa State University in the mid-1930s, experiments were conducted to see what salable product could be made from a surplus of cornstalks. Such experimenting led to the making of fiberboard. Beaverboard was an early name given to this product, which became popular for use on ceilings. As time passed, many names and insular uses evolved. Some of the names are Celotex (a brand name),

fiberboard, building board, brownboard, and blackboard. For a period of years, blackboard was the standard sheathing material. It gained a reputation for causing a house to be snug, cozy, and other terms disassociated with the drafty character of the old wood-board-sheathed houses. More recently, sheet forms of Styrofoam are proving to be more heat conserving per inch of thickness than is fiberboard. As fuel costs soared beginning in the 1970s, a great amount of attention and concern was focused on and will continue to be directed toward energy-saving systems and materials.

ENERGY-SAVING SYSTEMS

There are three basic types of houses that will accomplish the energy conservation principle:

1. The earth-sheltered house
2. Solar-heated and solar-cooled house
3. Superinsulated house

There are some fine books available on earth-sheltered and solar-type construction. The remainder of this text will be devoted to innovative and practical superinsulated house designs. Construction methods and details are presented which are practical for the novice, the professional, and the tract builder. Each model described has been built, field tested, and is a proven system. Each is a cost-conscious winner.

HEAT TRANSFER

It is not the purpose of this text to make a heating and cooling engineer of the reader. The focus is not complicated formulas and computations. That is left to the theorists and the universities. They have given us the fruits of advanced technology in the form of readily available materials. The emphasis in this text is placed on how to use current materials to the best advantage of both builder and consumer.

The Btu (British thermal unit) rating is the term used to denote heat transfer through a material or combination of materials. Each type of material is given an R rating, which indicates resistance to the passage heat. A low R number means that passage is rapid. More heat is lost from a room because it passes through a wall more quickly. A high R number indicates a better insulating value. R values are established for materials per inch of thickness. On the wrapper the R number refers to the full thickness of the material. Roll-batt fiberglass insulation of 3 1/2" thickness is usually labeled R-11.

The superinsulation principle is simple. The higher the total R number from the addition of all the materials in the wall, the greater will be the potential resistance to the loss of heat or cool.

Conduction

In house construction there is a factor called *conduction* that can lead the builder and consumer astray. When heat is applied to an inside surface of an exterior wall, it passes through dense materials, such as studs and plates, to the cold side and is lost there. It becomes a false sense of comfort when an owner rationalizes that a wall has an adequate quantity of insulation in the stud and ceiling joist cavities. The system is fundamentally flawed by the fact that the whole framework structure is a conductive envelope, each member a potential bridge, which bleeds off precious heat. Add to this the quantity of glass in windows (especially those windows with aluminum frames) and doors, and it becomes quite clear where the weaknesses of conventional construction exist, and consequently where the greatest potential for improvement is concentrated. An objective to keep in mind is to follow or innovate practices that will balance component retention factors throughout a structure. To do otherwise is like insulating a wall, but omitting the insulation from every fourth or fifth stud cavity. This ludicrous example is comparable to the common practice of insulating all wall cavities adequately and then using the lowest R-rated doors and windows available because they are a "good deal" or money is getting tighter. Neither rationale is responsible in terms of the future. A little further along it will be shown how the loss by conduction can be effectively eliminated, or greatly reduced, when contemplated on a five to ten year consumption plan.

Infiltration

In addition to heat transfer through materials, there is another significant source of heat loss, called infiltration. A poorly constructed house can lose as much heat as if it perpetually had a window open. Infiltration means cracks that permit heat to escape or cold wind to blow in. A house that seems drafty when no circulating fans are operating is probably suffering from excessive infiltration. A minimum investment of a few dollars in caulking can make a tremendous difference in such a place. For new construction, however, there are better ways to prevent infiltration than the patch-and-putty, after-the-fact technique.

Key infiltration zones are well known. Poorly sealed doors that enter directly into a living area are first-rate culprits. Windows run a close second. Electric boxes that are not carefully surrounded with insulation allow cold air into a house. Fireplace chimneys draw a lot of warm air out on calm days and allow drafts to blow in on windy days when dampers fit loosely and there are no glass doors to seal the opening at the hearth. Brickwork that connects outdoors to indoors may have a poorly sealed junction with wooden framework that adjoins it. The list goes on and on.

The type of windows used has a major effect on conservation. It is not at all uncommon for a single window, of poor insulating character to lose more heat than all the rest of the wall. Buying cheap windows is one of the poorest economy measures a consumer can take.

There are three types and qualities of glazing. The poorest and least costly is the single glass pane in a metal frame (steel or aluminum). The insulating R factor is so low as to offer little more than a windshield. Next comes double glazing. There are several designs falling under this term (some of them masquerade as "thermo" or thermal windows). Originally "double glaze" indicated one framed sash with a second lightly framed insert which could be removed for washing. A more advanced form has two panes of glass set in mastic in a U channel. The thermal-conserving feature of the latter is a little superior to that of simple double glass. The design is supposed to produce an air-sealed dead air space. Most double-pane windows accomplish this objective. A common complaint after a few years of exposure, however, is that leaks develop, followed by fogging and condensation buildup between the panes. Reputable manufacturers will make adjustments in most cases. Tripple glazing is another way of adding an additional dead air space.

INSULATING GLASS

The most effective heat-conserving window is hermetically sealed insulating glass, best known by the name *Thermopane*. Similar to the way that a vacuum bottle contains heat in a confined liquid, a Thermopane window does the best job of containing the heated air in a house. Over a period of years Thermopane will be the best choice, even though the initial cost may be considerably more.

The economist on the job should consider all factors both initially and long range. For example, inexpensive aluminum-framed windows do not have integral casements (the surrounding interior jambs), whereas most wood-framed sash are complete with jambs. Windows such as those produced by Pella and Anderson may be had with all weather-affected parts encased in vinyl plastic. The initial cost of the unit may be as much as twice that of the other type. This is a deceptive comparison. The aluminum-framed window will require additional skilled labor and expensive finish lumber for the jambs and sill. Each piece is custom fitted to the individual opening. Although the glass may be on a par, the fact remains that the aluminum material conducts at a rate about 19 times that of wood.

Doors present a similar comparison, but the materials situation is reversed in the case of panel doors (Fig. 14-1). An exterior wood-panel door usually contains contoured panels with edges that are very thin. The coved edges that form the tongue in the groove may be as thin as 1/4″. One quarter-inch of wood between the heated side of a room and the outdoor winter elements could scarcely be considered adequate. Tightly sealing storm doors are required to salvage a modicum of economy.

Insulated doors (Fig. 14-2) are available in many styles and materials. They all have a common feature. The

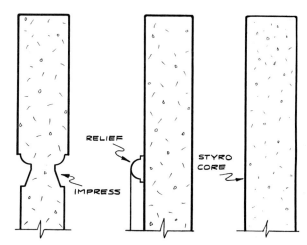

FIGURE 14-2 Insulated steel doors with impressed or reverse panels in relief offer reasonable thermal characteristics.

core of the door is filled with a rigid form of insulation. Less costly models are covered with prime painted steel. Some doors give the impression of carved and molded panels with overlays that do not detract from a full-thickness insulated core throughout. Others have shallow impressed panels which do not offer as much insulating quality but which nonetheless surpass wood doors by a considerable margin. More expensive doors are available with real wood overlays or vinyl pressure-molded wood imitations. As with the windows, it can be a false economy to install a seemingly economical unit.

COMPARTMENTED ENTRY

The compartmented entry principle has gained in interest as a result of the energy-saving concern. Designers of earth-sheltered and solar-heated homes stress the importance of a closable foyer (Fig. 14-3). A compartmented entrance is an anteroom. One can enter from the outdoors, close the exterior door against the drafts, and then proceed through another doorway into the living area. Frequently, it is possible to add this feature to an existing floor plan simply by adding a door in an existing archway. The compartment admits only a limited amount of cold or hot air upon entry or exit when the interior door is in the closed position. A sizable amount of energy can be preserved by having a compartmented entry design at all exterior entrances.

The principle does not necessarily preclude that an anteroom for the sole purpose is required. A secondary entrance can frequently be adapted to the compartmental type by incorporating it with an existing small room. A utility room or a laundry room that lends itself to a logical traffic flow may serve well as a compartment entrance. Care should be taken in the design, however, not to route the

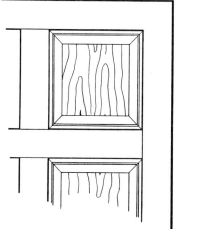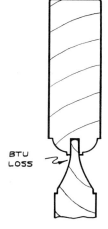

FIGURE 14-1 Solid wood doors with molded panels provide severely limited resistance to heat loss.

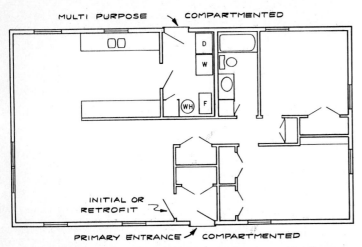

FIGURE 14-3   A compartmented entry may perform the conservation objective only or may also double in an auxiliary role.

traffic pattern directly through a work space (a common fault on many floor plans).

A modified compartment exists where the service entrance is inside an attached garage. The principle works only moderately with this design. To work at all, the garage door must be shut. Even then the efficiency is minimal, as the garage area is usually too large and too cold.

The floor plans of many existing homes lend themselves to minor remodeling which will make a compartmented entrance possible. An arch between an entranceway can be framed into a doorway. An entrance alcove can be separated with a retrofit partition, including a door.

It may be noted that most commercial buildings make use of compartmented entrances. The reduction in heat loss by this design is well known. The design is universally practiced by commercial architects. Compartmented entries are basic in the overall conservation principle.

TEMPERATURE RETENTION

Free Heat Source

Certain elements of free heat and cooling are available in most regions and climates of the earth. Throughout history, human beings have cycled to and away from the sources. Now, through necessity, it appears that in the United States, the pendulum is swinging back toward the use of our free sources of energy. What are these gifts of nature?

They come in several forms. It is only a task of finding a feasible way to harness each source that remains to be perfected. The sources are the *sun*, the *wind*, the *water* in the earth, and the *earth* itself. Solar energy is readily tapped with a variety of collector types. Wind is put to work with windmills and generators. Both of these sources

are free for the taking, but they suffer from a common feature, unreliability. Unless the sun shines or the wind blows, the energy gain may degenerate to nothing. By contrast, the earth, and the water in it, are more consistent sources of a known quality and quantity of heat and cooling potential.

There are devotees of these four sources who will expound at length on the advantages of one or another. There are a growing number of people who are taking advantage of feasible combinations of the four sources. As the technology improves, the use of the various combinations will be most attractive to contractors and individual builders alike.

HEAT AND COOLING RETENTION

Whether the structure is an earth-sheltered home, a solar-collector design, a conventional structure with a heat pump that draws water from a well, or some other type, one feature is supremely important. Once the heat has been gained, it must be efficiently retained. The methods of retention are well within the reach of the conscientious builder.

Insulating the Foundation Exposure Area

The above ground portion of the exterior face of a foundation wall is called the *exposure area*. Most building codes mandate a minimum exposure of 8 inches. Frequently the actual exposure is much greater, especially in heavy snow country, where home owners may be concerned about potential water damage to wood that is exposed to melting snow. It is quite common to see whole neighborhoods of houses sitting atop two or three courses of exposed concrete foundation blocks. Where there is a basement with approximately one-fourth of the wall exposed above ground, an extreme heat loss factor exists unless insulating measures are taken. Even a minimum 8" exposure will comprise a notable conductive escape zone all around the house. When one stops to consider, that the two sides of a concrete block comprise scarcely three inches of thickness of porous concrete, a visual picture is drawn. The cavities add no thermal barrier as they are not air tight. The webs in the blocks provide conductive bridges.

Solid concrete (poured) walls, though containing more mass, are also radical conductors. The installation of sheet Styrofoam, applied to one or both surfaces, will do much to eliminate the window of vulnerability that a basement wall represents. Such techniques successfully complete the overall envelope concept of house insulation.

A well coordinate system is to run the wall sheathing (Styrofoam) continuously down the frame wall, over the exposed foundation, and down to, or below, the frost line. This effectively blocks the thermal bridge (the sill and floor header). Another layer is then installed full height on the interior face of the basement wall.

Protecting the Styrofoam surface along the exposure area is mandatory. Styrofoam sheets are so vulnerable to damage that a shield is a must. The Styrofoam must be installed before backfilling as it should extend at least to the frost line. For basements that are intended to be used as full-time living space, a full wall covering of Styrofoam will add to comfort and to the economy of maintenance.

The shield is provided over the exposed part of the Styrofoam and extended down below grade line a few inches. Many material choices are available. There is copper, aluminum, galvanized iron, treated plywood, vinyl and other materials in sheet form. The shield is tucked up under the siding in rain shedding formation. It should be secured in a manner that is permanent. Though the shield is trapped at the top and pressed against the Styrofoam by dirt at the bottom, it still may benefit from adhesives or fasteners, particularly at the top.

Styrofoam may be fastened with adhesive to the masonry. A grid pattern is better than spotted pads. Some parge sealers will perform double duty as moisture sealers for the wall and adhesive backing for the Styrofoam. Obviously the Styrofoam must be placed on the wall while the asphalt sealer is wet and sticky. Spray on sealers will not hold Styrofoam in place.

In Chapter 7 the nominal-6″ exterior wall was explained. This 5 1/2″ cavity wall is a step up from the 3 1/2″ cavity of the traditional 2 × 4 stud wall. Obviously, it advances the cavity capacity for insulation by a little over 50%. In Btu resistance, this is an advance from R-11 to R-19 for fiberglass batts. This is a significant improvement. Teamed with a proportionate advance in the ceiling insulation, such as R-19 to R-38, the homeowner, new builder, or retrofitter will realize a substantial saving. There will be a cost-effective payback in a few years that will offset the additional initial material cost completely.

Superinsulation is a term that was coined to describe high-level R-rated house designs. An 8″ double-walled house was classed as superinsulated when it was first conceived. In reality, it is cost-effective in all but the warmest southern regions. Times change, and with them, life-styles. Full-house air conditioning is common throughout the summer heat belts. This means that superinsulation is feasible for most of the months of the year in many climates. This way of life gives impetus to the double-walled concept of building.

DOUBLE-WALL FRAME

The double wall, as designed by the author, is comprised of two wall frames made of 2 × 4 studs. The walls sandwich a 3/4″ core of 1 × 4 diagonal and horizontal braces

and spacer blocks. The headers are of unique design. The system is copyrighted against graphic reproduction but may be used in construction by a builder. Structurally, the framework is much stronger and more rigid than that of a conventionally framed wall. The reader will readily see why as the descriptions unfold.

Double-Wall Section

A cross-section is probably the best graphic view with which to begin the understanding of the double-wall concept (Fig. 14-4). From the sole plate to the top plate, there are subtle differences from a conventional wall frame. Basically, the double wall is comprised of two single walls attached together to form a nominal 8″ exterior frame wall.

Soleplates are conventional 2 × 4s. A small 1″ block is placed between the soleplates every 2 to 4′ as nailing progresses on the sole of the inside wall component. The purpose of this gauge is to maintain a uniform depth at the base of the wall. The block is placed on edge or end with its 3/4″ thickness separating the soles. It is merely a spacer and is removed after the sole is nailed at any point.

Rough window sills (Fig. 14-5) are comprised of a single 2 × 4 in each wall segment. This creates two pieces at each window on a common horizontal plane with each other. There is never a need for double sills in the conventional stacked manner. Therefore, no more material is expended in a double wall rough sill than in a single wall with double rough sills. The double-wall rough sill varies only in that the two pieces are side by side instead of stacked.

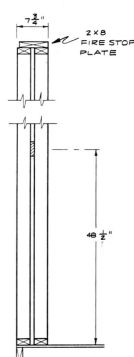

FIGURE 14-4 The author's copyrighted double-wall construction system is based on the section view of the wall shown above.

FIGURE 14-5   Rough window sills in the double wall are a pair of 2 × 4s side by side spaced apart by a 1 × 2.

Window and door headers are a complete departure from the conventional uniform double 2 × 12 type. The header is a hybrid of a plywood boxed header. It is boxed in the shape of an I-beam. The surrounding framework is of the old cripple stud type with a flat 2 × 4 on the lower edge. A solid piece of 3/4″ plywood is sandwiched between the frames (Fig. 14-6a). It is cut to a 12 3/4″ height. The header is sandwiched between the lower member of the upper plate, the surrounding studs, the lower flat 2 × 4 nailer, and the OC cripple studs (Fig. 14-6b). It fills the space normally occupied by a double 2 × 12 (11 1/4″) plus an additional 1 1/2″ of height where it goes up between the lower half of the double top plate (Fig. 14-6c). A conventional 2 × 12 header is 3″ longer than the rough opening, as it bears on top the 1 1/2″-thick trimmer stud on each end. The plywood header in the double wall is 6″ longer than the rough-opening width of the window or door (Fig. 14-6d). Its ends are sandwiched between the full-length stud posts of the opening framework. Note the section view in Fig. 14-7. This hybrid header will carry any conventional roof load to a span of 8′.

Headers over 8′ and up to 12′ can be designed and built as a combination I-beam and box beam. In addition to the sandwiched plywood, an additional plywood header is glued and nailed to the exterior in place of sheathing over the opening. The design may utilize vertical cripples in the boxed part, or it may incorporate diagonal-bridging-type webs (Fig. 14-8). The plywood pieces will have end joints when the header exceeds 8′ in length. The joint is purposely staggered so that the exterior ply joint is at the opposite end of the header ply joint. A 12′ header, for example, will have a vertical butt joint 4′ from one end of the sandwiched pieces. The plywood header on the exterior surface will have the joint toward the opposite end. Gen-

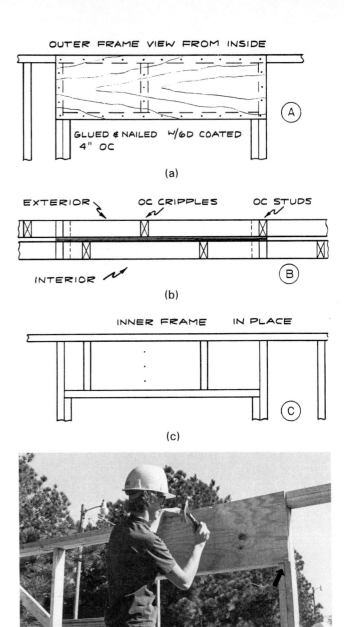

FIGURE 14-6   (a) The plywood header is nailed and glued to the inside of the external frame. (b) A horizontal section view through the header. Note that the common studs and cripples are on 2′ centers and staggered from each other. (c) Another exterior view of the completed header and wall assembly. (d) A double-wall header is 6″ longer than the rough opening, 3″ longer than a uniform header.

erally, spans from 8 to 12′ may be carried on boxed headers as described, which have only cripple studs in the core. From 12 to 16′ the box should hold well-fitted cripples and bridgework. Beyond these lengths and for exceptional loads, an engineered design should be sought.

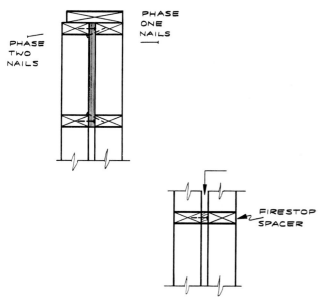

FIGURE 14-7 The plywood header and surrounding 2 × 4s form an effective I-beam of great strength. The side-by-side double rough sill serves all window openings. A 1 × 2 firestop surrounding the opening may be required.

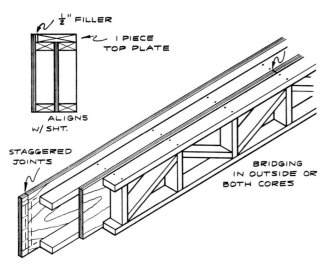

FIGURE 14-8 A plywood header of the I-beam type may be increased in load-bearing capacity for openings over 8′ wide by adding bridgebracing and/or boxing the exterior side with plywood. Remember to insulate the outer core before sealing it with the plywood.

The double top plate (Fig. 14-9) may be made in a conventional manner with two 2 × 4s on each of the walls. If constructed in this manner, a 1 × 2 continuous spacer strip will be required around the perimeter of the exterior wall. It is flush with the top surface of the double plate sandwiched between the two walls. Its purpose is nonstructural. It is required as a firestop.

Another efficient double top plate is made by using a 2 × 8 for the upper member. The 2 × 8 creates the firestop

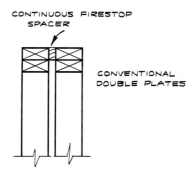

FIGURE 14-9 Two conventional top plates are an option for the double wall; however, a firestop of solid wood must be used between the tops.

and holds the two wall segments together. It is more efficient in locking the exterior corners together. The 2 × 8s are a little higher priced in board feet, but the cost of 1 × 2s is saved. The 2 × 8 top plate is aligned with the interior face of the combined wall frame. Its depth is 7 1/4″, whereas the wall depth is 7 3/4″.

Bracing is simplified in the double wall. Because the bracing forms a core between the frames, it is simply surface nailed to the inside face of the exterior wall frame. After the inside wall frame is raised, the existing braces are nailed to the studs from the outside. If desired, a 1 × 4 horizontal band may be installed between the inner and outer frame (Fig. 14-10). It is placed 4′ above the floor level. The band serves several good purposes. It stiffens the studs. It holds them in perfect alignment (plumb, straight, and correctly spaced). It ties the inner and outer walls together to form a superbly strong wall.

Studs in the double-wall design may be placed farther apart. Both the inner and outer wall frames will have their

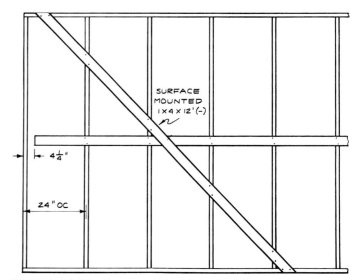

FIGURE 14-10 Outer wall bracing viewed from the inside. Stay back 4 1/4″ from the corner with the braces so that the perpendicular wall can butt against the corner stud.

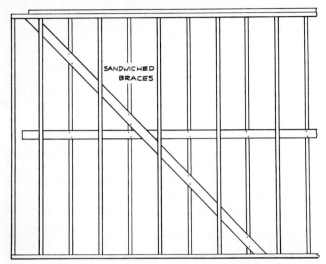

FIGURE 14-11   The inner frame shown in place installed against the outer wall. Note the staggered stud formation.

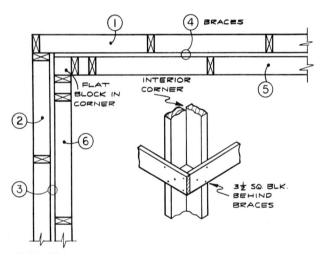

FIGURE 14-12   The top-view section shows corner and common stud positioning. The numbers indicate the order of assembly.

Material Savings

A theme of quality in both material and workmanship has run throughout this book. It may seem strange at this point to receive advice toward the purchase of cheaper materials. The case in point does exist with the double-wall design. The author was pleasantly surprised to find that studs costing as much as 40% less than others could be used successfully in the double-wall frame. It would seem logical that making two walls would cost twice what one wall would cost. It does not come out that way. The wider spacing (24″ instead of 16″) saves a stud in each 4′ of linear wall. The outer wall does not require extra studs to form internal backing corners at intersections or corners of the external walls. A small square block centered behind the braces connects the inner and outer wall and provides rigidity. Another 3 1/2″ × 3 1/2″ block may be placed at the bottom on top of the sole and a third block at the top if desired although they are not essential. In the final accounting, after a track record of several pilot houses, it was concluded that the only excess expenditure was the cost of additional insulation. Since the objective was to create the space for this least costly form of insulation (fiberglass blankets), the payback was assured by advance planning. More rationale for the economy of the double-wall concept will follow as the construction technique is explained.

Double-Wall Framing Procedure

Phase 1.   The outer wall is constructed first. It is assembled on the floor adjacent to where it will be raised. Construction progresses as with a conventional wall with a few exceptions. Only one stud is placed at each end of the

studs on 24″ spacing centers. The studs are staggered from one frame to the other so that, in reality, there is a stud every foot (Fig. 14-11). The exterior studs are on even-numbered spacing (0, 2, 4, 6, 8′, and so on). The inside frame studs are spaced on 1, 3, 5, 7, 9′, and so on. The staggered formation (Fig. 14-12) accomplishes several positive objectives. The braces and bands can be surface nailed to both walls since the nailing locations are exposed. Insulating blankets in each wall are staggered, which breaks up potential infiltration spots (no cold electric outlets). Wiring requires little or no drilling, as the wires are simply passed between the walls.

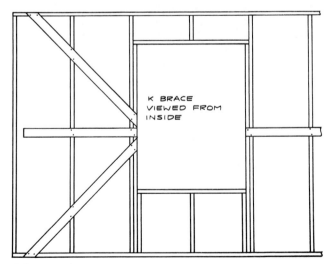

FIGURE 14-13   A K brace, viewed from the interior, is an alternative to a full-length brace where an opening interferes.

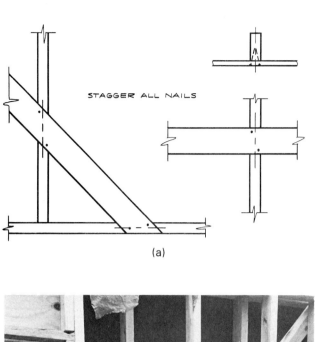

STAGGER ALL NAILS

(a)

(c)

(b)

(e)

FIGURE 14-14 (a) Holding power of each nail is improved by avoiding the possibility of adjacent nails going into the same grain line, which forms a double wedge and advances the potential for splitting the stud. (b) Braces are nailed to the core faces of both the external and internal wall frames (c) Glue is spread on the framework and the header before nailing. (d) The plywood header is fastened to the frame. (e) A sheathed double wall opening reveals the 1 × 2 filler/spacer.

frame. All common studs are placed on 24″ centering. A window rough sill is made of one 2 × 4 only. A flat 2 × 4 is placed on top of the window and door trimmers. Between the lower top plate and this flat 2 × 4, a cripple stud will be put at each 24″-OC spacing mark. No second top plate or headers are installed yet. The frame wall is now raised, plumbed in two directions, and braced.

Phase 2.   Diagonal corner braces are nailed from the top corners to the sole. The preferred angle is 45°. A brace should not be steeper than 60°. Where a window or door intereferes at a corner, the brace may be moved to the other side of the opening or a K brace used (Fig. 14-13). A 1 × 4 brace will have two 8d common or 8d coated nails placed into each stud. Offset the nails from the centerline of the stud so that they do not enter the stud in the same grain line. Place each nail at the farthest corner of the diagonal coverage over the stud (Fig. 14-14a). Aim the point of the nail toward the center axis of the stud. At the sole and top plate, stay away from the ends of the brace at least 1″ to avoid splitting. Hold a straightedge along the flat vertical surface of the stud when setting the first nail. Push the stud to the straightedge. A 6′ level is a good tool for this purpose. Do not squeeze the level and stud together, however, as this will bend the level and not accomplish the purpose of fixing the stud in a straight line. Check the spacing at 4′ above the floor after the brace is nailed. Each stud should be centered on 24″. It may be wise to recheck the plumbness of the corner before commencing this permanent bracing, to avoid polarizing a wall full of parallel but bowed studs.

Next, nail the bands across the studs halfway up the studs (Fig. 14-14b). Strike a chalk line where the top edge of the board should be. Strike the line from where the board will start to where it will end. Cut the end of the band at an angle to butt against the diagonal corner brace. Nail the ends first. Pull each bowed stud into straightness, testing with a straight edge, and nail through the band. Place the nails in the upper left and lower right segments of the coverage.

Headers are installed after the bracing is completed. Because the headers stiffen the wall, they are not installed while the wall is on the floor. By making the wall rigid on the floor, it would be difficult, if not impossible, to plumb the frame after it was raised. Set a nail in each corner of the 3/4″ plywood header. Hold the header in place. Tap these four nails in only far enough to form an indexing hole at each corner. Mark an up-pointing arrow in the center of the header board to indicate the top edge. From the exterior side of the frame, draw an outline with a pencil around all the rectangular openings covered by the header. In other words, trace all around the 2 × 4s. This will outline all the areas where glue will be placed. Take the header board down. Place it in a horizontal position. Apply glue in a continuous bead on all contact areas that

have been outlined (Fig. 14-14c). Spread the glue with a finger or a small stick. Tube adhesive may be used in a caulk gun. When two workers are available, the other person will be applying glue to the faces of the 2 × 4s in the wall frame where the header will contact. Place the header back on the frame (Fig. 14-14d). Seat the four nails in the indexing holes and drive them home. Place nails at 4″ intervals on all contact points. 7 or 8d coated or box nails are adequate with the glue system. Larger nails are detrimental at this close spacing because they split the 2 × 4s. This is a case for many small nails that contribute to an all-over contact of the plywood with the structural framing members. Surrounds are nailed around all the window and door openings. Flush the edge of the 1 × 2 with the rough opening. These 1 × 2 fillers will be on the interior edge of the trimmers and the rough window sills (Fig. 14-14e). Where a table saw is available, the least costly fabrication of these 1 × 2s is to rip them from utility-grade precut studs. Set the saw fence for a 3/4″ cut. The stud will net three 1 × 2s at a cost considerably lower than that of mill-cut 1 × 2s.

Where double 2 × 4 top plates are to be used on both the inner and outer walls, the firestop 1 × 2 will be nailed on next. The uppermost 2 × 4 top plate will probably have already been installed while the wall was lying on the floor. The 1 × 2 may also be nailed to the top plate while it lies on the floor.

After all exterior-wall components have been assembled and raised, the inside frames of the double wall will be assembled. The layout of stud locations is different. The soles and top plates are cut to butt snugly against the edges of the erected frame spacers. Spacing for studs is then laid out at the midpoint between the outer wall studs. Hook the 100′ tape measure to the building-line side of the outer wall. Make adjustments if the outer frame is inset. Mark all the odd-foot locations. Place two marks at each stud location. The marks will be 3/4″ before and 3/4″ after the odd-foot marks. For example, a mark is placed at 11 1/4 and 12 3/4″, 35 1/4 and 36 3/4″, 59 1/4 and 60 3/4″, and so on. This places a stud midway between each of the outer frame studs, which are on 24″ even numbers. Remember to take the sheathing thickness into consideration where the inset-frame technique has been practiced.

Partition intersecting studs are placed in the inside frame only (Fig. 14-15). Also, the blocked double corner stud will be required on the inside frame only. A full stud can be saved at the corner by use of 3 1/2 × 3 1/2″ 2 × 4 squares instead of three blocks and an extra stud. As shown in Fig. 14-16a, a block is placed on the sole in the corner. Another is placed under the top plate. A third square block is placed midway up the corner behind the studs. Since these blocks are trapped behind the corner studs, only one 10d box nail is needed to hold them to the plates. The center block is held with one nail through each corner stud and a small nail through the end of each brace.

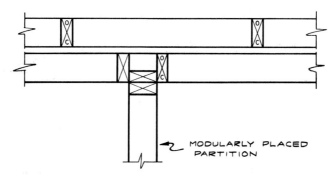

MODULARLY PLACED PARTITION

FIGURE 14-15 Only the inner wall contains the partition post.

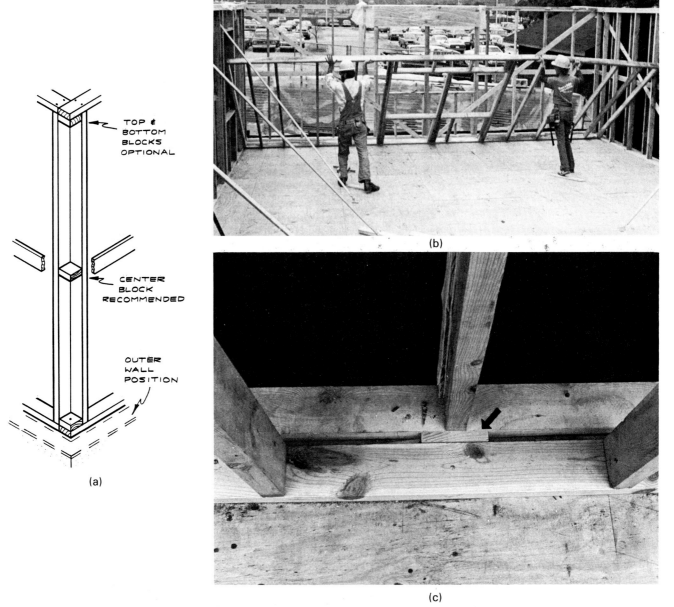

TOP & BOTTOM BLOCKS OPTIONAL

CENTER BLOCK RECOMMENDED

OUTER WALL POSITION

(a)

(b)

(c)

FIGURE 14-16 (a) This view of the exterior side of the inner wall frame exposes the little spacer blocks that may be used to tie the corner studs together. (b) Raising the inner wall. (c) Sole plates are gauged apart with little 1″ blocks until nailed to a chalk line.

Raise the wall frames in an order that will interlace the corners. For example, raise the two end frames of the outer walls first. Second, raise the long outer walls. Follow this same order with the inner walls. The corners will be interlaced as seen in Fig. 14-16b.

Nailing the sole is perfected with the use of a couple of 1″ gauge blocks (3/4″ thick; Fig. 14-16c). Cutoffs from a brace will serve. A chalk line is snapped on the floor where the interior edge of the sole will be. Use the gauges between the soles where the nail is being driven to prevent the sole from being driven closer to the outer wall than it should be. If the outer wall curves in, do not parallel and reproduce the error. Omit the block and lay to the chalk line. Any gross error in the outer wall should be corrected.

Drive each nail over, and anchored into, a floor joist. Since the joists are on 16″ centers and the common studs are on odd-numbered 24″ centers, there will be no studs over the joists in the inner wall. On the other hand, there will be a joist under every other stud in the outer frame, those which are on 4′ modules. This knowledge helps locate joists quickly. Added to the visible joints in the ends of the modular sheathing, which tells where a joist is, there remains only the 16″ intermediate joist locations, which can be identified quickly with a tape measure or framing-square tongue.

Frames with double 2 × 4 top plates will benefit by having metal ties across the top plates. A small sheet metal tie can be snipped from band iron, or ties can be purchased for the purpose. Place a string line along the inner or outer plate. Space it out away from the plate with an equal-thickness block at each end. Bring the plate with the string line into perfect straightness and secure it with braces to the floor. Interior bracing from the top plate of the outer wall, which is holding the wall plumb, will not interfere with the construction and raising of the inner wall because the stud centering is staggered. The braces will be between the studs of the second inner wall. The inner frame is assembled around the braces and simply straddles them as it is being raised. Use a bar clamp across the tops of the upper plates to close any gap between the inner and outer plates. Put on the metal tie to hold the plates together at any point required. *Place each tie at a location that is not over a stud in the outer wall* frame. The roof trusses will be resting over these studs.

Installing an upper top plate of 2 × 8 girth removes the need for ties. Each 2 × 8 plate board must have one straight edge. Saw, plane, or joint it straight. Line up the straight edge of each plate board with the interior edge of the inner wall. This board will not completely cover the double wall. The 2 × 8 is 7 1/4″ wide. The wall is 7 3/4″ deep. The disparity is unimportant as long as the inside is made flush. The resulting 1/2″ inset on the exterior side will be up under the plancier, where it is of no significance. In fact, it can be made functional by nailing 1/2″ plysheath insulation stops to it.

Cutouts should be made in the 2 × 8 at each partition intersection (Fig. 14-17a). The cutout will be 3 1/2″ × 3 1/2″ to accept the upper member of the interior partition top plate. The cross-lap tieing function is thereby accommodated. To locate the partition cutout, the 2 × 8 plate is put in place and temporarily tacked with a couple of nails (Fig. 14-17b). The location of a cutout is marked by projecting lines up from the partition blocks found in the partition post below. Occasionally, these partition locking cutouts are overlooked until after the 2 × 8 plates are nailed

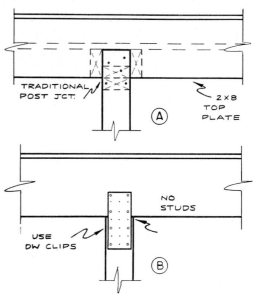

FIGURE 14-17 Top view showing a partition plate notched into a 2 × 8 plate on top of a double wall containing a conventional intersection post; (b) butted partition held fast with a truss plate.

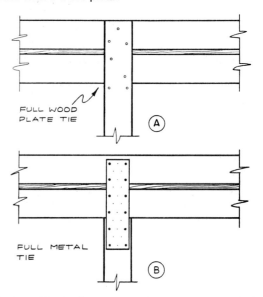

FIGURE 14-18 Partition ties where conventional double plate sets are used may be of wood or metal. (a) Top plate of the partition serving as the tie; (b) butted partition and a metal plate performing the tying function.

down. This poses no serious problem. A small sheet metal tie is nailed over the intersection to substitute for the usual crosslap interlock joint. The sheet metal tie may be used routinely. Some builders prefer the metal tie method. It takes less time, and there is no possibility of misaligning a notch.

Nail the 2 × 8 plate at 1′ intervals, staggering from the outer to inner plates below. 10d nails are adequate and will not penetrate through. Visualize the corner joints underneath the 2 × 8 so that nails are driven into effectual wood and not on top of other nails that are in the lower half of the double plate. The front and rear top plates may be allowed to extend beyond the end walls to support the birdbox cornice work (described in Chapter 3).

Should the plate of preference be the traditional doubled 2 × 4 on both inner and outer frame, the top partition plate should run through to the outer wall (Fig. 14-18a) or be metal strapped clear to the outer wall (Fig. 14-18b), thereby sustaining the perpendicular brace of both frames.

Salvaging Studs

The house builder who is not into tract building or production work can save a significant amount of cost by machining unstraight studs for use in a double wall. Many number 3 graded studs ("utility" or "economy") can be purchased at about one-half the price of number two ("structural") studs. Most of the lower-grade studs are warped. A bowed stud is not a problem, as it can be pulled into alignment and held straight with the sheathing. A crooked stud is a problem. A crooked stud is curved on its edge. This characteristic will be found in the better studs to some extent, but is more prevalent in the lower-grade studs. When the curvature is greater than 1/8″, the stud should not be used in a wall frame. The soft sheathings currently being used (blackboard, Styrofoam, and the like) exert no straightening effect on a crooked stud as shiplap boards and five-ply plywood sheathing once did.

A crooked stud *can be used* in a double wall by straightening either the concave or the convex edge. Machine off an equal depth amount from each end of the concave edge, as shown in Fig. 14-19. The convex edge can be straightened, but more wood will usually be removed, as the taper cut cannot be controlled accurately. In the double wall, only one straight edge is required of each stud. The curved edge is faced toward the core. A brace is not nailed tight if it crosses a stud at a narrowed point.

Straightening a convex or concave edge can be done by sawing or jointing. The typical construction job is not likely to boast a long bed jointer. The cost of one could be justified with the savings from several house jobs. A jointer of 1/2″-depth capacity is preferred. A power hand plane is also usable. To saw the board straight, a chalk line is snapped on the edge of your choice and the curved portion is sawed off.

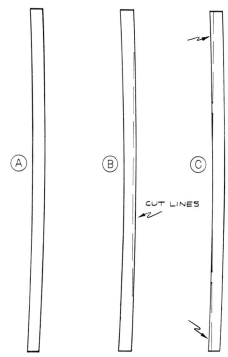

FIGURE 14-19 Crooked studs may be straightened on one edge only and used in a double-wall frame. Part (c) shows the preferred edge to straighten. Exaggerated for graphic emphasis.

What determines which edge should be straightened by sawing? It is a toss-up. Sawing off the convex edge leaves the ends of a stud at a full 3 1/2″ depth (preferred nailing-end surface). On the other hand, a badly crooked stud will be materially narrowed as it approaches the central area. This complicates the application of the diagonal braces and a central horizontal spacer band. The convex cut side is preferred where no band or diagonal brace is nailed to both inner and outer walls as with deeper wall cavities. Where a band is used and both wall frames are secured together, it is better to leave the central stud area at full depth by cutting the concave edge of the stud to form a straight edge. The latter will reduce the ends to less than 3 1/2″ in depth. This undersizing is of no consequence, as it will be on the inner core of the double frame.

Avoid misassembling the studs that are machined straight on one edge by indexing the straightened side with large coded crayon marks. Three Xs a foot apart make a good code. Assemble the outer wall with the studs placed on the floor *with the Xs up*. At the ends of each stud, the upper edge is nailed flush with the top edge of the plates. This produces an outer wall surface that is adequately straight. The studs for the inner wall are placed *with the marks down* so that when it is raised the true surface will face toward the interior. These stud ends must line up flush with the underside of the plates.

Another malformed warp shape is the *twisted* stud. This propeller-type configuration can also be remedied by

FIGURE 14-20 The deep window sill that is common to the double wall lends a feeling of grandeur and strength to the interior.

jointing. The board is started on edge on the jointer at a central point. The protruding angled edge is jointed off in a series of passes. The board is then reversed, end for end, and the same relative edge is leveled on the remaining end. One final pass on the newly planed edge produces a straight surface. All alignment pressure on the board with the hands is directed toward the jointer tables (infeed and outfeed). No pressure is exerted against the fence. The only true surface, the jointed edge, is marked with the code Xs. This rectified stud can only be used in the field of the frame wall. It will cause problems if placed adjacent to a door or window opening or on the end of a wall or partition corner. Its use is limited to standing alone with no attached parts.

The remedial stud system may sound like a time-consuming nuisance. In reality, several hundred dollars can be saved in a few hours. The author is not suggesting that wood of an inferior structural quality be used. However, much of the stud material available has been downgraded due to warpage alone. Since the double-wall design incorporates a centering system equal to 12″ OC and the two

wall segments are tied together into a structural unit, the structural strength is far in excess of the usual minimum stud girth requirement.

In addition to economy, a much straighter frame wall is produced both inside and outside. The crooked edges that remain on the straightened studs are toward the cavity of the wall, where they have no effect on the lines of the wall.

Superior vertical rigidity is a fringe benefit of the double wall. This feature is compelling in cyclone-, tornado-, and earthquake-prone areas of the country.

An aesthetic feature of note is the deep windowsill area (Fig. 14-20). It provides a potential planter shelf for flowers and knickknacks. With a small extension, it adapts well to an attractive cushioned window seat. For those interested in heat retention, the deeper window cavity provides an ideal setting for various forms of intermittent insulating (day and night), such as the blown bead wall or the roller insulation blanket.

OTHER DOUBLE WALL DESIGNS

There are several other double wall designs being used that are meeting with good results in the quest for heat and cool retention. One such assembly of the exterior wall is a direct spin-off from the old balloon framing design. It is so close that it actually provides a viable retrofit option for the restorer of an old historical house. If lost square footage is no great drawback, the interior face of the exterior walls is gutted. The old walls are insulated and a new inside wall is erected. The cavity can be made as deep as desired and filled with insulation.

DOUBLE-WALL COORDINATES

The effectiveness of the double wall is directly proportionate to an overall coordinated design. A ludicrous example of misapplication would be to have single-glass windows in abundance on the north side of a double-wall house. Similarly, a single-panel uninsulated exterior door with or without an accompanying storm door poses a weak link in the concept. The concept of superinsulation for the purpose of maximum heat or cooling retention must be an all-systems philosophy. Anything else is like toting water from a faraway well using a bucket with a hole in it.

A problem of concern has been observed with family building and small budget projects. It is repeated too often to be considered insignificant. Basically, the person(s) responsible for the budget is interested in heating, cooling, and maintenance economy and is also prone to be very cost conscious during the construction phase. This can lead to inconsistency in the long-range plan. As the building progresses, the harsh reality of large bills mounting up creates a poor psychological climate. The builder becomes more cautious, wary, and even stingy. Unfortunately, the timing is critical. One example of false economy that frequently strikes is in the selection of windows. Cheap single-pane windows in metal frames can be the undoing of the whole superinsulation objective. Many windows are represented to the market as thermal type simply because two panes of glass are set in butyl rubber surrounded by a thin metal channel. This type of ''thermalizing'' does not compare in resistance with genuine hermetically sealed glass such as Thermopane. Obviously, double-glazed windows, as the rubber-set panes are termed by accurate describers, are more efficient than a single-pane window. The cost-saving gain, however, does not rank it as an optimum coordinate to accompany the double-walled frame concept. Inexpensive windows are only cost saving initially. After five years or so, they become a perpetual expense to the owner. The expense could have been a saving had the budget for good windows been adequate and sustained.

Whether a house is double or single walled, the heat- and cooling-retention features should be coordinated to form a logical balance. The insulation ratio between walls and ceiling, for example, is important. An old-style wall with noninsulating sheathing and 3 1/2″ of blanket insulation (R-11) should have at least 6″ of insulation in the ceiling (R-18). A better-insulated wall, such as a blanketed 6″ frame with Styrofoam sheathing (about R-23), will profit significantly from a ceiling in the R-38 category. The ceiling should have a resistance value about 50% greater than that of the walls. Any variation from this theme will create an imbalance that is not cost-effective.

Floor Insulation

Floor insulation seems to be a subject of little concern with builders and consumers alike. Out of sight, out of mind would seem to characterize feelings about this coordinate area of insulation philosophy. The author has been sandwiching 2″ of tightly fitted Styrofoam into floor-joist cavities for several years. On the first occasion a utility company assessed the payback effectiveness on the first model at 18 years. The assessment was made on the utility cost of that date projected into the future. The next year the utility rate went up 25%. The following year it rose 25% again. In two years the payback figure had dropped dramatically. Present utility costs virtually warrant insulation in all crawl space homes and perimeter insulation for slab-floor homes. Homes with unheated basements will also benefit during the winter heating season.

The crawl space house is the type most needing insulation in the floor. There are conventional methods of insulating between the floor joists which have met with moderate to poor success. These techniques involve hang-

ing blanket insulation with cross wires, chicken wire, or some other invention on the site. Much of the poor success achieved stems from the inadequacy of the suspension techniques; poor fitting of the blankets around pipe, bridging, and other construction obstructions; and to inherent dampness in the crawl space. Several jobs, supposedly done by reputable and knowledgeable contractors, have been seen where the insulation with a vapor backing was installed upside down (the vapor barrier should face up next to the floor). There is a natural inclination to place it with the paper down, as it can be stapled easily to joists from beneath. Some of these jobs were left with no other support but the staples. Naturally, there were many places where the paper had torn loose from the staples, allowing the roll batt to fall down.

Three elements are needed for successful insulating of a floor:

- The insulation must fit tightly throughout the entire floor space.
- The insulation should perform a vapor-barrier function or have an integrated vapor barrier.
- The ground beneath the floor should be treated to maintain a dry air climate in the crawl space (ground cover barrier, adequate vents, etc.).

Treating the ground is done successfully in the following manner. Prepare the floor of the crawl space by removing all debris, rocks, and clods. Smooth the surface so that it is fairly flat and has no sharp protrusions or distinct cavities. Spread a thin layer (1/2″) of sand or crusher dust over the entire area. Lay a full-size sheet of plastic film over the entire area. Six mil is preferred, but 4 mil will suffice. At initial construction time the sheet is suspended over the piers until their location can be identified quite precisely. Cut an X over each pier and let the plastic slip snugly down around the pier. If more than one sheet is required to span the distance, lap over the edges at least 2 to 4′. Permit the sides and ends to rise up the foundation wall a few inches. Place a thin layer of sand all over the plastic to hold it in place and to cushion walking and crawling over it. Obviously, the plastic is vulnerable to punctures and tears. Construction crews will need to be made aware of the need for carefulness while it is exposed. Some more affluent contracts will specify a 2″ layer of concrete over the plastic to form a permanent shield.

Roll-type fiberglass is the least costly form of insulation per R unit of value. It becomes more costly by the coverage foot when a suspension system is added to the total cost. For this reason the consideration of sheet forms of insulation is worthy.

Blackboard in 2′ × 8′ V-grooved edge form is a favorite subsheathing material in some localities. It is laid across the floor joists with end joints staggered and V joined edges tightly compressed. Only four nails are needed on the ends of the sheets. Three nails are adequate in the field. The sheathing to come will hold the blackboard down. The sheathing installation should follow directly behind the blackboard. With this procedure the potential for breaking through the blackboard will be greatly lessened. Only 100% asphalt-impregnated fiberboard should be used. A single layer of 3/4″ tongue-and-groove plywood completes the floor. The T&G ply serves as both subfloor and underlayment for wall-to-wall floor covering. Such a floor must be built upon and closed in against the weather as quickly as possible to avoid rain damage.

Styrofoam insulation in sheet form is installed between the floor joists. One or more layers may be used to accumulate as great an R value as desired. In relation to the proportion of insulation between floor, walls, and ceiling, the floor requires the least. In numerical form the floor can be assigned one unit, the walls two units, and the ceiling four units. For example, in a superinsulated house with R-40 insulation in the ceiling and about R-25 in the walls, R-11 or R-12 in the floor will meet the criterion. Two inches of Styrofoam is a little over R-11 in value.

Installing 2″ of Styrofoam is accomplished most effectively by double layering (Fig. 14-21). Two 1″ layers are installed. The end joints of the pieces in the top layer are staggered above the bottom layer (Fig. 14-22). This technique eliminates infiltration through joint cracks. No separate vapor barrier is required, as Styrofoam is impervious to moisture. To serve as its own vapor barrier, the Styrofoam must be tightly fitted.

Installation of the Styrofoam involves a press-fit technique and a conscientious philosophy. Ledger strips are installed first around the perimeter of each joist cavity. The least costly material for the ledgers is precut economy studs ripped into four equal strips. The strip will be about 3/4″ thick by 1 1/2″ wide. Where a budget is very limited,

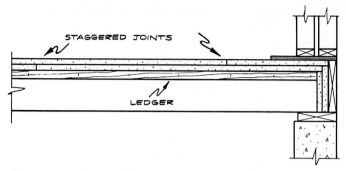

FIGURE 14-22 Stagger the end joints of layered Styrofoam to ensure against infiltration.

each of these can be ripped in half to net strips that are about 11/16″ × 3/4″ in girth. The latter case will net about 60 linear feet of ledger material for the cost of one inexpensive stud.

The ledgers are power stapled or nailed in place. To control the exact location of the Styrofoam, a gauge is used to hold the ledger the correct distance down from the top surface of the joists. A chalk line is of no value for this detail. The ledger must be parallel to the top edge of the joist. Most of the joists will have a slight crown when installed correctly. Two short boards are nailed together as seen in Fig. 14-23. The gauge piece will be 1/32″ narrower than the depth of insulation being installed. The gauge is held down over the edge of the joist. The ledger is held up firmly against the bottom edge of the gauge. The nail or staple is driven home opposite the gauge. Two men, one holding the gauge and ledger strip while the other operates the staple gun, can install the ledgers in a very short time.

The gauge is made to control the placement of the ledgers at a level 1/32″ higher than the total Styrofoam thickness. This position will cause the top surface of the Styrofoam to protrude 1/32″ above the top of the joists.

FIGURE 14-21 Layered Styrofoam provides an effective floor insulation when installed tightly throughout.

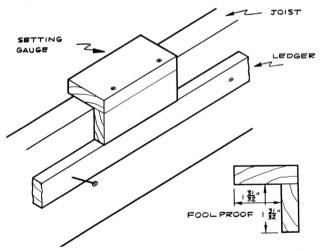

FIGURE 14-23 A simple foolproof gauge is used to position the ledger boards accurately.

When the subfloor is put on, it will compress the Styrofoam tightly, giving an excellent sealing effect.

The most economical Styrofoam unit to buy is the 4' × 8' large-bead type, carried in stock by most suppliers. It is fabricated by ripping into slabs 14 1/2" × 8'. The 4 1/2" remaining scrap is saved to fill corner post and partition post cavities in exterior walls. Use a notched story pole to hold the joists in correct parallel spacing. Hump each 8' slab a few inches in the middle while pressing the ends in. Leave it humped while putting in the next piece. After all pieces are in at their ends, go back and compress the middles down into position. This will cause the ends to compress tightly together. The last piece in a row will be custom cut to length. Cut it about 1/8" long. A little experimentation with the first row will tell how high to hump each piece and how much excess to leave on the custom-cut piece. Reverse ends when starting the second layer. In most house depths this will stagger the joint adequately. The 24'-deep floor is the exception. With this floor one should start the second layer with a half length (4') slab and save the other half for the custom-cut piece on the other side.

Leave the joist spaces at the ends of the floor until last. These spaces are less than 14 1/2" wide since the POB is on the outer edge of the joist instead of the center. Other custom-cut widths may be required where double joists have been installed under partition locations or reinforced zones. These should be filled as they are reached, as the workers should not have to walk out over the Styrofoam on either side later to install these odd pieces.

Fitting around the ends of lapped joists is time consuming but can be kept to a minimum by starting the coursing at the edge of the lap and working out. This requires custom cutting to length at each end of the run for the first layer. The second layer is started at either end. At the lapped joist point a piece is notched to fit precisely. A big-toothed wallboard saw is an efficient tool for this customizing. Assembly-line ripping of the duplicate slabs to go in the majority of the cavities is done on a table saw.

Double-Wall Insulation

A further saving can be realized with the double-wall concept because the blanket-type insulation is the least expensive form. The double wall's extra-deep cavity permits the installation of two layers of 3 1/2" blanket insulation. Both the outer and inner layers may be laid up with the nonpaper-backed type. It is called "friction fit" and comes in 48" and stud lengths. These convenient-size batts are handily worked into the outer wall cavities. The electric wiring is snaked between the studs after the first layer of insulation is in place. Any plumbing fixtures that are located adjacent to the exterior walls are rough plumbed. Vents and drains are installed. Freeze-ups of exterior wall plumbing are vir-

tually nonexistent with the double wall because the outer layer of insulation is between the pipes and the exterior side of the wall.

The inner layer of insulation is installed next. It can be the friction-fit type covered with a continuous piece of plastic sheet or the vapor-barrier paper-backed type in stud lengths. Because the studs are staggered from inner to outer frames, the insulation blankets are also staggered. The effect is a tight infiltration-proof wall of R-22 value (just the insulation rating). By using the less costly blackboard for sheathing and any form of siding, the total wall value is about R-25 or more. In the final accounting, the double-wall cost of the design shown in this text falls somewhere between those of the conventional 2 × 4 stud wall and the 2 × 6 stud wall. It is cost-effective in all respects when the plan is carefully devised (modular overall sizes and modular placement of openings and partitions) and the materials proportionately matched.

THERMAL ROOF DESIGNS

When considering heat and cooling retention, one must recognize the window of vulnerability that exists with conventional rafters. At the location of the birdsmouth (the seat cut), the distance from the surface of the top plate to the underside of the roof sheathing in some cases is smaller than the wall cavity depth. It is therefore virtually impossible to produce a 1 1/2-to-1 ratio (ceiling to wall) of insulation value in this area. The largest conventional rafters are seldom over 2 × 8 in girth (7 1/4"). A seat cut over a conventional wall plate lowers the height for insulation to about 6" or less. The conventional roof frame limits the area above the top plate from about 2" for 2 × 4 rafters to about 6" for 2 × 8 rafters (Fig. 14-24). Regardless of what depth of insulation exists over the rest of the ceiling, the area over the top plate is limited. A few attempts have been made to raise this area with cripple studs and an additional

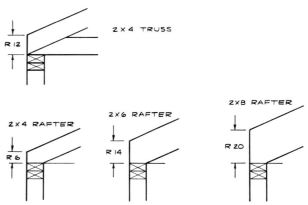

FIGURE 14-24 The space above a conventional wall between the top plate and the roof is limited for insulation containment.

top plate. The design suffers from instability, labor-time consumption, and high cost. None has caught on seriously.

Thermal Truss

The thermal truss has become commonplace. Designs vary, but most factory-made thermal trusses contain extra webs and cripple studs positioned to be above the wall (Fig. 14-25). With this design, any depth for insulation can be had. A drawback develops when the extended height becomes excessive. Unless enough overhang can be planned, a high frieze-board area develops over the windows. It is difficult to make this space look natural and intended. Americans are accustomed to seeing boxed eaves and possibly some frieze board just above the windows. Brick houses are especially vulnerable. An economy plan will not tolerate angle-iron lintels so that brick can be continued over the windows and doors. The finish carpenter is then burdened with the chore of filling in the void over the windows and doors with some nonmasonry material. It seldom looks anything but after-planned. An advantage of the high-thermal-truss design is that it works well with the inter-

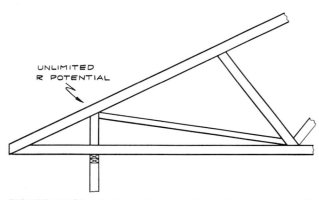

FIGURE 14-25 A thermal truss where the upper chord is raised with vertical cripples and webs can provide unlimited insulating capacity over the top plates. This design is especially adaptable to the midrange of pitches, such as 5 through 10 in 12.

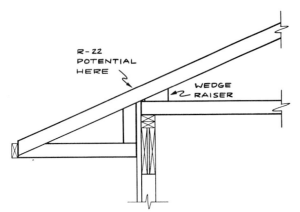

FIGURE 14-26 A plumb-cut bottom chord (square cut) and a pitched wedge will effectively double the insulation capacity over the top plates.

mediate pitches because the steeper angle contains the overhanging tail closer and lower on the wall.

A pitch wedge is another way to raise the upper chords (Fig. 14-26). The wedge is obtained from the end of the return piece or is custom cut from scrap stock. The lower chord is square cut.

Extended Span Truss

The author has employed an extended span truss design with great success for many years. It is a simple, cost-conserving concept which closes the window of insular vulnerability. It works on all roofs with horizontal boxed plancier returns.

The design formula simply calls for a truss of a modular span one size larger than the house span. The builder who designs and builds his own trusses will find it easy to lay out the truss on paper and on the floor.

Observe some specific examples. For a 24′ spanned house, a 26′ spanned truss is laid out (Fig. 14-27). One foot of the lower chord overhangs the wall. The mitered cutoff piece from the end of the lower chord is retained and used as a chock-block wedge to reinforce the bearing characteristic of the chords above the top plate (Fig. 14-28). It also serves as a solid backing for the gusset. The wedge is cost free, compared to a cripple, as it would normally be discarded. Another feature of the overhanging lower chord is that it provides a level under edge to which brick pocket drops can readily be fitted (Fig. 14-29). Square junctions are always less critical to join than are mitered junctions on the rake.

A truss that is one size larger than the house span will provide an insulation depth potential of about 10″ clear out to the building line. This is right in line with present-day cost-effective planning.

The depth potential for the insulation is variable with a nonmodular spanned house when a modular truss of greater span is used. As the house span approaches closer to the span of the lower chord, the space above the exterior wall will diminish. Stated a different way, the space above a conventional truss of 2 × 4 components will be just slightly more than 3 1/2″ at the building line when the truss nominal span is equal to the house span. As the lower chord is extended out away from the wall, the roof line appears to rise. It will gain in height (the space for insulation) in proportion to the distance that the wall is from the end of the lower chord.

The principle is so simple that it has other applications. For example, a rule of thumb emerges. It is not necessary to have a custom-spanned truss built to fit a nonmodular span. An odd-sized span of 25′ (not uncommon) is simply roofed with 26′ trusses. The extra 6″ overhang of the lower chord on each side is an asset. A 26′ truss will usually cost no more to make than a 25′ custom-built truss. If purchased, it may cost less.

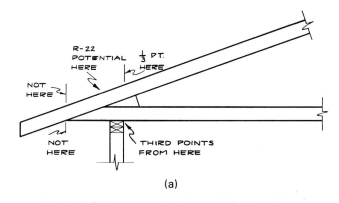

(a)

(b)

FIGURE 14-27 (a) Wedges that are cut from the ends of the chords are used in the joint to reduce actual span. (b) A standard truss that is 2′ wider than a modular span raises the insulating capacity above the plates.

The same system works throughout the various spans. House spans in the range 26 to 28′ will accept 28′ trusses; those above 28′ will accept 30 and 32′ standard trusses.

Web Location on Extended Trusses

When a standard truss is purchased, the webs will be connected to the chords at standard third and quarter points of the truss span. These locations will not coincide with the actual quarter and third points on the house, which has a shorter span. This is not a problem, as the truss has been designed for its own span. For the builder who makes his own trusses, the opportunity is there to create equal spans on the lower chord and thereby rectify the disparity. For example, a 28′ W truss on top of a 2 × 4 platee conventional wall will have a clear-span factor of 27′5″ (28 minus two 3 1/2″ plates). The third points of this span are about 9′–1 5/8″. Placing this standard 28′ truss on a house span of 26′ (a clear span of 25′5″) causes the central "third" to be much greater than the outer two actual clear spans. To overcome this discrepancy, the builder can lay out his

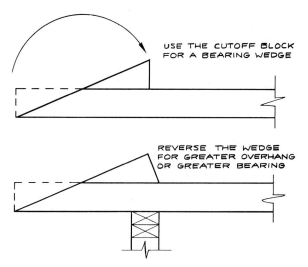

FIGURE 14-28 An accurately cut piece will fit the opening between chords and provide solid backing for a one-piece gusset of wood or metal.

truss jig to accommodate the third and quarter spacing according to the shorter span of the house by measuring from a centerline outward while the upper and lower chords are laid out on the profile of the next-larger modular truss. In this way the best of two objectives is achieved.

The potential of greater disproportionate third or quarter spans in the lower chord exists with a deeper-walled house. On a double wall it is recommended that an extended truss have its webs at the actual clear-span third points. This will guarantee equal spans, which in turn provides for the greatest inherent ceiling and roof support. When purchasing trusses the buyer can furnish the factory with a simple drawing including dimensions to centerlines (Fig. 14-30). This *should* assure the exact web locations desired. It does not, however, as workers are creatures of habit. Some will ignore the dimensions. Others will assume that the designer has misplaced the locations, especially if he is not a professional. It will help to avoid later

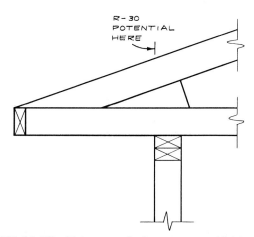

FIGURE 14-29 This truss design causes a higher frieze board area above windows but provides a ready-made soffit return with no drop to construct.

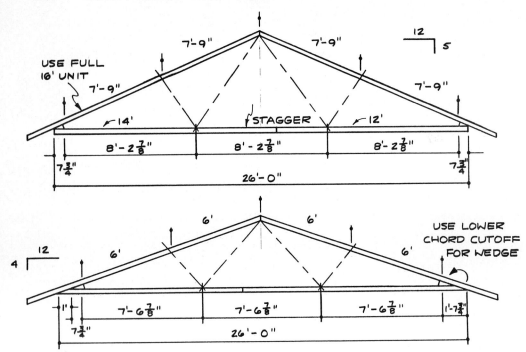

FIGURE 14-30 Sample truss drawings that will clearly help a manufacturer or a self-builder to construct what is correct and accurate. Each example is for a double-walled structure.

confrontation if the designer is on hand to oversee that the jig is properly set up in accordance with his plan. And, of course, a simple contract agreement to follow the drawing specifications will help in case error occurs.

VENTILATION OF THERMAL STRUCTURES

Problems of condensation were experienced when insulation first came into widespread use. A pessimistic philosophy is still encountered from time to time which says, "Too much insulation can be as bad as too little." The philosophy is grounded in some truth and some fiction.

A primary breakdown of early forms of fiberboard and blanket insulation came about because of the condensation that was created. Old-timers still have visions of windows with water dribbling down the inside of the panes and wood siding from which the paint peeled annually. The peeling paint was usually caused by fiberboard sheathing that did not have an asphaltum impregnation. Placed on uninsulated walls, the heat in the house would penetrate to the back side of the sheathing and cause condensation to form on the cold surface. The resulting condensation soaked the fiberboard, which in turn soaked the back side of the siding, usually cedar, which absorbed it like a sponge. This phase took place during the World War II period and on into the early 1950s. It was overcome by moisture-proofing the various brands of fiberboard and by paper-backing the batt insulation with a moisture barrier. In these transition years, the theory was born that a house could be overinsulated. In reality, there is no such thing as overinsulating. But there is a point of diminishing return which makes it nonfeasible. Too much insulation is not harmful; it simply may not pay back its initial cost in fuel savings over the life of the house.

Ventilation, vapor blocking, and air exchange are the keys to the conservation of heat- and cooling-generating fuels. Obviously, the greatest economy is to use the free sources—the sun, the wind, and the earth—to as great an extent as possible for heating and cooling. When other costly fuels are used, the next-best system of conservation is to superinsulate. It will work best when it is accompanied by adequate ventilation and occasional exchange of interior air.

Roof Ventilators

All the mechanical and powered roof ventilators are of moderate use for removing hot air from an attic. Static vents are too small. Nonpowered turbines do not suck out the air as they appear to. They turn on windless days from the impetus of the rising hot air. A turbine would be more effective as a simple screened chimney. Gable vents are directional. The most effective vent is the full eave and ridge vent combination. Full-length ridge and soffit vents do the best job.

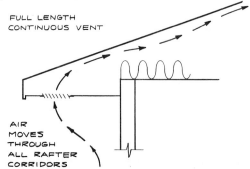

FIGURE 14-31 A full-length eave venting system permits cooled air to enter all rafter corridors.

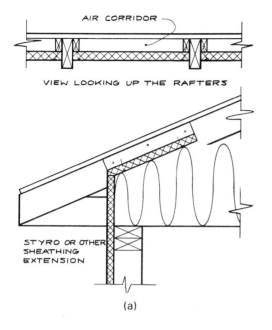

VIEW LOOKING UP THE RAFTERS

(a)

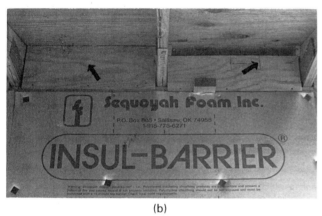

(b)

(c)

FIGURE 14-32 (a) The air corridor must be kept open with an insulation stop. (b) An exterior view of insulation stops and the vent corridors above the plates. (c) An interior view of the vent corridor stops (Styrofoam) which hold back the insulation. Note the suspended prenailed interior top plates.

To clear an attic of all hot spots, the air must be moved out of all the spaces between the rafters. This is accomplished most effectively with a combination of full-length venting entrances in the eaves and a full-length ridge vent. The air will move freely and naturally up all of the channels between the rafters with this combination (Fig. 14-31). Care must be taken to provide a protected corridor above the insulation over the plate area (Fig. 14-32a, Fig. 14-32b, and Fig. 14-32c). Manufactured ridge vents are obtainable in some areas. A simple and attractive vent can be built on site. A section view with dimensions is explained and represented graphically in Chapter 10.

Air exchange inside the house is another important factor in controlling condensation during the heating season. Condensation is a heating-season problem. Occasionally, the statement is heard, "The house has to breathe to be free of condensation." The breathing need not be accomplished via skimpy insulation and certainly not by tolerated infiltration. The theory that a house can be too tight is not logical if it implies that built-in leaks are good. The practical situation is for the tenant to be in control of conditions and still sustain and contain the heat that is being introduced as long as possible. Such control is maintained by periodic air exchange when humidity becomes excessive.

Partial air exchange occurs every time an exterior door is opened. Vent fans over the kitchen range will remove air on command. Vent fans in the bathrooms take care of steamy air.

Full air exchange is achieved by opening doors and windows on opposite sides or ends of the house for a few minutes. One might think such a practice was in direct conflict with the heat-saving objective. Not so. The heat loss is only momentary and quickly recouped. The dumping of stale, moisture-laden air will take only a few minutes, not long enough to cool down all the heat-holding objects and materials in the house.

The chimney flue in a fireplace is another excellent venting source. Once the air seems fresh and crisp, all the openings are closed. A hot-air furnace should be turned off during the air exchange; however, the blower may be operated manually to circulate new air rapidly, after which the thermostat may be returned to the desired operational settings. In a matter of minutes, the condensation is eliminated.

COST-EFFECTIVENESS OF THERMAL CONSTRUCTION

The term *cost-effective* relates to a comparison of the initial cost to construct or install something compared to the long-range saving it will generate. Scientists tell us that the world's fossil-fuel sources are diminishing at an alarming rate. Costs go up as supplies become precious. Obviously a home requiring no consumable fuels will be the most cost-effective if initial cost is reasonable.

Two doors are open to the designer/builder to approach this ultimate objective. One door leads to the use of the sun and the earth as the only truly free sources of heating and cooling. The other door leads to ways and means of holding onto the heat or cool that is put into a house as long as possible. The decade of the 1980s will be remembered as the time when solar and earth use for homes became feasible and cost-effective. The reader and homebuilder now has enough information from this text to construct a suitable habitat within the same cost range as a house of conventional (old-fashioned?) utilities.

Consistency is stressed when developing the cost-effective plan. Certain things go together. The mismatching of philosophies will nullify or diminish the effects of the super features. The conservation and retention theme must prevail with all systems and materials in a particular structure. Cost must not dominate a selection of materials. The quality coefficient is the criterion of importance.

Build a house to fit the land. If a plan is admired and selected first, a suitable lot must be found to fit the plan. Orient and size windows according to solar gain or loss. Extend eaves in accord with the sun's angle in summer and winter. Orient exterior doors in accord with the effects of prevailing winds. Include compartmented entrances. Use a 1-to-2-to-3 insulation proportion for the floor, the exterior wall, and the ceiling. A cost-effective example for a crawl space structure is 4″ of fiberglass blanket in the floor, 8″ in a double wall, and 12″ over the ceiling. Windows to match will be thermopane with a combination storm sash. Insulated doors are a must, with a combination storm door in front. Use light roof shingles in predominantly hot climates, dark shingles in the predominantly cold areas of the country.

Long-range planning is a moral responsibility. This concept is worthy of exploring although usually avoided by authors. The cost-effectiveness of materials should take into account the fact that someone will be paying utility bills for many years. Fifty years might be considered a minimum expectation.

The most flagrant and obvious example of short-range planning, visible in most housing developments, is witnessed in the quality of windows. It can only be accounted for by the naiveté of the average purchaser, who does not recognize window quality by sight. The typical buyer is likely to be impressed by the appearance of a house rather than by the quality of the components. It is a rare buyer who is brand conscious of such things as windows, doors, air conditioners, and furnaces. The average buyer is usually under some degree of pressure to acquire and establish a home without delay. In this atmosphere of anxiety (it is the biggest purchase of a lifetime for most), it is almost axiomatic that the buyer takes the word of the seller for about everything that is not obvious.

There is a broad degree of latitude between pure fiction and whole truth when it comes to describing the assets or liabilities of a house. Many of the features affecting the long-range utility costs are not visible on a cursory inspection. For example, the buyer has picked up a few terms in his or her quest. The question is asked, "Is this house of a thermal-constructed type?" The "yes" response puts the issue to sleep and the wife goes about admiring the fancy kitchen while the husband fantasizes at the workbench counter in the garage. What a heavenly change from the cramped apartment or the live-in situation with in-laws. The trap in which they may be snared lies in the term "thermal." The word "thermal" can be used to describe a house with any type of insulating material in it that does not classify as a structural component.

One time in his legal expert-witness role, the author uncovered an entire subdivision of houses with only a sheet of 4-mil plastic under the plastered walls. No insulation was present in the cavities. The houses were advertised as "fully insulated." This was an extreme case of misrepresentation in the moral sense. It would never have come to light had it not been for the comparing of heat bills between neighbors in homes built by more scrupulous contractors.

INSPECTION BY THE BUYER

The prospective buyer can inspect some places in a house in order to judge its thermal efficiency. There will be an access port into the attic somewhere. Armed with a flashlight and a tape measure, get up there and check the depth of insulation. Check for full coverage throughout. If it is blown insulation, is it evenly spread? If it is blanket type, has it been fitted around rafters, webs, strongbacks, or has it simply been rolled up around them? Are the furnace ducts in the attic (the poorest location for conservation)? If so, are they wrapped to a depth equal to the ceiling insulation? The customary system is to wrap them with 1 1/2 or 2″ of vinyl-backed, fiberglass blanketing.

Inspect the basement. Is the foundation insulated where it is exposed to the outdoors? Adhesive-bonded Styrofoam is cost-effective. Is there insulation behind the wood header (above the foundation) between each joist? Is there insulation the full length of the band headers at the ends of the house? Are the basement windows of thermal type (double glass, Thermopane, or with storms)? If these thermal characteristics do not exist around the exposed part of the foundation, the heat loss can be as great from this seemingly insignificant area as it is from the whole first-floor exterior wall.

Check the crawl space. Plan to don some old clothes and crawl under there with a flashlight. Can you smell any evidence of termite treatment (chlordane odor)? Is there insulation between the joists? If not, is there Styrofoam sheathing glued to the foundation? Are there enough foundation vents to let the stale air out of the corners? Is there a vapor barrier, a layer of sand and plastic over the dirt?

Inspecting a slab floor for thermal characteristics is more difficult but not completely impossible. A slab, to be considered thermal, must have a barrier between the exposed foundation and the interior floor. Styrofoam is the usual material. Somewhere in the house it may be exposed. If there is a plumbing access behind a tub adjacent to an outer wall, it could reveal a Styrofoam strip between the foundation and the floor slab. Behind a washer and dryer, the baseboard may be omitted, exposing the Styrofoam barrier. The junction between the floor slab and an attached garage slab may furnish a clue. Sometimes, taking up an aluminum door sill from this junction will reveal the needed barrier. All these things failing, there is still hope. On a cold winter day or hot summer day, feel the surface of an exposed part of the slab floor that is adjacent to the outer wall. It should feel comparable to the temperature inside the house if there is a barrier. Where all these potential clues are absent and the house is a new one in a tract-built home addition, there is one last possibility. Locate a new house-start at the end of the tract, one where the foundation is in but the floor is not yet poured. If it is the same builder, the construction will probably be the same. Try to be on hand just before the slab is poured. The full picture of the insulation and vapor barrier as well as the slab reinforcing will be evident.

Any attempt to make a house more successful at retaining heat or cooling will net dividends. In the long run, the greatest success will be achieved by balancing the systems and approaches and keeping it simple. In a new house, cost-effectiveness will result from a concept of total adaptation, as compared to fragmented schemes. Go with a complete plan of procedure from the outset. Do not be dissuaded by costs or by undocumented gossip. The end result for those who hang tight will be a house good to live in throughout the ages.

For those whose motivation is money by selling, it is a proven fact that good-quality houses, those with documented utility bills, sell more easily and quicker than the house where a track record is obvious by its absence.

SOLAR COLLECTION

No discussion of fuel conservation would be complete without some reference to the potential of solar gain in the superinsulated house. The double-walled design presents an ideal opportunity to incorporate built-in solar panels. Sandwiched into the outer walls these panels will not give the appearance of retrofited boxes. Panels of 2 or 4' width are attractively coordinated alongside windows or doors to give the appearance of shutters and coordinated glass units. For example, a 4'-wide glass-faced collector can be placed on either or both sides of a 6' sliding patio door. With the

top and bottom coordinated on the same level, the entire complex is trimmed as a unified multiple opening. It gives off the same aesthetic sense of beauty as is achieved with a broad expanse of glass doors or full-length windows.

Orienting the Collector

A solar collector's efficiency is in direct proportion to two factors. One is the length of time that the collector surface is exposed to the sun's rays. The second is the angle of the sun's rays against the collector.

The time-exposure factor will be at its optimum when the collector is facing directly south. The sun will contact a stationary south-facing collector for a longer period than if it were placed facing any other direction. A rotating collector that begins its day facing east and follows the sun's path toward the west is the ultimate concept. This concept can be followed in a limited way by having several collectors facing in different directions. An east-to-southeast exposure will accommodate the morning sun. The southeast-to-south-to-southwest span on the compass will be exposed to the late morning, noon, and early afternoon period. The southwest-exposed collector takes over late in the afternoon. A direct-west exposure is least efficient, as the sun is too far away and beginning its heat shutdown.

The fixed or built-in collector, according to these principles, is most beneficially placed on the south side of a house. Those consumers and builders who are interested in free heat by means of a solar collector will consider the house design and the building site orientation as critical elements of the planning phase. For example, a floor plan may have a limited number of places along the exterior walls where a collector, or more than one, can fit in both aesthetically and functionally. Usually, the longer side of a basically rectangular house will present more expanse for collector location. Once it is determined into which wall of the house the collector(s) will be built, it is possible to specify the required orientation of the lot and its size. When a lot is owned before a house is planned, it will be necessary to design the house around the fixed orientation of the lot. Urban lots will not present the flexibility that is found in most rural plots, where a house is not confined by setback regulations and parallelism requirements. A house in the country can usually be rotated to face the sun to advantage and still blend with its surroundings.

Collector Angle

The angle of the collector to the ground that will be most efficient is when the sun's rays strike the collector surface at 90°. The sun arcs across the sky in such a way that the rays never strike on the same degree line as time passes. The optimum angle for a collector surface is that which matches or is close to the latitude in a specific locality. Many early wall collector designs featured sloping glass

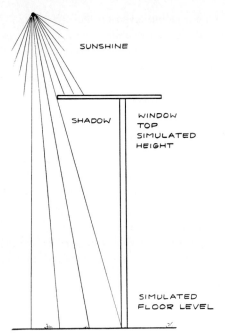

FIGURE 14-33. A quick assessment of the amount of shade on a wall can be made any sunny day of the year by moving a board back and forth across a pole that is about 7′ high (the approximate height from floor to window tops).

walls. The track record of a few years proved the affects of this design to be uncontrollable (*Popular Science*, August 1983, p. 70). The summer heat gain is too great to be turned away with blinds, ventilators, or any other internal mechanism. One such award-winning collector two stories high has been converted to a vertical posture and is working successfully. The principle defies theory but proves out in practice.

The boxed collector does not suffer from the same problem, as it heats through the movement of hot air. In the summer the hot air is vented outdoors. Unlike the direct-gain principle of the glass wall, the boxed collector's registers are shut during nonheating times.

Coordinating the eave overhang will virtually eliminate overheating of the collector itself. The eaves are designed to be long enough to shade the collector completely during the nonheating season. This eave length can be found nontechnically on the longest day of the year, June 20 or 21. Hold a 7′ board in vertical posture. Hold another board horizontally on top of the vertical board. Extend the end of the horizontal board toward due south until its shadow touches the bottom of the vertical board (Fig. 14-33). The horizontal distance that the board extends beyond the upright post will be the required amount of soffit depth above the windows in order to cast shade to the level of the floor. Take the reading at noon when the sun is at its highest point.

This test shows how much eave is needed to eliminate all sun from a collector surface on the longest day of

the year. That is part of the analysis. The object of the collector is to supply heat in the winter. In some latitudes an eave long enough to completely shade a collector to floor level would also shade the top part of it on short winter days.

The problem of determining the collector size of a built-in box-type collector can be approached from several different objectives. Following are two approaches.

1. The eave method starts with a predetermined eave depth. The shadow-line boundaries on the wall are established. The effective collector surface zone will start from the top line (the winter line) and extend to ground level. The effective shade line in summer will be the lower line. The height between these two lines is the optimum height for both collector panels and windows in terms of efficient heat collection in winter and rejection in summer. Where this height does not provide enough square-foot area, the difference may be made up by broadening the collector width. The box is expanded into another stud cavity to make up the loss in height.

2. Another systematic design approach is to design collector sizes and shapes to fit the wall elevation design. Then the eave length is custom coordinated.

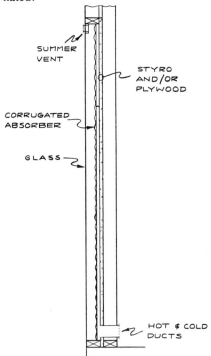

FIGURE 14-34 An integrated solar collector fits conveniently into the outer cavities of a double-walled frame. The black-painted corrugated sheet metal collector catches the sun's rays from all seasonal angles. The collector is vented in the summer.

Some compromise is mandated, as it is rarely possible to have a full-height panel that will be fully exposed in winter and fully shaded in summer. Each day presents a different exposure situation. This is the basic problem to be compromised with all forms of fixed-mount collectors. The most efficient fixed collectors will be those placed in locations not affected by eaves, such as ends of a gable-roofed house or on the roof.

Where the collector is built into the wall in a vertical position (Fig. 14-34), the exposure angle is attained by another means. The vertical collector suffers a little efficiency loss due to the vertical-angle discrepancy. It is regained by the use of corrugated aluminum sheet metal for the absorber. The corrugations are arranged horizontally so that regardless of the angle of the sun, it will play on some part of the curved surface.

Sizing an Integral Collector

The size of the collector relates to the quantity of heat desired. A basic formula for the type being described and illustrated herein will produce enough heat for homes in central and southern belt climates at a rate of 1 square foot of collector surface for 10 square feet of floor area. A 4′ × 8′ collector heats about 300′. There are so many variables, such as R values in walls and ceiling, that it is a difficult task to quote a reliable formula that will meet more than an isolated situation. It is logical, however, that any substantial quantity of heat that can be transferred into a home by the free use of the sun will net a saving over the cost of fossil fuels *if* the initial cost of the collector system is reasonable. Herein lies the feasibility of the collector design being described.

Constructing an Integral Collector

The collector for the double-wall house is basically a passive type although a small amount of electricity is used to power a minifan. Each 2′ cavity between the studs of the outer wall of the double-wall house can be used to form the shell of a collector. From test results it has been found that the use of two cavities side by side provides the most effective module.

The back of the collector is a single sheet, or combination of material sheets, 4′ × 8′ in size. The thickness fills the 3/4″ space between the inner and outer walls. A single sheet of 3/4″ CD-grade plywood works well. In addition to its collector function, it provides an ideal bracing feature to the wall in the same manner as corner-bracing plywood. Another combination of materials is to place a 1/4″ sheet of plywood to form the back of the collector, followed by a 1/2″-thick sheet of Styrofoam. A 3/4″ sheet of foil-backed Styrofoam provides the highest R rating against heat loss when the collector is not functioning.

Details of Construction. Following are the sequential steps to follow when constructing a built-in collector.

1. The first step is to block off an area at the top of the two stud cavities. Two blocks of 2 × 4 stock exactly 22 1/2″ long are required. The blocks are placed at a height that is 3/4″ above the underside of the door and window jambs (not the rough opening but the finish casement jambs). This location permits trimming of the collector to coincide exactly with doors and windows. The blocks should be glued and/or caulked so that the joints are airtight.

2. Next, a long notch is cut in the upper part of the center stud. This notch provides a crossover opening under the absorber through which the warm air moves from one side to the other. The notch is 3/4″ deep by 21″ long. As shown in Fig. 14-35, it starts under the top blocks and goes down the interior side of the center stud.

3. Center and nail an aluminum strip 4″ × 21″ on the interior face of the notch. The aluminum can be 22 gauge or heavier. This strip forms a ledger on which the absorber metal will rest.

4. Nail the plywood back to the collector opening before raising the inner wall. A bead of adhesive is spread around the perimeter of the collector into which the plywood is pressed and then nailed. Give attention to perfect centering of the middle stud throughout its length. Also, the side studs should be exactly half covered by the plywood backboard. If the floor is level, the plywood sheet acts as a squaring device to plumb the wall.

At this stage, work on the collector is discontinued until the house framing is completed and the house is closed in. It is prudent to cover the entire opening with a plastic

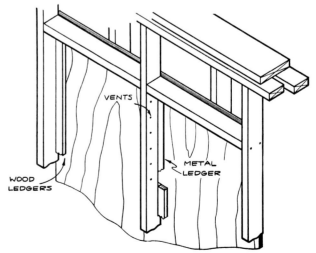

FIGURE 14-35 Notch the center stud, nail on the 4″ × 21″ metal ledger, and glue and nail the back panel on before raising the inner wall.

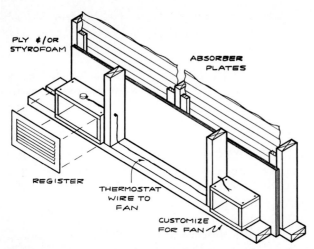

FIGURE 14-36 The inner wall contains the inlet and outlet ducts. The return air goes in one side and up the back side of the absorber, crosses over at the top, and is forced down and out by a mini-fan of 200 cubic feet per minute (CFM) or more. Locate the thermostat to touch some part of the metal absorber.

sheet lapped over the top edge of the plywood to protect it from the weather.

5.   Surround the perimeter of both cavities with a 1 × 2 board laid flat against the plywood back. These pieces can be ripped from stud material at minimum cost. The strips form a ledger for the absorber.

6.   Cut the rectangular openings in the plywood back for the intake and outlet ducts (Fig. 14-36). Make the ducts of wood or metal to fit your register and fan sizes. Install them glue tight.

7.   Cut the corrugated roofing aluminum absorber pieces to the exact distance across each stud cavity (should be 22 1/2"). Clean the metal surface with vinegar or cleaning acid. Nail each piece on the ledger strips (omit nails over the metal ledger at the top of the center stud). Use only enough nails to hold the panels in place until the casing jambs are put in. Start the absorber plates at the bottom, lapping one or two corrugations. Place a heavy bead of latex or silicone on the crest of the lapped corrugation at each joint. After all absorbers are permanently in place, caulk along all the edges around the perimeter of the absorbers to form an airtight seal.

8.   Drill several 3/8- to 1/2"-diameter crossover holes through the upper and lower 16" of the center stud. Center each hole in the area adjacent to the concave corrugation of the absorber.

9.   Glue and nail, or screw a triangular quarter-octagon or quarter-circle piece of 3/4" wood into the upper left corner of the collector and a duplicate in the upper right corner. A 2" hole is drilled through this block to form a summer vent (Fig. 14-37). An automatic control may be installed in this hole or a simple manually operated wood or metal closer can be placed over it with one screw to

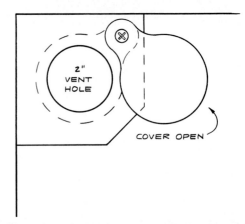

FIGURE 14-37 Exhaust vents are located at the top in one or both corners of the collector.

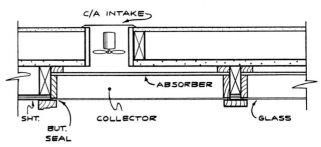

FIGURE 14-38 A top-section view showing how the jambs and casing blend the collector into the architecture while holding the glass front.

pivot on. There will be another duplicate board over the fiberglass (e.g., Filon) cover so that the Filon is sandwiched between them. With hard glass, only one surface board is needed on top of the glass. A corner is cut off the glass where the vent hole is.

10.   Install jamb strips around the inside perimeter of both absorber compartments (Fig. 14-38). These will be 3/4"-thick wood as deep as the distance from the surface of the absorber plates to the sheathing or siding level. These jambs are the nail backing for the exterior trim casing. On a brick- or stone-veneered house, match the depth to that of the windows and doors. A filler strip is required on the center stud to bring its surface to the same plane as the vertical face of the jambs. Reduce the jamb by as much as the thickness of the glass or film.

11.   Paint all the internal surfaces of the collector with a flat-black heat-resistant paint such as Krylon or Rustoleum. Engine manifold or cast-iron stove paint is also suitable.

12.   Install the window cover and casing simultaneously (Fig. 14-39). Have the glass cut to allow a clearance of about 3/16" on all four sides. Block the glass up in the bottom rabbet so that it is centered. Center it horizontally. Hold it in place with triangular putty darts or small nails. Run a continuous bead of butyl or silicone caulk all around the glass in the gap. The junctions should be air-

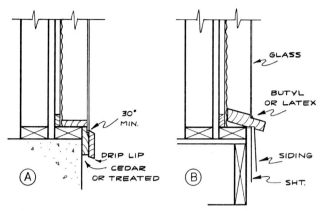

FIGURE 14-39 (a) Built-in collector sill will deflect water as long as the seal holds up; (b) better-quality construction where there is much rain. Both custom sills can be fabricated on a table saw.

tight but made in such a way that the glass can be removed without damage. With real glass, care must be taken not to hit the glass under the trim with a screw. Galvanized or brass screws are a better choice than rustable iron. Although many trouble-free years are possible, there may come a time when it is desirable to remove the glass to repaint the absorber, to clean the glass or to reseal the glass edges, or to replace damaged Filon. Pilot holes are drilled for screws to avoid splitting and to assure that no contact with the glass is made by the screw. An alternative method is to rabbet the casing instead of undercutting the jamb.

The bottom filler board will be rabbeted on its top edge to shed rain. A thin bead of latex is placed along the upper edge of the rabbet to seal the joint against the glass. A noticeable squeeze-out should exist to assure a seal that is free of voids. In very wet areas, a genuine rabbeted sill board is advisable. The rabbeted shoulder rises behind the glass about 1/2". All the trim boards will be set in butyl or window caulk where they contact the glass.

13. Interior completion of the blower and the hot-air register is all that remains to complete the collector. A low-cost adjustable thermostat is installed in the heat duct. A squirrel cage blower or fan, delivering approximately 200 cubic feet per minute or more, is installed in the cold-air return opening. A thermostat and blower may be wired to plug into a duplex externally, or they can be wired internally as for any other permanent electrical fixture in the house. **Full-house heat assisting** is possible by running the heat duct from the collector into the furnace main duct or plenum. The added heat will be a direct subtraction from what the furnace would be called upon to produce. During mild demand times the central service fan can be switched manually to distribute the solar-collected heat throughout the whole house.

Solar heat is a genuine "freebie" in our age of high cost fuels. Solar harnessing is something to be considered by anyone wishing to reduce home heating costs and dependence on utility companies.

HEAT PUMP

No discussion of heating and cooling a residence would be complete without consideration of the heat pump. Unlike furnaces, which derive their energy from gas, oil, or electricity directly, the heat pump takes advantage of nature's elements (at no cost) to assist in cooling or heating. It uses the most constant source that exists, earth temperature. Windmills work only when the wind blows. Solar works only marginally on sunless days and not at all after dark. In winter, when needed most, the nights are longest. The temperature of the earth below a certain surface level maintains a fairly constant temperature. The heat pump extracts this temperature and uses it to temper the air in a home night and day, summer and winter.

The water-to-air type heat pump is the most efficient, due to the constancy of the temperature of groundwater. Air-to-air heat pumps, although more efficient than fossil-fuel air exchangers, suffer from outside temperature variation. As temperatures progressively drop below freezing, the ability of the heat pump to draw warmth from the air diminishes to a point of little use. In the cooling cycle, a parallel effect takes place. As temperatures outdoors increase, the ability of the heat pump to convert hot air to cool air decreases. By contrast, the water-to-air heat pump deals with a temperature variable in the water from about 50° in the north to about 65° in the south. The variation of the earth's temperature, transmitted to earth water, below the frost line, is very small from season to season. Therefore, the water-to-air heat pump ranks at the top of the efficiency and consistency scale as a means of both heating and cooling.

COP

The degree of efficiency is ranked on the basis of 1 kilowatt-hour of electricity. This is called the *coefficient of performance* or COP. A high COP rating is desirable. A low COP translates to high fuel bills. In money terms a dollar's worth of electricity may furnish 3.5 to 4 COP with a water-to-air heat pump, compared to about 2 COP for oil or gas or 1 COP for direct electric heat furnaces. These figures, though general, represent a great saving over a period of years.

The initial cost of a heat pump exceeds conventional fossil-fuel systems by about one and a half to two times. The difference is usually recouped in three to five years. From then on it is pure gain through savings to the homeowner. Should the buyer need additional rationale or motivation, it may also be considered patriotic to use the free sources of energy, thus saving our country's fossil-fuel reserves.

Two Water-to-Air Systems

Closed loop is the name of one design for supplying ground-temperature water to the heat pump. In this system, several hundred feet of plastic pipe are buried below the ground in a looped formation. The loop is placed far enough below the grade line and frost line to be virtually isolated from aboveground temperature extremes. The same clean water is circulated through the loop whenever the heat pump places a demand on it. It is a dependable and constant source of heat and cool transmission.

The open system takes its water directly from a well, a spring-fed pond, or sometimes from a river (river sources are frequently too polluted to use). The water is circulated directly through the pump to cool or warm its coils and is then discharged. It may be dumped into a discharge well at a distance from the drawing well, into a stream, a pond, or used to water the yard or the garden. A combination of these discharge means can be set up with diverting gate valves so that watering potential exists during the growing season and unattended dumping during the winter season.

The water supply must be adequate for the open-loop system. A pond must be deep enough year round to furnish constant-temperature water. A well must have an adequate recovery table rate to supply both domestic and heat pump demands. An artesian well provides an ideal water source.

Comparison of open- and closed-loop systems must take the foregoing characteristics into consideration, as well as the initial cost. A closed-loop system involves much more pipe burying as a rule. The cost of pipe and the labor to bury it will be substantial. On the other hand, the constant nature of the permanent water source trapped in the loop removes all concerns about water supply.

Water-Heating Assistance

An auxiliary benefit of the heat pump is its ability to effect a substantial savings in domestic water heating. Heated water, which normally would be discharged, is utilized to add to the temperature requirements of the water heater, thereby lessening the demands on the conventional water heating source.

REVIEW TOPICS

1. Discuss the pros and cons of each of the three basic conservation types of houses.
2. Explain and discuss the meaning of Btu as applied to housing.
3. Explain the difference and significance between single-pane, double-glazed, and Thermopane glass windows.
4. Explain in detail why a solid wood door with molded and carved panels has such poor insulating characteristics.
5. Describe a compartmented entry, and explain how it saves energy.
6. Explain how each of the following elements is harnessed to provide temperature control in a house: wind, sun, earth, and ground water.
7. Describe the general characteristics of the double-wall house described in detail in this chapter.
8. Describe the fabricated I-beam window header that evolves during double-wall erection when a single piece of plywood forms the header.
9. Describe the designs for a boxed header that may be used for openings from 8 to 12′ and from 12 to 16′.
10. Recite the sequence (the order) of raising the walls of the double-wall design described and illustrated in this chapter.
11. Describe a K brace and explain its use.
12. Explain the reason for staggering nails where a diagonal brace is fastened to a stud or plate.
13. Explain fully a procedure that may make it possible to cut the cost of the stud inventory by 50%.
14. Explain what is meant by layering Styrofoam insulation in the floor joist cavities and how to go about placing all the components.
15. Explain how a stick-built roof will suffer from insulation starvation above the top plates of the exterior wall. Describe the effect of a 100% seat-cut birdsmouth.
16. Describe graphically on paper or chalkboard how a cripple raised truss is built. Describe and illustrate the effects of this design on the frieze board area as related to roof pitch.
17. Describe graphically the method of gaining insulation capacity above the top plates by the extended-lower-chord technique.
18. Describe the plumb-cut chord and wedge block technique of increasing the insulation area.
19. Explain precisely where the webs should be located in a W truss that has an extended lower chord *and* double walls. Use a specific set of dimensions for your example.
20. Explain in detail how to construct an integral solar collector of a two-stud cavity size into a double-walled building.
21. Describe the different types of heat pumps: air to air, closed-loop water, and open-water. State what COP means.

APPENDICES_____

APPENDIX 1   Nails Per Pound

Size	Length (in.)	Common		Box	
		Diameter (in.)	Number per Pound	Diameter (in.)	Number per Pound
4d	1 1/2	.102	316	.083	473
5d	1 3/4	.102	271	.083	406
6d	2	.115	181	.102	236
7d	2 1/4	.115	161	.102	210
8d	2 1/2	.131	106	.115	145
10d	3	.148	69	.127	94
12d	3 1/4	.148	63	.127	88
16d	3 1/2	.165	49	.134	71
20d	4	.203	31	.148	52

APPENDIX 2   Fastening Schedule

Component Joint	Fastener	Number or Spacing
Joist to sill or girder, toenail	8d common	3
Bridging to joist, toenail each end	8d common	2
Sole plate to joist or blocking, face nail	16d common	16″ OC
Top or sole plate to stud, end nailed	16d common	2
Stud to sole plate, toenail	8d common	4
Doubled studs, face nail each side	10d common	24″ OC
Doubled top plates, face nail	10d common	16″ OC
Top plates, laps and intersections, face nail	16d common or 10d common	2 16d or 3 10d
Continuous header, two pieces	10d common	16″ OC along each edge
Ceiling joists to plate, toenail	8d common or 10d box	3 3
Ceiling joists laps over partitions, face nail	16d common or 10d common	3 #16d or 4 #10d
Ceiling joists to parallel rafters, face nail	16d common or 10d common	3 #16d or 4 #10d
Rafter to plate, toenail	8d common or 10d box	3 #8d common or 10d box
1″ brace to each stud and plate, face nail	8d common	2
Built-up corner studs	12d common or 16d sinker	2 per block
Built-up girders and beams of three members	20d common	32″ OC at top and bottom and staggered two ends and at each splice

APPENDIX 2 Fastening Schedule (*cont.*)

Component Joint	Fastener	Number or Spacing
Plywood subflooring		
1/2″	6d common, annular, or spiral thread	6″ OC edges and 10″ OC intermediate
5/8″, 3/4″	8d common or 6d annular or spiral thread	6″ OC edges and 10″ intermediate
1/2″	16-gauge galvanized wire staples, 3/8″ minimum crown	4″ OC edges and 7″ OC intermediate
5/8″	1 5/8″ length	2½″ OC edges and 4″ OC intermediate
Plywood roof and wall sheathing		
1/2″ or less	6d common	6″ OC edges and 12″ OC intermediate
5/8″ or greater	8d common	6″ OC edges and 12″ OC intermediate
1/2″	16-gauge galvanized wire staples, 3/8″ minimum crown; length of 1″ plus plywood thickness	4″ OC edges and 8″ OC intermediate
1/2″ fiberboard sheathing	1½″ galvanized roofing nail, 6d common nail	3″ OC at edges and 6″ OC at other bearings
25/32″ fiberboard sheathing	1 3/4″ galvanized roofing nail, 8d common nail	3″ OC at edges and 6″ OC at other bearings
1/2″ gypsum sheathing	12-gauge 1¼″ large-head corrosion-resistive	4″ OC at edges and 8″ OC at other bearings

Note: Use annular or spiral nails for combination subfloor–underlayment.

APPENDIX 3   Nail Sizes

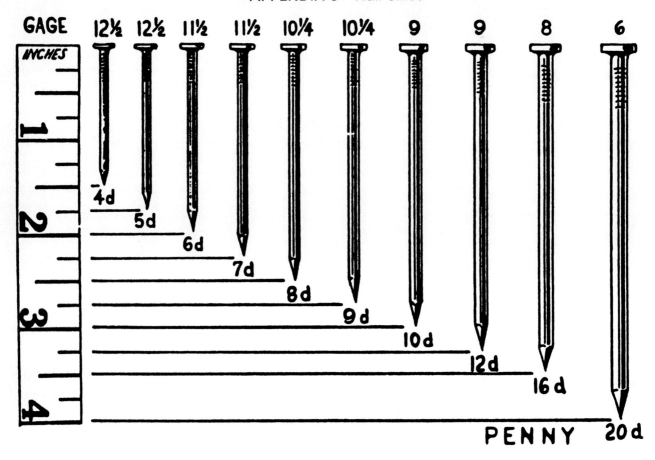

Appendix 4   Maximum Girder Spans (FHA-MPS)

Width of Structure	Girder Size	Supporting Bearing Partition		Non-bearing Partition
		1 story	1 1/2 or 2 Story	
Up to 26′	6 × 8	7′-0″	6′-0″	9′-0″
	8 × 8	9′-0″	7′-6″	11′-6″
	6 × 10	9′-0″	7′-6″	11′-6″
	8 × 10	10′-6″	9′-0″	12′-0″
	6 × 12	10′-6″	9′-0″	12′-0″
26–32′	6 × 8	6′-6″	5′-6″	8′-6″
	8 × 8	8′-0″	7′-0″	10′-6″
	6 × 10	8′-0″	7′-0″	10′-6″
	8 × 10	10′-0″	8′-0″	11′-6″
	6 × 12	10′-0″	8′-0″	11′-6″

APPENDIX 5   Maximum Floor and Ceiling Spans

SOUTHERN FOREST PRODUCTS ASSOCIATION

POST OFFICE BOX 52468
NEW ORLEANS, LOUISIANA 70152
TELEPHONE: AREA CODE 504 - 443-4464

SPANS FOR SOUTHERN PINE ONLY

Spans in the following tables are given in feet and inches of horizontal projection of the clear distance between the support of the member as follows:

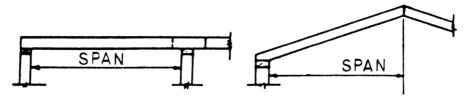

For sloped roofs the actual length of the member is obtained by converting the horizontal span length to the sloped length.

End-jointed lumber may be used interchangeably with solid sawn lumber of the same grade.

▶ Floor Joist Spans for 30 and 40 psf Live Loads, 10 psf Dead Load and 1/360 Deflection Limitation.

Grade		#1 Dense KD		#1 KD		#2 Dense KD		#2 KD		#3 KD	
Size and Spacing	Load PSF	30	40	30	40	30	40	30	40	30	40
2x6	12	12-6	11-4	12-3	11-2	12-0	10-11	11-10	10-9	10-5	9-4
	16	11-4	10-4	11-2	10-2	10-11	9-11	10-9	9-9	9-0	8-1
	24	9-11	9-0	9-9	8-10	9-7	8-8	9-4	8-6	7-4	6-7
2x8	12	16-6	15-0	16-2	14-8	15-10	14-5	15-7	14-2	13-9	12-4
	16	15-0	13-7	14-8	13-4	14-5	13-1	14-2	12-10	11-11	10-8
	24	13-1	11-11	12-10	11-8	12-7	11-5	12-4	11-3	9-9	8-8
2x10	12	21-0	19-1	20-8	18-9	20-3	18-5	19-10	18-0	17-6	15-8
	16	19-1	17-4	18-9	17-0	18-5	16-9	18-0	16-5	15-2	13-7
	24	16-8	15-2	16-5	14-11	16-1	14-7	15-9	14-4	12-5	11-1
2x12	12	25-7	23-3	25-1	22-10	24-8	22-5	24-2	21-11	21-4	19-1
	16	23-3	21-1	22-10	20-9	22-5	20-4	21-11	19-11	18-6	16-6
	24	20-3	18-5	19-11	18-1	19-7	17-9	19-2	·17-5	15-1	13-6

▶ Ceiling Joist Spans for 10[1] and 20[2] psf Live Loads, 10 psf Dead Loads and 1/240 Deflection Limitation.

		10	20	10	20	10	20	10	20	10	20
2x4	12	13-2	10-5	12-11	10-3	12-8	10-0	12-5	9-10	11-6	8-2
	16	11-11	9-6	11-9	9-4	11-6	9-1	11-3	8-11	10-0	7-1
	24	10-5	8-3	10-3	8-1	10-0	8-0	9-10	7-9	8-2	5-9
2x6	12	20-8	16-4	20-3	16-1	19-11	15-9	19-6	15-6	17-0	12-0
	16	18-9	14-11	18-5	14-7	18-1	14-4	17-8	13-9	14-9	10-5
	24	16-4	13-0	16-1	12-5	15-9	12-3	15-6	11-2	12-0	8-6
2x8	12	27-2	21-7	26-9	21-2	26-2	20-10	25-8	20-5	22-5	15-10
	16	24-8	19-7	24-3	19-3	23-10	18-11	23-4	18-1	19-5	13-9
	24	21-7	17-2	21-2	16-5	20-10	16-2	20-5	14-9	15-10	11-3
2x10	12	34-8	27-6	34-1	27-1	33-5	26-6	32-9	26-0	28-8	20-3
	16	31-6	25-0	31-0	24-7	30-5	24-1	29-9	23-1	24-10	17-6
	24	27-6	21-10	27-1	20-11	26-6	20-7	26-0	18-10	20-3	14-4

Note 1.   Load contemplates no attic storage and no future sleeping rooms.
Note 2.   Load contemplates limited access for attic storage and no future sleeping rooms.

APPENDIX 6   Maximum Rafter Spans

Lumber in the S–Dry grade category which is dried to 19% or less moisture content will have spans several inches less than the KD grade which is dried to 15% or less moisture content.

Spans are determined on the same basis as those given in the nationally recognized Span Tables for Joists and Rafters, published by the National Forest Products Association. More detailed span information for Southern Pine can be found in the SFPA Bulletin No. 2 on Maximum Spans for Joists and Rafters.

The conditions of loading are those recognized by HUD, the Model Building Codes and National Association of Home Builders.

Grademarked lumber is recommended and should be identified by the grademark of an agency certified by the Board of Review of the American Lumber Standards Committee.

LUMBER SIZES

Nominal Sizes, Inches	Dressed Sizes, Inches — 19% Max. MC
2 x 4	1½ x 3½
2 x 6	1½ x 5½
2 x 8	1½ x 7¼
2 x 10	1½ x 9¼
2 x 12	1½ x 11¼

▶ Rafter Spans for Any Slope---Drywall Ceiling---20[1] and 30[2] psf Live Load---15 psf Dead Load.

Grade		#1 Dense KD		#1 KD		#2 Dense KD		#2 KD		#3 KD	
Size and Spacing	Load PSF	20	30	20	30	20	30	20	30	20	30
2x6	12	16-4	14-4	16-1	14-1	15-9	13-9	16-3	13-9	12-5	10-6
	16	14-11	13-0	15-8	13-3	15-5	13-1	14-2	11-11	10-9	9-1
	24	13-9	11-8	12-9	10-10	12-7	10-8	11-7	9-9	8-9	7-4
2x8	12	21-7	18-10	21-2	18-6	20-10	18-2	21-6	18-2	16-3	13-3
	16	19-7	17-2	20-8	17-6	20-4	17-3	18-7	15-9	14-2	12-0
	24	18-2	15-4	16-10	14-3	16-7	14-0	15-2	12-10	11-7	9-9
2x10	12	27-6	24-1	27-1	23-8	26-6	23-2	27-5	23-2	20-10	17-7
	16	25-0	21-10	26-4	22-3	25-11	21-11	23-8	20-1	18-0	15-3
	24	23-1	19-6	21-6	18-2	21-2	17-11	19-4	16-5	14-8	12-5
2x12	12	33-6	29-3	32-11	28-9	32-3	28-2	33-4	28-3	25-4	21-5
	16	30-5	26-7	32-0	27-1	31-7	26-8	28-10	24-5	21-11	18-7
	24	28-1	23-9	26-2	22-1	25-9	21-9	23-7	20-0	17-10	15-2

▶ Rafter Spans for Low and High Slopes[3]--- No Ceiling --- 20 psf Live Load --- 10 and 7 psf Dead Load Respectively.

Size and Spacing		Low	High	Low	High	Low	High	Low	High	Low	High
2x4	12		11-6		11-3		11-1		10-10		9-6
	16		10-5		10-3		10-0		9-10		8-3
	24		9-1		8-11		8-9		9-2		6-9
2x6	12	16-4	18-0	16-1	17-8	15-9	17-4	15-6	18-6	13-4	14-1
	16	14-11	16-4	14-7	17-10	14-4	15-9	15-3	16-1	11-7	12-3
	24	13-0	15-8	13-9	14-6	13-7	14-4	12-5	13-2	9-5	10-0
2x8	12	21-7	23-9	21-2	23-4	20-10	22-11	20-5	24-5	17-7	18-7
	16	19-7	21-7	19-3	23-6	18-11	20-10	20-1	21-2	15-3	16-1
	24	17-2	20-8	18-3	19-2	17-11	18-10	16-4	17-4	12-6	13-2
2x10	12	27-6	30-4	27-1	29-9	26-6	29-2	26-0	31-2	22-6	23-8
	16	25-0	27-6	24-7	30-0	24-1	26-6	25-7	27-0	19-5	20-6
	24	21-10	26-3	23-3	24-6	22-10	24-1	20-11	22-0	15-11	16-9
2x12	12	33-6		32-11		32-3		31-8		27-5	
	16	30-5		29-11		29-4		31-2		23-8	
	24	26-7		28-3		27-9		25-5		19-4	

Note 1.   Where there is no snow load of any consequence a minimum of 20 psf live load is anticipated to occur occasionally from construction loads of short duration (7 days) and for design purposes building codes permit a 25% increase in the allowable fiber stress in bending. Such an increase is reflected in the spans.

Note 2.   The 30 psf loading is based on snow loading conditions generally considered by building codes to be of short duration and warrant a 15% increase in allowable fiber stress in bending. Such an increase is reflected in the spans.

Note 3.   Low slope: 3 in 12 or less; high slope: over 3 in 12. Reflects construction load increase (see Note 1.).

APPENDIX 7 Maximum Window and Door Header Spans

WINDOW AND DOOR HEADERS FOR EXTERIOR OPENINGS

Width of structure	Header size (on edge)	* Roof Construction		
		Roof joist with bearing partition, slope 3 in 12 or less / Brace rafters with bearing partition, Slope over 3 in 12	Rafters with bearing partition, Slope over 3 in 12 / Trussed rafters, Slope 3 in 12 or less	Trussed rafters slope over 3 in 12 / Rafters with bearing partition, Habitable space
	1 Story and Second Floor of 2 Story			
Up to 26 feet wide (span)	2 - 2x4s	3' 6"	3' 0"	2' 6"
	2 - 2x6s	6' 6"	5' 0"	4' 6"
	2 - 2x8s	8' 6"	7' 0"	6' 0
	2 - 2x10s	11' 0"	8' 6"	* 8' 0"
	2 - 2x12s	13' 6"	*10' 6"	* 9' 6"
	1½ or 2 Story			
	2 - 2x4s	2' 6"	------	------
	2 - 2x6s	4' 6"	4' 0"	3' 6"
	2 - 2x8s	6' 0"	5' 6"	5' 0"
	2 - 2x10s	7' 6"	* 6' 6"	* 6' 0"
	2 - 2x12s	9' 0"	* 8' 0"	* 7' 6"
	1 Story and Second Floor of 2 Story			
26 to 32 feet wide (span)	2 - 2x4s	3' 0"	2' 6"	------
	2 - 2x6s	6' 0"	4' 6"	4' 0"
	2 - 2x8s	8' 0"	6' 0"	5' 6"
	2 - 2x10s	*10' 0"	* 8' 0"	* 7' 0"
	2 - 2x12s	*12' 0"	* 9' 6"	* 8' 6"
	1½ or 2 Story			
	2 - 2x4s	------	------	------
	2 - 2x6s	4' 0"	3' 6"	3' 6"
	2 - 2x8s	5' 6"	5' 0"	4' 6"
	2 - 2x10s	* 7' 0"	* 6' 0"	* 5' 6"
	2 - 2x12s	* 8' 6"	* 7' 6"	* 7' 0"

Note: The above spans are based on allowable fiber stresses as follows: For 2 x 4s, 800 psi; for 2 x 6s and larger, 1,200 psi. These allowable stresses are average values taking into consideration upgrading for doubling of members. Where 2 x 4s having allowable fiber stress exceeding 800 are used, the spans for 2 x 4s may be increased by 20 percent. Where conditions vary from these assumptions, design the headers in accordance with standard engineering practice.

* **Triple studs at jamb opening; headers to bear on two 2 x 4 trimmers on each side.**

* **The roof construction affects the bearing weight placed on a header. Read the header span maximum in the column under the roof type and pitch (slope). Crossmatch this column with the house width and story height categories.**

APPENDIX 8   Stairway Design (FHA-MPS)

	Private Exterior Stairs (Attached to Dwelling)		Private and Common[a] Interior Stairs	
	Entrance	Basement	Main	Basement
Minimum clear headroom	—	—	6'-8"	6'-4"
Minimum width[b]	2'-8"	2'-8"	2'-8"	2'-8"
Minimum tread[c]	11"	11"	9"	9"
Minimum nosing			d	d
Maximum riser[c,e]	7 1/2"	7 1/2"	8 1/4"	8 1/4"
Winders[e,f]	Run at point 18" from converging end shall not be less than straight portion.			

[a]Stairway serving two living units.
[b]Clear of handrail.
[c]All treads shall be the same width and all risers the same height in a flight of stairs.
[d]Closed riser, 1 1/8" nosing; open riser, 1/2" nosing.
[e]In a building required to be accessible to the physically handicapped, the maximum riser is 7 1/2". Winders or open risers shall not be used in such buildings.
The width of a landing shall be not less than the width of the stairs and its depth shall be not less that 2'-6". The swing of a door opening on a stairway shall not overlap the top step.
[f]Winders are not permitted in common stairs.

APPENDIX 9   Stair Stringer Hypotenuse Tables

9" Unit Run: $a^2 + b^2 = c^2$					
Rise		Square of the Rise, a^2	Square of the Run, b^2	Unit Hypotenuse, c	
Fraction	Decimal			Decimals	Fractions
7"	7	49.	81.	11.40	11 13/32
7 1/16	7.0625	49.88	81.	11.44	11 7/16
7 1/8	7.125	50.77	81.	11.48	11 15/32
7 3/16	7.1875	51.66	81.	11.52	11 1/2
7 1/4	7.25	52.56	81.	11.56	11 9/16
7 5/16	7.3125	53.47	81.	11.60	11 19/32
7 3/8	7.375	54.39	81.	11.64	11 5/8
7 7/16	7.4375	55.32	81.	11.68	11 11/16
7 1/2	7.5	56.25	81.	11.72	11 23/32
7 9/16	7.5625	57.19	81.	11.76	11 3/4
7 5/8	7.625	58.14	81.	11.80	11 25/32
7 11/16	7.6875	59.1	81.	11.84	11 27/32
7 3/4	7.75	60.06	81.	11.88	11 7/8
7 13/16	7.8125	61.04	81.	11.92	11 29/32
7 7/8	7.875	62.02	81.	11.96	11 31/32
7 15/16	7.9375	63.	81.	12.00	12
8	8	64.	81.	12.04	12 1/32

APPENDIX 9   Stair Stringer Hypotenuse Tables (*cont.*)

9 1/8″ Unit Run: $a^2 + b^2 = c^2$					
Rise		Square of the Rise, a^2	Square of the Run, b^2	Unit Hypotenuse, c	
Fraction	Decimal			Decimal	Fraction
7″	7	49.	83.27	11.50	11 1/2
7 1/16	7.0625	49.88	83.27	11.54	11 17/32
7 1/8	7.125	50.77	83.27	11.58	11 9/16
7 3/16	7.1875	51.66	83.27	11.62	11 5/8
7 1/4	7.25	52.56	83.27	11.65	11 21/32
7 5/16	7.3125	53.47	83.27	11.69	11 11/16
7 3/8	7.375	54.39	83.27	11.73	11 23/32
7 7/16	7.4375	55.32	83.27	11.77	11 25/32
7 1/2	7.5	56.25	83.27	11.81	11 13/16
7 9/16	7.5625	57.19	83.27	11.85	11 27/32
7 5/8	7.625	58.14	83.27	11.89	11 7/8
7 11/16	7.6875	59.1	83.27	11.93	11 15/16
7 3/4	7.75	60.06	83.27	11.97	11 31/32
7 13/16	7.8125	61.04	83.27	12.01	12
7 7/8	7.875	62.02	83.27	12.05	12 1/16
7 15/16	7.9375	63.	83.27	12.09	12 3/32
8	8	64.	83.27	12.14	12 1/8

9 1/4″ Unit Run: $a^2 + b^2 = c^2$					
Rise		Square of the Rise, a^2	Square of the Run, b^2	Unit Hypotenuse, c	
Fraction	Decimal			Decimal	Fraction
7″	7	49.	85.56	11.60	11 19/32
7 1/16	7.0625	49.88	85.56	11.64	11 5/8
7 1/8	7.125	50.77	85.56	11.68	11 11/16
7 3/16	7.1875	51.66	85.56	11.71	11 23/32
7 1/4	7.25	52.56	85.56	11.75	11 3/4
7 5/16	7.3125	53.47	85.56	11.79	11 25/32
7 3/8	7.375	54.39	85.56	11.83	11 13/16
7 7/16	7.4375	55.32	85.56	11.87	11 7/8
7 1/2	7.5	56.25	85.56	11.91	11 29/32
7 9/16	7.5625	57.19	85.56	11.95	11 15/16
7 5/8	7.625	58.14	85.56	11.99	12
7 11/16	7.6875	59.1	85.56	12.03	12 1/32
7 3/4	7.75	60.06	85.56	12.07	12 1/16
7 13/16	7.8125	61.04	85.56	12.11	12 3/32
7 7/8	7.875	62.02	85.56	12.15	12 5/32
7 15/16	7.9375	63.	85.56	12.19	12 3/16
8	8	64.	85.56	12.23	12 7/32

APPENDIX 9   Stair Stringer Hypotenuse Tables (*cont.*)

9 3/8" Unit Run: $a^2 + b^2 = c^2$					
Rise		Square of the Rise, a^2	Square of the Run, b^2	**Unit Hypotenuse, c**	
Fraction	Decimal			Decimal	Fraction
7″	7	49.	87.89	11.70	11 11/16
7 1/16	7.0625	49.88	87.89	11.74	11 3/4
7 1/8	7.125	50.77	87.89	11.78	11 25/32
7 3/16	7.1875	51.66	87.89	11.81	11 13/16
7 1/4	7.25	52.56	87.89	11.85	11 27/32
7 5/16	7.3125	53.47	87.89	11.89	11 7/8
7 3/8	7.375	54.39	87.89	11.93	11 15/16
7 7/16	7.4375	55.32	87.89	11.97	11 31/32
7 1/2	7.5	56.25	87.89	12.01	12
7 9/16	7.5625	57.19	87.89	12.05	12 1/32
7 5/8	7.625	58.14	87.89	12.08	12 3/32
7 11/16	7.6875	59.1	87.89	12.12	12 1/8
7 3/4	7.75	60.06	87.89	12.16	12 5/32
7 13/16	7.8125	61.04	87.89	12.20	12 3/16
7 7/8	7.875	62.02	87.89	12.24	12 1/4
7 15/16	7.9375	63.	87.89	12.28	12 9/32
8	8	64.	87.89	12.32	12 5/6

9 1/2" Unit Run: $a^2 + b^2 = c^2$					
Rise		Square of the Rise, a^2	Square of the Run, b^2	**Unit Hypothenuse, c**	
Fraction	Decimal			Decimal	Fraction
7″	7	49.	90.25	11.80	11 13/16
7 1/16	7.0625	49.88	90.25	11.84	11 27/32
7 1/8	7.125	50.77	90.25	11.87	11 7/8
7 3/16	7.1875	51.66	90.25	11.91	11 29/32
7 1/4	7.25	52.56	90.25	11.95	11 15/16
7 5/16	7.3125	53.47	90.25	11.99	12
7 3/8	7.375	54.39	90.25	12.03	12 1/32
7 7/16	7.4375	55.32	90.25	12.07	12 1/16
7 1/2	7.5	56.25	90.25	12.10	12 3/32
7 9/16	7.5625	57.19	90.25	12.14	12 1/8
7 5/8	7.625	58.14	90.25	12.18	12 3/16
7 11/16	7.6875	59.1	90.25	12.22	12 7/32
7 3/4	7.75	60.06	90.25	12.26	12 1/4
7 13/16	7.8125	61.04	90.25	12.30	12 9/32
7 7/8	7.875	62.02	90.25	12.34	12 11/32
7 15/16	7.9375	63.	90.25	12.38	12 3/8
8	8	64.	90.25	12.42	12 13/32

APPENDIX 9   Stair Stringer Hypotenuse Tables (*cont.*)

9 5/8″ Unit Run: $a^2 + b^2 = c^2$					
Rise		Square of the Rise, a^2	Square of the Run, b^2	Unit of Hypotenuse, c	
Fraction	Decimal			Decimal	Fraction
7″	7	49.	92.64	11.90	11 29/32
7 1/16	7.0625	49.88	92.64	11.94	11 15/16
7 1/8	7.125	50.77	92.64	11.98	11 31/32
7 3/16	7.1875	51.66	92.64	12.01	12
7 1/4	7.25	52.56	92.64	12.05	12 1/16
7 5/16	7.3125	53.47	92.64	12.09	12 3/32
7 3/8	7.375	54.39	92.64	12.13	12 1/8
7 7/16	7.4375	55.32	92.64	12.16	12 5/32
7 1/2	7.5	56.25	92.64	12.20	12 3/16
7 9/16	7.5625	57.19	92.64	12.24	12 1/4
7 5/8	7.625	58.14	92.64	12.28	12 9/32
7 11/16	7.6875	59.1	92.64	12.32	12 5/16
7 3/4	7.75	60.06	92.64	12.36	12 11/32
7 13/16	7.8125	61.04	92.64	12.40	12 13/32
7 7/8	7.875	62.02	92.64	12.44	12 7/16
7 15/16	7.9375	63.	92.64	12.48	12 15/32
8	8	64.	92.64	12.52	12 1/2

9 3/4″ Unit Run: $a^2 + b^2 = c^2$					
Rise		Square of the Rise, a^2	Square of the Run, b^2	Unit Hypothenuse, c	
Fraction	Decimal			Decimal	Fraction
7″	7	49.	95.06	12.	12
7 1/16	7.0625	49.88	95.06	12.04	12 1/32
7 1/8	7.125	50.77	95.06	12.08	12 1/16
7 3/16	7.1875	51.66	95.06	12.11	12 1/8
7 1/4	7.25	52.56	95.06	12.15	12 5/32
7 5/16	7.3125	53.47	95.06	12.19	12 3/16
7 3/8	7.375	54.39	95.06	12.23	12 7/32
7 7/16	7.4375	55.32	95.06	12.26	12 1/4
7 1/2	7.5	56.25	95.06	12.30	12 5/16
7 9/16	7.5625	57.19	95.06	12.34	12 11/32
7 5/8	7.625	58.14	95.06	12.38	12 3/8
7 11/16	7.6875	59.1	95.06	12.42	12 13/32
7 3/4	7.75	60.06	95.06	12.45	12 7/16
7 13/16	7.8125	61.04	95.06	12.49	12 1/2
7 7/8	7.875	62.02	95.06	12.53	12 17/32
7 15/16	7.9375	63.	95.06	12.57	12 9/16
8	8	64.	95.06	12.61	12 19/32

APPENDIX 9   Stair Stringer Hypotenuse Tables (*cont.*)

9 7/8″ Unit Run: $a^2 + b^2 = c^2$					
Rise		Square in the Rise, a^2	Square in the Run, b^2	Unit Hypotenuse, c	
Fraction	Decimal			Decimal	Fraction
7″	7	49.	97.52	12.10	12 3/32
7 1/16	7.0625	49.88	97.52	12.14	12 1/8
7 1/8	7.125	50.77	97.52	12.18	12 3/16
7 3/16	7.1875	51.66	97.52	12.21	12 7/32
7 1/4	7.25	52.56	97.52	12.25	12 1/4
7 5/16	7.3125	53.47	97.52	12.29	12 9/32
7 3/8	7.375	54.39	97.52	12.33	12 5/16
7 7/16	7.4375	55.32	97.52	12.36	12 3/8
7 1/2	7.5	56.25	97.52	12.40	12 13/32
7 9/16	7.5625	57.19	97.52	12.44	12 7/16
7 5/8	7.625	58.14	97.52	12.48	12 15/32
7 11/16	7.6875	59.1	97.52	12.51	12 1/2
7 3/4	7.75	60.06	97.52	12.55	12 9/16
7 13/16	7.8125	61.04	97.52	12.59	12 19/32
7 7/8	7.875	62.02	97.52	12.63	12 5/8
7 15/16	7.9375	63.	97.52	12.67	12 21/32
8	8	64.	97.52	12.71	12 23/32

10″ Unit Run: $a^2 + b^2 = c^2$					
Rise		Square of the Rise, a^2	Square of the Run, b^2	Unit Hypotenuse, c	
Fraction	Decimal			Decimal	Fraction
7″	7	49.	100	12.21	12 7/32
7 7/16	7.0625	49.88	100	12.24	12 1/4
7 1/8	7.125	50.77	100	12.28	12 9/32
7 3/16	7.1875	51.66	100	12.32	12 5/16
7 1/4	7.25	52.56	100	12.35	12 11/32
7 5/16	7.3125	53.47	100	12.39	12 3/8
7 3/8	7.375	54.39	100	12.43	12 7/16
7 7/16	7.4375	55.32	100	12.46	12 15/32
7 1/2	7.5	56.25	100	12.50	12 1/2
7 9/16	7.5625	57.19	100	12.54	12 17/32
7 5/8	7.625	58.14	100	12.58	12 9/16
7 11/16	7.6875	59.1	100	12.61	12 5/8
7 3/4	7.75	60.06	100	12.65	12 21/32
7 13/16	7.8125	61.04	100	12.69	12 11/16
7 7/8	7.875	62.02	100	12.73	12 23/32
7 15/16	7.9375	63.	100	12.77	12 3/4
8	8	64.	100	12.81	12 13/16

APPENDIX 10   Heating Zone Map and Insulation Ratings

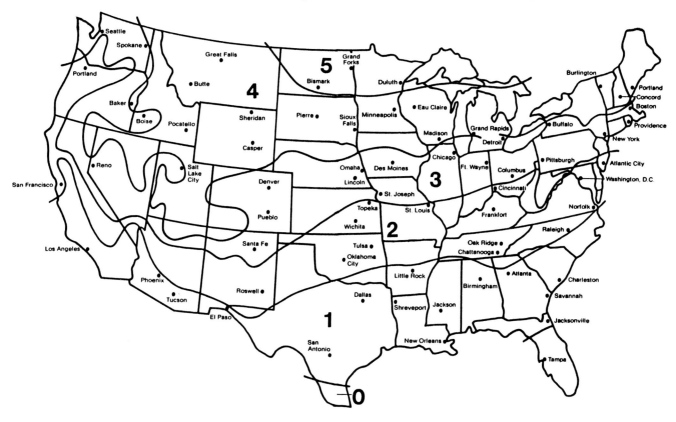

Recommended R-Values			
Heating Zone	Attic Floors	Exterior Walls	Ceilings Over Unheated Crawl Space or Basement
1	R-26	R-Value of full wall	R-11
2	R-26	insulation, which is	R-13
3	R-30	3½" thick, will depend	R-19
4	R-33	on material used.	R-22
5	R-38	Range is R-11 to R-13.	R-22
Source: U.S. Department of Energy			

R-Values Chart					
	Batts or Blankets		Loose Fill (Poured In)		
	glass fiber	rock wool	glass fiber	rock wool	cellulosic fiber
R-11	3½"–4"	3"	5"	4"	3"
R-13	4"	4½"	6"	4½"	3½"
R-19	6"–6½"	5¼"	8"–9"	6"–7"	5"
R-22	6½"	6"	10"	7"–8"	6"
R-26	8"	8½"	12"	9"	7"–7½"
R-30	9½"–10½"	9"	13"–14"	10"–11"	8"
R-33	11"	10"	15"	11"–12"	9"
R-38	12"–13"	10½"	17"–18"	13"–14"	10"–11"

APPENDIX 11   Heating Degree-Days

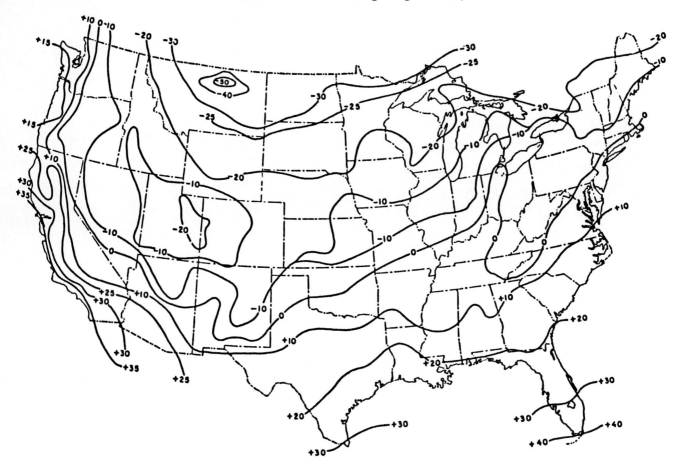

APPENDIX 12   Sun-Angle Chart and Eaves Chart

The sun's rays strike the earth at different times of day. Measure on your plan or house the number of feet the south windows extend below the eave of the roof or horizontal overhang. This measurement is the shadow height. Then for that specific latitude and shadow height, you will find, from the table given here, the exact width of overhang needed. For example, in a latitude of 35° and for a shadow height of 5', the width of overhang needed is 3'.

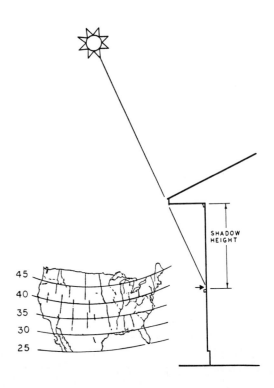

North Latitude (deg)	Shadow Height (ft)					
	3	4	5	6	7	8
	Width of Overhang (ft)					
25	1.1	1.5	1.9	2.2	2.6	3.0
30	1.4	1.9	2.4	2.9	3.4	3.8
35	1.8	2.4	3.0	3.5	4.1	4.7
40	2.1	2.8	3.6	4.3	5.0	5.7
45	2.6	3.4	4.3	5.1	6.0	6.8
50	3.0	4.1	5.1	6.1	7.1	8.2

APPENDIX 13   Solar Heater Specifications

MATERIAL SPECIFICATIONS FOR THE DOUBLE-WALL INTEGRAL SOLAR HEATER

- Panel backing should be exterior-grade plywood or other exterior-grade material.
- Lumber should be No. 2 or better, free of knots, checks, splits, or other openings.
- Fasteners should be galvanized or rust resistant.
- Absorber should be either aluminum or galvanized and free of rust or oxidation.
- Absorber paint should be able to withstand temperatures up to 200°F.
- Silicone caulk should be used to make a formed-in-place gasket for an airtight seal where absorber fastens to frame.
- Glazing should be ultraviolet treated if fiberglass is used. Glass should be tempered.
- Squirrel cage blower should be sized to provide 3 cubic feet per minute per square foot of panel at 1/2″ static pressure.
- Thermostat should be weathertight and operate between 85 and 115°F. Adjustable thermostats within the same temperature range can be used.
- All wiring should be in accordance with safe practices and building codes.
- Ducting should be airtight and of suitable material.
- Aluminum nails or fasteners should be used when aluminum absorber materials are used.

Where to Obtain Materials For Your Solar Heater

- Plywood, lumber, wood glue, nails, screws, paint, caulk, corrugated metal, metal for the panel edge and absorber support, electric wire, floor register, and insulation board are all available at local hardware, building supply, or lumber stores. Shop around, as prices vary greatly.
- Try your grocery store for vinegar for cleaning the absorber.
- Sears sells Filon glazing. Some building supply stores also stock Filon.
- Surplus Center, P.O. Box 82209, Lincoln, NB 68501 sells a 200CFM blower for $14 plus shipping. Ask for their catalog (price subject to change).
- Many hardware stores carry Grainger catalog equipment. Stock No. 4C006 blower (200CFM) is available, as are many other larger blowers for larger solar air panels. Also available from Grainger is a remote bulb thermostat No. 2E206. But a better bargain is Grainger's automatic Snapdisc control No. 2E245.
- Temp-Vents and Temp-Valves are available from Solar Usage Now, Box 306, Bascon, OH 44809 or Solar Components Division of Kalwall, P.O. Box 237, Manchester, NH 03105. Both companies offer good-quality solar equipment catalogs worth having.

APPENDIX 14   Thermal Sales Prospectus

The following prospectus is included to illustrate the author's conception and example of a truly thermally designed and constructed house at a competitive cost.

THERMAL PROSPECTUS

The idea of a superinsulated dwelling is not new. However, until recently there was a "con" factor called cost-effectiveness which made it less desirable in some areas. Universal air conditioning and the present cost of energy fuels now make the super insulation concept not only feasible but extremely practical. It presents the owner with a realistic bonus in the future as fuel costs continue to rise.

- "Doub L Wall," as designer Hop's house is called, features an outer and inner exterior wall of 2 × 4 studs separated by a 1″ nominal core.

- The core contains all the electrical wiring in such a way that no holes are drilled through the studs.
- The core also contains diagonal wind bracing continuously throughout the perimeter of the house frame. This creates a super-rigid wall with far greater potential to withstand hurricane- and cyclone-type storms.
- Superinsulation in the nominal 8" cavity wall is attained by installing two layers of fiberglass. The first layer is placed next to the exterior, followed by the wiring.
- Infiltration is nil with the second layer of insulation in place in the inner wall. The outer wall studs are on 2' spacing. The inner wall studs are also on 2' spacing but staggered to the center of the outer studs. In this way all joints between studs and insulation are lapped by the other layer.
- Street noise is minimized. The extra insulation is an effective sound deadener.
- The R value in the double wall is about 25 with 1/2" blackboard sheathing.
- Window and door headers are of double-box I-beam design. The pocketed cavities contain full insulation, a great improvement over conventional header areas.
- Attic insulation is also formed by double layering. The R value is 38.
- An extended roof truss yields a higher insulation capability over the wall top plates.
- The attic access is a lightweight box of 12" depth filled with insulation.
- The 36" attic fan is centrally located in a corridor to expel unwanted heat or humidity. A complete change of air can be effected in a few minutes by opening a window in each room a couple of inches while running the fan.
- Venting the attic takes place at all times without power, turbines, or scuppers to mar the roof appearance. Full-length eave venting and full-length ridge venting are at work constantly.
- Thermopane windows with storms (triple glass) complement the conservation theme of the wall and ceiling design. Vinyl clad with snap-on grids, there is never a need for painting. Glass cleaning is made easy. All windows are screened.

- The front door is of steel thermal design with insulating double-glass window lights.
- The 6' patio door is vinyl clad with Thermopane glass.
- A ceiling fan hangs from the peak of the cathedral ceiling to circulate the rising air in the spacious open zone of the living and dining area.
- Underfloor insulation is rated at R-19. Foundation vents allow condensation to escape.
- Superinsulation conclusions: There have been no problems with the "too tight" or "needs to breathe" theory so frequently heard. Both the main entrance and the secondary entrance are of the vestibule, "compartmented" type, so the loss or gain of heat or cool is minimized. The house is built tight to be draft free and infiltration proof. Every cavity is fully insulated, including the stud wall corner posts and partition intersections. Comparative studies rank this design in the same class with earth shelters for thermal retention.
- Construction costs, including all the features above, are comparable with a conventional 6" walled house due to complete modular synchronization of materials, dimensions, and methods.

Other Features

- Deep window sills present an ideal location for flowers. A small build-out can turn the picture window into a window seat.
- Backer boards are placed behind the wallboard to the right and left of all windows in the area where drapes or valances are mounted. No nails or screws will pull out from the weight of the drapes.
- Abundant wiring for electrical needs is provided. Duplex outlets are reachable from not more than 6' away from any spot along a wall. Six cable-TV plug-ins are in the various rooms. Several telephone jacks are internally wired into convenient locations.
- Kitchen appliances include a range, refrigerator, dishwasher, disposer, compactor, and microwave.
- Bathroom features include a 5' lavatory, a fiberglass shower tub and color-matched

water closet, a heater/vent/light ceiling fixture, fluorescent mirror light, and a generous linen closet. This centrally located bathroom services the two internal bedrooms.

- The master bedroom boasts a segmented privacy room, lavatory, and shower area. There are two large closets, one a walk-in.
- The cathedral ceiling rises over the entire living room/dining and kitchen area. Light and ventilation pass over the partition wall that furnishes the backstop for 12' of the 24' of linear cabinet and counter space. A 4' pass-through and a fold-up counter tabletop provide a snack or breakfast nook from which to watch the living room TV.
- Central vacuum cleaning provides access to all corners of the house via baseboard

hose plug-ins. The collection unit is located in the garage for convenient servicing and noise-segregated operation.

- A woodburning stove is centrally located to furnish a major part of the required heat. An auxiliary furnace is closeted off the corridor. Cool air is provided via built-in fans and air conditioning.
- The construction method is adaptable to any house design. Little or no builder reeducation is needed other than a review of the blueprint details.
- Construction throughout meets and exceeds local, state, and FHA minimum standard building codes.
- Designed and built by a certified and licensed contractor.

APPENDIX 15   Sample Quality Sales Promotion

SAMPLE SALES BROCHURE

Following is a sample of a sales brochure listing documented features of a well-constructed house. Documentation is effectively caught on color films at the time each feature is exposed during construction. Include some identifying feature of the lot or surroundings to verify that the photos are those of a specific house. This house contains the following quality features:

Steel-Reinforced Full Perimeter Footing

- Continuous 24"-wide footing and 8" foundation wall, including under the attached garage door opening
- Interior footing under the main bearing wall
- Three continuous 1/2" steel reinforcing rods: bent around corners, staggered end lap joints, double tight wired, controlled suspension level

All Concrete Slabs Steel Reinforced

- Continuous and tied steel grid in the house slab, the front porch, the driveway, and the garage

Insulation Ground Barrier

- Twenty-four-inch-wide Styrofoam perimeter thermal barrier between the floor and the earth and the foundation wall; no conductivity areas to lose heat

Insulated Attached Garage

- Walls insulated to R-16 value

Insulated for Thermo Saving

- House walls insulation sheathed
- Full cavity of blanket insulation with vapor barrier
- Ceiling with over 10" of cellulose, for an R-40 rating

Ventilation Features

- Full-length soffit vents to ensure air current movement up and out of ridge vent
- Full-length ridge vent

Designer Overhangs

- Large overhangs provide needed shade and protection from the sun's rays in summer and let the sun in during the cold months of winter

Triple-Pane Windows

- Thermo double-pane windows plus storms and screens; the ultimate in heat and cool saving

Insulated Doors

- All exterior doors of insulated core type and fireproof steel
- Combination storm and screen doors, all exterior entrances

Interior Sound Barrier

- Sound-barrier insulation between bathrooms, garage, and living areas

Strategic Cable-TV Outlets

- Six outlets wired in strategic areas

Solid Wall Backers

- Wood, nail, and screw backing in all areas where curtain rods are attached: behind towel bar areas, closet rungs, bookcases, and shelf brackets; backed drywall joints; recessed end joints

High-Quality Framing Features

- Passes or exceeds all known codes
- Framed gable overhangs with cantilevered ladder lookouts
- Steel tornado ties holding roof securely to walls, walls to floor, and floor to foundation
- Roof sheathing clips reduce flexibility and strengthen the surface

The features listed here are for the information of the discriminating buyer and homeowner. Most of the important structural components are covered from view after completion of the house. We document our high-quality construction as it occurs with photographs, so that you, the prospective consumer, can see for yourself what has gone into your life's largest purchase.

Glossary

A

Actual size Finished (dressed) size of lumber or real size of masonry unit.

Aggregate The sand and stone components of concrete.

Air-dried lumber Lumber that has been stacked to permit air to circulate around each piece to dry it.

Airway A space between roof insulation and roof boards for movement of air.

Anchor bolts Bolts embedded in a masonry foundation or slab to which the sole plate of a wall is attached.

Apron The flat member of the inside trim of a window placed against the wall immediately beneath the stool. Also, a sloping concrete approach to a garage door.

Architect's scale A triangular measuring tool with 11 scales, one of which is a full-sized ruler.

Asphalt A residue from evaporated petroleum. It is insoluble in water but soluble in gasoline and melts when heated. Used widely in building for waterproofing roof coverings of many types, exterior wall coverings, flooring tile, and the like.

Asphalt impregnated Saturated throughout with asphalt waterproofing solution.

Attic access (scuttle) A passageway opening through a ceiling into the attic.

Attic ventilators Screened openings provided to ventilate an attic space. *See also* Louver.

Awning window A single-section window hinged at the top which opens out.

B

Backfill To replace excavated earth into a trench around and against a basement foundation.

Balloon framing *See* Framing, balloon.

Bands Headers around the house at the ends of joists to form a box floor frame.

Base or baseboard A trim board on the bottom face of a wall around a room next to the floor.

Base shoe Molding used next to the floor on interior baseboard. Sometimes called carpet strip.

Batten Narrow strips of wood used to cover joints or as decorative vertical members over plywood or wide boards.

Batter board One of a pair of horizontal boards nailed to posts set at the corners of an excavation. Used to indicate outlines of foundation walls with string lines.

Beam A structural member horizontally supporting a load; A girder.

Bearing capacity The maximum capacity of a structural member to support a load.

Bearing partition A partition that supports a vertical load in addition to its own weight.

Bearing point The point where a surface takes on the support of a load.

Bearing wall A wall that supports a vertical load in addition to its own weight.

Bed molding A molding in an angle, as between the overhanging cornice, or eaves, of a building and the sidewalls.

Bevel An angled edge or end from one surface to the opposite surface.

Bituminous coat An asphalt (tar) product for waterproofing masonry walls.

Blind nailing Nailing in such a way that the nailheads are not visible on the face of the work, usually at the tongue of matched boards.

Block bridge A solid block placed between two joists to stiffen them.

Board *See* Lumber, boards.

Bolster A short horizontal timber or steel beam on top of a column to support and decrease the span of beams or girders.

Bonded Attached with masonry mortar or cement.

Bonded shim A spacer fastened in place with mortar (or adhesive).

Bowed board The flat side of a board which curves lengthwise.

Boxed header A fabricated header of dimension members and plywood glued and nailed together.

Brace An inclined piece of framing lumber applied to wall or floor to stiffen the structure. Often used on walls as temporary bracing until framing has been completed.

Brick ledge A masonry bearing surface to accommodate brick. Part of a foundation wall.

Brick tie A small, galvanized, corrugated (or rippled) strip of metal to tie hollow-core masonry walls together and to tie veneer brick to frame walls.

Brick veneer A facing of brick laid adjacent to sheathing of a frame wall or tile wall construction.

Bridging Small wood or metal members that are inserted in a diagonal position between the floor joists at midspan to act as floor stiffeners.

Building paper Asphalt- or resin-saturated paper ("felt") used for floor, siding, and shingle underlayment to block moisture and infiltration.

Built-up girder A beam assembled from individual pieces of dimension lumber.

Built-up roof A roofing composed of three to five layers of asphalt felt laminated with coal tar, pitch, or asphalt. The top is finished with crushed slag or gravel. Generally used on flat or low-pitched roofs.

Butt joint The junction where the ends of two timbers or other members meet in a square-cut joint.

Buttress A supportive pilaster bonded to a wall.

C

Cabinet soffits A boxed-in framework above upper cabinets.

Callout A short notation with an arrow leader pointing to a detail on a drawing.

Cantilever A structural member or component system that overhangs it bearing support.

Cap block (cored) An 8″ × 8″ × 16″ block with a closed top surface. It has three dome-shaped cavities to reduce weight.

Cap block (solid) A 4″ × 8″ × 16″ solid block for capping walls. Also used as a termite-protection course below grade.

Carriage *See* Stair carriage.

Casement frames and sash Frames of wood or metal enclosing a sash, which may be opened by means of hinges affixed to the vertical edges.

Casement window A window hinged at the side.

Casing Molding of various widths and thicknesses used to trim door and window openings at the jambs.

Ceiling backer A board nailed to the top of an upper plate which overhangs the edges to provide a surface to which ceiling material is nailed.

Center line A narrow line with short and long dashes showing the center of an object or location.

Chalkline A string saturated with chalk used to mark long, straight lines.

Checking Fissures that appear with age in many exterior paint coatings, at first superficial, but which in time may penetrate entirely through the coating.

Chords The ceiling joists and rafter members of a roof truss.

Clamp A device for holding objects tightly together. Handscrews, bar clamps, and C clamps are handy types in construction.

Clear span The *actual* span between, and not supported by, bearing points.

Collar beam A horizontal board connecting opposite roof rafters in the upper third of the rafter triangle.

Column A supporting post of wood or steel.

Combination doors or windows Self-storing or removable glass and screen in a seasonally convertible exterior protective door.

Composition shingles *See* Shingles, composition.

Compression stress A stress that is pressing together (or down).

Condensation In a building: Beads or drops of water (and frequently frost in extremely cold weather) that accumulate on the inside of the exterior covering of a building when warm, moisture-laden air from the interior reaches a point where the temperature no longer permits the air to sustain the moisture it holds.

Construction, frame A type of construction in which the structural parts are wood or depend on a wood frame for support.

Conventional roof framing A stick-built method of assembling a roof, one piece at a time.

Coped joint A cut on the end of a piece of molding which mates it to the face contour of a piece it butts perpendicularly at an internal corner. *See also* Scribing.

Corbel out To build out one or more courses of brick or stone from the face of a wall, to form a support for timbers. A chimney may be corbeled to change its vertical direction.

Corner bead A strip of formed sheet metal, placed on external corners of gypsum drywall or plaster lath before plastering, to reinforce them.

Corner block (a) A standard-size concrete block with a solid end (uncupped end). (b) A block of 2 × 4 nailed to the lower end of a stud corner post in a frame wall to provide a nail backing for baseboard.

Corner boards Used as trim for the external corners of a house or other frame structure against which the ends of the siding are finished.

Corner braces Diagonal braces at the corners of frame structure to stiffen and strengthen the wall.

Corner post An assembly of studs and blocks to form nailing surfaces on the inside and outside of a wall frame corner.

Cornice Overhang of a pitched roof at the eave line, usually consisting of a facia board, a soffit for a closed cornice, and appropriate moldings.

Cornice return The portion of the cornice that returns on the gable end of a roof overhang.

Corridor kitchen A kitchen with parallel cabinets on opposite walls with a traffic pattern running through.

Counterflashing A flashing usually used around chimneys above the roofline to cover shingle flashing and prevent moisture entry.

Course Any single layer or row of material units (bricks, blocks, shingles, etc.).

Cove Molding A molding with a curved concave face used as trim to finish interior corners.

Crawl space A shallow space below the living quarters of a basementless house, normally enclosed by a foundation wall.

Cricket A small drainage-diverting roof structure of single or double slope placed at the junction of the common roof and the upper side of a chimney; a saddle.

Cripple stud Short studs above or below a window opening (any stud less than full length).

Crooked board A board curved lengthwise on its edge.

Cross-bridging Diagonal bracing between adjacent floor joists, placed near the center of the joist span to prevent joists from twisting and to stiffen the floor.

Crown Placing a board or plank in position with the convex edge or side up.

Crown molding A molding used on a cornice or wherever an internal horizontal corner is to be covered (between the wall top and the ceiling).

Crushed stone Stone that has been crushed and sorted into uniform sizes.

Cubic yard A standard measurement of wet concrete (27 cubic feet).

Cul-de-sac A dead-end street with a circular turnaround at the end.

Cupola A hip- or gable-roofed four-sided ventilator on the ridge of a roof.

Cupped board A warped board that is curved across its width.

Curtain wall A nonbearing wall that protects from the elements of weather.

Cut-in-brace A diagonal brace that is recessed into the studs and plates flush with the frame surface.

D

Dado A rectangular groove across the width of a board or plank.

Dead load The weight of materials that are nonmovable (static) after construction.

Decay Disintegration of wood or other substance through the action of fungi.

Deck sheating Sheating on floor or roof. *See also* Sheathing.

Dimension *See* Lumber, dimension.

Dimension lines A narrow line with figures telling the size of something or distance between two points.

Direct nailing To nail perpendicular to the initial surface or to the junction of the pieces joined. Also termed *face nailing*.

Distribution panel An auxiliary breaker or fuse box at a distance from the main service entrance.

Door header A lintel above a door to channel the bearing weight of the roof onto the trimmer studs.

Doorjamb, interior The surrounding case into which and out of which a door closes and opens. It consists of two upright pieces, called side jambs, and a horizontal head jamb.

Dormer An opening in a sloping roof, the framing of which projects out to form a vertical wall suitable for windows or other openings.

Double-acting door A door that swings two ways into both adjoining rooms.

Double-hung window A window where the top and bottom sections move up and down.

Double plate Two-piece, upper horizontal member of a frame wall, tying partitions and walls together.

Double wired Attaching lapped ends of rerods together in two places with wire.

Downspout A pipe, usually of sheet metal, for carrying rainwater from roof gutters to a suitable drain.

Drain tile Underground piping used to carry off unwanted water. Synthetic or vitreous clay material.

Dressed and matched (tongue and groove) Boards or planks machined in such a manner that there is a groove on one edge and a corresponding tongue on the other.

Dressed lumber Lumber that has been planed.

Drip (a) A member of a cornice or other horizontal exterior-finish course that has a projection beyond the other parts for carrying off water. (b) A groove in the underside of a sill or drip cap to cause water to drop off on the outer edge instead of convecting back and running down the face of the building.

Drip cap A molding placed on the exterior top side of a door or window frame to cause water to drip beyond the outside of the frame.

Drip edge A preformed sheet metal strip that overhangs a roof eave and supports the overhang of composition shingles.

Dry rot A fungus disease of wood derived from dampness, causing the wood fibers to disintegrate into powder.

Drywall Interior covering material, such as gypsum board, which is applied in large sheets.

Ducts In a house, usually round or rectangular metal pipes for distributing warm or cool air.

Duplex outlet An electrical outlet with two openings for plugs.

Durawal Lateral reinforcing steel placed in the horizontal bonding mortar joint between concrete block courses.

Dutch door A door with upper and lower halves separately hinged which may be opened independently.

E

Eaves The margin or lower part of a roof projecting over the wall.

El A pipe or tile joint connecting lines that meet at a corner. Shaped like the letter "L."

Elevations Vertical views of each side of a house or building.

El kitchen A kitchen with counters at right angles around one corner. L-shaped cabinetry.

Expansion joint A bituminous fiber strip used to separate blocks or units of concrete to prevent cracking due to expansion as a result of temperature changes. Also used on concrete slabs.

Extension lines A narrow, short line extending from an object to show where a dimension line ends.

F

Facia or fascia A flat board, band, or face, used sometimes by itself but usually in combination with moldings, located at the outer face of the cornice.

Fall The amount of slant (or slope) per foot, of a drain pipe or surface.

Filler (wood) A heavily pigmented preparation used for filling and leveling off the pores in open-pored woods.

Fire stop A solid, tight closure of a concealed space, placed to prevent the spread of fire and smoke through such a space. In a frame wall, this will usually consist of 2×4 cross-blocking between studs.

Fishplate A wood or plywood piece used to fasten the ends of two members together at a butt joint with nails or bolts; a splice; a strap.

Five-sack concrete Five sacks of cement per cubic yard of mixed concrete.

Fixture (electric) A lighting device to hold a light bulb.

Flanker window Venting-type window alongside another picture window (by a door, they are nonventing).

Flared footing Wall and footing are poured at the same time. Bottom of the footing is twice as wide as the wall part and slants up to the wall part at 60°.

Flashing Sheet metal or other material used in roof and wall construction to protect a building from water infiltration.

Flatwork Poured masonry laid more or less horizontally, such as slabs, sidewalks, and driveways.

Flitch plate A sheet of steel plate sandwiched between dimension lumber header boards. Used for wide-span openings such as double-size garage doors.

Flue The space or passage in a chimney through which smoke, gas, or fumes ascend. Each passage is called a flue, which together with other flues and the surrounding masonry make up the chimney.

Flue liner A 2′ length of vitrious clay, modularly sized, to line masonry chimneys flues.

Flue lining Fireclay or terra-cotta pipe, round or square, usually made in all ordinary flue sizes and in 2′ lengths, used for inner lining of chimneys with the brick or masonry work around the outside.

Fly rafters End rafters of a gable overhang supported by roof sheathing and lookouts.

Footing A masonry section, usually concrete, in a rectangular form; wider than the bottom of the foundation wall or pier it supports.

Footing cove A curved layer of cement where the foundation joins the footing.

Footing-grade stake Stakes driven in a footing trench, the tops of which are the level of the intended footing top.

Footing key A formed keyway in the footing surface to prevent a poured wall from shifting.

Footing projection That part of the footing which extends beyond the faces of the wall.

Form A temporary structure to hold concrete until it becomes hard.

Form spreaders Boards used to hold warped form boards apart or together.

Foundation The supporting portion of a structure below the first-floor construction, or below grade, including the footings.

Foundation baseline The starting line of the foundation, from which the layout is made. Usually the longest line.

Foundation bed The earthen material on which a footing bears or rests.

Foundation exposure The part of the foundation seen above the grade line.

F.P.H.B. Frostproof hose bib.

Fracture lines A place where concrete fails and makes a crack in a wall, footing, or slab.

Frame wall. A structural wall made of studs, plates, and sheathing.

Framing, balloon A system of framing a building in which all vertical structural elements of the bearing walls and partitions consist of single pieces extending from the top of the foundation sill plate to the roof plate and to which all floor joists are fastened.

Framing, platform A system of framing a building in which floor joists of each story rest on the top plate of the story below or on the foundation wall of the first story.

Frieze In house construction, a horizontal trim piece between the top of the siding and the soffit of the cornice.

Frostline The depth of frost penetration in the earth. This depth varies in different parts of the country.

Fungi, wood Microscopic plants that live in damp wood and cause mold, stain, and decay.

Furring Strips of wood or metal applied to a wall or other surface to serve as a fastening base for finish material.

G

Gable The sided portion of the roof above the eave line at ends of a double-sloped roof.

Gable end An end wall having a gable.

Gable vent A triangular or rectangular ventilating area high in the end of a gable wall.

Girder A large or principal beam of wood or steel used to support concentrated loads such as floor joists.

Grade level Surface contour of the earth at a particular place; where the surrounding earth meets a foundation.

Grain The direction, size, arrangement, appearance, or quality of the fibers in wood.

Grain, edge (vertical) Edge-grain lumber has been sawed parallel to the pith of the log and approximately at right angles to the growth rings (i.e., the rings form an angle of 45 to 90°, or more, with the face of the piece).

Grain, flat Flat-grain lumber has been sawed parallel to the pith of the log and approximately tangent to the growth rings (i.e., the rings form an angle of less than 45° with the surface of the piece).

Grain, quartersawn Another term for edge grain.

Grounds Guides used around openings and at the floorline to strike off wet plaster; narrow strips of wood or wide subjams at interior doorways. They provide a level plaster line for installation of casing and other trim.

Grout Mortar made of such consistency (by adding water) that it will just flow into the joints and cavities of the masonry work and fill the voids.

Gusset A flat-wood, plywood, or metal piece, surface mounted to provide a connection at intersection of wood members. Most commonly used at joints of wood trusses. A gusset is fastened with nails, screws, or bolts, and adhesives.

Gutter or eave trough A shallow channel or conduit of metal or wood set below and along the eaves of a house to catch and carry off rainwater from the roof.

Gypsum board A sheet form of plaster covered with paper ready to be installed on walls and ceilings.

H

Habitable structure A building that will be lived in by people.

Hardware cloth 1/4″ or 1/2″ galvanized mesh.

Header A beam placed perpendicular to joists and to which joists are nailed in framing around a chimney, stairway, or other openings.

Header band A dimension board nailed perpendicularly across the ends of floor joists.

Header trimmer A shortened stud that supports the ends of a header.

Headroom (clearance) The total distance vertically from a floor or step nosing level to the nearest obstruction above.

Hearth The inner or outer floor of a fireplace, usually made of brick, tile, or stone.

Hip The external angle formed by the meeting of two sloping sides of a pyramid-shaped roof (hip roof).

Hip roof A roof that rises by equally sloped inclined planes from all four sides of a building.

Hollow-core door A door made with two plywood faces and a core filled with stiffeners.

Hopper window A single-section window hinged at the bottom which opens it.

Hose bib A plumbing tap with threads on it to except a hose connector; a faucet.

I

I-beam A steel beam with a cross section resembling the letter "I." Used in a house as a girder to support floor joists ends.

Impregnated Injected or saturated throughout.

INR (Impact noise rating) A single-figure rating which provides an estimate of the impact sound-insulating performances of a floor–ceiling assembly.

Insulation blanket Fiberglass insulation packaged in continuous rolls or precut stud-length pieces, unfaced or backed with a vapor barrier.

Insulation board, rigid A structural building board made of coarse wood or cane fiber in 1/2 and 25/32″ thicknesses. It can be obtained in various size sheets, in various densities, and with several treatments. Some forms are rated high enough for corner bracing. Blackboard, fiberboard, insulboard.

Insulation, thermal Any material high in resistance to heat transmission that when placed in the walls, ceiling, or floors of a structure will reduce the rate of heat flow.

Interior finish Material used to cover the interior framed areas, or materials of walls and ceilings.

J

Jack rafter A rafter that spans the distance from the wall plate to a hip, or from a valley to a ridge.

Jamb The side and head lining of a doorway, window, or other opening.

Jig A devised setup to aid in assembly-line cutting or assembling. Stud jig; truss jig.

Joint A junction where two materials are joined together by a specific method.

Jointer An adjustable table machine to plane smooth one edge or surface of a board at a time.

Joint seal Asphalt (tar) applied to a keyway to form a sealing gasket between wall and footing.

Joint strap A piece of wood nailed to the face of two boards across a butt joint. Also, splice or tie.

Joist One of a series of parallel beams, usually 2″ thick (nominal), used to support floor and ceiling loads, and supported in turn by larger beams, girders, or bearing walls.

Joist hangers Metal brackets to hold joist ends to the face of a girder.

K

Kiln-dried lumber Lumber that has had moisture removed by drying in a kiln to a remaining content of 6 to 12%. Common varieties of softwood lumber, such as framing lumber, may be dried to a somewhat higher moisture content.

King post The center supporting post in an M truss.

Knot In lumber, the portion of a branch or limb of a tree that appears on the edge or face of the piece.

L

Laminated solid header Stacked and glued dimension pieces prearched for stress. Used over long spaces such as a two-car garage door opening.

Landing A platform between flights of stairs or at the termination of a flight of stairs.

Lap joint Two boards that run past each other and are nailed together.

Lapped joist Joist ends that are fastened together face to face over a girder.

Lateral movement Horizontal shifting of material.

Ledger beam A girder with ledger boards attached.

Ledger board A board attached to the lower face of a girder to support joists.

Let-in brace Nominal-1″-thick boards applied into notched studs diagonally at the corners of a frame wall.

Level cut Any cut on a rafter or slanted board that is horizontal after installation.

Light Space in a window sash for a single pane of glass; also, a pane of glass.

Lintel A horizontal structural member that supports the load over an opening such as a door or window; masonry lintel.

Live load Loads that are occasional or movable; not built in.

Lookout One of several small cripple rafters attached at right angles to a common rafter of a gable roof to form and support an overhanging eave on the end of a roof.

Louver An opening with a series of horizontal slats so arranged as to permit ventilation but to exclude rain, sunlight, or vision. *See also* Attic ventilators.

Lower chord The ceiling joist member of a roof truss.

Lumber Lumber is the product of the sawmill and planing mill not further manufactured other than by sawing, resawing, and passing lengthwise through a standard planing machine, crosscutting to length, and matching.

Lumber, boards Yard lumber less than 2″ thick and 2 or more inches wide.

Lumber, dimension Yard lumber from 2″ to, but not including, 5″ thick and 2 or more inches wide. Includes joists, rafters, studs, planks, and small timbers.

Lumber, dressed size The dimension of lumber after shrinking from green dimensions and after machining to size or pattern.

Lumber, matched Lumber that is dressed and shaped on one edge in a grooved pattern and on the other in a tongued pattern.

Lumber module Standardized thickness, width, and length, as applied to spacing.

Lumber, shiplap Lumber that is edge dressed to make a rabbeted, lapped joint.

Lumber, timbers Yard lumber 5 or more inches in least dimension. Includes beams, stringers, posts, caps, sills, girders, and purlins.

Lumber, treated Wood that is treated under pressure with a chemical to preserve it indefinitely while exposed to moisture or subsoil.

Lumber, yard Lumber of those grades, sizes, and patterns that are generally intended for ordinary construction, such as framework and rough coverage of houses.

M

Masonry Stone, brick, concrete, hollow tile, concrete block, gypsum block, or similar building units or materials or a combination of the same, bonded together with mortar to form a wall, pier, buttress, or similar mass.

Mastic An adhesive pasty material used as a cement (as for waterproofing a foundation wall).

Match lumber *See* Lumber, matched.

Metal strap anchor A metal strap iron, used in a course to tie intersecting masonry walls.

Millwork Generally, all building materials made of finished wood and manufactured in millwork plants and planing mills are included under the term "millwork." Millwork includes such items as inside and outside doors, window and door frames, blinds, porchwork, mantels, panelwork, stairways, moldings, and interior trim. It normally does not include flooring, ceiling, or siding material.

Minimum bearing Least amount of surface that is acceptable on the bearing member (girder end in a pocket, joist end on a sill, rafter seat on a top plate, and so on).

Minimum footing formula The depth of the footing equals the thickness of the wall; the width of the footing equals twice the wall thickness; the projection is 1/2 the wall thickness.

Miter joint The joint of two pieces at an angle that bisects the corner. For example, the miter joint at the side and head casing of a door opening is made at a 45° angle.

Modular design A working plan conceived to accept standardized units of material without custom fitting and excessive waste.

Modular material A material fabricated to a coordinated size. Typical units such as a 4 × 8′ plywood sheet and an 8″ × 8″ × 16″ concrete block.

Module A selected unit of measure.

Module tub or shower Synthetic (fiberglass) one-piece unit (combination tub and shower or shower alone).

Modulus A small measure; A divisible part of a larger module.

Moisture content of wood Weight of the water contained in the wood, usually expressed as a percentage of the weight of the oven-dry wood.

Molding A wood strip having a curved or projecting surface used for decorative purposes.

Monolithic slab An integral concrete floor slab and foundation poured all at one time.

Mortice A rectangular slot cut into a board, plank, or timber, to receive the tenon of another board, plank, or timber to form a locking joint.

M truss (Howe) An assembled set of rafters, ceiling joists, and webs with two bearing points whose webs are arranged like the letter "M."

Mullion A vertical bar or divider in the frame between windows, doors, or other openings.

Muntin A small member that divides the glass or openings of sash or doors.

N

Nail pattern A specific or designated place to put nails in a board; an organized spacing pattern.

Newel A post to which the end of a stair railing or balustrade is fastened. Also, any decorative turned post.

Nominal The specified size of a building product or material. Lumber size before dressing.

Nominal span Full width of the house in the direction that the joists run. Center-to-center of columns and piers.

Nonbearing partition A dividing wall that carries only its own material weight. Does not support ceiling or roof components.

Nonbearing wall A wall supporting no load other than its own weight.

Nonstructural Materials or position not intended to support additional loads, other than its own weight (such as a nonbearing partition).

Nosing The projecting edge of a molding or drip. Usually applied to the projecting edge of a stair tread.

Notched joist A joist with a notch in the end where it bears on a ledger.

O

OA (Overall) The largest dimension of height, width, or length.

OC (On Center) The measurement of spacing for studs, rafters, joists, and the like from the center of one member to the center of the next.

OG (ogee) A molding with a profile in the form of a letter S; having the outline of a reverved curve. OG rain gutter.

Outrigger An extensiion of a rafter beyond the wall line. Usually, a smaller member nailed to a larger rafter to form a cornice or roof overhang.

P

Panel In house construction, a thin flat piece of wood, plywood, or similar material, framed by stiles and rails as in a door or fitted into grooves of thicker material with molded edges for decorative wall treatment.

Paneling Thin wall covering of wood or fabricated synthetics; usually, 4 × 8' size.

Paper, building A general term for papers, felts, and similar sheet materials used in buildings without reference to their properties or uses.

Paper, sheathing A building material, generally paper or felt, used in wall and roof construction as a protection against the passage of air and sometimes moisture.

Parge Two 1/4″ coats of Portland waterproof cement plastered on a block foundation wall for moisture proofing.

Partition A wall that subdivides spaces within any story of a building.

Partition post An assembly of studs and wood-block spacers to form two nailing surfaces where a wall intersects another.

Penny As applied to nails, it originally indicated the price per hundred. The term now serves as a measure of nail length and is abbreviated by the letter d.

Perimeter drain A drain system surrounding the exterior footing.

Perimeter footing A linear perimetrical footing, supporting foundation walls.

Perlite A pour/fill-type insulation made from obsidian or other vitreous rock. Looks like glass pellets.

Pier A column of masonry used to support other structural members (beams and girders).

Pilaster A supporting masonry column to carry girder ends. Usually bonded to an end wall. Intermediate bonded or integral vertical supports along a long masonry wall.

Pitch The incline slope of a roof or the ratio of the total rise to the total width of a house; an 8′ rise and 24′ width is a one-third pitch roof. Roof slope is expressed as inches of rise per foot of run (e.g., ″8-in-12 pitch″).

Pitch pocket An opening extending parallel to the annual rings of growth in a board that usually contains, or has contained, either solid or liquid pitch.

Pit run Gravel from a pit without processing. Sometimes used as the aggregate in concrete.

Plaster grounds *See* Grounds.

Plate Sill plate: a horizontal wood dimension member anchored to a masonry wall. Sole plate: bottom horizontal member of a frame wall. Top plate: top horizontal member of a frame wall to which ceiling joists, rafters, and partition plates are secured.

Platform framing *See* Framing, platform.

Plenum The main heat distribution box of a furnace duct system.

Plinth (plynth) A concrete pedestal on which a wood column stands (to keep the wood above the moisture of a basement floor).

Plot plan A plan showing things such as existing contours, future contours, elevation, septic systems, house location, flat masonry (sidewalks, driveways, etc.), roof top styles, lot size and shape, house overall size, north-indicating arrow, existing trees or other natural things, street or road, dropback and side clearance dimensions, lot shape and size, and so on.

Plough To cut a lengthwise groove in a board or plank.

Plumb Vertical.

Plumb cut Any cut on a rafter or slanted board that is vertical after installation.

Plumbing access A wall opening behind rough plumbing for inspection and repair purposes.

Ply A term to denote the number or layers of veneer in plywood or layers in built-up materials in any finished piece of such material.

Plywood A sheet of wood made of three or more layers of thin wood joined with glue. Usually laid with the grain of adjoining plies at right angles. Most plywood has an odd number of plies to create stiffness and a nonsplitting character.

Pocket clearance Air space between the end and sides of a wood girder and the bearing pocket.

Points 1/3, 1/5, 1/4, and 1/6. The divisions of a length on upper and lower chords where webs are attached. An equal division of the clear span.

Pores Wood cells of comparatively large diameter that have open ends and are set one above the other to form continuous tubes. The openings of the vessels on the surface of a piece of wood are referred to as pores or grain.

Poured concrete A concrete structure or slab that was formed and poured in a liquid state. Poured foundation.

Precut stud A 2 × 4 cut to a length of 92 5/8″ to fit the modular frame wall height system.

Preservative Any substance that for a reasonable length of time will prevent the action of wood-destroying fungi, borers of various kinds, and similar destructive agents when the wood has been properly coated or impregnated with it.

Primer The first coat of paint in a paint job that consists of two or more coats; also the paint used for such a first coat.

psi Pounds per square inch.

P trap A ''P''-shaped piece of drain equipment used to stop fumes from backing up into a room.

Putty A type of filler usually made of whiting and boiled linseed oil, beaten or kneaded to the consistency of dough, and used in sealing glass in sash, filling small holes and crevices in wood, and for similar purposes.

Q

Quarter round A small molding that has the cross-section shape of a quarter-circle.

Queen post A vertical supporting post at quarter points in the simple M truss.

R

Rabbet A rectangular longitudinal ell cut out of the edge of a board or plank; shiplap.

Radial saw An overtable cutting circular power saw that runs on a track. There are two axis adjustments which facilitate cutting simple and compound miters in addition to basic perpendicular cross cutting and ripping. Basically, a cutoff saw.

Rafter One of a series of parallel structural members of a roof in a sloped position.

Rafter, hip A rafter that forms the intersection of an external roof angle on a hip roof.

Rafter, valley A rafter that forms the intersection of an internal roof angle. The valley rafter is normally made of double 2″-thick members.

Rake Trim members that run parallel to the roof slope and form the finish between the wall and a gable roof extension.

Rebar ''Nickname'' for reinforcing bars.

Recessed entrance An entrance back from the regular wall line or one lower than floor level.

Recessed floor A floor constructed at a lower level than the other floors. Sunken living room.

Reflective insulation Sheet material with one or both surfaces of comparatively low heat emissivity, such as aluminum foil.

Reinforced concrete Poured concrete with steel reinforcing gridwork and/or rebar.

Reinforcing Steel rods or welded metal mesh placed in concrete slabs, beams, or columns to increase their strength. Also, Dura-wall.

Relative humidity The amount of water vapor in the atmosphere, expressed as a percentage of the maximum quantity that could be present at a given temperature.

Rerod ''Nickname'' for reinforcing rods.

Retempering (masonry) Adding water after hydration has begun. Destroys strength and surface.

Ribbon (girt) Normally, a 1 × 4 or 1 × 6 let into the studs horizontally to support ceiling or second-floor joists.

Ridge The horizontal line at the junction of the top edges of two sloping roof surfaces.

Ridge board The board placed on edge at the ridge of the roof against which the upper ends of the rafters are fastened.

Ridge cap The top-lapped course of shingles over a roof ridge, faced away from the prevailing wind direction.

Ridge cut A plumb cut at the upper end of a rafter which bears on the ridge board.

Ridge vent A single or continuous vent at the peak of a gable roof.

Rise In stairs, the vertical height of a step or flight of stairs.

Rise The vertical leg of a roof pitch triangle.

Riser Each of the vertical boards closing the spaces between the treads of stairways.

RO (Rough Opening) An opening in rough framework for windows, doors, chimneys, stairways, and so on.

Roll roofing Roofing material composed of fiber and saturated asphalt, supplied in 36″-wide rolls with 108 square feet of material. Weights are generally 45 to 90 lb per roll.

Roof capping The final shingles or another capping material on a roof ridge.

Roof pitch The angle or slant of the roof.

Roof sheathing The boards or sheet material fastened to the roof rafters on which the shingles or other roof covering is laid.

Roof truss A prefabricated roof unit incorporating ceiling joists, rafters, and braces (upper and lower chords and webs).

Roof vent An attic ventilator placed at the surface of the upper part of a roof.

Rough framing Construction of the wooden structural frameworks of a building, such as the floor, walls, ceiling, and roof frames.

Rough sill A single or double frame member placed horizontally below a window opening.

Run In stairs, the net depth of a step or the horizontal distance covered by a flight of stairs. On a roof or floor, one-half the span.

S

S4S A board surfaced on all four surfaces.

Saddle Two sloping surfaces meeting in a horizontal ridge, used on a roof behind a chimney; a cricket.

Sag A downward curve in a structural member from overstress or undersize material.

Sash A single window light frame containing one or more lights of glass. The opening part of a window casement.

Saturated felt A felt that is completely impregnated with tar or asphalt.

Scaffold A temporarily erected platform from which to work.

Scaffold nail A double-headed nail; sometimes called a duplex or form nail.

Scale (a) A measurement instrument used by drafters to draw plans proportionately. (b) The proportionate size to which plans are reduced.

Scratch coat The coat of plaster that is scratched to form a bond for the next coat.

Screed (a) A small strip of wood, usually the thickness of the plaster coat, used as a guide for plastering. (b) A straightedge for leveling concrete over forms.

Screwjack post A one-piece tabular steel column with a screw jack to adjust the height.

Scribing (a) Fitting woodwork to an irregular surface. In moldings, cutting the end of one piece to fit the molded face of the other at an interior angle instead of mitering. (b) Marking with a sharp instrument.

Sealer A finishing material, in paste or liquid form, either clear or pigmented, that is usually applied directly over uncoated wood for the purpose of sealing the surface.

Seasoning Removing moisture from green wood to improve its serviceability. Allowed to age.

Seat cut A plumbcut and a level cut joint on a conventional rafter which forms the bearing point on the plate; a birdsmouth.

Section view A cutaway view that reveals all the parts and assembly.

Septic drain A drain pipe that carries human or animal waste.

Service panel The main electrical entrance box into the house containing breakers or fuses.

Shake A thick handsplit shingle, resawed to form two shakes.

Sheathing The structural covering, usually wood boards, waferboard, or plywood, used over joists, studs, or rafters of a structure; also called ''sheeting.''

Sheathing paper *See* Paper, sheathing.

Sheer stress A compression stress with support on one side.

Shim A thin piece of material used to separate or hold up parts.

Shingles Roof covering of asphalt, asbestos, wood, tile, slate, or other material cut to various stock lengths, widths, and thickness.

Shingles, composition Shingles made of asphalt-saturated material coated with a weather-resistant material.

Shingles, siding Various kinds of shingles, such as wood shingles or shakes and nonwood shingles, that are used over sheathing for exterior sidewall covering of a structure.

Shiplap *See* Lumber, shiplap.

Shutter Usually louvered or flush wood window covers. Wood, metal, or fiberglass frames in the form of doors located at each side of a window. Some are made to close over the window for protection; others are fastened to the wall as a decorative device.

Siding The finish covering of the outside wall of a frame building. Made of horizontal weatherboards, vertical boards with battens, shingles, or other materials (aluminum, steel, vinyl, brick veneer, and stone).

Siding, bevel (lap siding) Wedge-shaped boards used as horizontal siding in a lapped pattern.

Siding, Dolly Varden Beveled wood siding that is rabbeted on the bottom edge.

Siding, drop Usually 3/4″ thick and 6 and 8″ wide with tongue-and-groove or shiplap edges. Often used without sheathing in secondary buildings.

Sill The lowest member of the wood frame of a structure, resting on the foundation and supporting the floor joists or the uprights of the wall. The member forming the lower side of an opening, as a door sill, windowsill, rough sill.

Sill plate *See* Sill.

Six-by-six reinforcing Welded wired in a grid pattern of 6″ squares used to reinforce concrete slabs. Comes in rolls 5′ wide by 150′ long. $6 \times 6 \times \#10$ (No. 10 wire size).

Slab A flat piece of concrete, such as a floor, sidewalk, or driveway; flatwork.

Slab floor A concrete floor.

Slab footing (monolithic) Integral footing and floor poured at the same time.

Slump Test A test used to determine the firmness or fluidity of concrete as it comes from the mixer.

Soffit Usually, the underside of an overhanging cornice; also, kitchen cabinet soffit.

Soffit vent Single, multiple, or continuous venting under the eave which directs an upflow of air over the top plate into the attic.

Soil cover (ground cover) A light covering of plastic film, roll roofing, or similar material used over the soil in crawl spaces of buildings to minimize moisture permeation of the area.

Soil stack A general term for the vertical main of a system of soil, waste, or vent piping.

Sole or sole plate *See* Plate.

Solid bridging A solid member placed between adjacent floor joists near the center of the span to stiffen the joists. Also called *blockbridge*.

Span The nominal distance across structural supports such as walls, columns, piers, and openings.

Specs A shortened spelling of the word ''specifications.''

Splash block A small grooved masonry block on the ground surface to carry away rainwater from downspouts.

Splice A wood or metal piece fastened over a butt joist to hold two joists or chords together.

Split-wired outlet A duplex with one outlet live and the other switched.

Spreader A board cut to a specific length to hold concrete forms apart.

Square A unit of measure, 100 square feet. Usually associated with roofing material.

Stable soil Soil composition that does not shift or more readily.

Stack A plumbing vent pipe that exists through the roof.

Staggered nails Nails not placed in the same grain line nor in a straight line.

Staggered sheathing A pattern of layment where the butt joints of adjacent courses of sheathing do not end on the same joist or rafter.

Stair carriage Supporting member for stair treads. Usually, a 2″ plank notched to receive the treads; sometimes called a ''rough horse.''

Staircase An assemblage of stairs.

Stair landing *See* Landing.

Stair rise *See* Total rise *and* Unit rise.

Stairway The area in which a stairs is constructed. Also called *stairwell*. The way to reach another level.

Standard I-beam A steel girder with narrow flanges.

Standpipe A vertical drain pipe for an automatic washing machine.

STC (Sound Transmission Class) A measure of sound stopping of ordinary noise.

Steel-plated header A two-piece wood header built up with a steel flitch plate core. *See* Flitch plate.

Steel shim Small rectangles of steel plate to shim up columns and girders.

Step footing (inclined) A footing used for hillside construction.

Stepped footing (pyramid) More than one footing stacked on another with uniform projections.

Stile An upright framing member in a panel door.

Stool An interior flat molding fitted on top of the sloping surface of the windowsill jamb. Forms a weather seal for the sash.

Storm drain A drain that carries away any type of nonpolluting water, such as rain, footing drainage, and surface water.

Storm sash or storm window An extra window usually placed on the outside of an existing one as additional protection against cold weather.

Story The habitable area between floors.

Story Pole A marked or notched board used to control brick course vertical spacing and horizontal siding. Also, a notched board to space joists, studs, and rafters temporarily.

Strap A wood or metal piece, surface mounted, to hold two components together (joist ends).

Stretcher block The most commonly used concrete block in the wall. Both ends cupped.

Stringline A tightly drawn string with which to judge straightness of building components.

Stringer A timber or other support for cross members in floors or ceilings. In stairs, the support on which the stair treads rest; also, *stringboard*.

Strip flooring Wood flooring consisting of narrow, matched strips (tongue and groove).

Structural masonry Concrete or masonry units designed and assembled to carry or support a load.

Stud One of a series of slender wood or metal vertical structural members placed as supporting elements in walls and partitions. Plural: studs or studding.

Subfloor Boards or plywood laid on joists over which a finish floor is to be laid. A work surface during construction.

Sump A small cistern to collect excess water around a footing.

Suspended ceiling A ceiling system supported by hanging it from the overhead structural framing.

T

T (T post) Three studs joined with spacer blocks to form the intersection of walls and partitions.

Tail joist A less-than-full-length joist fastened perpendicularly to a header.

Tee A pipe or tile component which connects lines that meet at right angles. Shaped like a "T".

Telepost An adjustable steel column. Two telescoping sections and a screwjack.

Tensile stress A stress that pulls in opposite directions.

Termites Insects that superficially resemble ants in size, general appearance, and habit of living in colonies; hence they are frequently called "white ants." Subterranean termites establish themselves in buildings not by being carried in with lumber, but by entering from ground nests *after* the building has been constructed. If unmolested, they eat out the woodwork, leaving a shell of sound wood to conceal their activities, and damage may proceed so far as to cause collapse of parts of a structure before discovery.

Termite shield A shield, usually of noncorrodible metal, placed in or on a foundation wall or other mass of masonry or around pipes to prevent passage of termites.

Three-tab-thick butt A triple-tab, heavyweight asphalt composition shingle.

Three-way switch One of a pair of switches that controls a light from two locations.

Threshold A strip of wood or metal with beveled edges used over the finish floor and the sill of exterior doors.

Timbers *See* Lumber, timbers.

Toenailing To drive a nail at a slant with the initial surface in order to hold it to another board at right angles (more or less).

Tongue and groove *See* Dressed and matched.

Topography The lay of the land.

Top plate *See* Plate.

Total rise (stairway) The total distance from one floor level to an adjacent floor level.

Total run (stairway) The total horizontal distance from the place where the first step drops off to where the last step drops off. First riser face to last riser face.

Tract-built house One of a group of houses built on a site, usually by the same contractor.

Transit An optical instrument or scope used to show straight directions and levels.

Tread The horizontal step board in a stairway.

Treated lumber *See* Lumber, treated.

Trench footing A footing formed and poured in firm earth without forms.

Trench foundation A vertical foundation poured in an earthen trench. The base is wide enough to serve as a footing.

Trim The finish materials in or on a building, such as moldings, applied around openings (window trim, door trim) or at the floor and ceiling of rooms (baseboard, cornice, and other moldings).

Trimmer A short stud that supports the end of a header for a doorway or window.

Trimmer joist A full-length additional joist nailed to an OC joist.

Truss A framework designed with diagonal members to strengthen its resistance to compression. Girder truss, roof truss, floor joist truss. Used for long spans.

Twenty-eighth day The point at which concrete reaches its maximum strength after pouring.

Twist A propeller-shaped warp in a board.

U

U kitchen A kitchen with counters and appliances arranged in the shape of a rectangular U. No through traffic.

Undercoat A coating applied prior to the finishing or top coats of a paint job. It may be the first of two or the second of three coats. Prime coat.

Underlayment A material placed under finish coverings, such as flooring or shingles, to provide a smooth, even surface for applying the finish.

Uniform double header A common-sized header used throughout the frame walls.

Uniform header, nonspaced A header assembled with no spacer which is placed flush with the exterior wall surface and has a lower horizontal trimmer.

Uniform single header A one-piece 2 × 10 header approximately centered over a horizontal trimmer. Used throughout the interior partitions.

Unit rise The *height* of one step.

Unit run The horizontal depth of a level cut on a stair stringer.

Upper chord The rafter member of a roof truss.

V

Valley The internal angle formed by the function of two sloping sides of a roof.

Valley rafter *See* Rafter, valley.

Vapor barrier Material used to retard the movement of water vapor through walls or floors and prevent condensation in living quarters. Applied separately over the warm side of exposed walls or as a part of the batt or blanket insulation. Plastic under concrete slab floors.

Veneer Thin sheets of wood made by rotary cutting or slicing of a log.

Vent stack A plumbing vent pipe that exists through the roof.

Vermiculite A mineral closely related to mica, with the faculty of expanding on heating to form lightweight material with insulation quality. Used as bulk insulation and also as aggregate in insulating and acoustical plaster and in insulating concrete floors.

W

Wall backers Wood backing boards placed behind areas in the wall where things will be fastened (towel racks, curtain rods, etc.). Provides solid screw anchorage.

Warped A board that is bent out of shape in various formations.

Water-repellent preservative A liquid designed to penetrate wood and impart water repellency and preservative protection. Used for millwork, such as sash and frames.

Weather stripping Narrow or jamb-width sections of thin metal or other material to prevent infiltration of air and moisture around windows and doors.

Webs Tension and compression braces in a roof truss. Connects upper and lower chords.

Wide-flange I-beam A steel girder with wide upper and lower surfaces.

Wind (wynd) A board with a twist.

Window header A lintel above a door to channel the bearing weight of the roof onto the trimmer studs.

Window well A retainer made of masonry or metal which holds the earth away from a window that is partly below grade.

Wire ties Wires used to hold steel reinforcing components together while concrete is poured around them.

Work triangle A traffic pattern between the three basic kitchen appliances: the sink, range, and refrigerator.

W truss (Fink) An assembled set of rafters, joists, and webs with two bearing points. The web formation looks like the letter "W."

Y

Yard lumber *See* Lumber, yard.

INDEX